ALGEBRA: ITS BIG IDEAS AND BASIC SKILLS

BOOK I

DAYMOND J. AIKEN is Director of Curriculum and former Head of the Mathematics Department, Lockport Township High School, Lockport, Illinois. He taught mathematics, including algebra, in high schools in Shawneetown and Anna, Illinois; Akron, Ohio; and Lake Geneva, Wisconsin. Mr. Aiken brings to this algebra textbook a background of highly successful experience in mathematics teaching and curriculum development.

KENNETH B. HENDERSON has taught mathematics in both junior and senior high school. He is Professor of Mathematics Education, University of Illinois. He taught mathematics in the South Amherst and Rocky River, Ohio, schools and was Assistant Professor of Education, University of Pennsylvania.

ROBERT E. PINGRY is Supervisor of Student Teaching in Mathematics and Professor of Mathematics and Education, University of Illinois. He is Editor of *The Mathematics Teacher*. Formerly he taught junior high school mathematics in the Griffith, Indiana, schools and taught mathematics in the Mitchell, Indiana, High School.

Algebra:

ITS BIG IDEAS

AND BASIC SKILLS

BOOK I
MODERN
MATHEMATICS
EDITION

Daymond J. Aiken

Kenneth B. Henderson

Robert E. Pingry

Illustrations by RAMON GORDON

McGRAW-HILL BOOK COMPANY, INC.

New York   Chicago   San Francisco   Dallas   Toronto   London

BIG IDEAS AND BASIC SKILLS SERIES

USING MATHEMATICS, 7	Henderson and Pingry
USING MATHEMATICS, 8	Henderson and Pingry
USING MATHEMATICS, 9	Henderson and Pingry

ALGEBRA: *Its Big Ideas and Basic Skills, Book I*
Aiken, Henderson, and Pingry
ALGEBRA: *Its Big Ideas and Basic Skills, Book II*
Aiken, Henderson, and Pingry

ALGEBRA: *Its Big Ideas and Basic Skills*, Book I, Third Edition

Copyright © 1960 by the McGraw-Hill Book Company, Inc.
Copyright 1950, 1954, © 1957 by the McGraw-Hill Book Company, Inc. Printed in the United States of America. All rights reserved. This book, or parts thereof, may not be reproduced in any form without permission of the publisher.

00712

Library of Congress Catalog Card Number: 59–15043

TO THE TEACHER

ALGEBRA: Its Big Ideas and Basic Skills, Book I, Modern Mathematics Edition, is modern in content and modern in teaching method. We have been guided by the publications of the Commission on Mathematics of the College Entrance Examination Board. In addition, we have put into practice other modern knowledge about the teaching and learning of algebra and have included features which will simplify your job of teaching.

To ensure that you have a textbook that presents ideas in a modern way to pupils: We define *variable* as a symbol which can be replaced by an arbitrary number from a set of numbers. We define *function* as a set of ordered pairs of numbers such that for every different first number there is one and only one second number. We treat an equation as a conditional or propositional function which does not have truth value as long as it contains a variable but becomes true or false upon substitution of a number for the variable. We use absolute value of numbers in appropriate places throughout the book. We treat inequalities and call them *inequations*, the modern term. We use modern applications. For example, we lay the foundation for linear programing by including the topic on systems of inequations.

Throughout this textbook pupils are reminded that mathematics is systematic and sequential and that ideas of mathematics relate to each other in patterns. We use the associative, commutative, and distributive principles in appropriate places to highlight the structure of mathematics for the pupil.

The subject matter is organized around big ideas and basic skills. This organization has been enthusiastically received by users of previous editions. Teachers have found that by concentrating on the big ideas and basic skills they have the time they need for careful explanation, for review, and for reinforcement of skills by reteaching. Psychologists have found that information organized around big ideas in a systematic way is remembered much longer than are isolated facts and skills. The pupil who has organized knowledge in mathematics can solve problems and can rediscover ideas for himself much better than the pupil who has only a set of isolated, memorized skills and ideas in algebra.

The big ideas of algebra in *Book I* are: number, using letters for numbers, equation, exponent, function, and graph. The basic skills are: using and interpreting symbols of algebra, fundamental operations, evaluating expressions, using exponents, solving equations, solving word problems, drawing and reading graphs, and factoring. The sequence of presentation is based on the sound principle of proceeding from the known and familiar to the unknown and the unfamiliar. On the end sheets of this book you will find charts that show you where the big ideas and basic skills are introduced and systematically developed throughout the book.

To simplify your job of teaching and help assure sound learning, we have provided the following special aids and features:

The *big ideas and basic skills* to be developed or reinforced are listed on the opening page of each chapter. Pointing out the big ideas and basic skills to the pupil helps him to organize his learning around these ideas and skills.

Your Aim, which also appears on the first page of each chapter, states for the pupil what he should seek to accomplish as he studies the chapter. He can also turn back to *Your Aim* from time to time to check on his progress.

Problems on Your Aims, which appears at the end of each chapter, is composed of a brief problems test on each of the aims stated at the beginning of that chapter. These tests help the teacher diagnose the pupil's learning relative to the objectives of the chapter.

The *Chapter Test* evaluates the pupil's grasp of the big ideas and basic skills developed in each chapter. This test provides mixed problem-solving experience. The *Chapter Test* is more for the purpose of grading the pupil rather than diagnosing gaps in his knowledge.

Self Tests at strategic points within chapters enable the pupil to check on his understandings and skills before going on to other topics.

The *Do You See?* feature applies the discovery method of teaching. Instead of being taught a principle directly, the pupil is led through a series of graded exercises to discover certain generalizations for himself. As the pupil works through these exercises, he is led to the point where he has the necessary experience background to make his own discovery. He thus gets the thrill of discovery that is missed if he is simply told how to do something and then requested to do it. He also gets practice in creative thinking so essential to future work in mathematics and science. The *Do You See?*, emphasized by a red symbol, then provides a concise statement that is meaningful to him at this point. More problems now provide opportunity to apply and test the generalization.

Study Tips, spotlighted by illustrations in color, help the pupil become aware of ways he can improve his study habits and guide him in efficient use of his textbook.

Summary of Important Things to Remember at the end of each chapter lists important words and expressions, understandings, and skills. It directs the pupil's attention to the most important outcomes of his study of the chapter.

Abundant problems provide both challenge and practice. Numerous exercises provide adequate drill. Verbal problems throughout the book provide substantial experience in application of the big ideas and basic skills. The problems in each set gradually increase in difficulty. Many sets include *optional problems* which challenge the more able pupils. A star in the margin marks the beginning of a group of such optional problems, and the special group ends where new instructions introduce a further section of the set.

Optional topics provide additional subject matter which is valuable and stimulating for the more able pupils. Optional topics are marked with a star, and they are not prerequisite to the study of any subsequent topic.

Illustrations of various types help teach certain important mathematical ideas. Some of the verbal problems have an accompanying illustration that helps the pupil visualize the action or situation described in the verbal problem. Color is used to make the visual aids more effective in a functional way.

Cumulative Review Problems at the end of each chapter contains problems that review all the ideas and skills in the book previous to the chapter. Thus the principle of spacing the review at intervals through the book helps the pupil fix his knowledge and retain his efficiency with the skills of algebra. Regular review provided by *Cumulative Review Problems* is an essential feature of any sound program of instruction in mathematics.

Valuable Skills Practice, provided at the end of each chapter, helps the pupil retain and improve his skill in arithmetic. Without an attempt to keep arithmetic skills alive during the course in algebra, pupils may actually be less skillful in arithmetic at the end of the course than they were at the start. *Valuable Skills Practice* enables the teacher to provide practice in arithmetic in an interesting way.

Mathematics is the foundation of the science and technology that have given us the highest standard of living in the world. Mathematics is also a subject alive with challenging intellectual experiences, valuable for their own sake for many pupils. You, the teacher, are the most important link between mathematical knowledge and its enjoyment and use on the part of the pupils. *Algebra: Its Big Ideas and Basic Skills, Book I*, provides the instructional materials for your important work.

DAYMOND J. AIKEN
KENNETH B. HENDERSON
ROBERT E. PINGRY

CONTENTS

ACKNOWLEDGMENTS

WE ARE GRATEFUL to many whose suggestions and criticisms have helped in the preparation of this book. Dr. Gilbert Ulmer, Professor of the Teaching of Mathematics and Assistant Dean, College of Liberal Arts and Sciences, University of Kansas; Miss M. Kathleen Lowther, Head of the Mathematics Department, Central High School, Oklahoma City; and Mr. Gordon D. Mock, Instructor of Mathematics, Wisconsin High School, University of Wisconsin, read the entire manuscript and offered many valuable comments. Dr. Eugene D. Nichols, Associate Professor and teacher of mathematics in the University School, Florida State University, provided many important refinements throughout. Others whose contributions we wish to acknowledge include Dr. Aaron Bakst, New York University; Professor William F. Brenizer, San Bernardino Valley College, San Bernardino, California; Miss Vivian Strand, Burlington High School and College, Burlington, Iowa; Miss Laura M. Wagner, Fort Atkinson, Wisconsin, High School; Miss Hortense Wilson, Elgin, Illinois, Senior High School; Mr. David Rappaport, Lane Technical High School, Chicago; and Miss Lorina Goerz and Mr. Charles Beseman, Lockport, Illinois, Township High School. While assuming full responsibility for the content of the book, we wish to thank everyone who has assisted us in any way.

DAYMOND J. AIKEN
KENNETH B. HENDERSON
ROBERT E. PINGRY

LEARNING AIDS

xiv

BIG IDEAS	LETTERS FOR NUMBERS
	EXPONENT
BASIC SKILLS	Using and interpreting symbols of algebra
	Fundamental operations
	Evaluating algebraic expressions
	Using exponents

CHAPTER **1** *Using Letters for Numbers*

THE FIRST TIME you used numbers was probably when you began counting—one, two, three, and so on. Then, when you began studying arithmetic, you learned to write number symbols—1, 2, 3, and so on. Later you were taught to add, subtract, multiply, and divide numbers.

In algebra, letters are used as **placeholders** for numbers. In your study you will learn to work with letters in addition, subtraction, multiplication, and division. You will learn how these placeholders are used to make general statements about operations with numbers.

Knowledge of algebra is important in many kinds of work, especially in the fields of science and engineering. The high standard of living that Americans enjoy is to a great extent due to the work of our scientists and engineers. They use their knowledge of algebra in addition to their other skills to improve our way of life.

In this chapter you will take some of your important first steps in the study of algebra.

YOUR AIM

1. **To learn how letters are used in algebra.**

2. **To learn how to add, subtract, multiply, and divide using letters to stand for numbers.**

3. **To learn how to work with formulas and other algebraic expressions.**

4. **To learn the importance of the commutative principles and the distributive principle.**

1

Symbols

EGYPTIAN | MAYAN | MODERN

How do you write the number twelve? Of course you use the symbol 12. People did not always use this symbol. For example, the Egyptians and the Mayan Indians used symbols like those shown above.

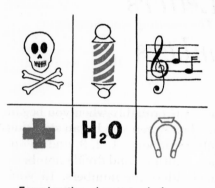

Examine the above symbols.
What does each one stand for?

Using symbols is not new to you. Your language is made up of words which are symbols. The words you are now reading are symbols representing ideas.

In your study of arithmetic you learned to use mathematical symbols like $+$ to mean addition, $-$ to mean subtraction, $\times$ to mean multiplication, $\div$ to mean division, and others. How well you know algebra will to a large extent depend upon your understanding of the various symbols of algebra and of the ways of using them.

PROBLEMS

Tell the meaning of each of the following symbols:

1. $\$$ 2. $\%$ 3. $=$ 4. π 5. $^\circ$
6. $\sqrt{9}$ 7. $\times$ 8. $\div$ 9. $\frac{3}{4}$ 10. $4\frac{1}{2}$
11. 0 12. $+$ 13. XII 14. $-$ 15. 2.6

Tell in words what the following symbols express:

16. $9 + 3$ 17. 5×8 18. $12 - 3$ 19. $1\frac{3}{2}$ 20. $\sqrt{25}$

Write each of the following using mathematical symbols:

21. Divide
22. Square root
23. Three inches
24. Four degrees
25. One divided by ten.
26. Twenty degrees and thirty seconds
27. Three feet and six inches
28. Two added to one
29. Divide twenty by three and add five.
30. Multiply six by seven and divide by nine.

2 *ALGEBRA: ITS BIG IDEAS AND BASIC SKILLS*

Letters for Numbers

In arithmetic you learned that, to find the area of a rectangle, you multiply the length of the rectangle by the width. You can write this rule, using letters, as $A = l \times w$. When you do this, you are using letters to stand for numbers. For example, if the length were 12 inches and the width were 4 inches, you would replace l by 12 and w by 4 and get $A = 12 \times 4$, or 48 square inches.

How would you write the following using mathematical symbols: "When you multiply any number by 1, the answer is the same number you started with"? A way of writing this in algebra is to let some letter, say a, stand for any number and write $1 \times a = a$. You can replace the letter a by any number, and the statement you get will be true. Examine the following examples.

When you replace a by:	The resulting statement is:
3	$1 \times 3 = 3$
19	$1 \times 19 = 19$
1572	$1 \times 1572 = 1572$
$\frac{3}{5}$	$1 \times \frac{3}{5} = \frac{3}{5}$
1.76	$1 \times 1.76 = 1.76$

Is each of the resulting statements above true?

PROBLEMS

In $1 \times a = a$, replace a by the following numbers and see if the resulting statements are true:

1. 5
2. 23
3. 3.47
4. $\frac{2}{3}$
5. $4\frac{3}{4}$
6. 0.0076
7. 339,426
8. $\frac{29}{32}$

DO YOU SEE? When a in $1 \times a = a$ is replaced by any number, the resulting statement is true.

9. You learned in arithmetic that any number multiplied by zero equals zero. Write this principle by using the letter y to stand for any number.

10. Test the statement you wrote for Problem 9 by replacing y by the numbers in Problems 1–8.

Symbols That Mean Multiply

There are various ways of writing a product using mathematical symbols. For example, you can write 5 times 4 in three different ways:

They all mean multiply!

(5)(4)   5 · 4   5 × 4

However, a number and one or more letters that are to be multiplied are usually written side by side without a multiplication symbol. Two or more letters to be multiplied are also written side by side without a multiplication symbol. For example, $5a$ means 5 times a; xy means x times y; $7mn$ means 7 times m times n.

Numbers that are multiplied to form a product are called **factors**. Thus, in 3×2, 3 and 2 are factors, and in $5m$, 5 and m are factors.

PROBLEMS

Tell what each of the following means:

1. $7x$
2. $x \cdot y$
3. xx
4. $10 \cdot a$
5. $(5)(k)$
6. $4y$
7. $5xy$
8. $\frac{1}{2}c$
9. $2.8y$
10. $0.6(a)$

Find what number each of the following stands for when $x = 5$:

11. $8x$
12. $(3)(x)$
13. xx
14. $\frac{3}{2} \cdot x$
15. $6.5x$
16. $6 \cdot 5x$
17. $(4\frac{1}{5})(x)$
18. $(x)(8)$
19. $(x)(\frac{1}{3})$
20. $0.6x$

Find what number each of the following stands for when $x = 3$ *and* $y = 4$:

21. $(7x)(y)$
22. $6 \cdot 5 \cdot x \cdot y$
23. $\frac{1}{2}xy$
24. $10y \cdot x$
25. $\frac{6}{4} \cdot \frac{x}{2} \cdot y$
26. $(\frac{4}{5})(2x)(y)$
27. $\frac{x}{y}$
28. $\frac{y}{x}$
★ 29. $\frac{4x}{y}$
30. $\frac{xx}{xy}$
31. $0 \cdot x \cdot y$
32. $\frac{x - x}{3x + 4y}$

SELF TEST

Find what number each of the following stands for when $x = 4$.

1. $x + 4$
2. $x - 2$
3. $x + x$
4. $5 - x$
5. $5 \cdot x$
6. $4x$
7. $(3)(x)$
8. $(x)(\frac{1}{2})$
9. $8 \div x$
10. $\frac{12}{x}$
11. $\frac{x}{8}$
12. $(x)(x)(x)$

13. Write the following rule using letters: Any number, except zero, divided by itself gives 1 as the quotient.

Find the answer to each of the following:

14. $14.53 \div 14.53$
15. $29\frac{3}{4} - 29\frac{3}{4}$
16. $0 \times 16\frac{2}{3}$
17. 1×11.3
18. $a \div a$
19. $a - a$
20. $0 \times b$
21. $1 \times c$

★ See page vii for explanation of starred problems.

4 *ALGEBRA: ITS BIG IDEAS AND BASIC SKILLS*

Writing the Four Fundamental Operations

In the study of algebra it is important that you become skillful in writing expressions involving addition, subtraction, multiplication, and division. Below are four examples of expressions written both in mathematical symbols and in words.

$x + y$ is a *sum*, the result of adding x and y.
$x - y$ is a *difference*, the result of subtracting y from x.
xy is a *product*, the result of multiplying x by y or y by x.
$\dfrac{x}{y}$ is a *quotient*, the result of dividing x by y.

PROBLEMS

1. What is the sum of 4 and 2? The difference? The product? The quotient?
2. What is the sum of $\frac{1}{2}$ and $\frac{1}{4}$? The difference? The product? The quotient?
3. What is the sum of 0.6 and 0.2? The difference? The product? The quotient?
4. What is the sum of 5 and 5? The difference? The product? The quotient?

Write the following, using the symbols of operations and letting x *stand for some number:*
5. Some number added to 7.
6. Some number subtracted from 7.
7. 7 multiplied by some number.
8. 15 divided by some number.

Tell what each of the following means:

9. $6 \times k$	10. $6 + k$	11. $k \times k$	12. $4 + k$
13. $k \div 5$	14. $k + k$	15. $k - 3$	16. $k + 6$
17. $k - k$	18. $k \times 12$	19. $k - 8$	20. $k \div k$

21. Find the numbers that the expressions in Problems 9–20 stand for when $k = 10$.

What numbers do the following expressions stand for when t = 14?

22. $3 \times t$	23. $t + t$	24. $t \div 2$	25. $t + 14$
26. $24 - t$	27. $t \times t$	28. $t \times 5$	29. $\dfrac{t}{2}$
30. $\dfrac{28}{t}$	31. $t - t$	32. $t + t + t$	33. $13 \times t$

34. What numbers do the expressions in Problems 22–33 stand for if $t = 4$?

★ **35.** What numbers do the expressions in Problems 22–33 stand for if $t = 5.9$?

36. What numbers do the expressions in Problems 22–33 stand for if $t = 2\frac{1}{2}$?

If a *and* b *stand for numbers, use mathematical symbols to write the following:*

37. The sum of a and b.

38. b subtracted from a.

39. The product of a and b. Write the product in four different ways.

40. The quotient of a divided by b.

41. 6% of a. Write 6% as a decimal.

42. a subtracted from b.

43. The square root of the product of a and b.

44. The quotient of b divided by a.

45. The sum of a and b divided by their product.

46. The product of a and b divided by their sum.

Find in Column 2 the algebraic expression for each word expression in Column 1:

Column 1	Column 2
47. The sum of 3 and x.	**a.** $3x$
48. Four less than b.	**b.** $a + b + c$
49. Four more than b.	**c.** $3 + x$
50. The product of 3 and x.	**d.** $\dfrac{a + b}{c}$
51. The quotient of 3 divided by x.	**e.** $b - 4$
52. Three less than x.	**f.** abc
53. The product of a, b, and c.	**g.** $b + 4$
54. The sum of a, b, and c.	**h.** $\dfrac{a}{b} + c$
55. The sum of a and b, divided by c.	**i.** $\dfrac{3}{x}$
56. The product of a and b, divided by c.	**j.** $\dfrac{a}{b} - c$
57. The quotient of a divided by b, increased by c.	**k.** $\dfrac{ab}{c}$
58. The quotient of a divided by b, decreased by c.	**l.** $x - 3$

6 *ALGEBRA: ITS BIG IDEAS AND BASIC SKILLS*

Writing Formulas

To find the circumference of any circle, you multiply pi, π, by the diameter. You can state this briefly by using mathematical symbols:

$$C = \pi d$$

This boy is finding the circumference. He could also find the circumference by measuring the diameter and using the formula.

A statement like $C = \pi d$ is called a **formula**.

PROBLEMS

Rewrite the following rules as formulas:

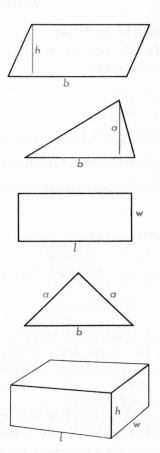

1. The area of a parallelogram is equal to the product of its base and altitude.

2. The area of a triangle is equal to one-half the product of its base and its altitude.

3. The area of a rectangle is equal to the product of its length and its width.

4. The perimeter of an isosceles triangle may be found by doubling the length of one of its equal sides and adding the length of the base.

5. The volume of a rectangular solid may be found by multiplying its length by its width by its height.

★ **6.** The area of a circle is equal to the product of pi and the square of its radius.

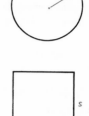

7. The area of a square is equal to the square of one of its sides.

8. The perimeter of a square may be found by multiplying the length of one side by 4.

DO YOU SEE? 👉 **You can state mathematical relationships more briefly in algebraic symbols than in words.**

Evaluating Formulas

Example for Study

In the formula $A = \frac{1}{2}ab$, find the value of A if $a = 6$ inches and $b = 12$ inches.

SOLUTION:

Copy the formula:	$A = \frac{1}{2}ab$
Note which values are known:	$a = 6, b = 12$
Replace the letters by their known values:	$A = \frac{1}{2} \cdot 6 \cdot 12$
Do the indicated operations to find the value of A:	$A = 36$ square inches

PROBLEMS

1. In $A = \frac{1}{2}ab$, find A when a is 9 feet and b is 10 feet.
2. In $d = rt$, find d when r is 35 miles per hour and t is 3 hours.
3. In Problem 2, find d when r is 30 miles per hour and t is 4 hours and 20 minutes.
4. In $c = 2\pi r$, find c when r is 28 feet. Use $\pi = 3\frac{1}{7}$.
5. In Problem 4, find c when r is 3.6 inches. Use $\pi = 3.14$.
6. In $i = prt$, find i when p is $1200, r is 2%, and t is 3 years.
7. In $A = lw$, find A when l is 25 yards and w is 15 yards.
8. In $p = a + b + c$, find p when a is 10 inches, b is 12.2 inches, and c is 8.9 inches.
9. In $V = lwh$, find V when l is 3 feet, w is 4 feet, and h is 2 feet.
10. In Problem 9, find V when l is $2\frac{1}{2}$ feet, w is $2\frac{1}{4}$ feet, and h is $2\frac{3}{4}$ feet.

In the following formulas, find X *if* $a = 2$, $b = 5$, *and* $c = 1$:

11. $X = ab + c$

12. $X = 2ab - c$

13. $X = \dfrac{10a}{b} + c$

14. $X = 2a + 3b + 5c$

15. $X = \frac{1}{2}ab - 5c$

16. $X = \dfrac{3}{4}bc - \dfrac{a}{c}$

★ *Find* Y *if* $m = \frac{2}{3}$, $n = \frac{1}{6}$, *and* $p = 0$:

17. $Y = 36mn - p$

18. $Y = \dfrac{m}{n} - 3p$

19. $Y = 6m - 12n + 10p$

20. $Y = m + n + p$

21. $Y = \dfrac{10n}{m} + 8mn$

22. $Y = mp + \dfrac{n}{m}$

23. $Y = 197.3mnp$

24. $Y = nm - mp + np$

25. $Y = 5m \cdot n$

26. $Y = \frac{1}{2}m + 2n$

Exponents

If you let A stand for the number of square units in the area of a square and let s stand for the number of units in a side, then you can write the formula for the area of the square in terms of its side:

$$A = s^2$$

In s^2, 2 is the **exponent** and s is the **base.** The exponent 2 tells you that s is a factor twice. s^2 means the same as $s \times s$. It is read "s square."

The expression 8^3 means the same as $8 \times 8 \times 8$. The exponent 3 tells you that the base 8 is used as a factor three times. The entire symbol 8^3 is the third **power** of 8. It is read "8 to the third power" or simply "8 to the third." It is also read "8 cube." The third power of 8 is thus $8 \times 8 \times 8$, or 512.

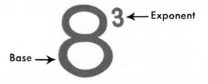

The product $a \cdot a \cdot a \cdot a$ contains four identical factors. It may be written as a^4, which is read "a to the fourth." The exponent 4 indicates that the base a is used four times as a factor.

When the exponent is not written, it is understood to be 1. Thus the exponent of, say, x is 1, or $x = x^1$.

If you wanted to find the successive powers of, say, 4, then the beginning of your work would look like this:

$$4^1 = 4 \qquad 4^2 = 16 \qquad 4^3 = 64 \qquad 4^4 = 256$$

1, 2, 3, and 4 are the exponents, and 4, 16, 64, and 256 are the first, second, third, and fourth powers of 4.

Examples for Study

1. $6 \cdot 6$, or 6^2, is read "6 square" or "6 to the second."
2. aaa, or a^3, is read "a cube" or "a to the third."
3. $bbbbb$, or b^5, is read "b to the fifth."
4. $aaaa \ldots a$ (to n factors), or a^n, is read "a to the nth." The three dots mean that some a's have not been written if n is greater than 5.

PROBLEMS

Rewrite each of the following using exponents:

1. aaa
2. $bbbb$
3. $2 \cdot 2 \cdot 2 \cdot 2 \cdot 2 \cdot 2 \cdot 2$
4. $3a \times aa$
5. $aa \times bb$
6. $10 \cdot 10 \cdot 10 \cdot 10 \cdot aaa$
7. $3x \cdot xxxx$
8. $4aaa \cdot aaa$
9. $aaa \times bbbb \times cc$
10. What does 5^4 mean?
11. What does 5^4 equal?
★ 12. What does $(\frac{1}{2})^3$ mean?
13. What does $(\frac{1}{2})^3$ equal?
14. What is the fifth power of 2?
15. Which is larger, the fourth power of 5 or the fifth power of 4?

Write each of the following as a single number:

16. $8^3 \cdot 7^2$
17. $(0.01)^3$
18. $(\frac{2}{3})^4$
19. $(0.5)^4$
20. $(1.5)^2 (0.6)^2$
21. 1^2
22. 1^{59}
23. 0^3
★ 24. 2^{10}
25. $(\frac{3}{4} \cdot 2)^2$
26. $(\frac{1}{2})^2 (\frac{3}{4})^3$
27. $8^3(\frac{1}{8})^3$

Order of Operations

In evaluating algebraic expressions, you must know which operation to do first. Take, as an example, this problem:

$$6 + 4 \times 3 = \underline{\ ?\ }$$

Should you add first and then multiply? Or should you multiply first and then add? If you add 6 and 4 and then multiply the sum by 3, you get 30 as an answer. But if you multiply 4 by 3 and then add 6, you get 18 as an answer. Without a guide to follow, either answer seems reasonable. It is desirable, however, to get only one answer. Therefore, in cases like this one, mathematicians agreed on the following:

> 1. **Do the multiplication and division operations first.**
> 2. **Then do the addition and subtraction operations.**

When you follow this agreement, you will work the problem as follows:

$$6 + 4 \times 3 = \underline{\ ?\ }$$
$$6 + 12 = 18$$

Expressions, Terms, and Coefficients

In algebra such expressions as $4y$, $1.7ax$, $156mnr$ are called **terms**. The expression $2x + 3y$ has two terms: $2x$ and $3y$. The expression $x + 2y - 5$ has three terms: x, $2y$, and 5. In an expression, addition and subtraction signs separate the terms; multiplication signs do not.

In an algebraic term such as $16x$, 16 is the coefficient of x, and x is the coefficient of 16. In the term $5ax$, 5 is the coefficient of ax; a is the coefficient of $5x$; x is the coefficient of $5a$; $5a$ is the coefficient of x; ax is the coefficient of 5; and $5x$ is the coefficient of a. However, 16 is the *numerical coefficient* of x in $16x$, and 5 is the *numerical coefficient* of ax in $5ax$. In this course, you will use the word **coefficient** to mean "numerical coefficient."

If an algebraic term consists of only one letter, say y, it actually means $1 \cdot y$. So the coefficient of y is 1. Similarly, a means $1 \cdot a$; mn means $1mn$; and x^2y^2 means $1x^2y^2$. The coefficient 1 is usually not written.

PROBLEMS

Name the coefficient in each of the following algebraic terms:

1. $3x$ 2. ax 3. $2ax^2$ 4. x^3 5. $0.01x$ 6. b^2x^2
7. $\frac{1}{2}x$ 8. $x \cdot 4$ 9. $x \cdot a$ 10. $\frac{4}{3}x$ 11. x 12. $1x$

The Distributive Principle

Parentheses around an expression, such as $(x + y)$ or $(10 - 2b)$, mean that the expression within the parentheses is to be considered as a whole. Read the parentheses as "the quantity." For example, read $(x + y)$ as "the quantity x plus y," $(a^2 - 4)$ as "the quantity a^2 minus 4," and $2(10 - 2b)$ as "2 times the quantity 10 minus $2b$."

Consider the following formula:

$$a(b + c) = ab + ac$$

Suppose $a = 2$, $b = 6$, and $c = 5$. Evaluating this formula, you obtain:

$$2(6 + 5) = 2 \times 6 + 2 \times 5$$

In finding $2 \times 6 + 2 \times 5$, multiply before adding:

$$2(6 + 5) = 12 + 10$$
$$2(11) = 12 + 10$$
$$22 = 22$$

For the set of values used above, the formula gives a true statement. Try other values for a, b, and c to see whether the formula

USING LETTERS FOR NUMBERS **11**

always gives a true statement. See if you can find any set of three numbers, one replacing a, another b, and the third c, which will not give a true statement.

DO YOU SEE? For every value of a, b, and c, $a(b + c) = ab + ac$.

The formula $a(b + c) = ab + ac$ states a very important relation in mathematics. It is called the **distributive principle**. When the multiplication by a is done, a is distributed to each expression within the parentheses.

Because it is an equality, the distributive principle may be written either $a(b + c) = ab + ac$ or $ab + ac = a(b + c)$. When the letters are replaced by numbers, for example, $2(6 + 5) = 2 \times 6 + 2 \times 5$, the formula shows that you get the same answer if you *first add* 6 and 5 and *then multiply* by 2 or if you *first multiply* 6 by 2 and 5 by 2 and *then add* the products. The distributive principle holds no matter how many letters or numbers are inside the parentheses.

PROBLEMS

1. If $a = 5$ and $b = 2$, show that $3(ab)^2$ and $3ab^2$ give two different answers.

Write each of the following as a single number:

2. $3(7 + 2)$
3. $8(9 + 3)$
4. $(5 + 1)(3)$
5. $7(9 - 5)$
6. $13(5 - 2)$
7. $(7 - 4)(2)$
8. $(3 \cdot 7)^2$
9. $3(7^2)$
10. $(4 \cdot 2 \cdot 5)^2$
11. $4(2 \cdot 5)^2$
12. $(4 \cdot 2)^2 (5)$
13. $4^2(2 \cdot 5)$

Find the value of each of the following when $a = 2$ *and* $b = 4$:

14. $3(a + b)$
15. $4(b - a)$
16. $5(2a - b)$
17. $a(7 - a)$
18. $b(10 - b)$
19. $3(ab - 2)$
20. $9(a^2 + b^2)$
21. $a(a^2b - 10)$
22. $3a(ab - a)$
23. $5(3a^2b - 6)$
24. $ab(ab - b)$
25. $b^3(b^2 - 3a^2)$

Evaluate each of the following if $a = 3$, $b = 5$, $c = 6$, *and* $d = 1$:

26. $bc - ad$
27. $4a + bc - ad$
28. $ab + b(c - d)$
29. $\dfrac{c}{a} + ab$
30. $\dfrac{3(a + c)}{a}$
31. $\dfrac{2(c - b)}{d}$
32. $8c - a(c - b)$
33. $a^2 + b^2$
34. $d^3 + (c - 2d)$
35. $b^3 - (bc - ad)$
36. $(5b - 5a) - d^2$
37. $c^3 - b^3$
38. $\dfrac{4(c - d)}{b}$
39. $\dfrac{10cd}{a + b}$
40. $\dfrac{ac - bd}{abc}$
41. $\dfrac{20d - d(b + c)}{3c}$
42. $\dfrac{a^3 + b^3}{b^2}$
43. $\dfrac{bc - 10a}{6d^3}$

Example for Study

Using the distributive principle, write an expression equal to $mx + my$.

SOLUTION:
$$\text{Distributive principle: } ab + ac = a(b + c)$$
Let $a = m$, $b = x$, and $c = y$
$$\text{Substituting: } mx + my = m(x + y)$$

So $m(x + y)$ is equal to $mx + my$.

Using the distributive principle, write an expression equal to each of the following:

44. $ac + ad$ 45. $xt + xs$ 46. $dn + dm$

47. $8a + 8c$ 48. $3r + 3p$ 49. $10z + 10y$

50. $cx + dx$ 51. $ay + by$ 52. $ma + na$

53. $8a + 3a$ 54. $5b + 5b$ 55. $62r + 36r$

56. $6m + 12m$ 57. $10.4t + 2t$ 58. $15n + 15n$

Writing Algebraic Expressions

As you continue your study of algebra, you will gain skill in changing word expressions into algebraic expressions that have the same meaning. Study the following examples:

Word Expression	*Algebraic Expression*
The sum of x and y, divided by three	$\dfrac{x + y}{3}$
The product of a and b, increased by four	$ab + 4$

PROBLEMS

Change the following word expressions into algebraic expressions. Use parentheses when needed.

1. The sum of m and n.
2. The product of b and $3a$.
3. The product of a and b, decreased by 6.
4. The quotient of p divided by q.
5. The sum of $3x$ and y, divided by 10.
6. The product of r and s, increased by the product of m and n.
7. Twelve more than the quotient of x divided by y.
8. One-fifth of t decreased by one-half.
9. The cube of x plus the square of y.
10. The difference of the square of a subtracted from the square of b.
11. a raised to the fourth power, increased by b raised to the third power.

12. x raised to the nth power.
13. The product of a, b, and c.
14. Ten times the square of the product of a, b, and c.
15. Six times x, plus y.
16. Six times the sum of x and y.
17. Twice m plus n.
18. Twice the quantity of m plus n.
19. Three times the quantity a minus b.
20. One-half of the sum of $3p$ and $5q$.

★ 21. Fifteen times the square of x, diminished by ten times the cube of y.
22. Thirteen times the product of m and n, divided by seven times r raised to the second power.
23. The difference of the cube of c subtracted from the cube of d.
24. n times the quantity s square minus t square.
25. The product of m and the sum of $5r$ and $6s$.

Study the following examples to see how algebraic expressions are changed to word expressions.

Algebraic Expression	Word Expression
$2k$	Twice some number
$x + 2y$	The sum of one number and twice another number

Change the following algebraic expressions into word expressions:

26. $5n$ 27. $a + b$ 28. $2m + 8$

29. $n - \frac{1}{2}n$ 30. ab 31. d^2

32. $\dfrac{x + y}{2}$ 33. $\frac{1}{4}(m - n)$ 34. $5(ab)^3$

★ 35. $n(3x - y^2)$ 36. $(a + b) \div 5$ 37. $7(m + n)$

38. $5(x + y)^2$ 39. $5(x^2 + y^2)$ 40. $3(5x^2 + y)$

The Commutative Principle for Addition

Replace a by 4 and b by 5 in the formula $a + b = b + a$. Do you get a true statement? Is this formula true for other values (replacements) of a and b? Can you find values for a and b for which the formula becomes a false statement?

DO YOU SEE? ☞ **For every value of a and b, $a + b = b + a$.**

This formula states a principle which you have used for a long time; namely, the order of adding two numbers makes no difference. This principle is called the **commutative principle for addition.**

The Commutative Principle for Multiplication

Replace a by 6 and b by 7 in the formula $ab = ba$. Do you get a true statement? Is this formula true for other values (replacements) of a and b? Can you find values for which the formula becomes a false statement?

DO YOU SEE? 👉 **For every value of a and b, $ab = ba$.**

This formula states a principle which you have used for a long time; namely, the order of multiplying two numbers makes no difference. This principle is called the **commutative principle for multiplication**.

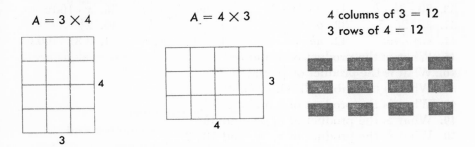

The commutative principle for multiplication can be used to good advantage in algebra, as you will see in the two examples below.

Examples for Study

Find the indicated products:

1. $2a \cdot 3a = \underline{\ ?\ }$

SOLUTION:
The product can be written: $2 \cdot a \cdot 3 \cdot a$

Rearranging the factors: $2 \cdot 3 \cdot a \cdot a = 6a^2$

2. $2a \cdot 3ab \cdot 6ab = \underline{\ ?\ }$

SOLUTION:
The product can be written: $2 \cdot a \cdot 3 \cdot a \cdot b \cdot 6 \cdot a \cdot b$

Rearranging the factors: $2 \cdot 3 \cdot 6 \cdot a \cdot a \cdot a \cdot b \cdot b = 36a^3b^2$

In doing multiplication problems similar to the two examples above, it is not necessary to rearrange the factors on paper. You can rearrange them mentally, using your pencil only to write the result.

PROBLEMS

Multiply:

1. $3 \cdot 8x$
2. $5 \cdot 10a$
3. $(13b)(3)$
4. $(2)(19c)$
5. $(ab)(11)$
6. $(10)(20x)$
7. $8 \cdot 8a$
8. $9 \cdot 7b$
9. $(5a)(6c)$
10. $(10c)(4ab)$
11. $8a \cdot 7a$
12. $(6x)(9x)$
13. $(14d)(4d)$
14. $9mn \cdot mn$
15. $6 \cdot 7c$
16. $ab \cdot a$
17. $2x \cdot 49$
18. $ab \cdot ab$
19. $\frac{1}{2}a \cdot 4a$
20. $\frac{1}{2}m \cdot \frac{1}{2}m$
21. $\frac{3}{4}k \cdot 2k$
22. $5xy \cdot 2x$
23. $mn \cdot 7mn$
24. $13a^2b \cdot 3ab$

25. $5y$
    $\underline{2y}$
26. $3s$
    $\underline{4s}$
27. $3x$
    $\underline{6x^2}$
28. $5xy$
    $\underline{7y}$

29. $3k$
    $\underline{7k^2}$
30. $9a^2bc$
    $\underline{2ab}$
31. $4xyz$
    $\underline{5xyz}$
32. $9.3r^2$
    $\underline{0.4s}$

33. $20 \cdot 2k \cdot k$
34. $x \cdot 3x \cdot 2x$
35. $5a \cdot 5a \cdot 5a$
36. $x \cdot 100x$
37. $3f \cdot 2f \cdot 5$
38. $a \cdot a \cdot a \cdot a$
39. $\frac{1}{2}h \cdot \frac{1}{2}h \cdot \frac{1}{2}h$
40. $2\frac{1}{4} \cdot 3a$
41. $mn \cdot mn$
42. $ab \cdot ab \cdot ab$
43. $0.1u \cdot 0.1u$
44. $0.3x \cdot 0.03y$

45. What is the product of x and $3x$?
46. What is the product of $\frac{1}{4}a$ and $\frac{1}{4}b$?
47. What is the cube of 3? Of 5? Of $4a$?
48. What is the product of k and k^2?
49. What is the product of 5, $3a$, and $4b$?
50. What is the product of x, $3x$, and $10x^2$?

Division

The operation of division is related to the operation of multiplication, as you will see in the following examples.

$$14 \div 2 = \underline{\ ?\ } \qquad \underline{\ ?\ } \times 2 = 14$$

The two examples above tell you that the question "What is the quotient of 14 divided by 2?" is equivalent to the question "What number multiplied by 2 gives 14?" The answer, of course, is 7. Therefore, 14 divided by 2 equals 7, or $14 \div 2 = 7$. We say that division is the **inverse** of multiplication.

In trying to find an answer to a problem like $10 \div 5 = \underline{\ ?\ }$, you should ask yourself, "What number multiplied by 5 gives 10?" The answer, of course, is 2. Therefore, 10 divided by 5 equals 2, or $10 \div 5 = 2$.

Suppose you have the following:

$$6 \div 0 = \underline{\ ?\ }$$

This problem is the same as finding a number which when multiplied by zero gives 6. Of course you know that there is no such number, because any number multiplied by zero is zero. Therefore, we say that division by zero is meaningless.

In algebra it is often helpful to write a division problem as a fraction. For example, you can write $14 \div 2 = 7$ as $\frac{14}{2} = 7$. The meaning is the same. To check the answer, multiply the quotient 7 by the divisor 2. The result should be the dividend 14. The answer checks.

In arithmetic you reduced fractions to lower terms by dividing both the numerator and the denominator by the same number.

FOR EXAMPLE:

$$\frac{35}{50} = \frac{35 \div 5}{50 \div 5} = \frac{7}{10} \qquad \frac{7 \times \overset{1}{\cancel{5}}}{10 \times \underset{1}{\cancel{5}}} = \frac{7}{10} \qquad \frac{36 \times 5}{9} = \frac{\overset{4}{\cancel{36}} \times 5}{\underset{1}{\cancel{9}}} = 20$$

In algebra, too, you can divide the numerator and the denominator by the same number, term, or expression.

Examples for Study

1. $\dfrac{36 \cdot a}{9} = \dfrac{\overset{4}{\cancel{36}} \cdot \overset{a}{\cancel{a}}}{\underset{1}{\cancel{9}}} = 4a$ $\qquad$ CHECK: $4a \cdot 9 = 36a$

Both the numerator and the denominator are divided by 9.

2. $\dfrac{70a}{10a} = \dfrac{\overset{7}{\cancel{70a}}}{\underset{1}{\cancel{10a}}} = 7$ $\qquad$ CHECK: $7 \cdot 10a = 70a$

Both the numerator and the denominator are divided by $10a$.

3. $\dfrac{24ab}{6a} = \dfrac{\overset{4b}{\cancel{24ab}}}{\underset{1}{\cancel{6a}}} = 4b$ $\qquad$ CHECK: $4b \cdot 6a = 24ab$

Both the numerator and the denominator are divided by $6a$.

4. $\dfrac{100k}{25} = \dfrac{\overset{4k}{\cancel{100k}}}{\underset{1}{\cancel{25}}} = 4k$ $\qquad$ CHECK: $4k \cdot 25 = 100k$

Both the numerator and the denominator are divided by 25.

When dividing, keep in mind one important principle: Any number —except zero—or term or expression divided by itself equals one.

FOR EXAMPLE:

$$\frac{6}{6} = 1 \qquad \frac{100}{100} = 1 \qquad \frac{a}{a} = 1 \qquad \frac{ab}{ab} = 1 \qquad \frac{5xyz}{5xyz} = 1$$

PROBLEMS

Divide:

1. $\dfrac{8y}{4}$ 2. $\dfrac{16x}{8}$ 3. $\dfrac{2b}{b}$ 4. $\dfrac{100ab}{ab}$

5. $\dfrac{63m}{7}$ 6. $\dfrac{72a}{24}$ 7. $\dfrac{28d}{7d}$ 8. $\dfrac{400mn}{100m}$

9. $\dfrac{96k}{12}$ 10. $\dfrac{30ab}{5a}$ 11. $\dfrac{2.6n}{1.3n}$ 12. $\dfrac{4xy}{2x}$

13. $\dfrac{20a^2}{20}$ 14. $\dfrac{ab}{a}$ 15. $\dfrac{1.8a}{0.9a}$ 16. $\dfrac{1.2y}{0.02}$

17. $18a \div 3$ 18. $12x \div 4$ 19. $32a^2 \div 8a$

20. $42d \div 6$ 21. $36m \div 9m$ 22. $100xy \div 50y$

23. $24k \div k$ 24. $48xy \div 3xy$ 25. $95xyz \div 5xz$

★ 26. $1000p \div 100p$ 27. $2.5x \div 0.05$ 28. $35a^2 \div 50a$

29. $\frac{1}{2}m \div \frac{1}{2}$ 30. $3a \div \frac{1}{2}$ 31. $15xy \div 30x$

32. $\frac{1}{4}y \div 4$ 33. $12a \div \frac{1}{3}$ 34. $4r^2 \div 8r^2$

35. $3a^2 \div 0.003$ 36. $a \div 0.01$ 37. $17xy \div 17xy$

Find the quotient in each of the following problems:

38. 1 divided by 2.   39. a divided by $2a$.

40. 2 divided by 20.   41. $2ab$ divided by $20ab$.

42. x divided by $100x$.   43. $0.01x$ divided by $0.01x$.

44. a divided by a.   45. $\frac{1}{2}k$ divided by $2k$.

46. $\frac{1}{4}p$ divided by $\frac{3}{4}p$.   47. $\frac{7}{16}st$ divided by $\frac{7}{8}st$.

Addition

By using the distributive and commutative principles, you can often simplify the sum of a number of terms.

Examples for Study

1. Add $5x^2$, x^2, and $7x^2$ and simplify the answer.

SOLUTION:

Commutative principle: $5x^2 + x^2 + 7x^2 = x^2 \cdot 5 + x^2 + x^2 \cdot 7$

Distributive principle: $= x^2(5 + 1 + 7)$

Adding 5, 1, and 7: $= x^2 \cdot 13$

Commutative principle for multiplication: $= 13x^2$

2. Add $4b$ and $2b$ and simplify the answer.

SOLUTION:

Commutative and distributive principles: $4b + 2b = b(4 + 2)$

Adding 4 and 2: $= b \cdot 6$

Commutative principle for multiplication: $= 6b$

3. Add $8x$ and $2y$.

SOLUTION: $8x + 2y$ is the sum. It is not possible to simplify.

18 *ALGEBRA: ITS BIG IDEAS AND BASIC SKILLS*

PROBLEMS

Find a simple answer for the sum of the terms in each of the following:
1. $6a, 2a$
2. $10c, 5c$
3. $x, 7x, 21x, 16x$
4. $b, 14b, b, 29b$
5. $3y, 30y, 15y$
6. $13x^2, 7x^2, 9x^2, x^2$

7. Compare your answers to Problems 1–6 with the sum of the coefficients of the terms. State a short-cut rule for finding a simple answer for these problems.

The idea of like terms is helpful in simplifying, where possible, the answers to addition problems. To learn how to decide whether terms are like terms or unlike terms, study the following examples.

Like terms: (1) $3a, 2a, a, \frac{1}{2}a$ (2) $8cx, 3cx, cx$ (3) $x^2, 4x^2, 8x^2, 10x^2$
Unlike terms: (1) $b, c, 2a, x$ (2) y, y^2, y^3 (3) $2m, 2m^2, 2m^3$

When you have a sum consisting of like terms, you can get a simpler answer merely by adding the coefficients. Remember: when no coefficient is written, it is understood to be 1.

Add like terms by adding coefficients; indicate the sums of unlike terms:

8. $3x$
   $4x$
9. $2a$
   $5a$
10. a
    a
11. $2a$
    $3b$
12. $7d$
    d
13. $2ab$
    $6ab$

14. mn
    mn
15. $2x$
    $8y$
16. $4k$
    10
17. $5a^2$
    $3a^2$
18. m^3
    m^3
19. xy
    $3xy$

20. $12ab$
    $8ab$
21. $12ab$
    $3ac$
22. m^2n
    $2m^2n$
23. x^4
    x^4
24. x
    7
25. a^2
    a

26. $3a$
    $4a$
    $5a$
    $6a$
27. am
    am
    am
    am
28. $10x$
    x
    $3x$
    $2x$
29. $1\frac{1}{2}x$
    $2\frac{1}{4}x$
    $5\frac{1}{2}x$
    $4\frac{3}{4}x$
30. $2.1a$
    $3.2a$
    $6.0a$
    $3.8a$
31. x^2y
    x^2y
    $3x^2y$
    x^2y

Simplify whenever possible by adding like terms:
32. $mn + mn$
33. $9k + 10k + k$
34. $2a + 3a + b$
35. $x + 5 + 2$
36. $a + b + a$
37. $3x^2y + 2x^2y + x^2y$
38. $3m + 4m + 10m$
39. $y + 3y + 4y + y$
40. $a + b + c$
41. $10 + 10a$
42. $x + 3 + 3x$
43. $2a + 8a + 4b$
44. $a^2 + a + 2a$
45. $5x^2 + x^2 + y^2 + 5y^2$

★ 46. $2s + s^2 + 3s + 4$
47. $0.01x + 3.7x + x$
48. $\frac{1}{2}x + \frac{2}{3}x + \frac{1}{4}x$
49. $2.7xy + 3.2xy + 4.8xy$
50. $7x^2 + 7y^2 + 7x^2$
51. $4xyz + xyz + 0.1xyz$
52. $5r^2 + 2r + 6r^2$
53. $5x^3 + 2x^2 + 7x^3 + 4x^2$

Subtraction

You can use the distributive and commutative principles to find a simple answer to some subtraction problems.

Examples for Study

1. Subtract $3y$ from $8y$.

SOLUTION:

Distributive principle: $\qquad\qquad ab - ac = a(b - c)$

Let $a = y$, $b = 8$, and $c = 3$

Substituting: $\qquad\qquad\qquad y8 - y3 = y(8 - 3)$

Subtracting 3 from 8: $\qquad\qquad\qquad = y \cdot 5$

Commutative principle for multiplication: $\qquad = 5y$

2. Subtract $5a$ from $7b$ (b is larger than a).

SOLUTION: $7b - 5a$ is the simplest answer.

As in addition, the idea of like terms is helpful in subtraction. If two terms are like terms, you can simplify the answer merely by subtracting the coefficients.

PROBLEMS

In each of the following, subtract the second term from the first:

1. $10x, 5x$
2. $14a, 8a$
3. $6x, 3y$
4. $21a^2, 11a^2$
5. $9m, 2m$
6. $3ab, 2ab$
7. $4a, 3b$
8. ab, a
9. $3x^2, x^2$
10. mn, mn
11. $12k, 6$
12. $10x, x$
13. $3mn, 2mn$
14. $8ab, ab$
15. $1\frac{1}{2}x, \frac{1}{4}x$
16. $2\frac{1}{2}b, \frac{3}{4}b$
17. $7ab, 5ac$
18. $3a, a$
19. $18b - 10b$
20. $16x - x$
21. $12a - a$
22. $x^2 - x^2$
23. $15ab - 8ab$
24. $23a^2 - 17a^2$
25. $a^2 - a^2$
26. $a^3 - a^2$
27. $2a - a$

28. From the sum of $9b$ and $8b$ subtract $6b$.

29. From the sum of $4x$ and $7x$ subtract x.　　30. Subtract a from a^2.

31. By how much does $23a$ exceed $11a$?

32. How much larger is $1\frac{1}{2}a$ than a?

33. If a is larger than b, what is the difference between $5a$ and $4b$?

Add or subtract like terms in the following problems as indicated:

34. $6d - 3d + 2d$
35. $5a - a + 2a$
36. $m + m - m$
37. $ab + ab + 3ab$
38. $7x - 2x - x$
39. $3a^2 - 2a^2 + a^2$
40. $x^2 + x^2 - x^2$
41. $x^2 + x - x$
42. $4a + a - 3$
43. $2 + 3 + 2a - 2$
44. $ab - ab + a$
45. $4x + 4 - x - x - 1$
46. $12y + 3y + 8 - y - 4$
47. $xy^2 + 3y - xy^2$
48. $4mn - m$
49. $20 - xy - 10 - x$
50. $a^3 + 2a^2 - a^2$
51. $c - \frac{2}{3}c - \frac{1}{4}c$

SELF TEST

Find y *in the following when* s $= 3$ *and* t $= 5$:

1. $y = s + t$ **2.** $y = st$ **3.** $y = \dfrac{5s}{t}$ **4.** $y = s^2$

5. $y = 4t + s$ **6.** $y = s^2 + t^2$ **7.** $y = s(4 + t)$ **8.** $y = 5(t^2 + 5)$

9. $y = \dfrac{s}{s} + \dfrac{t}{t}$ **10.** $y = 8(s + t)$ **11.** $y = 5s + 6t$ **12.** $y = \frac{1}{2}st$

Find a simple answer for each of the following:

13. $5x + 3x$ **14.** $2y + 8y + y$ **15.** $8x - 2x$

16. $5x + 2 - 3x$ **17.** $9x^2 + 3x^2 - 7x^2$ **18.** $ab + ab + 3$

19. $8 \cdot 4a$ **20.** $(7x)(3x)$ **21.** $4a^2 \cdot 5a$

22. $\dfrac{24y}{3}$ **23.** $\dfrac{72b^2}{12b}$ **24.** $\dfrac{100ab}{5b}$

SUMMARY OF IMPORTANT THINGS TO REMEMBER

1. Words and Expressions

algebraic expression	formula
base	inverse
coefficient	like terms
commutative principle for addition	parentheses
commutative principle for multiplication	placeholder
distributive principle	power
exponent	symbol
factor	term

2. Understandings

Letters are used to stand for numbers. A letter may be replaced by any number from a set of numbers.

Letters that stand for numbers can be added, subtracted, multiplied, and divided.

It is not possible to divide by zero.

For every value of a, b, and c, $a(b + c) = ab + ac$.

Like terms can be added or subtracted by adding or subtracting the coefficients.

For every value of a and b, $ab = ba$ and $a + b = b + a$.

3. Skills

You should be able to:

Use the distributive and commutative principles to simplify answers.

Identify like terms.

Multiply and divide using letters that stand for numbers.

Change word expressions into algebraic expressions and change algebraic expressions into word expressions.

Evaluate formulas and algebraic expressions.

PROBLEMS ON YOUR AIMS

YOUR AIM To learn how letters are used in algebra.

1. If $x = 4$, what number is represented by $5x$? $\frac{1}{2}x$? $\frac{1}{x}$? $x - \frac{1}{x}$? $x - x$?

If y *stands for some number, write the following in the language of algebra:*
2. Twice some number
3. One-half some number
4. Six more than some number

If x *stands for the smaller of two numbers and* y *stands for the larger number, write the following expressions in the language of algebra:*
5. The difference of the two numbers
6. Six less than the larger number
7. One more than the smaller number
8. Three more than the sum of the two numbers
9. Ten less than the difference of the two numbers

YOUR AIM To learn how to add, subtract, multiply, and divide using letters to stand for numbers.

If a *and* b *stand for two numbers and* b *stands for the larger of the two numbers, write each of the following in the language of algebra:*
1. Their sum
2. Their difference
3. Their product
4. The quotient of the larger divided by the smaller

Find a simple answer for each of the following:
5. $2a + a$
6. $3a \cdot 3a$
7. $4ab \cdot 2a$
8. $6x \div x$
9. $5a + 5b$
10. $m \cdot m \cdot m$
11. $x + x + x$
12. $2a \div ab$
13. $2x + x - x$
14. $3a - 3 - a$
15. $m + 2 + m$
16. $ab + a + ab$

YOUR AIM To learn how to work with formulas and other algebraic expressions.

If x $= 5$ *and* y $= 2$, *find the value of:*
1. xy
2. $5x - y^2$
3. x^2y
4. xy^2
5. $\dfrac{x + y}{y}$
6. $\dfrac{x - y}{x}$
7. $\dfrac{10 - xy}{x}$
8. $\frac{1}{3}x - \frac{1}{2}y$

If a $= 10$ *and* b $= 3\frac{1}{2}$, *find the value of* A *in each of the following:*
9. $A = ab$
10. $A = \frac{1}{2}ab$
11. $A = a^2$
12. $A = 2a + 2b$

YOUR AIM To learn the importance of the commutative principles and the distributive principle.

1. Write in four ways the product of 3 and x.
2. Solve $4(3 + 8)$ in two ways using the distributive principle.
3. Using the commutative principles, complete the following:
$$x + y = ? \qquad xy = ?$$

22 *ALGEBRA: ITS BIG IDEAS AND BASIC SKILLS*

VALUABLE SKILLS PRACTICE

1. Copy the following table and work the problems in each column. To check, add your answers to the four problems in each column and compare the sum with the total given in each column.

$\frac{1}{2}$ of $3\frac{1}{2}$ = _?_	1% of 1 = _?_	$1\frac{1}{2} + 1\frac{3}{4}$ = _?_	$10 \times \frac{1}{2}$ = _?_
$\frac{3}{4}$ of 7 = _?_	10% of 30 = _?_	$1\frac{5}{6} - \frac{1}{3}$ = _?_	$10 \div \frac{1}{2}$ = _?_
$\frac{1}{5}$ of $3\frac{3}{4}$ = _?_	4% of 2.5 = _?_	$1\frac{1}{2} + 2\frac{1}{3}$ = _?_	$\frac{1}{2} \div 10$ = _?_
$\frac{1}{2}$ of $\frac{1}{2}$ = _?_	$2\frac{1}{2}\%$ of 10 = _?_	$2\frac{1}{5} - 1\frac{3}{4}$ = _?_	$\frac{1}{2} \div 1\frac{1}{2}$ = _?_
Totals $\quad$ 8	3.36	$9\frac{1}{30}$	$25\frac{23}{60}$

2. Copy the following table. Do the operations indicated at the top of each column for the different values of a and b listed in the first two columns. Write the answers in the proper spaces of your table. To check, add the answers in each column and compare your sum with the total given in each column.

a	b	$a + b$	$a - b$	ab	$\dfrac{a}{b}$	$\dfrac{b}{a}$	$\dfrac{a}{b} + \dfrac{b}{a}$	$\dfrac{a}{b} - \dfrac{b}{a}$
5	$\frac{1}{2}$	?	?	?	?	?	?	?
6	$\frac{2}{3}$	?	?	?	?	?	?	?
$1\frac{1}{2}$	$\frac{1}{4}$	?	?	?	?	?	?	?
Totals		$13\frac{11}{12}$	$11\frac{1}{12}$	$6\frac{7}{8}$	25	$\frac{17}{45}$	$25\frac{17}{45}$	$24\frac{28}{45}$

3. Copy the following table. Do the operations indicated at the top of each column for the different values of c and d listed in the first two columns. Write the answers in the proper spaces of your table. To check, add the answers in each column and compare your sum with the total given in each column.

c	d	$c + d$	$c - d$	cd	$\dfrac{c}{d}$	$\dfrac{d}{c}$	$\dfrac{c}{d} + \dfrac{d}{c}$	$\dfrac{c}{d} - \dfrac{d}{c}$
$\frac{1}{2}$	$\frac{1}{3}$	?	?	?	?	?	?	?
$\frac{3}{5}$	$\frac{1}{2}$	?	?	?	?	?	?	?
$\frac{3}{4}$	$\frac{1}{4}$	?	?	?	?	?	?	?
Totals		$2\frac{14}{15}$	$\frac{23}{30}$	$\frac{157}{240}$	$5\frac{7}{10}$	$1\frac{5}{6}$	$7\frac{8}{15}$	$3\frac{13}{15}$

CHAPTER TEST

Copy and complete each of the following statements:
1. In $8ax^3$ the coefficient of x^3 is ___?___.
2. In $8ax^3$ the exponent of x is ___?___.
3. In the expression $6a + 2a - b$, the terms $6a$ and $2a$ are ___?___ terms.
4. The result of adding two numbers is called a ___?___.
5. The result of multiplying two or more numbers is called a ___?___.
6. The result of dividing one number by another is called a ___?___.
7. The product of x and y is ___?___.
8. The quotient of x divided by y is ___?___.
9. The number of feet in Y yards is ___?___.
10. $5m$ increased by x is ___?___.
11. When $a = 5$ and $b = 10$, $2a + 6b$ equals ___?___.
12. The sum of $2m$ and n, divided by their product is ___?___.
13. The number of inches in $2f$ feet and $3y$ yards is ___?___.
14. Four to the second power is ___?___.
15. The product of $3a$ and $2a$, decreased by the cube of d is ___?___.
16. $6x + x + 5 - 3x - 5$ written in the simplest form is ___?___.
17. If, in $Y = \dfrac{mn - 5}{m}$, $m = 10$ and $n = 6$, then Y equals ___?___.
18. Five times the quantity x minus $2y$ is ___?___.
19. Eight subtracted from eight times $2a$ is ___?___.
20. The cube of 8 plus the square of 5 equals ___?___.

REVIEW PROBLEMS

USING THE SYMBOLS OF ALGEBRA

1. What does $3x$ equal when $x = 7$?
2. Write four expressions for the product of a and b.
3. Write the square of x. The square root of x.
4. Indicate the quotient of m divided by n.
5. Indicate the sum of 5 and y, divided by their product.
6. What is the sum of $\frac{2}{3}$ and $\frac{2}{3}$? The difference? The product? The quotient?
7. What is the sum of 10 and 10? The difference? The product? The quotient?
8. What is the sum of x and x? The difference? The product? The quotient?
9. What is the sum of 0.5 and 0.05? The difference? The product? The quotient?

Write each of the following in the language of algebra. Use parentheses when necessary.
10. Three times the product of a and b.
11. The quotient of a divided by b, increased by 6.

24 *ALGEBRA: ITS BIG IDEAS AND BASIC SKILLS*

12. The product of x and y, increased by the square of x.
13. Fifteen times m decreased by ten times n.
14. Three times the sum of d and k.
15. a cube increased by the square of b.

WRITING FORMULAS

1. If one pencil costs 5 cents, how much will 3 pencils cost? n pencils? Write a formula for the cost C of n pencils at 5 cents each.
2. Write a formula for the cost C of n articles at c cents each.
3. Draw a triangle and label the sides a, b, and c. Write a formula for the perimeter p of the triangle.
4. Draw a rectangle and label its length l and its width w. Write a formula for the perimeter p of the rectangle.
5. Draw a square and label a side s. Write a formula for the perimeter p of the square.
6. How many nickels are there in \$1? In \$2? In D dollars? Write a formula for the number of nickels N in D dollars.

7. The area of a trapezoid is equal to the product of one-half the altitude and the sum of the bases. Write this rule as a formula. Use parentheses.

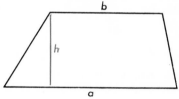

8. The rule for changing centigrade thermometer readings to Fahrenheit readings is: To find the number of degrees Fahrenheit, take $\frac{9}{5}$ of the centigrade reading and add 32. Write this rule as a formula, using F for Fahrenheit readings and C for centigrade readings.
9. The speed of the earth in traveling around the sun is about 18 miles per second. Write a formula for the distance d the earth will travel in s seconds.
10. m and n stand for two numbers. Write a formula for the average A of these numbers.
11. The volume of a cylinder may be found by multiplying the area of the base by its height. Write this rule as a formula, letting V stand for the volume, B for the area of the base, and h for the height.
12. Letting r stand for the radius of the base, write a formula for finding the volume of a cylinder without using the letter B. See Problem 11.

USING LETTERS FOR NUMBERS **25**

EVALUATING ALGEBRAIC EXPRESSIONS

If $a = 1$, $b = 2$, *and* $c = 3$, *find the value of each of the following:*

1. $a + b + c$
2. $2a + 3b$
3. $6a - 2b + c$
4. $a^2 + b^2 + c^2$
5. $3(a + b)$
6. $5a(b + c)$
7. $abc - 6$
8. $\dfrac{2bc}{3a}$
9. $10(bc)^2$
10. $3b^3 - 6a - c^2$
11. $(c - b)(a + b)$
12. $\dfrac{3a - c}{a + b}$

If $m = 2$, $n = 4$, *and* $p = 5$, *find the value of* x:

13. $x = mn + 2p$
14. $x = \frac{1}{2}mn + 3p$
15. $x = m(n + p)$
16. $x = p(5m - n)$
17. $x = \frac{1}{2}m^3 + \frac{1}{4}n^2$
18. $x = \dfrac{3m + 5n}{2p}$

★ 19. $x = \dfrac{2^m + 5^n}{2(p - n)}$
20. $x = (np)^m$
21. $x = \dfrac{6mn - 2p}{m + n}$
22. $x = m^n$
23. $x = p^n$
24. $x = (mp)^n$

If $a = 2\frac{1}{2}$, $b = 1\frac{1}{2}$, *and* $c = 5\frac{1}{4}$, *find the value of each of the following:*

25. ab
26. $a + b + c$
27. $bc - ab$
28. $8a - 10b$
29. $5a + 3c$
30. ac
31. $a^2 + b^2$
32. $c + (b + c)$
33. $\dfrac{a}{b}$
34. $\dfrac{a - b}{c}$
35. $\dfrac{c - b + a}{a - b}$
36. $\dfrac{b(c - a)}{c - b}$

USING THE FOUR FUNDAMENTAL OPERATIONS

Add:

1. $3mn$
   $2mn$
2. $4x^2$
   $5x^2$
3. ab
   $3ab$
4. $100x$
   x
5. $16d^2t$
   $38d^2t$

6. $m + m$
7. $0.01x + x$
8. $14a^2b + 28a^2b$
9. $abc + abc$
10. $1\frac{1}{2}y + \frac{1}{4}y + 2\frac{1}{4}y$
11. $a + 2\frac{3}{4}a + 5\frac{1}{2}a$

Subtract:

12. $6a$
    $3a$
13. $14am$
    $5am$
14. $10cd$
    cd
15. abc
    abc
16. $3d$
    $2d$

17. $7ab - 4ab$
18. $23mn - 9mn$
19. $40x - x$
20. $15k - k$
21. $16a - a - a$
22. $19xy - 10xy - 8xy$

Multiply:

23. $9a$
    3
24. $3x$
    7
25. $2ab$
    6
26. $11m^2n$
    11
27. $10x$
    x

28. $3x \cdot 3x$
29. $a \cdot a \cdot a \cdot a \cdot b \cdot b$
30. $4m \cdot 3m \cdot m$
31. $xxxyyy$
32. $14rh \cdot 14rh$
33. $2c \cdot 2c \cdot 2c \cdot 2c \cdot 2c$

Divide:

34. $\dfrac{42x}{6}$　35. $\dfrac{18bc}{9}$　36. $\dfrac{24m^2n}{12}$　37. $\dfrac{a}{a}$　38. $\dfrac{6x}{6x}$

39. $\dfrac{8b}{4b}$　40. $\dfrac{14mn}{2m}$　41. $\dfrac{36abc}{9bc}$　42. $\dfrac{12x}{x}$　43. $\dfrac{70rs}{10s}$

Add or subtract as indicated:

44. $6a - 2a + b - a + 2b$

45. $4x - x + 3y - x + y$

46. $12 + ab - 10 - ab - 1$

47. $5x^2 - x + 3x - 5x^2$

48. $3\frac{1}{2}m + m - 1\frac{1}{2}m - \frac{1}{2}m$

49. $\frac{2}{3}p - \frac{1}{6}p + \frac{1}{2}p$

50. $1.3r^2s + 8.8r^2s - 5.7r^2s$

51. $\frac{1}{5}mn + \frac{1}{10}mn - \frac{1}{20}mn$

52. $\frac{2}{3}x + \frac{3}{4}x + x$

53. $\frac{7}{8}xy + \frac{1}{8}x + \frac{1}{4}xy$

Follow these steps to success.

REVIEWS OFTEN

ASKS QUESTIONS IF IN DOUBT

DOES OWN WORK

DOES EACH DAILY LESSON

DAYS MISSED

LESSONS NOT MADE UP

BACK WORK

FAILED T...

DIDN'T GET DAILY LESSON

DAY DREAMED IN CLASS

DIDN'T ASK QUESTIONS

Avoid carrying this burden.

BIG IDEAS	LETTERS FOR NUMBERS
	EQUATION
BASIC SKILLS	Using and interpreting symbols of algebra
	Fundamental operations
	Evaluating algebraic expressions
	Solving equations
	Solving verbal problems

CHAPTER 2 *Equations*

IN CHAPTER 1 you learned to use letters to stand for numbers. You were able to write general statements about numbers using letters. This was not possible in arithmetic. In this chapter you will learn how to use letters to make equations and then solve them. The solutions of equations will provide you with answers to various problems.

Equations play a very important part in your everyday life. For example, the development of radio and television was made possible by equations. The existence of radio waves was first predicted by a Scottish physicist, James Clerk-Maxwell, in a set of equations. Later these equations were used as the basis of an experiment that led to the actual discovery of radio waves.

Equations affect your life in other ways, too. It is by means of equations that your electric-light bill is determined at the end of the month. Also, without the equation scientists would never have learned how to release atomic energy.

YOUR AIM

1. To learn the meaning of an equation.

2. To learn how to solve equations.

3. To learn how to use equations in solving problems.

Using Letters in Equations

You have learned that you can replace the letter in an algebraic expression such as $3x + 5$ by different numbers. For example, when x is replaced by 8, the expression $3x + 5$ equals 29. When x is replaced by 8, the expression $2x + 13$ also equals 29. Thus when $x = 8$, then $2x + 13 = 3x + 5$ is a true statement.

An expression such as $2x + 13 = 3x + 5$ is called an **equation.** Other examples of equations are $3x + 5 = 11$, $14 = 2y + 3$, $6b = 12$, and $18 = \frac{n}{3}$. Thus an equation is an expression of equality of two algebraic expressions or of a number and an algebraic expression.

PROBLEMS

1. What number does $3x + 5$ equal when $x = 2$? When $x = 3$?
2. What number does $4x + 1$ equal when $x = 4$? When $x = 3$?
3. What number does $5y + 6$ equal when $y = 2$? When $y = 1$?
4. What number does $9a$ equal when $a = 1$? When $a = \frac{1}{2}$?

When x is replaced by the number in this column	Then 2x + 9 is equal to the number in this column	And 4x + 1 is equal to the number in this column
0	9	1
1	11	5
2	13	9
3	15	13
4	17	17
5	19	21
6	21	25
7	23	29

5. Study the table above. When $x = 1$, what does $2x + 9$ equal? What does $4x + 1$ equal? Does $2x + 9 = 4x + 1$ when $x = 1$?
6. In the table above, when $x = 3$, does $2x + 9 = 4x + 1$?
7. In the table above, when $x = 4$, does $2x + 9 = 4x + 1$?
8. Which numbers used to replace x in the above table make $2x + 9 = 4x + 1$ a false statement?

DO YOU SEE? When x in the equation $2x + 9 = 4x + 1$ is replaced by some numbers, the equation is a false statement. Only $x = 4$ makes it a true statement.

9. What number does $x + 9$ equal when $x = 1$? When $x = 2$? When $x = 3$? When $x = 4$?
10. What number for x makes $x + 9 = 12$ a true statement?
11. Replace x in $x + 9 = 12$ by some numbers that will make the equation a false statement.

In each of the following equations replace the letter by the number that will make the equation a true statement. Do not use pencil and paper except to write the answer.

12. $5x = 15$
13. $3y = 12$
14. $4a = 28$
15. $a + 3 = 10$
16. $x + 5 = 30$
17. $y + 6 = 17$
18. $b - 3 = 12$
19. $k - 7 = 11$
20. $x - 15 = 15$
21. $\dfrac{x}{4} = 8$
22. $\dfrac{y}{3} = 6$
23. $\dfrac{k}{7} = 9$
24. $k + 4 = 5$
25. $x + 11 = 17$
26. $y + 3 = 17$
27. $4 + x = 17$
28. $19 - x = 15$
29. $15 - x = 1$
30. $7k = 21$
31. $5t = 10$
32. $5t = 30$
33. $5t = 60$
34. $3x = 9$
35. $3x = 18$
36. $\dfrac{50}{x} = 2$
37. $\dfrac{x}{50} = 2$
38. $50 \cdot x = 100$
39. $x + 4 = 6$
40. $x + 4 = 5$
41. $x + 4 = 4$
42. $x - 4 = 2$
43. $x - 4 = 1$
44. $x - 4 = 0$
45. $8x = 16$
46. $8x = 8$
47. $8 \cdot x = 0$

★ 48. $\frac{1}{2}x = 20$
49. $\frac{1}{3}x = 5$
50. $\frac{1}{6}y = 4$
51. $\dfrac{x}{4} = 2$
52. $\dfrac{x}{4} = 1$
53. $\dfrac{x}{4} = \dfrac{1}{2}$
54. $\dfrac{y}{5} = 4$
55. $\dfrac{y}{5} = 1$
56. $\dfrac{y}{9} = 1$
57. $\dfrac{k}{2} = \dfrac{1}{2}$
58. $\dfrac{k}{4} = \dfrac{1}{4}$
59. $\dfrac{k}{4} = \dfrac{1}{2}$

Solving Equations

In an equation the expression to the left of the equal sign is called the left side or the **left member** of the equation. The expression to the right of the equal sign is called the right side or the **right member** of the equation.

When you are given an equation like $3x = 12$, you replace x by a number that makes the left member equal the same number as the right member. When you do this, you are **solving the equation.** The number that makes the left member equal the same number as the right member is called the **root of the equation.** A root is said to **satisfy the equation.**

30 *ALGEBRA: ITS BIG IDEAS AND BASIC SKILLS*

AN EQUATION

$$\underbrace{3x+6}_{} \quad = \quad \underbrace{2x+11}_{}$$

Left side or   Right side or
left member   right member

PROBLEMS

*Find which of the following equations have the root 5. Do not use pencil
except to write the answers.*

1. $3x = 15$
2. $2x = 8$
3. $2x + 5 = 15$
4. $2x + 3 = 10$
5. $x + 5 = 10$
6. $20 - x = 14$
7. $18 - 2x = 8$
8. $7x = 36$
9. $5x = 2$

*Find which of the following equations have the root 6. Do not use pencil
except to write the answers.*

10. $x + 7 = 13$
11. $4x = 24$
12. $x - 2 = 4$
13. $x + 3 = 10$
14. $x - 5 = 7$
15. $3x = 21$
16. $2x + 4 = 16$
17. $5 + 3x = 23$
18. $7x - 40 = 2$

*In each of the following equations replace x by a number that will make the
left member equal the same number as the right member. Do not use
pencil except to write the answers.*

19. $2x = 18$
20. $x + 5 = 16$
21. $3 + x = 18$
22. $5 - x = 2$
23. $x - 6 = 3$
24. $\frac{x}{5} = 10$
25. $\frac{x}{4} = 4$
26. $3x = 33$
27. $\frac{30}{x} = 5$
28. $2x + 1 = 7$
29. $100 = 10x$
30. $2x = 88$

SELF TEST

*Copy the following and add a word or a phrase that will make each sentence
a true statement:*

1. In an equation the algebraic expression on the left side of the equal
   sign is called the ___?___.
2. The process of finding a number to replace x in the equation
   $5x = 15$ which will make the equation a true statement is called
   ___?___.
3. The number which when substituted for x makes the equation
   $5x = 15$ a true statement is called the ___?___ of the equation.
4. The number which when substituted for x makes the equation
   $5x = 15$ a true statement is said to ___?___ the equation.

EQUATIONS **31**

The Four Laws of Equations

You have solved equations by trying different numbers until you found the one that satisfied the given equation. This is a good method when you work with simple equations such as $3x = 15$ or $2x + 4 = 10$. When you work with more difficult equations like $6x - 15 = 51x - 39$, you need a more direct method of finding the roots.

Study the four laws of equations listed below. You will use these laws in solving equations.

THE FOUR LAWS OF EQUATIONS

1. The same number may be added to each side of an equation without destroying the equality.
2. The same number may be subtracted from each side of an equation without destroying the equality.
3. Each side of an equation may be multiplied by the same number without destroying the equality.
4. Each side of an equation may be divided by the same number (except zero) without destroying the equality.

Inverse Operations

In order to be able to use the four laws of equations, you must understand inverse operations. Operations which are opposite in their effect are called **inverse operations.**

Walking to school and walking home are examples of inverse operations. Putting a jigsaw puzzle together and taking it apart are also inverse operations. Can you think of some other examples of operations which are opposite in their effect?

Addition and subtraction are examples of inverse operations in mathematics.

Addition	Subtraction
$20 + 8 = 28$	$28 - 8 = 20$
$12 + 6 = 18$	$18 - 6 = 12$

From the examples above, you see what is meant by the phrase "operations which are opposite in their effect."

Multiplication and division are also inverse operations.

Multiplication	Division
$3 \times 9 = 27$	$27 \div 9 = 3$
$5 \times 11 = 55$	$55 \div 11 = 5$

Using the Law of Subtraction

You need to use the idea of inverse operations to solve an equation like $x + 8 = 15$. In the left member of the equation 8 is added to x. Since subtraction is the inverse of addition, subtract 8 from the left member of the equation. Then you must also subtract 8 from the right member of the equation in order to keep the equality. Thus $x + 8 - 8 = 15 - 8$, or $x = 7$.

To solve an equation like
$$x + 8 = 15$$
use the LAW OF SUBTRACTION
Subtract 8: $x + 8 - 8 = 15 - 8$
$$x = 7$$

CHECK: $7 + 8 \overset{?}{=} 15$
$$15 = 15$$

In solving equations like $x + 8 = 15$, state the operation and then do it mentally as shown in the following examples.

Examples for Study

1. *Solve:* $x + 9 = 20$

SOLUTION:
Subtract 9 from each member: $x = 11$

CHECK: $11 + 9 \overset{?}{=} 20$
$$20 = 20$$

2. *Solve:* $35 = x + 10$

SOLUTION:
Subtract 10 from each member: $25 = x$

CHECK: $35 \overset{?}{=} 25 + 10$
$$35 = 35$$

PROBLEMS

Solve the following equations by applying the law of subtraction. Check.

1. $x + 2 = 13$
2. $y + 9 = 11$
3. $a + 15 = 20$
4. $b + 23 = 30$
5. $m + 11 = 88$
6. $34 = y + 5$
7. $x + 27 = 69$
8. $c + 46 = 92$
9. $103 = n + 10$
10. $k + 55 = 100$
11. $x + 2.9 = 11.2$
12. $y + 0.04 = 9.4$
13. $s + 3.03 = 3.03$
14. $b + 0.2 = 2.02$
15. $28 = y + 8$
16. $35 = a + 15$
17. $112 = m + 97$
18. $7 + m = 7$

★ 19. $8.3 + x = 14.9$
20. $k + 2.13 = 3.75$
21. $3.20 + y = 7.05$
22. $k + 19.3 = 19.3$
23. $4\frac{1}{2} + z = 5\frac{3}{4}$
24. $x + 3\frac{1}{2} = 13\frac{1}{4}$

EQUATIONS **33**

Using the Law of Addition

In solving an equation like $m - 4 = 10$, note that in the left member of the equation 4 is subtracted from m. Since addition is the inverse of subtraction, add 4 to the left member of the equation. Then you must also add 4 to the right member of the equation in order to keep the equality. Thus $m - 4 + 4 = 10 + 4$, or $m = 14$.

To solve an equation like
$$m - 4 = 10$$
use the **LAW OF ADDITION**
Add 4: $m - 4 + 4 = 10 + 4$
$$m = 14$$
CHECK: $14 - 4 \overset{?}{=} 10$
$$10 = 10$$

Examples for Study

1. *Solve:* $x - 5 = 16$

SOLUTION:
Add 5 to each member: $x = 21$

CHECK: $21 - 5 \overset{?}{=} 16$
$$16 = 16$$

2. *Solve:* $3\frac{1}{2} = x - \frac{1}{2}$

SOLUTION:
Add $\frac{1}{2}$ to each member: $4 = x$ or $x = 4$

CHECK: $3\frac{1}{2} \overset{?}{=} 4 - \frac{1}{2}$
$$3\frac{1}{2} = 3\frac{1}{2}$$

PROBLEMS

Solve the following equations using the law of addition. Check.

1. $x - 10 = 4$
2. $a - 15 = 11$
3. $m - 12 = 27$
4. $r - 25 = 24$
5. $x - 51 = 57$
6. $a - 23 = 0$
7. $d - 100 = 100$
8. $b - 30 = 303$
9. $y - 3.2 = 19.8$
10. $x - 0.04 = 15.56$
11. $a - \frac{1}{2} = \frac{1}{2}$
12. $k - \frac{1}{4} = \frac{3}{4}$

★ 13. $h - 2\frac{1}{2} = 0$
14. $n - 0.3 = 8.2$
15. $5\frac{2}{3} - a = 0$
16. $11\frac{3}{5} = x - 4$
17. $16\frac{1}{2} = y - 7\frac{1}{8}$
18. $0.03 = z - 2.99$
19. $0 = k - 2\frac{1}{5}$
20. $m - 995 = 4$
21. $c - 0.06 = 9.2$

Solve using the law of addition or the law of subtraction. Check.

22. $x - 8 = 2$
23. $a + 3 = 7$
24. $k - 14 = 1$
25. $x - 1 = 1$
26. $y + 1 = 1$
27. $k - 1 = 0$
28. $m + 15 = 16$
29. $2 + x = 3$
30. $7 + g = 7$
31. $d - 7 = 7$
32. $m - 2\frac{1}{2} = 2$
33. $y - 3.2 = 8.8$
34. $h + \frac{1}{3} = 3$
35. $q - 2.33 = 1.66$
36. $x - \frac{3}{8} = 1$

Using the Law of Division

If an equation like $4y = 100$ were stated in words, it would read, "Four times some number equals one hundred." Since y, which stands for some number, is multiplied by 4, you must do the inverse operation in solving for the number; that is, divide each member of the equation by 4.

To solve an equation like
$$4y = 100$$
use the LAW OF DIVISION

Divide by 4: $\dfrac{4y}{4} = \dfrac{100}{4}$

$$y = 25$$

CHECK: $4 \times 25 \stackrel{?}{=} 100$

$$100 = 100$$

In solving equations like $4y = 100$, state the operation and then do it mentally as shown in the following examples.

Examples for Study

1. *Solve:* $8a = 24$

SOLUTION:
Divide each member by 8: $a = 3$

CHECK: $8 \times 3 \stackrel{?}{=} 24$
$24 = 24$

2. *Solve:* $2 = 3x$

SOLUTION:
Divide each member by 3: $\dfrac{2}{3} = x$

CHECK: $2 \stackrel{?}{=} 3 \times \dfrac{2}{3}$
$2 = 2$

PROBLEMS

Solve the following equations using the law of division. Check.

1. $4n = 40$
2. $7x = 63$
3. $2y = 11$
4. $3m = 17$
5. $2k = 1$
6. $3m = 2$
7. $6a = 3$
8. $5x = 4$
9. $14 = 7x$
10. $24 = 5y$
11. $100 = 8d$
12. $9x = 9$

★ 13. $3x = 17$
14. $5z = 8\frac{1}{2}$
15. $4k = \frac{2}{3}$
16. $\frac{1}{8} = 3m$
17. $2x = 0$
18. $3.24 = 9b$
19. $3.24 = 0.09x$
20. $1.06y = 2.438$
21. $(1\frac{2}{3})(y) = 17$
22. $0.88 = 2.4y$
23. $16.1 = 2\frac{1}{2}z$
24. $(6\frac{2}{3})a = 2\frac{1}{6}$

Using the Law of Multiplication

If an equation like $\frac{n}{3} = 5$ were stated in words, it would read, "Some number divided by three equals five." Since n, which stands for some number, is divided by 3, you must do the inverse operation in solving for the number; that is, multiply each member of the equation by 3.

To solve an equation like
$$\frac{n}{3} = 5$$
use the LAW OF MULTIPLICATION

Multiply by 3: $\quad 3 \cdot \frac{n}{3} = 3 \cdot 5$

$$n = 15$$

CHECK: $\quad \frac{15}{3} \stackrel{?}{=} 5$

$$5 = 5$$

In solving equations like $\frac{n}{3} = 5$, state the operation and then do it mentally as shown in the following examples.

Examples for Study

1. *Solve:* $\frac{x}{5} = 6$

SOLUTION:
Multiply each member of the equation by 5:
$$x = 30$$

CHECK: $\frac{30}{5} \stackrel{?}{=} 6$

$$6 = 6$$

2. *Solve:* $7 = \frac{y}{2}$

SOLUTION:
Multiply each member of the equation by 2:
$$14 = y \quad \text{or} \quad y = 14$$

CHECK: $7 \stackrel{?}{=} \frac{14}{2}$

$$7 = 7$$

36 *ALGEBRA: ITS BIG IDEAS AND BASIC SKILLS*

PROBLEMS

Solve the following equations using the law of multiplication. Check.

1. $\frac{a}{2} = 3$　　　　　2. $\frac{x}{4} = 4$　　　　　3. $\frac{m}{5} = 8$

4. $\frac{k}{9} = 2$　　　　　5. $\frac{x}{6} = 1$　　　　　6. $\frac{d}{4} = 12$

7. $\frac{y}{10} = 10$　　　　8. $\frac{g}{11} = 12$　　　　9. $3 = \frac{w}{5}$

10. $16 = \frac{b}{6}$　　　　11. $1.3 = \frac{k}{4}$　　　　12. $\frac{x}{2.5} = 2.5$

13. $\frac{k}{17} = 2$　　　　14. $\frac{k}{17} = 1$　　　　15. $\frac{k}{17} = 0$

★ 16. $\frac{y}{2.07} = 3.14$　　17. $1.05 = \frac{a}{0.01}$　　18. $\frac{y}{0.25} = 4.32$

19. $\frac{x}{2} = 3\frac{1}{3}$　　　　20. $\frac{z}{5} = \frac{3}{8}$　　　　21. $\frac{m}{12} = \frac{3}{4}$

22. $1 = \frac{b}{0.06}$　　　23. $1 = \frac{x}{1728.35}$　　24. $1 = \frac{y}{19.56}$

Solve the following equations using the law of multiplication or the law of division. Check.

25. $\frac{x}{8} = 8$　　　　　26. $8x = 8$　　　　　27. $\frac{b}{10} = 1$

28. $10n = 2$　　　　　29. $\frac{k}{6} = 12\frac{1}{2}$　　　　30. $5y = 0$

31. $7g = 7$　　　　　32. $\frac{h}{8} = 0$　　　　　33. $\frac{d}{12} = 1.2$

34. $\frac{m}{6} = \frac{1}{2}$　　　　35. $100a = 100$　　　　36. $\frac{a}{100} = 100$

For each of the following equations state the operation you must do in order to solve it; then write the root:

EXAMPLE: $\frac{1}{2}a = 5$ (Note that $\frac{1}{2}a$ is the same as $\frac{a}{2}$.) Multiply each member by 2; $a = 10$

37. $10m = 50$　　　38. $5h = 5$　　　　39. $\frac{1}{4}b = 4$

40. $a + 3 = 5$　　　41. $g - 6 = 7$　　　42. $m + 8 = 8$

43. $\frac{a}{3} = 9$　　　　44. $11d = 88$　　　45. $8x = 3$

46. $12y = 4$　　　　47. $7 + p = 10$　　　48. $\frac{1}{2} + q = 1\frac{1}{4}$

49. $d + \frac{1}{4} = 4$　　　50. $x - 13 = 0$　　　51. $13d = 26$

52. $147 = 7b$　　　53. $10k = 1$　　　　54. $\frac{d}{20} = 40$

55. $f - 20 = 40$　　56. $\frac{1}{3}x = 6$　　　57. $y - 5 = 0$

58. $\frac{a}{4} = 0$ 59. $5\frac{1}{2}m = 11$ 60. $5 = 10d$

61. $35 = f - 15$ 62. $35 = k + 15$ 63. $x + 3\frac{1}{4} = 13\frac{1}{2}$

64. $31 = 10 + x$ 65. $\frac{n}{4} = \frac{1}{2}$ 66. $9x = 21$

★ 67. $9 + m = 9$ 68. $\frac{3}{4}a = \frac{3}{4}$ 69. $40x = 10$
70. $0.5y = 10$ 71. $y + 1 = 1$ 72. $d - 1 = 1$

73. $f - 1\frac{3}{4} = 5\frac{1}{2}$ 74. $105 = 5x$ 75. $\frac{a}{16} = \frac{3}{4}$

General Methods for Solving Equations

So far you have solved equations that require only one operation; that is, you have either added, subtracted, multiplied, or divided to find the root of the equation. Now you will learn how to solve equations that require more than one operation to find the root.

Solving an equation is like untying a complicated knot. To untie a knot, you decide which minor knot was made last and untie it. Then you look for the next minor knot and untie it, and so on. Similarly, to solve an equation, you look for the last operation and undo it by performing the inverse operation on both members of the equation. Then you look for the next operation, undo it, and so on.

Examples for Study

   1. *Solve:* $3a + 4 = 16$

SOLUTION: 4 is added to $3a$. Do the inverse operation: subtract 4. To keep the equality, 4 must be subtracted from each member of the equation:

$$3a + 4 - 4 = 16 - 4$$
$$3a = 12$$

a is multiplied by 3. Do the inverse operation: divide $3a$ by 3. To keep the equality, also divide 12 by 3:

$$\frac{3a}{3} = \frac{12}{3}$$
$$a = 4$$

CHECK: $3 \times 4 + 4 \stackrel{?}{=} 16$
$12 + 4 \stackrel{?}{=} 16$
$16 = 16$

NOTE: Always check by substituting in the original equation. Can you explain why, in the example above, we did not check by substituting in the second equation, $3a = 12$?

2. *Solve:* $2x - 7 = 1$

SOLUTION: 7 is subtracted from $2x$. Do the inverse operation: add 7 to each member.

$$2x - 7 + 7 = 1 + 7$$
$$2x = 8$$

x is multiplied by 2. Do the inverse operation: divide each member by 2.

$$\frac{2x}{2} = \frac{8}{2}$$
$$x = 4$$

CHECK: $2 \times 4 - 7 \overset{?}{=} 1$
$$8 - 7 \overset{?}{=} 1$$
$$1 = 1$$

3. *Solve:* $\frac{n}{2} + 1 = 5$

SOLUTION: 1 is added to $\frac{n}{2}$. Do the inverse operation: subtract 1 from each member.

$$\frac{n}{2} + 1 - 1 = 5 - 1$$
$$\frac{n}{2} = 4$$

n is divided by 2. Do the inverse operation: multiply each member by 2.

$$2 \cdot \frac{n}{2} = 2 \cdot 4$$
$$n = 8$$

CHECK: $\frac{8}{2} + 1 \overset{?}{=} 5$
$$4 + 1 \overset{?}{=} 5$$
$$5 = 5$$

Study the following table. It will help you spot the operations to use in solving equations.

Examples of equations	Operation indicated	To solve, do the inverse operation
$x + 2 = 6$	addition	subtraction
$x - 2 = 6$	subtraction	addition
$2x = 6$	multiplication	division
$\frac{x}{2} = 6$	division	multiplication

PROBLEMS

Solve the following equations and list the steps as shown in the example:

EXAMPLE: $2x + 3 = 11$ *1.* Subtract 3 from each member: $2x = 8$

                           2. Divide each member by 2: $\dfrac{2x}{2} = \dfrac{8}{2}$

                           3. Write the root: $x = 4$

1. $5y - 8 = 7$ 2. $3a + 4 = 13$ 3. $6b - 9 = 3$

4. $\dfrac{n}{5} - 4 = 2$ 5. $\dfrac{s}{7} + 2 = 5$ 6. $\dfrac{x}{3} + 1 = 2$

Solve and check:

7. $5x - 8 = 27$ 8. $6t + 9 = 15$ 9. $2m + 7 = 17$

10. $8d - 1 = 7$ 11. $\dfrac{y}{4} + 9 = 12$ 12. $4x + 3 = 13$

13. $3x + 6 = 21$ 14. $1 + 2a = 7$ 15. $3p - 4 = 17$

16. $5p - 12 = 33$ 17. $3g - 15 = 0$ 18. $\dfrac{k}{6} + 7 = 9$

19. $\dfrac{x}{8} - 1 = 0$ 20. $\dfrac{m}{4} - 6 = 10$ 21. $\dfrac{x}{4} - 6 = 0$

22. $\frac{1}{2}x + 2 = 7$ 23. $8x + 8 = 8$ 24. $y + 17 = 17$

25. $\dfrac{d}{4} - 5 = 5$ 26. $7h - 2 = 5$ 27. $8z - 5 = 35$

28. $1 + x = 1$ 29. $16 = 3y - 5$ 30. $\dfrac{b}{3} + 3 = 11$

★ 31. $\dfrac{a}{3} + 3 = 3$ 32. $3 + \frac{1}{2}b = 4$ 33. $\dfrac{x}{5} + 7 = 7$

34. $12x - 3 = 1$ 35. $6 = 6x - 6$ 36. $\dfrac{x}{5} + 6.3 = 8.2$

37. $2 = 5x$ 38. $\dfrac{n}{6} = 12$ 39. $\dfrac{b}{2.8} - 3.5 = 1.3$

40. $\dfrac{n}{2} - 1 = 0$ 41. $31 = \frac{3}{4}x + 16$ 42. $\frac{2}{3}x + 4 = 4\frac{2}{3}$

Don't be a copycat. To learn and to remember what you have been taught, you must do your own work.

You may ask for help or suggestions from your teacher and from others, but do not ask them to do your work for you.

By working and studying faithfully, you will improve your skill in algebra.

By copying, you will gain nothing except writing and copying practice.

Combining Like Terms

When like terms appear in either member of an equation, combine the like terms by adding or subtracting as indicated.

Examples for Study

1. *Solve:* $2x + 3x - x - 11 = 9$

SOLUTION:

Combine the like terms: $\qquad 4x - 11 = 9$

Add 11 to each member: $4x - 11 + 11 = 9 + 11$

$$4x = 20$$

Divide each member by 4: $\qquad \dfrac{4x}{4} = \dfrac{20}{4}$

$$x = 5$$

CHECK: $2 \times 5 + 3 \times 5 - 5 - 11 \overset{?}{=} 9$

$10 + 15 - 5 - 11 \overset{?}{=} 9$

$9 = 9$

2. SOLVE: $4x + 5x - 2x = 30 + 2x + 2 + x$

NOTE: In this equation, both members have terms involving the same letter.

SOLUTION:

Combine the like terms in each member of the equation:

$$7x = 32 + 3x$$

Subtract $3x$ from each member: $\quad 7x - 3x = 32 + 3x - 3x$

$$4x = 32$$

Divide each member by 4: $\qquad \dfrac{4x}{4} = \dfrac{32}{4}$

$$x = 8$$

CHECK: $4 \times 8 + 5 \times 8 - 2 \times 8 \overset{?}{=} 30 + 2 \times 8 + 2 + 8$

$32 + 40 - 16 \overset{?}{=} 30 + 16 + 2 + 8$

$56 = 56$

PROBLEMS

Solve and check:

1. $5x + 2x = 14$
2. $8x - 5x + x = 12$
3. $5a + a = 24$
4. $b + b + b = 3$
5. $2m - m + m = 10$
6. $8y + y - y = 8$
7. $11x + 3x = 22 + 3x$
8. $15 = n + 4n$
9. $6a - 2a = 42 - 2a$
10. $3x - 8 - x = 10 - x$
11. $7d + 8 + 2d = 38 - d$
12. $x + x + 2x - 2 = 0$
13. $10 + b = 15 - 9b$
14. $\frac{1}{2}x + \frac{1}{2}x - 1 = 0$
15. $18x + 12 - 10x = 24 - 4x$
16. $\frac{1}{4}x = 10 - x$

17. $x = 9 + \frac{1}{4}x$

18. $9d + 16 = 20 - d$

19. $\frac{1}{2}x + \frac{3}{4}x - \frac{1}{4}x = 16$

20. $a + 3.2a = 31 + 1.1a$

21. $\frac{1}{2} = x + \frac{1}{4}$

22. $x - \frac{1}{2} = \frac{1}{4}$

23. $a + a - 2 = a$

24. $3 + k - 2 = 5$

25. $\frac{1}{2} + x + 2x = 1$

26. $0.2x + 0.3x = 4$

★ 27. $0.5b + b - 1 = 3$

28. $0.01 + 0.1d = 1$

29. $10m - m - 1 = 0$

30. $6 + n - 5 + 3n = 7$

31. $g + g + g = 0.21$

32. $1 = x - \frac{1}{4}x$

33. $4 = 2y - y$

34. $16 = 12 + p + 3p$

35. $\frac{1}{2}x + \frac{1}{3}x = 1\frac{1}{5}$

36. $0 = h - 4 + \frac{1}{2}h$

SELF TEST

Solve and check the following equations:

1. $x + 13 = 15$

2. $56 = y + 8$

3. $a - 14 = 13$

4. $15 = y - 3$

5. $2y = 13$

6. $\frac{1}{5} = 4x$

7. $\frac{x}{4} = 12$

8. $\frac{3}{5} = \frac{x}{4}$

9. $3x + 2 = 17$

10. $8x - 5 = 27$

11. $1 + 2a = 15$

12. $\frac{y}{3} + 1 = 10$

13. $\frac{k}{6} + 13 = 20$

14. $\frac{3}{4}y = 18$

15. $3x - 16 = \frac{1}{2}$

16. $5a + 6 = 3a + 12$

17. $8y - 2y = 14 - y$

18. $5d + 18 = 24 - d$

Using Equations to Solve Problems

One way to solve the problem pictured above is by trial and error. Guess what the numbers might be. Tom guessed that the numbers are 10 and 40. His reason was: "The larger number, 40, is 4 times the smaller number, 10." This much is true, of course, but the sum of the numbers must be 65. Hence, 10 and 40 are not the numbers.

Alice said, "The numbers are 45 and 20, because their sum is 65." But 45, the larger number, is not 4 times 20, the smaller number. Hence, Alice's guess, like Tom's, is incorrect.

How many guesses did you make before you found the right solution?

A great many of our problems could be solved by trial and error, but such a method is too costly in time, money, and even in human lives. Can you imagine relying on trial and error for designing modern airplanes or ocean liners?

By using equations, you can eliminate almost all trial and error in solving many problems. This is why algebra is a powerful tool—it saves time, money, and energy.

Study the following solution carefully, because it is the general method for solving problems by means of algebra.

SOLUTION TO PROBLEM PICTURED ON PAGE 42:

Step 1. Use a letter to stand for the unknown numbers.

$$\text{Let } n = \text{the smaller number}$$

Since the problem states that the larger number is 4 times the smaller number, then

$$4n = \text{the larger number}$$

Step 2. Write as an equation the facts stated in the problem: the sum of two numbers is 65.

$$n + 4n = 65$$

Step 3. Solve the equation.

$$n + 4n = 65$$
$$5n = 65$$
$$n = 13$$

Step 4. Answer the question in the problem.

Since the two numbers as represented are n and $4n$, the numbers are 13 and 4×13. Hence:

$$\text{The smaller number is 13.}$$
$$\text{The larger number is 52.}$$

Step 5. Check by comparing your answers with the facts given in the problem.

The sum of two numbers is 65.

$$13 + 52 \overset{?}{=} 65$$
$$65 = 65$$

The larger number is 4 times the smaller number.

$$52 \overset{?}{=} 4 \times 13$$
$$52 = 52$$

Hence, 13 and 52 are the numbers, and the solution is correct.

Writing Equations

You learned to change word expressions to algebraic expressions in Chapter 1. Now you will use this skill in writing equations. Then you will use your skill in writing equations to solve problems.

Example for Study

Write as an equation: Four times some number added to eight times the same number gives a sum of 36.

Use a letter to stand for the unknown numbers:

Let $y =$ the number
then $4y = 4$ times the number
and $8y = 8$ times the number

Write the word expression as an equation: $4y + 8y = 36$

PROBLEMS

Write the following word expressions as equations. Use parentheses when necessary.

1. Six times a certain number is eighteen.
2. A number added to five equals forty.
3. Three less than some number equals one.
4. Twelve more than some number is seventy-two.
5. One-half of a number is sixty-three.
6. A number increased by seven is equal to twenty-one.
7. Three times a number decreased by six is nine.
8. One-fifth of a number is eight.
9. Eleven times a number plus twenty is forty-two.
10. Two-thirds of a number increased by twice the number is twenty-four.
11. The product of twice a number and three, decreased by twelve is forty.
12. Twice a number decreased by one-half of the number is fifteen.
13. Eighteen more than one-half of a number is thirty-six.
14. The quotient of x divided by four is one.
15. Five times the quantity x plus seven is fifty-two.
16. Three times the sum of six and y is thirty-three.
17. Four times a number minus twice the number is fifteen.
18. When eight is added to three times a number, the result is thirty-three.
19. The product of a number and five, decreased by nine, equals eleven.
20. One-third of a number added to three-fourths of the number is twenty-six.

Solve the following problems by the use of equations:

21. The sum of two numbers is 81. If the larger number is twice the smaller, find the two numbers.

SOLUTION: Let n = the smaller number $\qquad n + 2n = 81$
then $2n$ = the larger number $\qquad\qquad 3n = 81$
$\qquad\qquad\qquad\qquad\qquad\qquad\qquad\qquad n = 27$

Hence, the smaller number is 27 and the larger number is 54. Check to see if these answers are correct.

22. One number is three times another. Their sum is 66. Find the numbers.

23. One number is one-third of another. If their difference is 18, find the numbers.

24. The sum of two numbers is 96. One of the numbers is 16 larger than the other. Find the two numbers.

25. If a certain number is multiplied by 6 and the product is increased by 44, the result is 68. Find the number.

26. Joe and George earned $7.50 selling newspapers. According to their agreement, Joe was to receive 1.5 times the amount George was to receive. How much did each receive?

27. Betty's weight is three-fourths of John's weight. Find the weight of each if the difference between their weights is 28 pounds.

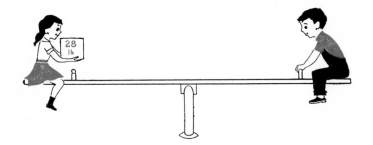

28. If three-fifths of a number is decreased by 13, the result is 50. Find the number.

29. One number is twice another, and one-half their sum is 18.6. Find the numbers.

30. One number exceeds another by 14.5. The sum of the two numbers is 109.7. Find the numbers.

31. One number is five times another. Their difference is 67. Find the two numbers.

32. The length of a rectangle is 8 inches more than its width. One half of its perimeter is 18 inches. Find its length and width.

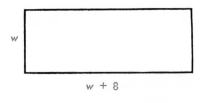

33. Find the length and the width of the rectangle in Problem 32 if the perimeter is 58 inches.

34. The sum of three numbers is 50. The second number is twice the first; the third number is 6 more than the first. What are the three numbers?

★ 35. The sum of three numbers is 96. The second number is 3 more than twice the first, while the third number equals the sum of the first two. Find the numbers.

36. Stanley is 5 years older than George. The sum of their ages is 37. How old is George?

37. A certain number when increased by three times its half equals 70. Find the number.

38. Find the length, width, and height of the hollow wire frame at the right if the total amount of wire used to make it was 42 feet.

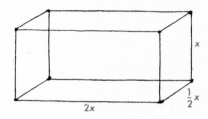

39. The length of a hollow wire frame something like the one in Problem 38 is twice the width, and the height is 2 inches more than the width. Find the length, width, and height if the total amount of wire used to make it is 68 inches.

40. If 10 is subtracted from one-fourth of a number, the result is 2. Find the number.

41. If $2\frac{2}{3}$ is added to one-sixth of a number, the result is 7. Find the number.

42. The larger can shown here is filled with a liquid; the smaller can is empty. Part of the contents of the larger can is poured into the smaller one until it is filled. After this is done, 10 pints remain in the larger can. Find the capacity, in pints, of each can.

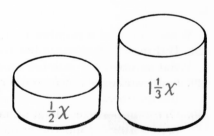

43. Find, by using an equation, the value of x that will make the expression $4x - 1$ equal the expression $2x + 15$.

44. Find, by using an equation, the value of y that will make the expression $y - 7$ equal the expression $\frac{1}{4}y + 2$.

45. The terms $\frac{2}{3}x$ and $\frac{1}{2}x$ stand for two consecutive numbers. Find the two numbers. Note: 6 and 7 are examples of consecutive numbers.

SUMMARY OF IMPORTANT THINGS TO REMEMBER

1. Words and Expressions
equation
four laws of equations
inverse operations
left member of an equation

right member of an equation
root of an equation
satisfy an equation
solve an equation

2. Understandings
Replacing the letter in an equation by some numbers results in false statements.

When the root replaces the letter in an equation, a true statement results.

It is important to check an equation to make sure that the number you find is the root.

Equations are very useful in solving problems.

When an arithmetic operation is performed on one side of an equation, it must be performed on the other side also to keep the equality.

3. Skills
You should be able to:
Solve equations by applying the four laws of equations.
Write equations in solving problems.

PROBLEMS ON YOUR AIMS

YOUR AIM **To learn the meaning of an equation.**

If x *is replaced by 3, which of the following result in true statements?*
1. $x + 1 = x + 3$ 2. $4x - 2 = x + 7$ 3. $2x + 1 = 5$

4. $3x - 3 = 4$ 5. $7x + 6 = 27$ 6. $\dfrac{12}{x} + x = 7$

7. When you find a number that satisfies an equation, the number is called the ___?___.
8. What is the only number that can be used to replace y so that $7y = 0$ will result in a true statement?

YOUR AIM **To learn how to solve equations.**

What is the inverse operation of each of the following?
1. Addition   2. Subtraction   3. Multiplication   4. Division

What operation would you use to solve each of the following equations?

5. $x + 3 = 12$ 6. $x - 6 = 14$ 7. $\dfrac{x}{5} = 7$ 8. $9x = 36$

Solve and check:

9. $5x = 60$ 10. $x - 5 = 18$ 11. $y + 3 = 19$ 12. $\dfrac{k}{7} = 11$

13. $5z - 4 = 21$ 14. $\dfrac{y}{4} + 9 = 14$ 15. $4x - 3 = 17$ 16. $y + 6 = 6$

YOUR AIM 👉 To learn how to use equations in solving problems.

1. The larger of two numbers is three times the smaller. How would you represent one number? How would you represent the other?
2. If the sum of the two numbers in Problem 1 is 42, write the equation to find the numbers.
3. One of two numbers is 10 larger than the other. How would you represent each of these two numbers?
4. Janet said, "To check a word problem, all I do is substitute in the equation." Is this a good method? Explain.

VALUABLE SKILLS PRACTICE

1. Copy the following table and work the problems in each column. To check, add your answers to the four problems in each column and compare the sum with the total given in each column.

$2 - \frac{3}{4} =$	_?_	$1 - \frac{3}{8} =$	_?_	$12\frac{1}{2}\%$ of \$8.00 $=$	_?_
$\frac{3}{4} \times \frac{1}{2} =$	_?_	$1\frac{1}{4} + 3\frac{7}{8} =$	_?_	2% of \$20.00 $=$	_?_
$\frac{3}{4} - \frac{1}{4} =$	_?_	$2\frac{1}{4} \times 1\frac{1}{8} =$	_?_	0.2% of \$100.00 $=$	_?_
$2 - \frac{3}{4} - \frac{1}{16} =$	_?_	$2\frac{5}{8} \times 2\frac{1}{3} =$	_?_	$1\frac{1}{2}\%$ of \$500.00 $=$	_?_
Totals	$3\frac{5}{16}$		$14\frac{13}{32}$		\$9.10

2. Copy the following table and change each of the numbers listed to their equivalents in the form of fractions, decimals, or percents. Check by adding the numbers in each column and compare the sum with the total given in each column.

Common fraction	Decimal fraction	Percent
$\frac{1}{2}$	?	?
?	0.4	?
$\frac{3}{8}$	?	?
?	1.5	?
$\frac{5}{6}$	?	?
?	?	$266\frac{2}{3}\%$
Totals $6\frac{11}{40}$	6.275	627.5%

CHAPTER TEST

Select the best answer. On a sheet of paper write each question number and beside it the letter of your choice of answer.

1. What is the root of $3x = 6$?　　　　**a.** 2　　　　**b.** 3　　　　**c.** 6

2. What value of x satisfies the equation $x - 1 = 3$?　　**a.** 2　　**b.** 3　　**c.** 4

3. Five times a number decreased by 6 is 49. What is the equation for this?　　**a.** $5n + 6 = 49$　　**b.** $5n - 6 = 49$　　**c.** $5n = 43$

4. The root of $7x - 2 = 3$ is:　　**a.** an odd number　　**b.** a fraction　　**c.** an even number

5. The root of $2y + 3 = 9$ is:　　**a.** an odd number　　**b.** a fraction　　**c.** an even number

6. If m and n stand for two numbers, what represents 5 more than their product?　　**a.** $m + n + 5$　　**b.** $mn + 5$　　**c.** $\dfrac{m}{n} + 5$

7. If a and b stand for two numbers, which of the following represents 2 less than their sum?　　**a.** $ab - 2$　　**b.** $a - 2b$　　**c.** $a + b - 2$

Select the best method for solving each of the following equations. **A** *means addition,* **S** *means subtraction,* **M** *means multiplication, and* **D** *means division.*

8. $x + 3 = 4$　　**a.** A　　**b.** S　　**c.** M

9. $3x + 1 = 9$　　**a.** A then D　　**b.** D then S　　**c.** S then D

10. $5x - 1 = 14$　　**a.** A then D　　**b.** D then S　　**c.** S then D

11. $\frac{1}{2}x + 8 = 12$　　**a.** S then M　　**b.** A then D　　**c.** A then M

Select the root of each of the following equations from the three choices at the right:

12. $7x - 12 = 16$　　　　**a.** $\frac{2}{7}$　　**b.** 4　　**c.** 21

13. $\frac{3}{4}y = 12$　　　　**a.** 9　　**b.** 16　　**c.** 36

14. $\dfrac{2m}{3} + 5 = 25$　　**a.** 18　　**b.** 20　　**c.** 30

15. $\frac{1}{2}k - \frac{1}{2} = \frac{1}{2}$　　**a.** $\frac{1}{2}$　　**b.** 1　　**c.** 2

16. $\dfrac{a}{4} - 4 = 0$　　**a.** 4　　**b.** 8　　**c.** 16

17. $2n + 2 = n + 2$　　**a.** 0　　**b.** 1　　**c.** 2

18. $\frac{1}{4}h - 1 = 0$　　**a.** $\frac{1}{4}$　　**b.** 1　　**c.** 4

19. $5a + 2 - a = 2a + 18$　　**a.** 8　　**b.** 10　　**c.** 12

20. $\dfrac{3n}{5} - \dfrac{1}{5} = 4$　　**a.** $\frac{3}{5}$　　**b.** 7　　**c.** 21

Solve the following problems by the use of equations:

21. One number is $2\frac{1}{2}$ times another number. Their difference is 18. Find the numbers.
22. The length of a rectangle is 5 inches more than the width. Find the length and the width if the perimeter is 50 inches.
23. If five-sixths of a number is increased by 17, the result is 62. Find the number.
24. The first side of a triangle is 2 inches less than the second side; the third side is 3 inches more than the second side. Find the length of each of the three sides if the perimeter of the triangle is 88 inches.
25. A wire 50 feet in length is cut in two parts. One part is 4 feet less than twice the other part. Find the length of each part.

CUMULATIVE REVIEW PROBLEMS

WORKING WITH ALGEBRAIC EXPRESSIONS

Rewrite the following expressions in their simplest form:

1. $x + 3x$
2. $a + a + a + a$
3. $a \cdot a \cdot a \cdot a$
4. $10m - 3n - 5m$
5. $7y^2 + 8y^2$
6. $aa + aa$
7. $2x \cdot 3x - 5x \cdot x$
8. $b - b$
9. $2a + b - a$
10. $6a \cdot 3b - 4b \cdot 4a$
11. $5x + x + x + 7x$
12. $2y - y + 8y - 5y$
13. $aaaa + aaa$
14. $16x + y + 5y - 8x - 3y$
15. $10ab + 4ab + 6a - a$
16. $a + a$
17. $14 + 6 - 2x - 7$
18. $45c - c$
19. $\frac{1}{2}ab + ab + \frac{1}{2}ab$
20. $\frac{1}{2}x^2 + 1\frac{1}{2}x^2$
21. $a^2 + a^2 + a^2 + a^2$
22. $a \cdot a \cdot a \cdot a \cdot a$

23. Write as an algebraic expression: five times the quotient of x divided by y.
24. Find the quotient of the product of 3 and 6 divided by their sum.
25. Which of the following are factors of 18: 1 and 8, 2 and 16, 2 and 9?
26. Which of the following are factors of $12a$: $12a$ and a, $3a$ and $9a$, 3 and $4a$?
27. Evaluate $2ab^2$ if a is 3 and b is 5.
28. Evaluate a^x if a is 2 and x is 3.
29. What is 3 raised to the fourth power?
30. In the expression $5ab^2$, what is the exponent of a?
31. How many days are there in $2w$ weeks? In w weeks and m months?
32. How many inches are there in $2f$ feet and $2y$ yards?

WORKING WITH EQUATIONS

1. By what number would you divide both members of the equation $8x = 4$ to find the value of x? What is the value of x?
2. What operation would you do first in solving the equation $4n - 2 = 10$? What would you do next? What is the root of the equation?
3. Does $\frac{1}{2}$ satisfy the equation $2x + 6 = 7$?
4. Does 3 satisfy the equation $9x = 36$?
5. What value of a satisfies the equation $\frac{a}{4} = 5$?
6. Make up three examples of equations that require addition for solving.
7. Make up three examples of equations that require division for solving.
8. Make up three examples of equations that require multiplication and addition for solving.
9. Make up three examples of equations that require division and subtraction for solving.

SOLVING EQUATIONS

Find the root of each of the following equations. Check.

1. $3x = 9.6$
2. $\frac{1}{2}y = 7.2$
3. $k - 2\frac{1}{2} = 2\frac{1}{3}$
4. $a + 3 = 12$
5. $m - 5 = 2$
6. $15x = 5$
7. $\frac{1}{3}d = 6\frac{2}{3}$
8. $b + 2 = 3$
9. $\frac{2}{3}c - 1 = 1$
10. $6x + 5x = 66$
11. $4y - 6 = 18$
12. $\frac{a}{5} - 1 = 1$
13. $2b - 14 = 44$
14. $22 = 17 + \frac{x}{7}$
15. $10m - m + 1 = 10$
16. $36 = 18x - 12x + 6$
17. $4 = 4b - b + b$
18. $x + x + x = 8$
19. $5x - x + x = 3$
20. $\frac{1}{4}x + 4 = 4$
21. $10a = 11 - a$
22. $10 + 3b = 9b$
23. $\frac{2}{3}x = 30$
24. $\frac{3}{5}x = 60$
25. $5n - 6 = 4n + 2$
26. $x - 2 = \frac{1}{2}x + 1$
27. $7x + 8 = 3x + 16$
28. $a - 7 = \frac{1}{3}a + 1$
29. $16 + 4x - x = x + 32$

Find the root of each of the following equations without using pencil and paper:

30. $3x = 9$
31. $x + 1 = 6$
32. $\frac{1}{2}x = 1$
33. $5a = 10$
34. $2n - 1 = 8$
35. $10 = 10y$
36. $5 = 10d$
37. $y - 3 = 13$
38. $2m - 7 = 17$
39. $x + x = 12$
40. $3x - x + x = 15$
41. $a + a - 4 = 19$

EQUATIONS **51**

42. $8 = \frac{1}{4}x$

43. $5 = \dfrac{x}{5}$

44. $\dfrac{2x}{3} = 6$

45. $3a = 7$

46. $\dfrac{3x}{5} = 10$

47. $26 = 14a - a$

48. $2c + 3c - c = 48$

49. $13a + 9 = 9$

Find the value of x *in each of the following equations if* a $= 2$ *and* b $= 5$:

50. $2x + a = 4b$

51. $x = \dfrac{10a}{b}$

52. $x = a^3 + b^2$

53. $\dfrac{x}{b} + a = ab$

54. $2ab - b = x$

55. $\dfrac{4b}{a} + x = 6a^2$

56. $bx = 10a^4 - b^3$

57. $\dfrac{x}{a} + 3a = a(b - a)$

58. $ax + bx = a + 4b$

59. $x(b - a) = 6a$

When you take a test:

Be sure that you understand the directions.

Read each problem carefully. Examine the facts that are given and decide how to find the answers to the questions that are asked.

Do the problems you are sure of first.

If you can't do a problem after working on it for a reasonable length of time, leave it. Go back to it later.

Check your work carefully to find any errors you may have made.

52 *ALGEBRA: ITS BIG IDEAS AND BASIC SKILLS*

BIG IDEAS	NUMBER
	EQUATION
	EXPONENT
BASIC SKILLS	Using and interpreting symbols of algebra
	Fundamental operations
	Solving equations
	Solving verbal problems
	Using exponents

CHAPTER **3** *Signed Numbers*

YOUR FIRST experience with numbers was in learning how to count. Then you learned how to work with whole numbers. Later you learned how to use fractions and decimal fractions.

Now you will learn how to use plus and minus signs with numbers. You will use these signs to indicate, for example, whether $5 is a $5 debt or a $5 credit without using the words "debt" or "credit" or whether a reading of 10° on a thermometer is 10° below freezing or 10° above freezing without using the words "below" or "above."

YOUR AIM 1. To learn what positive and negative numbers mean and how to use them.

2. To learn how to add, subtract, multiply, and divide signed numbers.

3. To be able to apply the laws of signed numbers in solving equations.

53

The Use of Signed Numbers

You probably have used signed numbers if you have told someone that the temperature was below zero. You know that $-20°$ means "20° below zero" and that $+20°$ means "20° above zero."

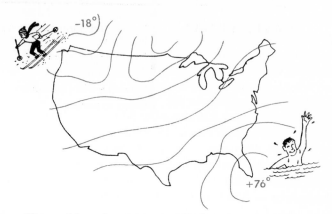

Numbers like -20 and $+20$ are called **signed numbers**. Numbers that are written with the plus sign or with no sign attached are called **positive numbers,** and numbers that are written with the minus sign are called **negative numbers.**

Signed numbers are used in many ways. For example, if $+50$ means a $50 profit in a business, then -50 would mean a $50 loss. If a gain of 10 yards in a football game were written $+10$, then a loss of 10 yards would be written -10.

PROBLEMS

The following words are usually associated with positive direction. For each word, name its opposite:

1. Profit
2. Up
3. North latitude
4. East longitude
5. A.D.
6. Above freezing
7. Above sea level
8. Right
9. In the black
10. Gaining weight
11. Above par
12. Gain

Write each of the following by using a positive or a negative number:

EXAMPLE: 35° south latitude would be written $-35°$ because south latitude is the opposite of north latitude. North latitude is usually considered positive.

13. 45° south latitude
14. 15 miles east
15. 3000 B.C.
16. 90° west longitude
17. $200 bank deposit
18. $50 withdrawal from bank
19. 15-yard penalty
20. A.D. 1776
21. 10° drcp in temperature
22. 10 pounds overweight

54 *ALGEBRA: ITS BIG IDEAS AND BASIC SKILLS*

Describe a situation which each of the following numbers might represent:

23. $+80\cent$ **24.** -10 yards   **25.** $-\$5$

26. $+16,000$ people   **27.** $+13°$ **28.** $-4°$

29. $+8$ miles an hour   **30.** -7 miles an hour   **31.** $+15$ feet

32. -30% **33.** $+14\%$ **34.** $+30$ hours

35. -50 hours   **36.** $+13$ miles   **37.** -15 miles

Write the result in each of the following problems as a signed number:
EXAMPLE: Earning $7, then spending $6. The result is written $+\$1$, because earning is considered positive and spending is considered negative.

38. Earning $10, then spending $6.

39. Depositing $100, then withdrawing $35.

40. Gaining 12 yards, then losing 15 yards.

41. Rising 500 feet, then descending 400 feet.

42. Gaining 10 yards, then gaining 12 yards more.

43. Walking 12 miles east and then 4 miles west.

44. Adding a debt of $200 to a credit of $100.

45. Adding a loss of $20 to a profit of $50.

46. Adding a debt of $20 to a debt of $5.

47. Adding a penalty of 15 yards to a gain of 40 yards.

48. Adding a gain of 5 yards to a gain of 10 yards.

49. Adding a penalty of 15 yards to a loss of 6 yards.

50. Adding a loss of $200 to a profit of $500.

51. Adding a profit of $50 to a debt of $30.

52. Adding a debt of $60 to a loss of $100.

53. Adding a loss of 8 pounds to a gain of 10 pounds.

The Number Zero

Zero is a number which has some characteristics that other numbers do not have. For example, you have seen that any number multiplied by zero is zero and that zero added to any number results in that number.

The number zero is used to indicate absence of quantities. For example, $\$0.00$ means "no dollars."

Zero is also used to mark a point on a line which divides the points on the right from the points on the left or the points above from the points below; for example, on the temperature scale and the altitude scale. Zero in these cases divides the points corresponding to the positive numbers from the points corresponding to the negative numbers.

"I have zero dollars."

The surface of the water is zero position.

PROBLEMS

Identify the following zero positions:
1. Zero position on a centigrade thermometer
2. Zero position in elevation
3. Zero position on a football field   4. Zero hour

★5. Zero latitude   6. Zero meridian

The Number Line

A scale, or line, for signed numbers is shown below. It is called the **number line.**

$$-10\ -9\ -8\ -7\ -6\ -5\ -4\ -3\ -2\ -1\ \ 0\ +1\ +2\ +3\ +4\ +5\ +6\ +7\ +8\ +9\ +10$$

You can make a number line by drawing any straight line, marking some point on the line and labeling it 0. Then mark off any desired number of convenient units to the right and to the left of the zero mark. Label in order the marks to the right of zero as $+1$, $+2$, $+3$, and so on, or as 1, 2, 3, and so on, and those to the left of zero as -1, -2, -3, and so on. The zero point is called the **origin.**

PROBLEMS

1. Draw a number line beginning with -20 and ending with $+20$.
2. Would it be possible to have a number line starting with -100 and ending with $+100$?
3. Would it be possible to have a number line starting with $-50,000$ and ending with $+50,000$?

DO YOU SEE? **The number line can be thought of as extending indefinitely in either direction from the origin. It has no ends.**

56 *ALGEBRA: ITS BIG IDEAS AND BASIC SKILLS*

Use the number line you drew for Problem 1 for the following problems:
4. Start with $+4$ and count the number of units to -4. How many units did you count?
5. Start with -7 and count the number of units to $+6$. How many units did you count?
6. Start with -15 and count the number of units to -8. How many units did you count?
7. Start with -3 and count the number of units to -15. How many units did you count?

In each of the following problems, state (1) which point is farther from zero and (2) whether the points are on the same or on opposite sides of zero:

8. $+7, +5$ 9. $-5, -9$ 10. $+3, -7$
11. $-2, -8$ 12. $-7, +6$ 13. $+7, -5$
14. $+9, +5$ 15. $+14, -3$ 16. $+11, +2$
17. $-7, -3$ 18. $-13, +9$ 19. $+14, -16$
20. $-6, +20$ 21. $+4, +7$ 22. $-5, -3$
23. $-4, +4$ 24. $+6, -6$ 25. $+7, +11$

26. In Problems 8–25, what part of the signed numbers shows which point is farther from zero? What part of the signed numbers shows on which side of zero the points are?

Absolute Value of a Number

The **absolute value** of a positive number is the number itself. Thus the absolute value of $+5$ is $+5$. The symbol used for absolute value of $+5$ is $|+5|$. So $|+5| = +5$, or 5.

The absolute value of a negative number is its opposite positive number. Thus $|-5| = +5$, or 5. Also $|0| = 0$.

PROBLEMS

What is the absolute value of each of the following numbers?
1. $+17$ 2. -3 3. $+8$ 4. -16 5. $+12$
6. -12 7. -50 8. $+0.6$ 9. $-2\frac{1}{2}$ 10. -8.2
11. Does the absolute value of $+15$ equal the absolute value of -15?

12. Where is the point for $|+15|$ on the number line?
13. Where is the point for $|-15|$ on the number line?
14. Where is the point for $|0|$ on the number line?

Which of the following statements are true? Why?
15. $|+5| = |-5|$ 16. $-3 = |-3|$ 17. $+6 = |+6|$
18. $|0| = 0$ 19. $|+6| + |-6| = 0$ 20. $10 - |+10| = 0$
21. $10 - |-10| = 0$ 22. $7 + |-7| = 0$ 23. $|-8| - |+8| = 0$

One Number Greater Than Another

If you start at the origin on a number line and you move to the right, the numbers increase. For example, 6 is to the right of 3, and 6 is greater than 3.

This characteristic holds for the entire number line; that is, any number on the number line is considered to be greater than every number to its left. For example, -5 is to the left of $+2$; therefore, $+2$ is greater than -5.

The mathematical symbol for *greater than* is $>$, and the symbol for *less than* is $<$. Thus, $+6 > +3$ is read, "Positive 6 is greater than positive 3"; $-6 < -2$ is read, "Negative 6 is less than negative 2"; and $|-10| > |+5|$ is read, "The absolute value of negative 10 is greater than the absolute value of positive 5."

PROBLEMS

Name the greater number in each of the following pairs of numbers:

1. $+8, +3$
2. $+5, +16$
3. $-3, -8$
4. $-4, -2$
5. $+3, -2$
6. $+3, -3$
7. $+3, -5$
8. $0, -2$
9. $0, +3$
10. $|+3|, |+2|$
11. $|+11|, |+15|$
12. $|-5|, |-3|$
13. $|-6|, |+2|$
14. $|+9|, |-15|$
15. $|5|, |-3|$
16. $|-8|, |-12|$
17. $|+1\frac{1}{2}|, |0|$
18. $|-3\frac{1}{2}|, |+2\frac{1}{4}|$
19. $|+1.5|, |+0.82|$
20. $|-9.1|, |-15|$

Write each of the following by means of symbols:

21. Positive 4 is greater than negative 9.
22. Negative 1 is less than positive 1.
23. Negative 3 is greater than negative 6.
24. The absolute value of negative 5 is greater than the absolute value of positive 4.
25. The absolute value of positive 50 equals the absolute value of negative 50.

In each of the following problems, show by a symbol whether the first number is greater than, less than, or equal to the second number:

26. $+6, -2$
27. $+8, +5$
28. $+2, -1$
29. $+2, -2$
30. $-6, -10$
31. $+3, +4$
32. $0, +5$
33. $-3, 0$
34. $\frac{5}{16}, \frac{3}{8}$
35. $|-1|, |+1|$
36. $|-5|, |+7|$
37. $|-3|, |-1|$
38. $|-4|, |0|$
39. $|-10|, |+10|$
40. $|-2|, |+1|$

Adding Signed Numbers

You can use the number line to help you learn how to add signed numbers.

EXAMPLE: A football team first gained 6 yards. Start with zero on the number line and count to the point $+6$. The team then gained 2 more yards. Start at $+6$ and count 2 more to the right. Why should you count to the right rather than to the left? To which point on the scale have you counted? This is the sum of $+6$ and $+2$.

PROBLEMS

Count on the number line to find the sum of each of the following:

1. $+3, +4$	2. $+5, +3$	3. $+1, +9$
4. $+7, +5$	5. $+5, +7$	6. $+8, +3$
7. $+3, +8$	8. $+1, +\frac{1}{2}$	9. $+\frac{1}{2}, +1\frac{1}{2}$
10. $+3.2, +4.1$	11. $+3, +5, +2$	12. $+6, +5, +6$

DO YOU SEE? To add two positive numbers, you add as you did in arithmetic. The sum is a positive number.

EXAMPLE: A football team first lost 3 yards. What point on the number line represents this number? The team next lost 10 yards. Start at the point -3 and count 10 to the left. Why to the left? To which point on the scale have you counted? This is the sum of -3 and -10.

Count on the number line to find the sum of each of the following:

13. $-3, -5$	14. $-2, -7$	15. $-1, -9$
16. $-8, -4$	17. $-6, -3$	18. $-2, -\frac{1}{2}$
19. $-\frac{1}{2}, -2\frac{1}{2}$	20. $-3.6, -2.8$	21. $-7, -5, -4$

DO YOU SEE? To add two negative numbers, you add as you did in arithmetic. The sum is a negative number.

EXAMPLE: On the first play a football team gained 8 yards. Find the point on the number line that represents this number. The team next lost 5 yards. Since this is a loss, count 5 to the left of $+8$. At what point did you end? What is the sum of $+8$ and -5?

22. On the first play a football team lost 15 yards. On the next play it gained 12 yards. What is the position of the team at the end of the two plays? What is the sum of -15 and $+12$?

Use the number line to find the sum of each of the following pairs of numbers:

23. $+4, -7$ 24. $-3, +5$ 25. $-5, +3$ 26. $-6, +2$
27. $+6, -2$ 28. $+8, -7$ 29. $-8, +7$ 30. $-15, +10$
31. $+15, -10$ 32. $-8, +8$ 33. $+12, -12$ 34. $+3, -3$
35. $+11, -6$ 36. $+\frac{1}{2}, -2$ 37. $+2\frac{1}{2}, -1$ 38. $-3.5, +2.3$

DO YOU SEE?   To add two numbers with unlike signs, find the difference between the numbers as you did in arithmetic. Give the answer the sign of the number which has the greater absolute value.

Examples for Study

1. *Add:*

$$\begin{array}{r} +12 \\ +11 \\ \hline +23 \end{array} \qquad \begin{array}{r} -11 \\ -6 \\ \hline -17 \end{array}$$

The signs are alike in these problems. Find the sum of the numbers as you did in arithmetic. Keep the same signs.

2. *Add:*

$$\begin{array}{r} +9 \\ -4 \\ \hline +5 \end{array} \qquad \begin{array}{r} +6 \\ -17 \\ \hline -11 \end{array}$$

The signs are unlike. To add, find the difference between the numbers as you did in arithmetic. Give the sum the sign of the number with the larger absolute value.

Use the rules for adding signed numbers in the following problems. If a number other than zero does not have a sign attached to it, the number is understood to be positive.

39. $\begin{array}{r} +7 \\ -4 \\ \hline \end{array}$ 40. $\begin{array}{r} -8 \\ -1 \\ \hline \end{array}$ 41. $\begin{array}{r} +5 \\ +9 \\ \hline \end{array}$ 42. $\begin{array}{r} -2 \\ +7 \\ \hline \end{array}$ 43. $\begin{array}{r} +3 \\ -3 \\ \hline \end{array}$

44. $\begin{array}{r} +5 \\ -4 \\ \hline \end{array}$ 45. $\begin{array}{r} -1 \\ -3 \\ \hline \end{array}$ 46. $\begin{array}{r} +4 \\ +4 \\ \hline \end{array}$ 47. $\begin{array}{r} -4 \\ -7 \\ \hline \end{array}$ 48. $\begin{array}{r} +9 \\ -9 \\ \hline \end{array}$

49. $\begin{array}{r} 0 \\ -5 \\ \hline \end{array}$ 50. $\begin{array}{r} +2 \\ +7 \\ \hline \end{array}$ 51. $\begin{array}{r} -8 \\ +7 \\ \hline \end{array}$ 52. $\begin{array}{r} -7 \\ +8 \\ \hline \end{array}$ 53. $\begin{array}{r} -3 \\ 0 \\ \hline \end{array}$

54. $\begin{array}{r} -13 \\ -10 \\ \hline \end{array}$ 55. $\begin{array}{r} -16 \\ 6 \\ \hline \end{array}$ 56. $\begin{array}{r} -13 \\ 10 \\ \hline \end{array}$ 57. $\begin{array}{r} 17 \\ -9 \\ \hline \end{array}$ 58. $\begin{array}{r} +15 \\ 15 \\ \hline \end{array}$

59. $\begin{array}{r} -5.3 \\ -2.8 \\ \hline \end{array}$ 60. $\begin{array}{r} -3.9 \\ 1.8 \\ \hline \end{array}$ 61. $\begin{array}{r} +1\frac{1}{4} \\ -2\frac{3}{4} \\ \hline \end{array}$ 62. $\begin{array}{r} -7\frac{1}{4} \\ +9\frac{1}{2} \\ \hline \end{array}$ 63. $\begin{array}{r} +3\frac{1}{2} \\ -8\frac{3}{4} \\ \hline \end{array}$

64. -23	65. -57	66. 20	67. -98	68. 0
14	-63	$+50$	89	-33

69. -13	70. 25	71. -97	72. 72	73. -92
$+81$	-35	-13	-83	76

★ 74. $+1\frac{1}{2}$ 75. $+\frac{3}{4}$ 76. $-\frac{1}{2}$ 77. $+\frac{1}{6}$ 78. $\frac{2}{5}$

      $-\frac{1}{2}$ $-\frac{1}{4}$ $-\frac{1}{3}$ $+\frac{1}{3}$ $\frac{5}{6}$

79. $(-5) + (-10)$ 80. $(+6) + (+9)$ 81. $(-11) + (+29)$

82. $(-8) + (+13)$ 83. $(19) + (-9)$ 84. $(75) + (-75)$

85. $(-\frac{1}{2}) + (-\frac{1}{4})$ 86. $(2\frac{1}{4}) + (-1\frac{1}{2})$ 87. $(-31) + (-13)$

You may write signed numbers that are to be added either in a column or horizontally as long as the same sign is attached to each number.

Vertical Arrangement			*Horizontal Arrangement*
(1) $+8$	(2) 3	(3) -1	(1) $-2 + 8 = 6$
-2	-10	4	(2) $3 - 10 = -7$
6	-7	-6	(3) $-6 + 4 - 1 = -3$
		-3	

NOTE: You may write the numbers in any order as long as you keep the same sign with each number.

Write the numbers in each of the following problems horizontally and add:

88. -3	89. -6	90. -10	91. 5	92. 2
-4	$+8$	$+5$	-5	-9

93. -3	94. -1	95. $+1$	96. 2	97. 4
4	-2	6	-3	-7
-6	-3	$+3$	-5	3

Add the numbers in each of the following problems:

98. $+2, -6, -7$ 99. $-8, -10, -4$ 100. $3, -11$

101. $6, -6, -4$ 102. $-10, +10, -5$ 103. $1, -15$

104. $-7, +8, +9$ 105. $2, -14, -12$ 106. $12, -4$

107. $-8, -8, -8$ 108. $-7, +3, -5$ 109. $4, -12$

110. $+7, -10, -3$ 111. $10, -14, -1$ 112. $\frac{1}{2}, -1$

113. $1\frac{1}{2}, -2\frac{1}{3}, +\frac{1}{3}$ 114. $-1\frac{1}{4}, -\frac{1}{4}, -\frac{1}{4}$ 115. $\frac{1}{4}, -1$

116. $|-6\frac{1}{2}|, -\frac{1}{2}, +7$ 117. $2, -7\frac{1}{2}, |-\frac{3}{4}|$ 118. $|0.01|, |-1|$

Subtracting Signed Numbers

You learned in Chapter 2 that addition and subtraction are inverse operations. For example, the subtraction $5 - 2 = \underline{\ ?\ }$ means that you are trying to find some number which when added to 2 will give 5. The number from which you subtract is called the "minuend," the number being subtracted is called the "subtrahend," and the result of subtraction is called the "difference." You use the idea of inverse operations when, in checking a subtraction problem, you add the difference to the subtrahend to obtain the minuend.

PROBLEMS

Check the following subtraction problems by adding the difference to the subtrahend. Some of the answers are wrong.

1.	15	2.	17	3.	28	4.	8	5.	19
	9		12		15		2		13
	6		5		23		5		6

6.	45	7.	18	8.	406	9.	287	10.	400
	12		15		199		84		368
	23		13		207		103		132

Subtract
```
6      6
4      4
?      2
```

In doing a problem like $6 - 4 = \underline{\ ?\ }$, you can ask yourself, "What number added to 4 equals 6?" The answer is 2, because $2 + 4 = 6$. This method of subtraction might be called the "checking method of subtraction."

Subtract
```
-5     -5
-3     -3
?     -2
```

You probably have never subtracted signed numbers, but in the last section you learned how to add signed numbers. So, in doing a problem like the one on the left, you can think, "What number added to -3 will equal -5?" The answer is -2. How can you check to be sure that -2 is the answer?

Examples for Study

Subtract:

1. $+15$ The answer is $+7$, since $+7$ added to $+8$ equals $+15$
   $+8$ $+15$. $+8$
   $\underline{\ ?\ }$ $+7$

2. -10 The answer is -16, since -16 added to $+6$ -10
   $+6$ equals -10. $+6$
   $\underline{\ ?\ }$ -16

3. $+8$ -5 ?   The answer is $+13$, since $+13$ added to -5 equals $+8$. $+8$ -5 $+13$

4. -4 $+12$?   The answer is -16, since -16 added to $+12$ equals -4. -4 $+12$ -16

5. -9 -6 ?   The answer is -3, since -3 added to -6 equals -9. -9 -6 -3

Use the checking method of subtraction to find the answers to the following subtraction problems:

11. $+8$ $+3$ 12. $+8$ -5 13. $+9$ -4 14. -8 -6 15. -8 $+4$

16. -9 -12 17. $+5$ $+9$ 18. $+6$ -3 19. $+2$ $+9$ 20. -12 -3

21. -8 $+6$ 22. -12 $+14$ 23. $+16$ $+28$ 24. -12 -2 25. -15 6

Here are the answers to Problems 11–25. If you made a mistake in any problem, find out why.

(11) $+5$ (12) $+13$ (13) $+13$ (14) -2 (15) -12
(16) $+3$ (17) -4 (18) $+9$ (19) -7 (20) -9
(21) -14 (22) -26 (23) -12 (24) -10 (25) -21

26. Copy Problems 11–25, changing the sign of the subtrahend in each problem. Now add the numbers by the methods you learned for adding signed numbers. Compare the answers with those given above. What do you find?

DO YOU SEE?   To subtract one signed number from another, change the sign of the subtrahend and apply the rules for adding signed numbers.

Examples for Study

1. *Subtract:* $+3$ -5

SOLUTION:
Change the sign of the subtrahend: $+3$ $+5$ Then add: $+3$ $+5$ $+8$

SIGNED NUMBERS **63**

2. *Subtract:* -4
                 -6

SOLUTION:

Change the sign of the subtrahend:

$$-4 \qquad \text{Then add:} \qquad -4$$
$$\underline{+6} \qquad\qquad\qquad \underline{+6}$$
$$\qquad\qquad\qquad\qquad\quad +2$$

When you subtract signed numbers, change the sign of the subtrahend in your mind. If you change the sign on your paper, you may become confused and forget whether or not you have changed it.

In each of the following problems find the difference between the signed numbers by changing mentally the sign of the subtrahend and adding. Check your answers.

27. $+12$	28. $+11$	29. -7	30. -15	31. $+30$
$\underline{+10}$	$\underline{-9}$	$\underline{-4}$	$\underline{+10}$	$\underline{+20}$
32. $+16$	33. -6	34. -5	35. 0	36. 0
$\underline{-8}$	$\underline{+9}$	$\underline{-10}$	$\underline{-6}$	$\underline{+6}$
37. $+10$	38. $+16$	39. -3	40. -14	41. -20
$\underline{-8}$	$\underline{+11}$	$\underline{-7}$	$\underline{+20}$	$\underline{-24}$
42. $+17$	43. -38	44. -11	45. $+9$	46. $+3$
$\underline{+10}$	$\underline{-33}$	$\underline{+6}$	$\underline{-12}$	$\underline{-12}$
47. -15	48. -16	49. -50	50. -45	51. $+40$
$\underline{-5}$	$\underline{-20}$	$\underline{-50}$	$\underline{+15}$	$\underline{-40}$
52. $+25$	53. 30	54. -75	55. 60	56. -85
$\underline{-15}$	$\underline{30}$	$\underline{-50}$	$\underline{+60}$	$\underline{100}$
57. $+100$	58. 500	59. 0	60. 0	61. -10
$\underline{-200}$	$\underline{700}$	$\underline{-20}$	$\underline{28}$	$\underline{-10}$
62. -1	63. $+4\frac{2}{3}$	64. -8.3	65. $+1\frac{1}{2}$	66. $-\frac{3}{4}$
$\underline{-50}$	$\underline{-8\frac{1}{2}}$	$\underline{+6.2}$	$\underline{+6\frac{1}{2}}$	$\underline{+9\frac{5}{8}}$

67. $(-8) - (+5)$ 68. $(+22) - (+44)$ 69. $(+1) - (-\frac{1}{2})$
70. $(-13) - (-5)$ 71. $(65) - |-45|$ 72. $|-\frac{1}{2}| - |-\frac{1}{4}|$

64 *ALGEBRA: ITS BIG IDEAS AND BASIC SKILLS*

Multiplying Signed Numbers

In multiplying two signed numbers, there are four possible combinations of signs:

Case 1: $(+3)(+2) = \underline{\ ?\ }$ $\qquad$ *Case 2:* $(+3)(-2) = \underline{\ ?\ }$

Case 3: $(-3)(+2) = \underline{\ ?\ }$ $\qquad$ *Case 4:* $(-3)(-2) = \underline{\ ?\ }$

An important principle of multiplication you have used is the principle of zero. This principle may be stated, "When any number is multiplied by zero, the product is zero." Or using symbols:

$$a \times 0 = 0$$

When the numbers of arithmetic were extended to include positive and negative numbers, it was necessary to define the rules for addition, subtraction, multiplication, and division of these numbers. These rules were made in such a way that the distributive principle and the principle of zero remained true. Let us see how these two principles helped us to know how to define multiplication of positive and negative numbers.

Case 1: A positive number multiplied by a positive number

The rule for Case 1 was defined so that a number with the positive sign, for example, $+5$, would be the same as the number without a sign; that is, $+5 = 5$, $+2 = 2$, $+10 = 10$, and so forth. Thus, since $5 \times 10 = 50$, then $(+5)(+10) = +50$. Or, in general, the product of any two positive numbers is a positive number.

PROBLEMS

What is the sum in each of the following?

1. $(+7) + (-7)$ $\qquad$ 2. $(+6) + (-6)$ $\qquad$ 3. $(-9) + (+9)$
4. $(-8.2) + (+8.2)$ $\qquad$ 5. $(+1) + (-1)$ $\qquad$ 6. $(-5) + (+5)$

Using the principle of zero, find the product in each of the following:

7. $(+9)(0)$ $\qquad$ 8. $(4)(0)$ $\qquad$ 9. $(0)(+3)$

Brackets, like parentheses, mean multiplication.

Example for Study

What is the value of $4[(3) + (2)]$?

METHOD 1

Combine inside the brackets first. Then multiply by 4.

$$4[(3) + (2)] = 4[3 + 2]$$
$$= 4[5]$$
$$= 20$$

METHOD 2

Use the distributive principle to first multiply by 4 and then combine.

$$4[(3) + (2)] = 4(3) + 4(2)$$
$$= 12 + 8$$
$$= 20$$

Case 2: A positive number multiplied by a negative number
Case 3: A negative number multiplied by a positive number

10. Since $(+5) + (-5) = 0$, what is the product $+3[(+5) + (-5)]$?
11. Since $(+2) + (-2) = 0$, what is the product $+5[(+2) + (-2)]$?
12. Since $(+2) + (-2) = 0$, then $+5[(+2) + (-2)]$ must equal zero if the principle of zero is to hold. However, if we use the distributive principle:

$$+5[(+2) + (-2)] = (+5)(+2) + (+5)(-2)$$
$$= +10 + \underline{\ ?\ }$$

We know that the product on the left is 0 and that the first product on the right is $+10$. What must be the product of $(+5)(-2)$ if the sum of the terms on the right side is to be 0?
13. If a is a placeholder for any number, what is the sum $(a) + (-a)$?
14. If a and b are placeholders for positive numbers, what is the product $b[(a) + (-a)]$?
15. Applying the distributive principle to the expression in Problem 14, we get $(b)(a) + (b)(-a)$. If $(b)(a) = +ba$, what must $(b)(-a)$ equal? What does $(-a)(b)$ equal?

DO YOU SEE? A negative number multiplied by a positive number results in a negative number for the product.

Case 4: A negative number multiplied by a negative number

16. What is the product -4×0?
17. What is the sum $(+7) + (-7)$?
18. What is the product $-3[(+7) + (-7)]$?
19. We know that $-3[(+7) + (-7)] = 0$. If we use the distributive principle, we get $-3[(+7) + (-7)] = (-3)(+7) + (-3)(-7)$. We know that $(-3)(+7) = -21$, so $(-3)(-7) = \underline{\ ?\ }$
20. $-8[(+5) + (-5)] = 0$
$$-8[(+5) + (-5)] = (-8)(+5) + (-8)(-5)$$
$$0 = -40 + \underline{\ ?\ }$$
What must $(-8)(-5)$ equal if $-8[(+5) + (-5)] = 0$?
21. If a and b represent positive numbers,
$$-a[(+b) + (-b)] = 0$$
$$-a[(+b) + (-b)] = (-a)(+b) + (-a)(-b)$$
$$0 = (-ab) + \underline{\ ?\ }$$

What must $(-a)(-b)$ equal if the right side of the equation is to be zero?

DO YOU SEE? A negative number multiplied by a negative number results in a positive number for the product.

66 *ALGEBRA: ITS BIG IDEAS AND BASIC SKILLS*

Find the products:

22. $(+4)(+9)$
23. $(-6)(-3)$
24. $(+7)(-4)$
25. $(-8)(-5)$
26. 8×7
27. $(4)(-3)$
28. $(-28)(5)$
29. $(+\frac{1}{2})(+16)$
30. $(+\frac{1}{2})(38)$
31. $(-\frac{1}{2})(+\frac{1}{2})$
32. $(-\frac{2}{3})(-\frac{3}{4})$
33. $(+\frac{2}{3})(-\frac{3}{4})$
34. $(0.7)(0.6)$
35. $(-0.3)(+0.4)$
36. $(-0.8)(-0.9)$
37. $(+0.01)(-0.001)$
38. $(-0.28)(-1.5)$
39. $(+4)(0)$
★ 40. $(0)(-7)$
41. $(-2\frac{1}{2})(-3\frac{1}{3})$
42. $(+10)^2$
43. $(+5)^2$
44. $(-2)^2$
45. $(+1)^2$
46. $|-1|^3$
47. $(-9.7)|-1|$
48. $-3(4-4)$

The Associative Principle for Multiplication

Consider the following equation:

$$(a \times b) \times c = a \times (b \times c)$$

Suppose $a = -2$, $b = -3$, and $c = -5$. Evaluating this equation, gives us:

$$(-2 \times -3) \times -5 = -2 \times (-3 \times -5)$$
$$6 \times -5 = -2 \times 15$$
$$-30 = -30$$

For the set of values we used, the equation becomes a true statement. Try other values for a, b, and c to see whether the equation always gives a true statement. See whether you can find any set of three numbers, one replacing a, another b, and the third c, which will not give a true statement.

DO YOU SEE? For every value of a, b, and c,
$(a \times b) \times c = a \times (b \times c)$.

This equation tells you that the order in which you multiply factors does not change the product. The product is always the same.

The equation, $(a \times b) \times c = a \times (b \times c)$, states a very important relation in mathematics. It is called the **associative principle for multiplication.**

PROBLEMS

Find the products:

1. $(+2)(-3)(-1)$
2. $(-1)(-1)(-1)$
3. $(-2)(-2)(-2)$
4. $(6)(+2)(3)$
5. $(-1)(+2)(-3)(+4)$
6. $(-2)(-3)(-8)$
7. $(-1)(-6)(0)(+7)$
8. $(+2)^2$
9. $(+2)^3$
10. $(-2)^2$
11. $(-2)^3$
12. $(-2)^4$

Dividing Signed Numbers

Division is the inverse operation of multiplication. Now that you know the rules for multiplying signed numbers, you can work out the rules for dividing signed numbers.

Recall that in the problem $8 \div 4 = \underline{\ ?\ }$, you asked yourself, "What number multiplied by 4 gives 8?" The answer was 2, so you said $8 \div 4 = 2$. Thus, in checking a division problem, you multiply the quotient by the divisor to obtain the dividend.

PROBLEMS

Check the following problems. One quotient is not correct.

1. $6\overline{)18}$ quotient 3
2. $6\overline{)24}$ quotient 4
3. $5\overline{)20}$ quotient 3
4. $9\overline{)36}$ quotient 4

You probably have never divided signed numbers, but you have multiplied them. You can use this ability to solve this problem:

$$-3\overline{)+15} \text{ quotient } ? \qquad -3\overline{)+15} \text{ quotient } -5$$

You can think, "What number multiplied by -3 will give $+15$?" Why is -5 the correct answer?

Examples for Study

1. $+4\overline{)+20}$ quotient $?$ The quotient is $+5$ because $(+5)(+4) = +20.$ $+4\overline{)+20}$ quotient $+5$

2. $+4\overline{)-20}$ quotient $?$ The quotient is -5 because $(-5)(+4) = -20.$ $+4\overline{)-20}$ quotient -5

3. $-4\overline{)+20}$ quotient $?$ The quotient is -5 because $(-5)(-4) = +20.$ $-4\overline{)+20}$ quotient -5

4. $-4\overline{)-20}$ quotient $?$ The quotient is $+5$ because $(+5)(-4) = -20.$ $-4\overline{)-20}$ quotient $+5$

Use the method shown in the examples for study above to solve the following division problems. Remember that another way to write $+2\overline{)-18}$ is $\dfrac{-18}{+2}$.

5. $+3\overline{)+6}$ 6. $-5\overline{)+10}$ 7. $+4\overline{)-12}$ 8. $-9\overline{)-18}$

9. $-4\overline{)+32}$ 10. $-5\overline{)-50}$ 11. $+12\overline{)+60}$ 12. $+12\overline{)-48}$

13. $\dfrac{+64}{-8}$ 14. $\dfrac{+52}{+13}$ 15. $\dfrac{-24}{-12}$ 16. $\dfrac{-49}{+7}$

17. $\dfrac{36}{-6}$

18. $\dfrac{-18}{2}$

19. $\dfrac{+11}{-11}$

20. $\dfrac{-15}{-15}$

21. $\dfrac{+150}{-75}$

22. $\dfrac{+4}{+8}$

23. $\dfrac{-4}{+8}$

24. $\dfrac{-4}{-8}$

DO YOU SEE? In deciding whether a quotient is positive or negative, you use the same rules as in deciding whether a product is positive or negative:

1. The quotient of two numbers whose signs are alike is positive.

2. The quotient of two numbers whose signs are unlike is negative.

Find the quotients using the rules for dividing signed numbers:

25. $\dfrac{-20}{+5}$

26. $\dfrac{+12}{-4}$

27. $\dfrac{-10}{-2}$

28. $\dfrac{+8}{+2}$

29. $\dfrac{-4}{-4}$

30. $\dfrac{26}{-2}$

31. $\dfrac{-27}{3}$

32. $\dfrac{30}{+3}$

33. $\dfrac{20}{-20}$

34. $\dfrac{-1}{-1}$

35. $(+24) \div (+3)$

36. $(-36) \div (-12)$

37. $(-33) \div (+3)$

38. $(+6) \div (+2)$

39. $(-10) \div (-20)$

40. $(+4) \div (-12)$

41. $(-2) \div (+2)$

42. $(-\frac{1}{2}) \div (-\frac{1}{2})$

★ 43. $(-\frac{1}{2}) \div (-\frac{1}{4})$

44. $(-\frac{1}{4}) \div (-\frac{3}{4})$

45. $4 \div (-\frac{1}{4})$

46. $(-\frac{1}{4}) \div (+4)$

47. $(-2) \div 500$

48. $(+12) \div (-\frac{1}{5})$

49. $\dfrac{+3\frac{1}{2}}{-1\frac{1}{2}}$

50. $\dfrac{+3\frac{1}{3}}{-10}$

51. $\dfrac{+67\frac{1}{2}}{100}$

52. $\dfrac{-83\frac{1}{3}}{100}$

Examples for Study

1. $(+3)(-4) = -12$ $+3$ and -4 are factors of -12.
2. $a \cdot b = ab$ a and b are factors of ab.
3. $a \cdot a = a^2$ a and a are factors of a^2.

53. $(-3)(+4) = -12$. If -3 is one factor of -12, what is the other factor?

54. $(+6)(-2) = -12$. If $+6$ is one factor of -12, what is the other factor?

55. $(-1)(-12) = 12$. If -12 is one factor of 12, what is the other factor?

56. If -4 is one of two factors of 20, what is the other factor?

57. If -6 is one of two factors of -18, what is the other factor?

58. If -5 is one of two factors of 30, what is the other factor?

Tell which of the following statements are true and which are false:

59. -7 and -6 are factors of 42.

60. -4 and 20 are factors of 80.

61. -1 and -1 are factors of 1.

62. If $+3$ is one factor of $+15$, then the other factor is $+5$.

63. If $+3$ is one factor of -15, then the other factor is -5.

64. If -3 is one factor of -15, then the other factor is -5.

Using Parentheses with Signed Numbers

A plus sign written in front of a letter means the same as $+1$ times whatever number the letter stands for. For example, $+x$ means $(+1)x$. If $x = +3$, then $+x$ means the same as $(+1)(+3) = +3$.

A minus sign written in front of a letter means the same as -1 times whatever number the letter stands for. For example, $-x$ means $(-1)x$. If $x = -2$, then $-x$ means the same as $(-1)(-2) = +2$.

Avoid using two signs in front of a number or a letter without separating the signs with parentheses. For example, write $- -3$ as $-(-3)$ which is the same as $(-1)(-3)$ or $+3$.

PROBLEMS

Write each of the following numbers using only one sign:

1. $+(+3)$	**2.** $-(+5)$	**3.** $+(-6)$	**4.** $+(+8)$
5. $-(-1)$	**6.** $-(+13)$	**7.** $+(+19)$	**8.** $-(-15)$
9. $+(-7)$	**10.** $+(+10)$	**11.** $+(+4)$	**12.** $+(+7)$
13. $+(-10)$	**14.** $+(-4)$	**15.** $-(+9)$	**16.** $-(-4)$
17. $-(-8)$	**18.** $-(-9)$	**19.** $-(+4)$	**20.** $-(+8)$

21. Look at your answers to Problems 9–14. What effect does the plus sign in front of the parentheses have on the sign of the number inside the parentheses?

22. Look at your answers to Problems 15–20. What effect does the minus sign in front of the parentheses have on the sign of the number inside the parentheses?

DO YOU SEE? 1. **A plus sign in front of parentheses does not change the sign of the number inside the parentheses when the parentheses are removed.**

2. **A minus sign in front of parentheses changes the sign of the number inside the parentheses when the parentheses are removed.**

23. If x stands for a positive number, does $+x$ stand for a positive or a negative number?
24. If x stands for a negative number, does $+x$ stand for a positive or a negative number?
25. If x stands for a positive number, does $-x$ stand for a positive or a negative number?
26. If x stands for a negative number, does $-x$ stand for a positive or a negative number?

★ *Tell when the following will be positive and when they will be negative:*
27. $(+2)(x)$ 28. $(-3)(y)$ 29. $+5a$ 30. $-4k$
31. $+3y$ 32. $-14x$ 33. $+10m$ 34. $-3s$

SELF TEST

1. What is the absolute value of -23?

In each of the following problems choose the greater number:
2. $+6, +3$ 3. $+8, -3$ 4. $-1, -5$ 5. $+2, -7$

Find the answer to each of the following:

6. $(+5) + (+3)$ 7. $(+5)(+3)$ 8. $\dfrac{-18}{-6}$ 9. $\dfrac{+12}{-4}$

10. $(-3) - (+2)$ 11. $(-8) + (+3)$ 12. $\dfrac{-3}{+1}$

13. $(-3)(-2)$ 14. $(+8)(-5)$ 15. $(-3) + (+6)$
16. $(-7) + (-9)$ 17. $(-15)(+3)$ 18. $(-8) - (-6)$

19. $(+9) - (-5)$ 20. $\dfrac{+36}{+9}$ 21. $|+14| - |+17|$

I pay attention to the meaning of words in heavy black type. I know they are important words.

Powers of Negative Numbers

In Chapter 1 you learned that a positive exponent indicates how many times the number should be taken as a factor in a product. For example, 5^4 means $5 \times 5 \times 5 \times 5 = 625$.

The meaning of positive exponents is the same when they are used with signed numbers.

FOR EXAMPLE:
$(+2)^4$ means $(+2)(+2)(+2)(+2) = +16$
$(-3)^2$ means $(-3)(-3) = +9$
$(-4)^3$ means $(-4)(-4)(-4) = -64$

PROBLEMS

1. Copy each of the tables on the right and fill in the values of a^2, a^3, a^4, a^5, a^6.

2. How many numbers in each of the three tables are positive? How many are negative?

3. Are positive results produced by even or odd exponents?

4. Are negative results produced by even or odd exponents?

a^1	a^2	a^3	a^4	a^5	a^6
-1	?	?	?	?	?

a^1	a^2	a^3	a^4	a^5	a^6
-2	?	?	?	?	?

a^1	a^2	a^3	a^4	a^5	a^6
-3	?	?	?	?	?

DO YOU SEE? When a negative number is raised to an even power, the result is a positive number. When a negative number is raised to an odd power, the result is a negative number.

Without using pencil and paper, decide which of the following will give positive results and which will give negative results:

5. $(-2)^8$ 6. $(-1)^7$ 7. $(-4)^2$ 8. $(-5)^4$
9. $(-6)^4$ 10. $(-3)^8$ 11. $(-1)^{11}$ 12. $(-1)^{12}$
13. $(-1)^{13}$ 14. $(-1365)^{18}$ 15. $(-17)^{432}$ 16. $(-12)^{519}$

Adding and Subtracting Like Terms

In Chapter 1 you learned to add like terms by adding the coefficients. Since you know how to add positive and negative numbers, you know how to add like terms with positive and negative coefficients.

Examples for Study

Add:

1. $+a$
$\underline{+a}$
$+2a$

2. $-a$
$\underline{+a}$
0

3. $+3x$
$\underline{-8x}$
$-5x$

4. $-ax$
$\underline{-ax}$
$-2ax$

PROBLEMS

Add:

1. $+3a$
   $+2a$

2. $+6x$
   $-3x$

3. $-2m$
   $+4m$

4. $5k$
   $-2k$

5. $-y$
   $2y$

6. $+n$
   $-2n$

7. $-4h$
   $-3h$

8. $+14x$
   $+10x$

9. $3p$
   $-p$

10. $-13g$
    $13g$

11. $20a$
    $-3a$
    $+a$

12. $+14ab$
    $-20ab$
    $+3ab$

13. x^2
    x^2
    x^2

14. $+a^2b$
    $-2a^2b$
    $-3a^2b$

15. mn^2
    $-mn^2$
    $-8mn^2$

Examples for Study

Subtract:

1. $(+a) - (+a) = (+a) + (-a) = 0$
2. $(-a) - (+a) = (-a) + (-a) = -2a$
3. $(+3ab) - (-ab) = (+3ab) + (+ab) = +4ab$
4. $(-4x) - (-5x) = (-4x) + (+5x) = +x$
5. $rs - (+5rs) = rs + (-5rs) = -4rs$
6. $cd - cd = cd + (-cd) = 0$

Subtract. Apply the rule: change the sign of the subtrahend and then add.

16. $9a$
    $5a$

17. $7x$
    $-3x$

18. $-30m$
    $10m$

19. $-13x$
    $-16x$

20. $4ab$
    $8ab$

21. $16d$
    $3d$

22. $19x$
    $20x$

23. $-5m$
    $15m$

24. $24h$
    h

25. mn
    $3mn$

26. $a - a$

27. $a - (-a)$

28. $(-d) - d$

29. $pq - (-pq)$

30. $0 - a$

31. $2a - (-5a)$

32. $(-10x) - (-11x)$

33. $7m - 2m$

34. $(-20ab) - ab$

Add or subtract as indicated:

35. $(-4x) - (-2x)$

36. $(-5a) - (+3a)$

37. $(-12m) + (-6m)$

38. $(+3y) - (-11y)$

39. $(+2x) + (-8x)$

40. $(-b) - (-b)$

41. $(ab) + (-ab)$

42. $(-6n) - (12n)$

43. $10a + (-7a)$

44. $9d - 14d$

45. $15s - (-15s)$

46. $(-6ab) + 9ab$

Do the operations indicated:

47. $8a + 5a - 6a + (-10a)$
48. $(-7x) - (-9x) + (-x) - (-x)$
49. $3ab + 5ab - (-ab) - (-ab)$
50. $(-10x^2) - 7x^2 + (-x^2) - (-20x^2)$
51. $4\pi - (-3\pi) + 2\pi - 10\pi$
52. $y^3 - (-3y^3) + (-y^3) + 2y^3$

When adding like terms, you may arrange them either horizontally or vertically.

Arranged Vertically   Arranged Horizontally

(1) $-3x$ (2) $-4a$ (1) $(-x) + (-3x) = -4x$
     $-x$ $7a$ (2) $-4a + 7a = 3a$
     $\overline{-4x}$ $\overline{3a}$

In each of the following problems arrange the terms horizontally and combine the like terms:

53. $-a$ 54. $3x$ 55. $+3a$ 56. $-10x$
     $+4a$ $-7x$ a $-10x$

57. $3x$ 58. $+ab$ 59. $-2x^2$ 60. $-m$
     $-x$ $-2ab$ $-x^2$ $2m$
     $+x$ $-4ab$ $5x^2$ -4

Combine the like terms:

61. $3k - 2k + 4$ 62. $7xy - xy - xy$
63. $10a - 10 - a$ 64. $15m - 10m - 5$
65. $20a^2 - a - 10a^2$ 66. $11x - 10 + x$
67. $19 - 2x - x$ 68. $31.5x - 0.2x + x$
69. $2.2a + 0.3a - 0.5a$ 70. $14k - 1\frac{1}{2}k - \frac{1}{4}k$
71. $x - 11x$ 72. $2a - 10a - a$
73. $2a - 12a$ 74. $9\frac{1}{3}x - \frac{2}{3}x - x$
75. $3x^2 - 3x$ 76. $\frac{1}{3}a - \frac{1}{4} - a + 1$

Multiplying and Dividing Terms

In a multiplication problem like $(+a)(-b)$, you can rewrite the problem as $(+1)a \times (-1)b$. Rearranging the factors, you get $(+1)(-1)ab$, or $-1ab$, or simply $-ab$. So $(+a)(-b) = -ab$.

Examples for Study

 1. *Multiply:* $(-x)(-x) = $ _?_   2. *Multiply:* $(+2a)(-3a) = $ _?_
SOLUTION: $(-x)(-x) = +x^2$ SOLUTION: $(+2a)(-3a) = -6a^2$

PROBLEMS

Multiply:

1. $+3m$ 2. $-6x$ 3. $-7y$ 4. $+12a$ 5. $-4a$
    $+2m$ $+5x$ $-8y$ $-8a$ $4a$

6. $+10a$ 7. $5d$ 8. k 9. $3ab$ 10. $-4x$
    $2a$ d $-k$ $-2ab$ $-1x$

11. $(+3a)(-2)$

12. $(-5x)(-2)$

13. $(-3g)(-2g)$

14. $(-5)(+a)$

15. $(-1)(-2x)(-x)$

16. $(-3m)(+m)(-2m)$

17. $5a(+2a)5$

18. $2a \cdot 2a \cdot 2a$

19. $(-10d)(-10)(-d)$

20. $(-x)(-x)(-x)$

Examples for Study

1. *Divide:* $\dfrac{-10a}{-5a} = \underline{\ ?\ }$

SOLUTION: $\dfrac{-10a}{-5a} = +2$

2. *Divide:* $\dfrac{+12a^2}{-6a} = \underline{\ ?\ }$

SOLUTION: $\dfrac{+12a^2}{-6a} = -2a$

Divide:

21. $\dfrac{-24a}{-12a}$

22. $\dfrac{+30m}{-10m}$

23. $\dfrac{-48x}{+12x}$

24. $\dfrac{-18d}{-9d}$

25. $\dfrac{-3d}{3}$

26. $\dfrac{+4a}{a}$

27. $\dfrac{+28x}{+14}$

28. $\dfrac{-x^2}{-x}$

29. $\dfrac{m}{m}$

30. $\dfrac{-a}{+a}$

31. $\dfrac{-10x}{-10}$

32. $\dfrac{-5k^2}{5k}$

33. $(+100a) \div (-10a)$

34. $(-4am) \div (-2a)$

35. $36a^2 \div (6a)$

36. $(+14ab) \div (+7a)$

37. $15x \div (-5)$

38. $(-13.3) \div (-13.3)$

Do the operations indicated:

39. $2a + 3a - 5a + a$

40. $3m(-m)(-4)$

41. $(+12a) + (-6a)$

42. $(-20d) - (-30d)$

43. $-(-6) - (-8)$

44. $-(-7) + 9$

45. $3(4) - 2(+5)$

46. $-2(-4) + 5(-4)$

47. $(-2a) - (-3a)$

48. $+3(-a) + 2a - 6a$

49. $(-a)5a + 3a(-3a)$

50. $2(-3a)(-5a)$

51. $-10(-7a)^2$

52. $-3(-2) - (-2)$

53. $(-21x) \div (-7x)$

54. $(3a)(-2a) \div a$

55. $(+11x) - (-11x)$

56. $(-3a)(+a) + (-4a)(-2a)$

57. $-6m + 17m - 8m - m$

58. $(+4y)^2(-2)$

★ 59. $(-6x)(x) \div 6$

60. $8g - (-7g) + (-7g)$

61. $(+20a)(-200)$

62. $(-8h)(-9h) + (+8h)(-9h)$

63. $3(-4)(-5a) - 5a$

64. $(-10n)(2n) \div 5n$

65. $(-x)20x + 2x(-x)$

66. $(-2a)(-3a) - (-3a)(-6a)$

67. $10(6y^2) \div 30y$

68. $(+2g) - (-g) - (-3g)(-10g)$

SIGNED NUMBERS **75**

Evaluating Algebraic Expressions

Now that you know how to perform the four basic operations with signed numbers, you will be able to evaluate algebraic expressions in which letters stand for signed numbers.

Examples for Study

1. Find the value of $5a - 8c$ if $a = -2$ and $c = -5$.

SOLUTION:
$$5a - 8c = \underline{\ ?\ }$$
$$5(-2) - 8(-5) = \underline{\ ?\ }$$
$$-10 + 40 = +30$$

2. Find the value of a^4 if $a = -2$.

SOLUTION:
$$a^4 = a \cdot a \cdot a \cdot a$$
$$= (-2)(-2)(-2)(-2)$$
$$= +16$$

3. Find the value of a raised to the power b if $a = -2$ and $b = 3$.

SOLUTION:
$$a^b = (-2)^3$$
$$= (-2)(-2)(-2)$$
$$= -8$$

Find the value of each of the following if $a = -2$, $b = 3$, *and* $c = -5$:

1. $a + b + c$ 2. $4a + 3b$ 3. $6b - 3c$ 4. $ac + b$

5. $5a - 4b$ 6. $a^2 + b^2$ 7. $(ab)^2 + c^2$ 8. abc

9. $c(a + b)$ 10. $\dfrac{ab}{c}$ 11. $\dfrac{2bc}{a}$ 12. $8a + 10b + 6c$

★ 13. $ab - bc$ 14. $a - b - c$ 15. $ab \div a$ 16. a^3

17. c^b 18. $\dfrac{6ab - 4bc}{-3a}$ 19. $\dfrac{4c^2 - 5ab}{ac}$ 20. $ac - bc$

SELF TEST

1. When $x = +2$, what is the value of $-(x - 3)$?
2. When x stands for a negative number, what kind of number does $-x$ stand for?

Add:

3. $(-2x) + (-3x)$ 4. $-(-4x) + (+2x)$ 5. $(-3ab) + (+8ab)$

Find the value of each of the following when $a = -3$ *and* $b = -2$:

6. $-a$ 7. $-ab$ 8. a^2b

9. $(-a)(-b)$ 10. $-(a + b)$ 11. $a - b$

12. $-\left(\dfrac{a}{b}\right)$ 13. $\dfrac{-a}{-b}$ 14. $\dfrac{-5a}{b}$

76 *ALGEBRA: ITS BIG IDEAS AND BASIC SKILLS*

Additive and Multiplicative Inverse Principles

Your understanding of signed numbers makes it possible for you to solve equations now by using only two of the laws of equations—the *law of addition* and the *law of multiplication*.

1. If $x + 4 = 3$, you can add -4 to both sides:
$$x + 4 + (-4) = 3 + (-4)$$
$$x = -1$$

2. If $4x = -12$, you can multiply both sides by $\frac{1}{4}$:
$$\tfrac{1}{4} \cdot 4x = \tfrac{1}{4} \cdot -12$$
$$x = -3$$

In addition, when operations such as $4 + (-4) = 0$ or $-5 + 5 = 0$ are performed, then -4 is said to be the **additive inverse** of 4 and 5 the **additive inverse** of -5, and so on.

In multiplication, when operations such as $\frac{1}{4} \cdot 4 = 1$ or $-5\left(-\frac{1}{5}\right) = 1$ are performed, then $\frac{1}{4}$ is said to be the **multiplicative inverse** of 4 and -5 the **multiplicative inverse** of $-\frac{1}{5}$, and so on.

The use of these two principles makes it possible for you to simplify your thinking in solving equations.

Example for Study

1. Solve $3x + 8 = 2$ for x.

SOLUTION: $\qquad\qquad\qquad 3x + 8 = 2 \qquad$ CHECK: $3(-2) + 8 \overset{?}{=} 2$

Add -8 to each side: $\qquad\quad 3x = -6 \qquad\qquad\qquad -6 + 8 \overset{?}{=} 2$

Multiply each side by $\frac{1}{3}$: $\qquad\quad x = -2 \qquad\qquad\qquad\qquad\; 2 = 2$

PROBLEMS

In each of the following, state whether you would use the additive or multiplicative inverse principle to solve, and give the method. For example, Problem 1: multiplicative inverse, multiply each side by $\frac{1}{3}$.

1. $3x = 10$
2. $x + 12 = 5$
3. $x + 5 = 15$
4. $-3x = 10$
5. $x - 12 = 5$
6. $-5x = 15$
7. $\dfrac{x}{3} = 10$
8. $\dfrac{x}{5} = -3$
9. $\dfrac{x}{5} = 15$
10. $2x = -6$
11. $12x = 5$
12. $-3x = -6$
13. $x + 7 = 5$
14. $x - 7 = 5$
15. $4x + 19 = 7$
16. $\frac{1}{2}x + 3 = 2$
17. $\frac{3}{4}x + 2 = 11$
18. $2x - 3x = 8$
19. $x - 2 - 4x = 18$
20. $16 - x = 10$
21. $7x - 8 = 2x + 7$

Solve by using the additive and multiplicative inverse principles:

22. $9 - 2x = 1$ **23.** $5 + x = 0$ **24.** $2x + 5 = 3$

25. $\dfrac{x}{4} - 4 = x$ **26.** $\dfrac{x}{6} + 3 = 1$ **27.** $\dfrac{x}{4} + 4 = 0$

28. $\frac{1}{2}x = -1$ **29.** $2x + 1 = 0$ **30.** $3x - 1 = 0$

31. $\frac{1}{2}x + 2 = 0$ **32.** $10 + x = 0$ **33.** $5x + 5 = 0$

34. $8 + x = 2x - 9$ **35.** $\dfrac{x}{3} - 4 = x$ **36.** $10x - 8 = 20x$

★ **37.** $20 - 2x = 2$ **38.** $0 = 11 + 2x$ **39.** $0 = 17 - 3x$

40. $19 + 5x = 6$ **41.** $x - \frac{1}{2} = 2x$ **42.** $17 - x = 2x + 17$

43. $2 - x = 4$ **44.** $3 - 9 = x$ **45.** $x - 2x = 3$

46. $x - \frac{1}{2}x = 2$ **47.** $\frac{1}{2}x - x = 1$ **48.** $3 - 4x = 0$

49. $7 + x = 0$ **50.** $x - 10 = 10 - x$ **51.** $3 - 9 = 9 - 3x$

52. $2 - x - 3 = 0$ **53.** $\frac{1}{2} - \frac{1}{2}x = 1$ **54.** $4 - 4x = 3 - 3x$

SUMMARY OF IMPORTANT THINGS TO REMEMBER

1. Words and Expressions

absolute value

associative principle for multiplication

additive inverse

multiplicative inverse

negative numbers

number line

origin

positive numbers

signed numbers

position of zero

2. Understandings

Zero is the number that separates the positive and the negative numbers.

To add two signed numbers with like signs, add the numbers as you did in arithmetic. The sum has the same sign as the two numbers you added.

To add two signed numbers with unlike signs, find the difference between the two numbers. The sum has the sign of the number with the greater absolute value.

To subtract one signed number from another, change the sign of the subtrahend and add the two numbers.

The product of two signed numbers whose signs are alike is positive.

The quotient of two signed numbers whose signs are alike is positive.

The product of two signed numbers whose signs are unlike is negative.

The quotient of two signed numbers whose signs are unlike is negative.

The even power of a negative number is a positive number.

The odd power of a negative number is a negative number.

3. Skills

You should be able to:

Add, subtract, multiply, and divide signed numbers.

Solve equations in which there are signed numbers.

Add, subtract, multiply, and divide algebraic terms in which the coefficients are signed numbers.

PROBLEMS ON YOUR AIMS

YOUR AIM **To learn what positive and negative numbers mean and how to use them.**

1. What is the starting position on a number line called?
2. Does the number corresponding to the starting position on a number line have a sign? Explain.
3. If a and b stand for two positive numbers, is their sum positive or negative? If a is greater than b, is $a - b$ positive or negative? If b is greater than a, is $a - b$ positive or negative?
4. What is meant by the absolute value of a number? What symbol is used for absolute value?
5. If the absolute value of b is greater than the absolute value of a and if a is positive and b is negative, is the sum $a + b$ positive or negative? If a is negative and b is positive, is the sum positive or negative?
6. If a and b stand for signed whole numbers and a is greater than b, what sign does a have when $b = 1$?

Which of the following statements are true?

7. $-2 > -6$ 8. $+2 < +4$ 9. $|-6| > |-4|$
10. $|-3| > -10$ 11. $3 \div 3 > -5$ 12. $(-3)(2) < 0$
13. $0 > -100$ 14. $-\frac{1}{2} > -50$ 15. $|-100| > |0|$

YOUR AIM **To learn how to add, subtract, multiply, and divide signed numbers.**

If m *and* n *stand for two numbers, what sign would you attach to the result of each of the following?*

1. Their sum when m and n are both positive. Both negative.
2. Their sum when m is positive, n is negative, and the absolute value of m is greater than the absolute value of n.
3. The difference, $m - n$, when both numbers are positive and n is greater than m.
4. Their difference when $m = n$.

SIGNED NUMBERS **79**

Which of the following statements are true and which are false?

5. $(-2)(-2)(-2) = +8$

6. $3 - (-4) = +1$

7. $3 - 8 = -5$

8. $2x - 7 - 5x + 8 = -3x + 1$

9. $24 \div (-4) = +6$

10. $(-1)^3 - (-1)^4 + (-1)^5 = -3$

11. Find the sum of each of the following pairs of numbers: -2 and $+3$, $+6$ and -2, -12 and $+4$, $+1$ and $+7$.

12. Subtract the second number from the first number of each pair in Problem 11.

13. Find the product of the two numbers in each pair in Problem 11.

14. Divide the first number by the second number of each pair in problem 11.

YOUR AIM

To be able to apply the laws of signed numbers in solving equations.

1. Explain why equations such as $x + 10 = 0$ were impossible to solve before the signed number idea was developed.

Which of the following equations have negative roots and which have positive roots?

2. $2x - 4 = 0$

3. $3x + 5 = 0$

4. $10 + 7x = 0$

5. $x - 8 = 3x + 9$

Which of the following equations have the number -2 as a root?

6. $x - 2 = 2$

7. $-x + 2 = 0$

8. $2x - 4 = 4x - 2$

9. $4 - 2x = 8$

VALUABLE SKILLS PRACTICE

1. Copy the following table and work the problems in each column. To check, add your answers to the four problems in each column and compare the sum with the total given in each column.

$1.7 + 1.8 - 0.3 =$ _?_	$4 =$ _?_ % of 40
$1.01 + 30.15 - 6 =$ _?_	$3 =$ _?_ % of 300
$3.2 - 10.6 =$ _?_	$2 =$ _?_ % of 10
$1 - 1\frac{1}{2} - 2\frac{1}{2} =$ _?_	$1 =$ _?_ % of 1
Totals 17.96	131%

Solve the equations in Problems 2–4. Then use the values of x, y, *and* z *to solve Problem 5.*

2. $x = -(-1)^3 + 10(-10)^2$

3. $z = (-2)^5 + (-5)^2 + (-10)^2(0)$

4. $y = (-5)(-8) - (-5)^2$

5. $x + 4y + 10z = \text{CMXCI}$

Solve the equations in Problems 6–8. Then use the values of a, b, *and* c *to solve Problems 9–14.*

6. $a = -2 + 5 - 6$ **7.** $b = 2 - 7$ **8.** $c = 8(-\frac{1}{2}) + (-2)(-5)$

9. $p = \dfrac{a + b}{c}$ **10.** $q = \dfrac{a - b}{c}$ **11.** $r = \dfrac{a - c}{b - c}$

12. $s = \dfrac{c - b}{ab}$ **13.** $t = \dfrac{c - a}{b - c}$ **14.** $u = \dfrac{b - c}{ab}$

15. Use the formula $p + q + r + s + t + u = -1$ to check your answers to Problems 6–14.

CHAPTER TEST

Add:

1. $\begin{array}{r} 16 \\ -8 \\ \hline \end{array}$ **2.** $\begin{array}{r} -20 \\ +25 \\ \hline \end{array}$ **3.** $\begin{array}{r} -100 \\ -200 \\ \hline \end{array}$ **4.** $\begin{array}{r} 2a \\ -3a \\ \hline \end{array}$ **5.** $\begin{array}{r} 3a \\ a \\ \hline \end{array}$

6. $\begin{array}{r} 5x \\ -2x \\ \hline \end{array}$ **7.** $\begin{array}{r} 10m \\ -m \\ \hline \end{array}$ **8.** $\begin{array}{r} c \\ -4c \\ \hline \end{array}$ **9.** $\begin{array}{r} -5x^2 \\ -4x^2 \\ \hline \end{array}$ **10.** $\begin{array}{r} 8ab \\ -8ab \\ \hline \end{array}$

Subtract:

11. $\begin{array}{r} +14 \\ 7 \\ \hline \end{array}$ **12.** $\begin{array}{r} 18 \\ -2 \\ \hline \end{array}$ **13.** $\begin{array}{r} -25 \\ -15 \\ \hline \end{array}$ **14.** $\begin{array}{r} 4x \\ x \\ \hline \end{array}$ **15.** $\begin{array}{r} -7y \\ 3y \\ \hline \end{array}$

16. $\begin{array}{r} 4ab \\ 3ab \\ \hline \end{array}$ **17.** $\begin{array}{r} a \\ -a \\ \hline \end{array}$ **18.** $\begin{array}{r} 2x^2 \\ 2x^2 \\ \hline \end{array}$ **19.** $\begin{array}{r} -20m \\ m \\ \hline \end{array}$ **20.** $\begin{array}{r} 6n^2 \\ n^2 \\ \hline \end{array}$

Multiply:

21. $\begin{array}{r} -6 \\ +6 \\ \hline \end{array}$ **22.** $\begin{array}{r} -10 \\ -10 \\ \hline \end{array}$ **23.** $\begin{array}{r} -3b \\ +2b \\ \hline \end{array}$ **24.** $\begin{array}{r} 4a \\ -5a \\ \hline \end{array}$ **25.** $\begin{array}{r} -a \\ -a \\ \hline \end{array}$

26. $\begin{array}{r} -3b \\ +9 \\ \hline \end{array}$ **27.** $\begin{array}{r} -4mn \\ -5m \\ \hline \end{array}$ **28.** $\begin{array}{r} -\frac{1}{2}a \\ 6a \\ \hline \end{array}$ **29.** $\begin{array}{r} m^2 \\ m^2 \\ \hline \end{array}$ **30.** $\begin{array}{r} -9xy \\ -4xy \\ \hline \end{array}$

Divide:

31. $\dfrac{24}{-3}$ **32.** $\dfrac{-16}{4}$ **33.** $\dfrac{32a}{-16}$ **34.** $\dfrac{-2x}{2x}$ **35.** $\dfrac{-10ab}{5a}$

36. $\dfrac{60a}{10a}$ **37.** $\dfrac{40mn}{-8n}$ **38.** $\dfrac{-a}{a}$ **39.** $\dfrac{-13m}{m}$ **40.** $\dfrac{-27a^2b}{-9ab}$

41. From $-16a$ subtract $-8a$.
42. If a is -3, how much is $-4a^2$?
43. If $m = -4$ and $n = -10$, what is the value of mn?
44. Simplify $-(-0.05) - (+11)$.
45. Simplify $-2(+10) - 3(-8)$.

If $a = 4$, $b = -6$, and $c = -1$, find the value of x in each of the following:

46. $x = a + b + c$
47. $ax = 2b$
48. $a^2x = b^2$
49. $ax = c$
50. $ax = bc$
51. $x = abc$

CUMULATIVE REVIEW PROBLEMS

WORKING WITH SIGNED NUMBERS

1. If two numbers have like signs, what is the sign of their product? Of their quotient?
2. If two numbers have unlike signs, what is the sign of their product? Of their quotient?
3. If a positive number is subtracted from a negative number, what is the sign of the difference?
4. If a negative number is subtracted from a positive number, what is the sign of the difference?
5. If a stands for a negative number and b stands for a positive number, what is the sign of the product ab?
6. What are two meanings of the plus sign? Of the minus sign?
7. If n stands for a negative number, what sign has n^2? n^3?
8. Which has the greater absolute value, -12 or $+10$?
9. -5 subtracted from $+6$ is -11. True or false?
10. What is the sum of -5 and the square of -5?
11. What is the product of -3 and $(-3)^2$?
12. What is the quotient of $(-4)^3$ divided by $(-2)^5$?
13. What is the product of -5 and $+6$ subtracted from the square of 7?
14. If a negative number is raised to an odd power, the result is positive. True or false?
15. If 3 is one of two factors of 12, what is the other factor?
16. If 5 is one of two factors of -15, what is the other factor?
17. If -7 is one of two factors of $+21$, what is the other factor?
18. What is the average of $+3$, -9, and 0?
19. Subtract -16 from $+16$.

WORKING WITH ALGEBRAIC EXPRESSIONS

If $a = 5$ *and* $b = -10$, *answer each of the following questions:*

1. What is the product of a and b?
2. What is the quotient of a divided by b?
3. What is the sum of a and b?
4. What is the difference of b subtracted from a?
5. What is the difference of a subtracted from b?

Find the average:

6. $-8, +1, -11, +7$, and -4
7. $+3a, -16a, -a$, and $+18a$

8. The length of a side of an equilateral triangle is $3m + 1$. What is its perimeter?
9. What is the coefficient of x in the term $3a^2x$?
10. $(-a)(-a)(-a) = a^3$. True or false?

Combine the like terms in each of the following:

11. $3a + 4b - 2a + b$ 12. $6x - x - 3y + y$
13. $14 - b + b - 8 + 4a$ 14. $15a^2 - 10a + a^2 + 9a$

15. If m is larger than n, how much larger is $m - n$ than $n - m$?

16. By how much does the line AB exceed the line CD?

$$A \underline{\overset{2a-3}{}} B$$
$$C \underline{\overset{a-10}{}} D$$

17. The length of a rectangle is $5a - 6$ and the width is 10 less than the length. Find the perimeter of the rectangle.

SOLVING EQUATIONS

1. Does 3 satisfy the equation $4x - 5 = 7$?
2. Which of the numbers 2, 4, or 5 is the root of $6x - 8 = 4$?

Find the root of each of the following:

3. $4x = 20$ 4. $5x = 35$ 5. $2x + 11 = 3$
6. $\frac{1}{2}x = 2$ 7. $3x + 2 = -14$ 8. $x + x - 4 = 6$
9. $3x - 6 + x = 10$ 10. $2x + 16 = x - 7$ 11. $32 = 3x - 7$
12. $\frac{3}{4}x - 2 = 1$ 13. $\frac{1}{2}x - 2 = \frac{3}{4}x + 5$ 14. $1 - \frac{1}{3}x = \frac{2}{5}x$

If $a = -2$ *and* $b = 4$, *find* x *in each of the following:*

15. $ax = b$ 16. $ax = ab$ 17. $bx = a^2$
18. $x = \dfrac{b}{a}$ 19. $ax = b^3$ 20. $x = a + b$
21. $x = b - a$ 22. $\dfrac{x}{b} = a$ 23. $bx - a = 0$
24. $abx = -b$ 25. $a^2x = b^2$ 26. $a^2b - ax = 0$
27. $\dfrac{b}{a} - x = 0$ 28. $\dfrac{x}{b} - a^3 = 0$ 29. $\dfrac{x}{b^2} = a^2 - b$

BANKERS USE ALGEBRA

A man visited a banker one day and said, "Nine months from now I will receive a check for $1000, but I need money now. How much can I borrow now so that in 9 months I can pay with my $1000 check the amount of the principal and the interest?"

Bankers and financial experts use algebra (or tables derived by algebraic methods) in their work, so this banker knew how to find the answer. He wrote:

Let P = the number of dollars to be borrowed

then $0.06P$ = the interest for 1 year at 6 %

and $\frac{3}{4}(0.06P)$ = the interest for 9 months

The banker then solved the following equation:

$$1000 = \tfrac{3}{4}(0.06P) + P$$
$$4000 = 0.18P + 4P$$
$$4000 = 4.18P$$
$$956.94 = P$$

The banker said, "You can borrow $956.94. In 9 months you will owe the bank $1000."

BIG IDEAS | NUMBER
EQUATION

BASIC SKILLS | Using and interpreting symbols of algebra
Fundamental operations
Evaluating algebraic expressions
Solving equations
Solving verbal problems

CHAPTER **4** *Addition and Subtraction*

IN THE FIRST three chapters you have studied some of the basic ideas of algebra. The purpose of this chapter is to help you develop skill in adding and subtracting algebraic expressions and to help you learn how to apply these basic skills and ideas in solving problems.

YOUR AIM

1. To gain a better understanding of some of the words used in algebra.

2. To gain greater skill in and understanding of addition and subtraction of algebraic expressions.

3. To learn how to add and subtract simple algebraic fractions.

4. To gain skill in solving problems by the use of equations.

85

Your Algebraic Vocabulary

It is time now for you to add a few new words to your vocabulary in algebra. The words are given in the following questions. Read the questions and see if you can discover the meaning of each new word.

PROBLEMS

1. How many wheels has a *bi*cycle? A *tri*cycle? A *mono*cycle?
2. How many angles has a *tri*angle? Into how many parts do you divide a line when you *bi*sect it?
3. The French flag is called a *tri*color. How many colors are there in the flag? Some airplanes are called *bi*planes. How many wings have such planes? How many wings has a *mono*plane (like the Air Force's jet planes)?
4. From your answers to the questions above, tell the meaning of the prefixes *mono-*, *bi-*, and *tri-*.
5. The stem *-nomial* comes from the Latin word *nomen*, meaning "name" or "term." Now that you know the meaning of the prefixes and of the word stem, define monomial, binomial, and trinomial.

The prefix *poly-* means "many." Hence, a **polynomial** is an algebraic expression that consists of two or more terms. Thus the algebraic expression $2a - b$ is a polynomial; since it has two terms, it is also called a **binomial.** The algebraic expression $x + y - 2$ is also a polynomial; since it has three terms, it is also called a **trinomial.** Now you can see that, in the illustration shown above, each of the three pupils is right: $3x - 4$ is an algebraic expression; it is a polynomial; and it is also a binomial.

Identify each of the following algebraic expressions as a monomial, a binomial, a trinomial, or a polynomial. If two words apply, give both.

6. $5xy - 2$
7. ab
8. $a - 2ab + c$
9. $10x^2y^2$
10. $x - 10 + 2y + 5a$
11. $16x^4 - x^3y^5$
12. $2a(3b)^2 - 5(2c)^3$
13. $4(-2a) - 6x + 5y - (3m)^2$
14. $(-3)^5 + 3(-a)$
15. $3x(-2x) + 7a(-ab) - a$

Adding Monomials

In Chapter 1 you learned how to add like terms. **Monomial** is another name for term. Thus $+7ab^2$ is a monomial. Other examples of monomials are $+2a^2b^2$, $-5xy$, $+17m^2n^2$, $-cdf$, and s^2t^3. These monomials are unlike monomials.

In Chapter 3 you learned how to solve a problem like this:

$$+7ab^2 + 2ab^2 + 8ab^2 + (-6ab^2) + (-2ab^2) = 9ab^2$$

You can also arrange monomials that are to be added in a column, as shown at the right. You then add the coefficients. The above problem has been checked by letting $a = +2$ and $b = +3$. The sum $+162$ was obtained in two ways: by adding the column of numbers on the right and by evaluating the sum $9ab^2$. This method of checking is used in algebra quite frequently. You can check this problem by replacing the letters by numbers other than $+2$ and $+3$. However, you must not replace the

CHECK: LET

$a = +2$ and $b = +3$

$$
\begin{aligned}
+7ab^2 &= +126 \\
+2ab^2 &= +36 \\
+8ab^2 &= +144 \\
-6ab^2 &= -108 \\
-2ab^2 &= -36 \\
\hline
9ab^2 &= +162
\end{aligned}
$$

letters by either 0 or 1 because, as you have seen, these two numbers have some characteristics which other numbers do not have.

PROBLEMS

Add, and check by letting a $= +3$ *and* b $= +2$:

1. $+5a$ $\quad +3a$	2. $+7b$ $\quad -3b$	3. $-5b$ $\quad +2b$	4. $-8a$ $\quad -7a$	5. $+5a$ $\quad -8a$
6. $-6ab$ $\quad -8ab$	7. $+4ab$ $\quad -9ab$	8. $+8a^2b$ $\quad -5a^2b$	9. $-2ab^2$ $\quad -3ab^2$	10. $+6b^2$ $\quad -3b^2$
11. $-18a^2$ $\quad -2a^2$	12. $-19a$ $\quad +a$	13. $-a$ $\quad -a$	14. $+a^2$ $\quad -a^2$	15. $+a^2b^2$ $\quad +a^2b^2$

Add:

16. $+8y$ $-2y$ $+3y$ 17. $-6x$ $-2x$ $+9x$ 18. $+2k$ $+8k$ $+9k$ 19. $3x$ x $-x$ 20. $+4y$ $-2y$ $-4y$

21. $+7x$ $-5x$ $+2x$ $+6x$ 22. $+4x^2y$ $-3x^2y$ $+9x^2y$ $-5x^2y$ 23. $8y^2$ $-2y^2$ y^2 y^2 24. $+6xyz$ $+9xyz$ $-7xyz$ $-8xyz$ 25. $-ax$ $-ax$ $-ax$ $-ax$

26. $3x + 9x$
27. $(+4x) + (-2x)$
28. $4x + (-5x)$
29. $-8y + 11y$
30. $(-13k) + (-6k)$
31. $(-2x^2y) + (-7x^2y)$
32. $(-8xyz) + (+11xyz)$
33. $(+5xy^2) + (-13xy^2)$
34. $-2x + 3x + 6x + 5x$
35. $+9y + (-2y) - (-3y) + (-8y)$
36. $5x + 7x + 3x + (-8x) + (-4x) + 6x$
37. $-8y + (-6y) + 3y + 5y + (-9y)$
38. $+9x^2 + (-15x^2) + (-6x^2) + 3x^2 + 8x^2$
39. $-13ab + 6ab + ab + 3ab + (-5ab)$
40. $ab^2 + ab^2 + (-5ab^2) + 3ab^2 + ab^2$
41. $+17xyz + xyz + 3xyz + (-4xyz) + 3xyz$
42. $8xy^2z + (-2xy^2z) + 6xy^2z + (-4xy^2z) + (-9xy^2z)$

★ 43. $+3.7x^2$ $+6.4x^2$ $-9.3x^2$ 44. $2.0y$ $-3.8y$ $-2.1y$ 45. $8.05xy$ $-7.32xy$ $+6.45xy$ 46. $0.04k$ $-6.83k$ $-5.92k$

47. $-0.72x^2y$ $-4.03x^2y$ $+2.87x^2y$ 48. $5abc$ abc $0.04abc$ 49. $-3.0k$ $-2.5k$ $+5.5k$ 50. $+0.01x$ $+0.01x$ $+0.99x$

51. $+\frac{1}{4}x$ $-\frac{7}{8}x$ $+\frac{5}{16}x$ 52. $3\frac{1}{2}x$ $-2\frac{1}{5}x$ $+6\frac{3}{10}x$ 53. $-2\frac{1}{3}ab$ $-4\frac{3}{5}ab$ $+9\frac{2}{5}ab$ 54. $4\frac{1}{2}k^2$ $2\ k^2$ $6\frac{1}{5}k^2$

55. $-3\frac{1}{2}k + 6\frac{2}{3}k + (-4\frac{1}{2}k) + 7\frac{1}{3}k$
56. $-9\frac{1}{8}abc + 3\frac{3}{4}abc + (-4abc) + 7\frac{5}{8}abc$
57. $0.03x^2 + 3.25x^2 + (-6.47x^2) + 9.08x^2$
58. $-4.03y + (-2.05y) + 5.98y + 6.95y$
59. $xy^2 + (-5.34xy^2) + 2.00xy^2 + 0.06xy^2$

60. $+4(a + b)$ $-3(a + b)$ $+8(a + b)$ 61. $-5(x^2 - y^2)$ $+6(x^2 - y^2)$ $+5(x^2 - y^2)$ 62. $+3(4x + 2)$ $-(4x + 2)$ $-6(4x + 2)$

Subtracting Monomials

In Chapter 3 you learned to solve subtraction problems involving signed numbers. To subtract one signed number from another, you changed the sign of the subtrahend and added. You will use the same procedure in subtracting one monomial from another.

Examples for Study

1. $+4ab^2 - (+2ab^2) = \underline{\;?\;}$
2. $-6xyz - (-5xyz) = \underline{\;?\;}$

SOLUTION:

$+4ab^2 + (-2ab^2) = 2ab^2$

SOLUTION:

$-6xyz + (+5xyz) = -xyz$

PROBLEMS

Subtract:

1. $+8a$
   $+6a$
2. $+5b$
   $-3b$
3. $-6k$
   $+7k$
4. $+9y$
   $-4y$
5. $-5x$
   $-6x$

6. $+4y$
   $+7y$
7. $-15x$
   $+6x$
8. $-9xy$
   $+6xy$
9. $+7ab^2$
   $-3ab^2$
10. $+4ab$
    $+2ab$

11. $+15r$
    r
12. $-16x$
    $+x$
13. $+x$
    $-13x$
14. $-x$
    $-16x$
15. $-7x$
    $+7x$

16. $-7x$
    $-7x$
17. $+7x$
    $+7x$
18. $+7x$
    $-7x$
19. $+y$
    $+y$
20. $-15k^2$
    $-15k^2$

21. $+75ab^2$
    $-25ab^2$
22. $+50xy$
    $+25xy$
23. $63y^2$
    $-27y^2$
24. $-15a^2b$
    $+14a^2b$
25. abc
    $-abc$

26. $(+3a) - (-5a)$
27. $(-6b) - (+2b)$
28. $(-4xy) - (-4xy)$
29. $(+9xy^2) - (+11xy^2)$
30. $49abc - 21abc$
31. $(ab^2) - (-ab^2)$

★ 32. $(-4.2x) - 3.7x$
33. $0.08x^2 - (-4.63x^2)$
34. $(-3.2xy) - (-5.1xy)$
35. $12.803y^2 - 18.009y^2$
36. $\frac{1}{8}xy - \frac{3}{4}xy$
37. $3\frac{2}{3}k^2 - 8\frac{1}{5}k^2$
38. $\frac{8}{3}t - t$
39. $\frac{1}{1000}m - 4\frac{1}{9}m$

To remember what you have learned:

Do each day's lesson thoroughly.

Do the Self Tests.

Study the Summaries of Important Things to Remember.

Adding and Subtracting Polynomials

Once you know how to add and subtract monomials, you can use this knowledge to add and subtract polynomials. One simple way of doing this is to arrange like terms in the same column and add or or subtract these terms. Study the examples below and on pages 91 and 92.

Examples for Study

1. *Add:* $2a - b$ and $3a + 5b$

SOLUTION:
Place like terms in columns and add the coefficients:

$$2a - b$$
$$3a + 5b$$
$$\overline{5a + 4b}$$

CHECK: Replace the letters by numbers. Let $a = 2$ and $b = 3$.
$$2a - b = 4 - 3 = 1$$
$$3a + 5b = 6 + 15 = 21$$
$$\overline{5a + 4b = 10 + 12 = 22}$$

2. *Add:* $6m + 2$, $3m - 4$, and $-m - 7$

SOLUTION:
Place like terms in columns and add the coefficients:

$$6m + 2$$
$$3m - 4$$
$$-m - 7$$
$$\overline{8m - 9}$$

CHECK: Let $m = 2$.
$$6m + 2 = 12 + 2 = 14$$
$$3m - 4 = 6 - 4 = 2$$
$$-m - 7 = -2 - 7 = -9$$
$$\overline{8m - 9 = 16 - 9 = 7}$$

PROBLEMS

Add:

1. $3y + 6$
   $2y + 5$

2. $8x - 9$
   $2x - 5$

3. $3m - 4$
   $4m + 9$

4. $a - b$
   $3a - b$

5. $16 + m$
   $8 - 2m$

6. $a^2 - 5$
   $a^2 + 8$

7. $10a - 3b + 5$
   $7a + 6b - 9$

8. $x + y - z$
   $x - y + z$

9. $2x + 5$
   $-3x - 6$

Place like terms in columns and add:

10. $4x + 6y$, $-7x + 3y$, $+8x - 7y$
11. $3x^2 + 4x$, $2x^2 - 5x$, $7x^2 + 6x$
12. $4ab - 9$, $-ab - 1$, $-3ab - 1$
13. $x^2y + 4y$, $3x^2y - 9y$, $-x^2y + 6y$
14. $9k + 6m$, $-k - m$, $-k - m$
15. $-a - b - c$, $-a - b - c$, $-a - b - c$
16. $2a + b - c$, $-a - 2b + 2c$, $-a + b - c$

90 *ALGEBRA: ITS BIG IDEAS AND BASIC SKILLS*

Add:

17. $13a - b$
    $4a + 2b$
    $-2a - 7b$

18. $40 - ab$
    $20 + ab$
    $-50 + 4ab$

19. $a^2 + ab - b^2$
    $2a^2 - 3ab + b^2$
    $a^2 + 5ab - 4b^2$

20. $4x + 3y - 7z$
    $-2x - y + z$
    $+6x - 4y - 8z$

21. $9a^2 - ab + 3b^2$
    $a^2 + 2ab + 2b^2$
    $3a^2 - 4ab - b^2$

22. $a^2 - 2a + 6$
    $a^2 - 5a + 3$
    $a^2 - 7a - 5$

Example for Study

Subtract: $3x - 6$ from $5x + 3$

SOLUTION:

Place like terms in the same column and subtract the coefficients:

$5x + 3$
$3x - 6$
$2x + 9$

CHECK: Let $x = 2$

$5x + 3 = 10 + 3 = 13$
$3x - 6 = 6 - 6 = 0$
$2x + 9 = 4 + 9 = 13$

Subtract:

23. $3y + 6$
    $2y + 5$

24. $8x - 9$
    $2x - 5$

25. $3m - 4$
    $4m + 9$

26. $a - b$
    $3a - b$

27. $16 + m$
    $8 - 2m$

28. $a^2 - 5$
    $a^2 + 8$

29. $10a - 3b + 5$
    $7a + 6b - 9$

30. $x + y - z$
    $x - y + z$

31. $2x + 5$
    $-3x - 6$

32. $5a + 10$
    $3a - 12$

33. $16x + 18$
    $12x - 23$

34. $11m - 2n$
    $3m - 5n$

35. $a + 8$
    $5a + 9$

36. $19 + 3b$
    $21 - 2b$

37. $1 - m$
    $2 + m$

38. $34r + s$
    $40r + s$

39. $a + 17$
    $-a + 18$

40. $ab - 60$
    $9ab - 70$

41. $45 - mn$
    $36 + 8mn$

42. $3x^2 - 2x + 5$
    $x^2 + x - 5$

43. $14m + mn - 16$
    $m + 8mn - 21$

Do the operations indicated:

44. Add 6 to $6a - 6$.
45. Find the sum of $3a + 4$ and $8a + 9$.
46. Find the sum of $6b - c$ and $3b - 8c$.
47. Find the sum of $3x + 8y - 4$ and $x - 5y + 10$.
48. Subtract $16x - 8$ from $20x + 12$.

49. Subtract $28 + x$ from $30 - x$.

50. Subtract $14a + 15b$ from $11a + 5b$.

51. Find the sum of $m + n$, $2m + 3n$, and $7m - n$.

52. Add $3k - 4h$, $k + h$, $-3k + 6h$, and $10k - h$.

53. From the sum of $5a + 8$ and $a - 9$ subtract $3a - 4$.

54. From the sum of $b - c$ and $3b + 4c$ subtract $5b + 5c$.

55. Subtract $x - y$ from $x + y$.

56. Subtract $a - 1$ from 0.

57. Subtract $a - b + c$ from the sum of $2a - b - c$ and $b + c$.

58. Subtract $x + y - 2$ from the sum of $3x - y - 1$ and $2x - 4y + 5$.

59. From the sum of 40 and $10x$ subtract $30 + x$.

This algebraic expression is arranged in descending powers of x:

$$x^4 + x^3 + x^2 + x + 1$$

And this expression is arranged in ascending powers of x:

$$1 + x + x^2 + x^3 + x^4$$

In adding and subtracting polynomials, you must place only like terms in the same column. Before doing that, it is good practice to arrange the terms in ascending or descending powers of a letter. If there is more than one letter in a polynomial, choose one letter and arrange the terms in ascending or descending powers of that letter.

Example for Study

Add: $3am + a^3 - a^2b^2$ and $-3a^3 + 4a^2b^2$

SOLUTION: First arrange each polynomial in descending powers of a. Note that the second polynomial is already arranged in descending powers of a.

$$3am + a^3 - a^2b^2 = a^3 - a^2b^2 + 3am$$

Now arrange the terms in columns, so that each column has only like terms, and add:

$$
\begin{aligned}
a^3 - \ \ a^2b^2 + 3am \\
-3a^3 + 4a^2b^2 \qquad \\
\hline
-2a^3 + 3a^2b^2 + 3am
\end{aligned}
$$

Arrange in descending powers of x *and add the polynomials:*

60. $13 + 6x^2 - x$ and $3x^2 - 1 - 9x$

61. $10x^2 - 11 - 5x$ and $-1 + x + x^2$

62. $2x - 4 + 6x^2$ and $8 + 3x + 7x^2$

63. $3xy + 2x^2 - y^2$ and $10x^2 + y^2 - xy$

64. $5y^2 + x^2 - 9xy$ and $13xy - 3x^2 - 2y^2$

92 *ALGEBRA: ITS BIG IDEAS AND BASIC SKILLS*

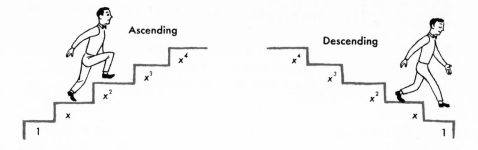

Ascending   Descending

Arrange in ascending powers of x *and subtract the first polynomial from the second:*

65. $5x^2 + 6 + 4x$ and $2x^2 - x + 1$

66. $8 + 7x^2 - 8x$ and $11 - x + x^2$

67. $xy + 3x^2 + y^2$ and $5y^2 - 2xy + x^2$

68. $x^3 - x^2 + 2$ and $8 - 4x^3 - 9x^2$

69. $ax^2 - a^2x - a^3$ and $a^3 + 2ax^2 - a^2x$

Fractions in Algebra

In your study of arithmetic you learned some important principles about fractions which will be useful in algebra. Two of these are:

> **1. The numerator and the denominator of a fraction may be multiplied or divided by the same number except zero without changing the value of the fraction.**
>
> **2. Fractions with unlike denominators must be changed to fractions with like denominators before they can be added or subtracted.**

PROBLEMS

Make use of the first principle stated above to reduce each of the following fractions to lowest terms:

1. $\dfrac{4}{6}$ **2.** $\dfrac{6}{8}$ **3.** $\dfrac{12}{20}$ **4.** $\dfrac{48}{100}$ **5.** $\dfrac{45}{70}$

6. $\dfrac{15}{25}$ **7.** $\dfrac{5 \times 3}{5 \times 5}$ **8.** $\dfrac{8 \times 2}{8 \times 3}$ **9.** $\dfrac{3 \times 6}{6 \times 5}$ **10.** $\dfrac{2 \cdot 2 \cdot 7}{2 \cdot 9 \cdot 2}$

11. $\dfrac{8x}{16}$ **12.** $\dfrac{15a}{25}$ **13.** $\dfrac{6ab}{8}$ **14.** $\dfrac{6ab}{8ab}$ **15.** $\dfrac{6ab}{8a}$

16. $\dfrac{12}{16x}$ **17.** $\dfrac{9}{12xy}$ **18.** $\dfrac{24a}{36ab}$ **19.** $\dfrac{ab}{a}$ **20.** $\dfrac{x}{xy}$

21. $\dfrac{17}{17}$ **22.** $\dfrac{3xy}{3xy}$ **23.** $\dfrac{5a^2b}{25a^2}$ **24.** $\dfrac{8}{12x^2}$ **25.** $\dfrac{7x}{28x^2}$

Make use of the second principle on page 93 to add or subtract the fractions in the following problems:

26. $\frac{1}{8} + \frac{4}{8}$ **27.** $\frac{5}{6} - \frac{3}{6}$ **28.** $\frac{3}{10} + \frac{4}{10}$

29. $\frac{5}{8} + \frac{3}{4}$ **30.** $\frac{2}{3} + \frac{4}{5}$ **31.** $\frac{7}{8} - \frac{2}{3}$

32. $\frac{7}{10} + \frac{4}{5}$ **33.** $\frac{5}{16} - \frac{1}{4}$ **34.** $\frac{2}{3} + \frac{3}{4}$

Examples for Study

1. $\dfrac{7}{x} + \dfrac{9}{x} = \underline{\;\;?\;\;}$

SOLUTION: Since the denominators in both fractions are the same, simply add the numerators:

$$\frac{7}{x} + \frac{9}{x} = \frac{7+9}{x} = \frac{16}{x}$$

2. $\dfrac{3}{x} + \dfrac{5}{2x} = \underline{\;\;?\;\;}$

SOLUTION: To get a common denominator, multiply both the numerator and the denominator of the first fraction by 2:

$$\frac{3}{x} + \frac{5}{2x} = \frac{6}{2x} + \frac{5}{2x}$$

Now you can add: $\dfrac{6}{2x} + \dfrac{5}{2x} = \dfrac{6+5}{2x} = \dfrac{11}{2x}$

NOTE: In Example 2 above, $2x$ is the lowest common denominator of 2 and x. The product of the denominators of the two fractions, x and $2x$, is $2x^2$. $2x^2$ is also a common denominator, but it is not the lowest common denominator. The product of the denominators is always a common denominator but not necessarily the lowest common denominator. In Chapter 10 you will learn a method for finding the lowest common denominator.

3. $3 + \dfrac{1}{a} = \underline{\;\;?\;\;}$

SOLUTION:

First write 3 as $\dfrac{3}{1}$: $\dfrac{3}{1} + \dfrac{1}{a}$

Next multiply both the numerator and the denominator of $\frac{3}{1}$ by a:

$$\frac{3a}{a} + \frac{1}{a}$$

Now add: $\dfrac{3a}{a} + \dfrac{1}{a} = \dfrac{3a+1}{a}$

4. $\dfrac{5}{x} - \dfrac{7}{y} = \underline{\ ?\ }$

SOLUTION: The common denominator is xy. Multiply both the numerator and the denominator of the first fraction by y, and multiply both the numerator and the denominator of the second fraction by x:

$$\dfrac{5y}{xy} - \dfrac{7x}{xy}$$

Now subtract: $\qquad \dfrac{5y}{xy} - \dfrac{7x}{xy} = \dfrac{5y - 7x}{xy}$

Add or subtract as indicated:

35. $\dfrac{5}{y} + \dfrac{2}{y}$　　　　36. $\dfrac{4}{k} - \dfrac{2}{k}$　　　　37. $\dfrac{3}{x} + \dfrac{k}{x}$

38. $\dfrac{2}{x^2} + \dfrac{4}{x^2}$　　　　39. $\dfrac{6}{x^2} - \dfrac{m}{x^2}$　　　　40. $\dfrac{x}{y} + \dfrac{x}{y}$

★ 41. $\dfrac{x}{y} + \dfrac{2x}{y}$　　　　42. $\dfrac{5k}{x} + \dfrac{7k}{x}$　　　　43. $\dfrac{11x}{a} - \dfrac{8x}{a}$

44. $\dfrac{3a^2}{b} + \dfrac{x}{b}$　　　　45. $\dfrac{15a^2b}{2x} + \dfrac{14a^2b}{2x}$　　　　46. $\dfrac{7xy}{5x} - \dfrac{2xy}{5x}$

47. $\dfrac{x}{y} + \dfrac{x}{y} + \dfrac{x}{y}$　　　　48. $\dfrac{3a^2}{b} + \dfrac{2a^2}{b} - \dfrac{4a^2}{b}$　　　　49. $\dfrac{11k}{k^2} - \dfrac{3}{k^2}$

In each of the following find a common denominator and add or subtract as indicated:

50. $\dfrac{4}{a} + \dfrac{3}{5a}$　　　　51. $\dfrac{2}{b} - \dfrac{5}{3b}$　　　　52. $\dfrac{1}{4k} + \dfrac{3}{k}$

53. $\dfrac{k}{5} + \dfrac{x}{3}$　　　　54. $\dfrac{2}{5a} + \dfrac{4}{a}$　　　　55. $\dfrac{11}{12a} - \dfrac{1}{a}$

56. $\dfrac{3}{2x} + \dfrac{5}{4x}$　　　　57. $\dfrac{1}{7x} + 2$　　　　58. $5 + \dfrac{y}{3}$

59. $k + \dfrac{5}{x}$　　　　60. $\dfrac{2}{y} + m$　　　　61. $\dfrac{2}{3a} + 9$

62. $\dfrac{1}{3x} + \dfrac{2}{x} + \dfrac{4}{x}$　　　　63. $\dfrac{7}{a} + \dfrac{5}{2a} + \dfrac{4}{5a}$　　　　64. $\dfrac{5}{x} + \dfrac{2}{3x} + \dfrac{4}{6x}$

65. $\dfrac{2}{3} + \dfrac{2}{x}$　　　　66. $\dfrac{5}{4} - \dfrac{6}{a}$　　　　67. $\dfrac{4}{a} + \dfrac{3}{b}$

68. $\dfrac{5}{m} - \dfrac{2}{n}$　　　　69. $\dfrac{4}{x^2} - \dfrac{2}{x}$　　　　70. $\dfrac{5}{xy} + \dfrac{3}{y}$

71. $\dfrac{2}{k} + \dfrac{x}{m}$　　　　72. $\dfrac{3}{5} + \dfrac{x}{y}$　　　　73. $\dfrac{a}{b} + \dfrac{c}{d}$

ADDITION AND SUBTRACTION **95**

★ 74. $\dfrac{a}{b} + \dfrac{c}{d} + \dfrac{5}{d}$

75. $\dfrac{x}{y} + 3 + \dfrac{1}{z}$

76. $\dfrac{5}{a} + \dfrac{2}{b} + \dfrac{3}{2a}$

77. $\dfrac{a}{b} + \dfrac{c}{d} + \dfrac{e}{b}$

78. $\dfrac{4}{k} + \dfrac{5}{k^2} + \dfrac{2}{3k^2}$

79. $\dfrac{x}{y} - \dfrac{2}{3xy}$

80. $\dfrac{6}{x^2} + \dfrac{3}{y^2}$

81. $\dfrac{3}{2a^2b} - \dfrac{1}{3a}$

82. $\dfrac{m}{n} - \dfrac{x}{y}$

SELF TEST

Add:

1. $4x + 3y$
   $-5x + 6y$

2. $4a^2 + 3b$
   $+2a^2 - 5b$

3. $-2x^2 - 4xy$
   $-5x^2 + 6xy$

Subtract:

4. $2x + 4y$
   $4x - 2y$

5. $8x^2 - 2y^2$
   $-9x^2 + 6y^2$

6. $-a^2 + 2b^2$
   $-a - 2b^2$

Add:

7. $\dfrac{2}{3} + \dfrac{1}{3}$

8. $\dfrac{3}{k} + \dfrac{2}{k}$

9. $\dfrac{2}{x} + \dfrac{4}{3x}$

10. $\dfrac{1}{a} + \dfrac{3}{b}$

11. $\dfrac{3}{x^2} + \dfrac{2}{x}$

12. $\dfrac{2}{3} + \dfrac{4}{5x}$

Two Mathematical Abilities

Your skill in solving problems depends to a large extent on:

(1) Your ability to understand what you read.

(2) Your ability to write relationships expressed in words as algebraic expressions.

The following problems will help you to develop these two abilities.

HOW TO READ

Read rapidly to get general ideas.
Read slowly to understand the details.

PROBLEMS

Test your ability to understand what you read by answering the following questions:

1. What is the sum of one-fourth of twenty and one-half of eight?
2. Six is how much less than three times ten?
3. How many inches are there in $1\frac{1}{4}$ feet? $1\frac{3}{4}$ yards?
4. What is the sum of forty, one-fourth of forty, and one-tenth of forty?

5. How many dimes are equivalent to three dollars, five quarters, and seven nickels?

6. How many workdays are there in six 5-day weeks?

7. Shirley has three quarters, one dime, and three nickels. How much will she have left after spending three-fourths of this?

8. How many ounces are there in two 3-pound boxes?

9. How much is the sum of ten and the square of ten?

10. What is the square of the sum of eight and four?

11. Lucille has one quarter, three dimes, and five nickels. If she had five quarters, three dimes, and one nickel, how much more money would she have?

12. Ann is two years older than Bob. Six years from now, Bob will be twenty-one. How old is Ann now?

13. What is the result if the quotient of six divided by three is multiplied by the product of six and three?

14. What is the result if the difference of twelve subtracted from fifteen is added to the sum of twelve and fifteen?

15. How much is five less than the product of five, eight, and two?

16. The sum of two numbers is thirteen and their difference is three. Find the product of the two numbers.

Test your ability to write relationships expressed in words as algebraic expressions by writing each of the following expressions in the simplest algebraic form:

17. The number of inches in m feet.

18. The number of inches in h feet and k yards.

19. The number of quarters in D dollars.

20. The sum of n and five times n.

21. The product of $2n$ and $3n$.

22. The number of days in $3w$ weeks. In $w - 2$ weeks.

23. The number of seconds in m minutes. In $m - n$ minutes.

24. The product of a, a, and 10. Their sum.

25. One-half of n plus eight.

26. Three less than two-thirds of x.

27. Five more than ten times p.

28. The number of nickels in q quarters and d dollars.

29. Five more than n. Five less than n. Five times n. Three less than twice n.

30. The width of a rectangle is w. What is the length of the rectangle if it is three times the width? What is the length if it is five more than twice the width?

★ 31. If a represents your age now, what represents your age ten years ago? Ten years from now? Your father's age if he is eight years more than twice your age?

32. A baseball team has scheduled x games and has played two-thirds of them. How many games remain to be played?

33. If n represents the first of three consecutive numbers, what represents the second number? The third? Remember that three consecutive numbers are numbers like 15, 16, 17.

34. If D dollars are invested and yield 10 percent profit, what is the total amount?

35. Paul is a years old now and is twice as old as Mary. Write the expressions for their ages four years ago.

36. What is the area A of a rectangle whose sides are $5a$ and $3b$? What is the perimeter p of this rectangle?

Solving Verbal Problems

In solving verbal problems, it is important to organize your work properly. You will find problem solving easier if you follow these steps:

1. **Read the problem.**
2. **Represent the unknown quantities by letters.**
3. **Write the equation and solve it.**
4. **Answer the question or questions asked in the problem.**
5. **Check by comparing your answer or answers with the facts stated in the problem.**

Example for Study

Step 1. Read the problem: The sum of three consecutive numbers is 96. Find the numbers.

Step 2. Represent the unknown quantities by letters:

Let n = the first consecutive number
Then $n + 1$ = the second consecutive number
And $n + 2$ = the third consecutive number

Step 3. Write the equation and solve it: As represented above, the sum of the three numbers is

$$n + (n + 1) + (n + 2) = 3n + 3$$

The sum is 96, hence,

$$3n + 3 = 96$$
$$3n = 93$$
$$n = 31$$

98 *ALGEBRA: ITS BIG IDEAS AND BASIC SKILLS*

Step 4. Answer the question: The numbers are 31, 32, and 33.

Step 5. Check by comparing your answers with the facts stated in the problem: The problem states that the numbers are consecutive (31, 32, and 33 are consecutive numbers) and that their sum is 96 $(31 + 32 + 33 = 96)$.

PROBLEMS

1. If 14 is added to four times a certain number, the result is 38. Find the number.
2. If 25 is subtracted from ten times a certain number, the result is 45. Find the number.
3. The sum of two numbers is 180. The larger number is five times the smaller number. Find the two numbers.
4. George is 5 years older than Mary. If the sum of their ages is 47, how old is each?
5. The sum of two numbers is 77. If one number is three-fourths of the other, find the two numbers.
6. The sum of two numbers is 98. If one number is six times the other, find the two numbers.
7. Divide $135 between Lois and Bob so that Lois will receive twice as much as Bob.
8. Divide 180 into two parts so that one part will be three times the other part.
9. The sum of two consecutive numbers is 111. Find the two numbers.
10. The sum of three consecutive numbers is 78. Find the three numbers.
★ 11. The sum of two consecutive odd numbers is 96. Find the two numbers.
12. The sum of two consecutive even numbers is 162. Find the two numbers.
13. The sum of three consecutive odd numbers is 105. Find the three numbers.
14. Mary is 4 years older than Jill. The sum of their ages is 32 years. How old are Mary and Jill?

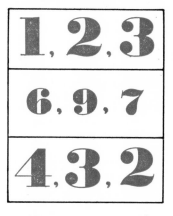

Which are consecutive?

15. Jerry is four times as old as his brother and half as old as his uncle. The sum of the three ages is 39 years. How old is each?

Using Algebra in Arithmetic Problems

It is likely that in arithmetic you memorized a certain rule which worked for a certain type of problem. Every time you had to solve a problem of that type, you remembered the rule to be used. Using algebra, you do not need to memorize which rule applies to which type of problem. You can express as an equation the relationships given in the problem. You get the answer to the problem by solving the equation.

Examples for Study

1. $24 is 30% of what amount?

SOLUTION: Let x = the amount sought in number of dollars
Since 30% of x is equal to $24, the equation is:
$$0.30x = 24$$
Solving for x: $x = 80$
Hence the answer is $80.   CHECK: 30% of $80 = $24

2. The retail price of butter this year has increased 25% over the price last year. What was the price last year if the price this year is 60 cents per pound?

SOLUTION: Let x = the price in number of dollars last year
    Then $0.25x$ = the increase in price

Price last year + increase in price = price this year

$$x \quad + \quad 0.25x = 60$$
$$1.25x = 60$$
$$x = 48$$

Hence, the price last year was 48 cents.   CHECK: 25% of 48 = 12
                                                                  $12 + 48 = 60$

3. What sum of money invested at $3\frac{1}{2}$% simple interest will amount to $1083 in 4 years?

SOLUTION: Let x = the number of dollars invested

Sum invested + interest = amount

$$x \quad + \ 4(0.035x) = 1083$$
$$1.14x = 1083$$
$$x = 950$$

Hence, the sum is $950.

Check this answer.

100 *ALGEBRA: ITS BIG IDEAS AND BASIC SKILLS*

PROBLEMS

Use the algebraic method in solving the following problems:
1. $45 is 15% of what amount?
2. $125.50 is 20% of what amount?
3. 105 miles is 35% of what distance?
4. $41.82 is the down payment required for a refrigerator. If this is 15% of the selling price, find the selling price.
5. The price of milk has increased 20% since last year. If the present price of milk is 22 cents per quart, what was the price last year?
6. A 6% discount of a bill is $1.83. What was the amount of the bill?
7. A customer saved $19.20 by paying cash for an article. If the discount was 12%, what was the original price of the article?
8. What sum at 2.5% simple interest will amount to $666.25 in one year? Base the equation on: Sum + interest on sum = amount.
9. What sum at 4% simple interest will amount to $1508 in one year?
10. What sum invested at $3\frac{1}{2}$% simple interest will amount to $846 in 5 years?
11. What sum invested at $4\frac{1}{2}$% simple interest will amount to $4760 in 8 years?
12. What sum at 3% simple interest will amount to $1072.50 in 10 years?
13. A radio sold for $69.70. This was 15% less than the marked price. What was the marked price?
14. At what price must a merchant sell an article that cost him $8.76 in order to have a margin of 40% of the selling price? The margin is the amount allowed for operating expenses and profit.

★ 15. A European airline announced that during April of one year it transported 65,311 Americans over its various European routes. This was a gain of 35.5 percent over the same month during the previous year. How many Americans did the airline transport in April of the previous year?
16. A salesman is paid a salary of $60 a week plus 4% commission on his sales. How much must he sell to make a total of $150 a week?
17. How much money must be invested at $4\frac{1}{2}$% simple interest to bring a return of $2500 in one year?
18. How much money must be invested at 2.9% simple interest to bring a return of $1000 in one year?
19. Show that a margin of 20% of the selling price is the same as a margin of 25% of the cost.
20. Mr. Franklin received a 5% cut in salary. What percent increase must he receive to bring his salary to what it was before the cut?

21. According to United States Treasury figures, individuals owned the biggest single block of United States government securities one year. Their holdings were approximately $68,850,000,000, which was estimated to be 34 percent of the aggregate liquid assets of individuals. Find the aggregate liquid assets of individuals in the United States for that year.

SELF TEST

Write each of the following using the symbols of algebra:
1. The number of inches in y feet.
2. The number of feet in k yards.
3. The number of yards in m inches.
4. Three consecutive numbers the least of which is x.
5. The interest received in one year on an investment of A dollars at 4% interest.
6. The distance a car goes in 10 hours at an average speed of a miles an hour.
7. The sum of two numbers is 15, and x stands for one of them. Represent the other number in terms of x.
8. The perimeter of a rectangle is 28 inches. w stands for the width. Express the length in terms of w.

FACTS....?

WHAT....?

HOW....?

HAVE I....?

DOES IT....?

When you solve problems, ask yourself questions:

What facts are given in the problem?
What am I trying to find?
How shall I solve the problem?
Have I used all the facts given?
Does my answer check?

Using Algebra in Geometry Problems

In solving some problems, it is helpful to make a diagram in addition to following the five steps listed on page 98.

Example for Study

Step 1. Read the problem: Find the width of a rectangle if its area is 192 square inches and its length is 16 inches.

Step 2. Make a diagram:

Step 3. Represent the unknown quantities by letters:
Let x = the number of inches in the width of the rectangle

Step 4. Write the equation and solve it: Since the area of a rectangle is the product of the length and the width, the equation is

$$16x = 192$$
$$x = 12$$

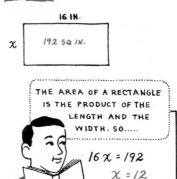

Step 5. Answer the question: The width of the rectangle is 12 inches.

Step 6. Check:
$$\text{Area} = \text{length} \times \text{width}$$
$$192 \overset{?}{=} 16 \times 12$$
$$192 = 192$$

PROBLEMS

1. Find the length of a rectangle if its area is 104 square inches and its width is 8 inches.

2. Find the altitude of a triangle whose base is 12 inches and whose area is 84 square inches.

3. The perimeter of a rectangle is 32 feet. Find the length and the width of the rectangle if the length is three times the width.

4. The perimeter of a rectangle is 64 feet. The length of the rectangle is 10 feet more than the width. Find the length and the width of the rectangle.

5. The perimeter of a rectangular plot of ground is 582 feet. The length is twice the width. Find the length and the width.

6. The perimeter of a rectangle is 630 feet. Find the dimensions of the rectangle if the length is 25 feet longer than the width.

7. In a triangle the longest side is twice the shortest side, and the third side is 5 inches less than the longest side. Find the three sides if the perimeter is 45 inches.

8. One angle of a certain triangle is three times a second angle, and the third angle is 16° smaller than the first. Find the number of degrees in each angle. Base the equation on this fact: The sum of the three angles of any triangle equals 180°.

9. If one angle of a triangle is 60° more than the smallest angle and the third angle is six times the smallest angle, find the number of degrees in each angle.

10. If two angles of a triangle are equal and the third angle is equal to the sum of the first two angles, find the number of degrees in each angle.

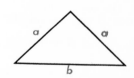

★ 11. Each of the two equal sides of an isosceles triangle is 24 inches longer than the base. The perimeter is 72 inches. Find the lengths of the equal sides and the base.

An isosceles triangle has two equal sides, a and a, which are called the "legs." The third side, b, is called the "base."

12. If each leg of an isosceles triangle is four times the base and the perimeter is 104 inches, find the lengths of the legs and the base.

13. The base of an isosceles triangle is 14 inches less than twice one of the legs. The perimeter is 54 inches. Find the length of each of the three sides.

Using Algebra in Distance Problems

In solving the problems below, you will need to use the relationship which exists between the rate of travel, time, and distance covered. This relationship can be written as:

$$d = rt$$

where d represents distance, r rate, and t time.

Example for Study

Two bicycle riders A and B start at the same time, 3:00 P.M., riding toward each other from points 20 miles apart. A rides 15 miles per hour and B rides 10 miles per hour. Where and at what time will they meet?

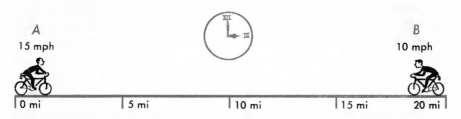

SOLUTION: Let $t = $ the number of hours of travel
In t hours A will travel $15t$ miles and B will travel $10t$ miles. Hence,

$$15t + 10t = 20$$
$$25t = 20$$
$$t = \tfrac{4}{5} \text{ hour, or 48 minutes}$$

Distance A will travel $15t$: $15 \times \tfrac{4}{5} = 12$ miles

Distance B will travel $10t$: $10 \times \tfrac{4}{5} = 8$ miles

Hence, A and B will meet at 3:48 P.M. at a point 12 miles from where A started.

PROBLEMS

1. If an automobile travels an average of 30 miles per hour, how far will it travel in 2 hours? In $3\tfrac{1}{2}$ hours? In $\tfrac{1}{2}$ hour? In one hour and ten minutes? In h hours?

2. At 30 miles per hour, how long will it take to travel 60 miles? 45 miles? 70 miles? m miles?

3. Find the average speed of travel if a distance of 90 miles is traveled in 2 hours. In one hour and 48 minutes. In t hours. In $2t$ hours. In $2.5t$ hours.

4. Bill starts riding a bicycle north 10 miles an hour at 1:00 P.M. Joe starts at the same time from the same point and rides 12 miles an hour south. At what time will they be 77 miles apart?

5. Two cars leave town at the same time and go in the same direction. One car averages 40 miles an hour and the other car averages 48 miles an hour. How long will it be before the cars are 36 miles apart?

6. If the hikers pictured in the drawing start out at 7 o'clock, at what time will they meet?

7. Two ships sailed from San Francisco at the same time. The slower ship traveled at 15 knots (nautical miles per hour). After one day of traveling, the ships were 264 nautical miles apart. What was the speed of the faster ship?

8. At 8:00 A.M. a train left Chicago for New Orleans, traveling at an average rate of 40 miles per hour. Three hours later, a second train, averaging 60 miles per hour, left Chicago for New Orleans. How far south will the trains be when the second train overtakes the first?

9. Two automobiles traveling in opposite directions meet on a highway. One averages 45 miles per hour and the other 30 miles per hour. In how many hours will they be 150 miles apart?

10. A plane averaging 120 miles per hour left Hickam Field, Hawaii, at 6:30 A.M. for San Francisco. At 9:45 A.M. a fast plane, averaging 250 miles per hour, took off for the same destination. At what time did the second plane overtake the first?

11. Using the facts in the drawing, find at what time the cyclist will overtake the hiker.

106 *ALGEBRA: ITS BIG IDEAS AND BASIC SKILLS*

SUMMARY OF IMPORTANT THINGS TO REMEMBER

1. Words and Expressions

algebraic fraction

ascending powers

binomial

descending powers

monomial

polynomial

trinomial

2. Understandings

Like monomials can be added or subtracted by adding or subtracting coefficients.

The numerator and the denominator of a fraction can be multiplied or divided by the same number except zero without changing the value of the fraction.

Fractions with the same denominator can be added or subtracted by adding or subtracting the numerators.

Algebraic methods of solving problems are very convenient.

3. Skills

You should be able to:

Add and subtract polynomials.

Reduce algebraic fractions to lowest terms.

Add and subtract algebraic fractions.

Solve problems using equations.

PROBLEMS ON YOUR AIMS

YOUR AIM   **To gain a better understanding of some of the words used in algebra.**

Define or give an example of each of the following:
1. Term   2. Factor   3. Coefficient

How many terms has each of the following expressions?
4. $x - 2$ 5. $a - b - 3$
6. $3ax^2$ 7. $3x - y - 4$

What is the meaning of each of the following prefixes?
8. Tri-   9. Bi-   10. Poly-   11. Mono-

Use the prefixes in Problems 8–11 to form words describing each of the following:
12. $3x - 4$ 13. $4m - 5n + 2$
14. $10x^3$ 15. $2x - 3y + z - 5$

16. Arrange $a^3x^2 - a^5 - a^4x + ax^4 + a^2x^3$ in descending powers of x.

ADDITION AND SUBTRACTION **107**

YOUR AIM **To gain greater skill in and understanding of addition and subtraction of algebraic expressions.**

In the following, arrange algebraic expressions in columns and add:
1. $3x - 4y$, $6x + 8y$, $-x - y$
2. $4xy - 1$, $xy + 2$, 3, xy, $8 - 2xy$
3. $x - y + 2$, $3x + y - 2$, $6 - 2x + y$, $5x - 7$

Arrange each of the following problems as a polynomial expression, then simplify by combining the like terms:

4.	$2x^2$	5.	$5ab^2$	6.	$-3x^2$	7.	$10a$
	$-3x$		$-2ab$		$-4x^2$		$-a$
	x^2		ab^2		$5x^2$		$3a$
	$-5x$		$-ab$		$2x$		-5

Add and check by letting $x = 2$ and $y = -3$:

8. $3x - xy + 2$
$6x + 2xy - 7$

9. $x^3 + xy - y^3$
$2x^3 - 2xy + y^3$

10. $x^3 - x^2y - xy^2 + y^3$
$2x^3 + x^2y - xy^2 + 3y^3$

Subtract and check by letting $x = -2$ and $y = +2$:

11. $3x - 2y - 5$
$5x - 4y - 8$

12. $x^2 - 2xy + y^2$
$-2x^2 + 3xy - 3y^2$

13. $x^2y - xy^2$
$3x^2y - 2xy^2$

YOUR AIM **To learn how to add and subtract simple algebraic fractions.**

Find the common denominator for each of the following sets of fractions:

1. $\dfrac{1}{2}, -\dfrac{1}{3}, \dfrac{5}{6}$

2. $\dfrac{1}{3}, \dfrac{1}{a}, \dfrac{3}{4}$

3. $\dfrac{a}{3}, \dfrac{b}{4}, \dfrac{c}{5}$

4. $\dfrac{1}{a}, \dfrac{2}{3a}, -\dfrac{x}{2a}$

5. $\dfrac{1}{2}, \dfrac{1}{x}, \dfrac{1}{x^2}$

6. $\dfrac{10}{xy}, \dfrac{3}{y}, -\dfrac{2}{x}$

Reduce each of the following fractions to lowest terms:

7. $\dfrac{3}{9}$

8. $\dfrac{2}{4a}$

9. $\dfrac{xy}{x^2}$

10. $\dfrac{-3am}{4am}$

11. $\dfrac{5x^2y}{6x^3y}$

12. $\dfrac{-5a}{-10a^2}$

13. $\dfrac{x^2}{x}$

14. $\dfrac{-3b}{-6b}$

Add or subtract as indicated:

15. $\dfrac{1}{3} - \dfrac{1}{4} - \dfrac{1}{2}$

16. $\dfrac{5}{m} - \dfrac{2}{m}$

17. $4 - \dfrac{1}{a}$

18. $\dfrac{2}{5} + \dfrac{8}{9} - \dfrac{2}{3}$

19. $\dfrac{1}{2x} + \dfrac{1}{x}$

20. $6 + \dfrac{2}{x}$

21. $\dfrac{1}{x} - \dfrac{2}{x} + \dfrac{3}{x}$

22. $\dfrac{1}{x} - \dfrac{1}{2x}$

23. $x - \dfrac{3}{y}$

YOUR AIM To gain skill in solving problems by the use of equations.

Write each of the following (1–11) using algebraic symbols:
1. The sum of x and 5. 2. The sum of x and $x - 2$.
3. Some number increased by four. 4. Some number decreased by six.
5. Three more than one-half of some number.
6. Seven less than four times some number.
7. Five more than some number.
8. Three less than some number.
9. The sum of two numbers is sixteen.
10. One number is seven more than twice another number.
11. Two of three numbers are consecutive numbers. Write the third number if it equals the sum of the two consecutive numbers.

12. List five steps to follow in solving verbal problems.
13. One number is 5 less than twice another number. The sum of the two numbers is 82. Find the two numbers.
14. The perimeter of a triangle is 37 inches. The first side is 3 inches more than the second side and the third side is 5 inches less than the sum of the first two sides. Find the length of each side.

VALUABLE SKILLS PRACTICE

Mt. Whitney, in California, has the highest elevation of any mountain in the United States: 14,495 feet. Most people, instead of trying to remember the exact figure, would say that the height of Mt. Whitney is 14,000 feet or 14,500 feet. That is, they would *round* the number.

16,492 rounded to the nearest 1000 is 16,000.
7821 rounded to the nearest 100 is 7800.
823 rounded to nearest 10 is 820.
0.175 rounded to nearest tenth is 0.2.

Round each of the following numbers to the nearest 1000:
1. 3587 2. 16,077 3. 29,900 4. 101,011
5. 888 6. 10,499 7. 3090 8. 99,999

Round each of the following numbers to the nearest 10:
9. 724 10. 97 11. 126 12. 203
13. 111 14. 333 15. 409 16. 94

Round each of the following numbers to the nearest tenth:
17. 2.16 18. 0.35 19. 0.65 20. 1.03
21. 3.33 22. 11.125 23. 9.05 24. 10.45
25. 10.05 26. 0.174 27. 0.05 28. 5.55

CHAPTER TEST

1. What is a binomial?
2. What is a polynomial?

Add:

3. $-3x$
   $+4x$

4. $-5ab^2$
   $-7ab^2$

5. $+4x$
   $+x$
   $-3x$

6. $-a^2$
   $-3a^2$

Add or subtract as indicated:

7. $(+5y) + (-3y)$

8. $(-4x^2y) + (-3x^2y)$

9. $(-6k) - (+3k)$

10. $(-4ab) - (-4ab)$

11. $3a + 5a - 6a - 8a + 7a$

12. $-15xy + 3xy - 7xy + 6xy$

Add:

13. $5a + b$
    $-3a + 4b$

14. $x^2 + 5$
    $6x^2 - 9$

15. $5x + 2y - 7z$
    $-4x + y - z$
    $-x + 6y - 9z$

16. $a^2 + ab + b^2$
    $2a^2 - ab + 6b^2$
    $5a^2 + ab - 3b^2$

Subtract:

17. $12m - 3n$
    $4m - 7n$

18. $15y^2 - 3y + 7$
    $y^2 - 2y - 15$

19. Find the sum of $8k - 3$ and $2k + 7$.
20. Subtract $16 - x$ from $13 + 5x$.
21. Subtract $17x + 3$ from 1.
22. Add $15 + 3x^2 + 2x$ and $6x - 13 + 2x^2$.

Reduce to lowest terms:

23. $\dfrac{8a}{24}$

24. $\dfrac{xy}{x}$

25. $\dfrac{6ab}{12a}$

26. $\dfrac{9}{12x^2}$

Add or subtract as indicated:

27. $\dfrac{4}{x} - \dfrac{2}{x}$

28. $\dfrac{a}{b} + \dfrac{c}{b}$

29. $\dfrac{15k}{y} - \dfrac{3}{y}$

30. $\dfrac{2}{x} - \dfrac{4}{3x}$

31. $7 + \dfrac{5}{6a}$

32. $\dfrac{4}{3y} + \dfrac{5}{6y}$

33. $\dfrac{3}{4} + \dfrac{2}{a}$

34. $\dfrac{5}{x} - \dfrac{6}{y}$

35. $\dfrac{x}{y} + \dfrac{3}{y} - \dfrac{4}{5y}$

Write each of the following using algebraic symbols:

36. Eight more than seven times some number.

37. The number of feet in b yards.

38. The number of hours in t minutes.

Solve:

39. The sum of two numbers is 102. One of the numbers is five times as great as the other number. Find the two numbers.

40. The sum of three consecutive numbers is 111. Find the numbers.

41. A 4% discount on a bill was $13.04. What was the amount of the bill before the discount?

42. A radio cost a merchant $21. At what price should he sell the radio to clear 30% of the selling price?

43. A rectangle has a perimeter of 640 feet. The length is three times as long as the width. Find the length and the width.

44. The area of a triangle is 30 square inches. The base is 8 inches. What is the altitude of the triangle?

45. A hiker walking 4 miles an hour leaves a camp at 2:00 P.M. A second hiker walking 5 miles an hour starts after him at 2:30 P.M. When will the second hiker catch up with the first one? How far will they have walked?

CUMULATIVE REVIEW PROBLEMS

DOING FUNDAMENTAL OPERATIONS

Add:

1. -56 -38	2. $+37$ -59	3. $+18$ $+21$	4. -19 $+32$	5. -14 -9

Subtract:

6. $+38$ -15	7. -62 $+49$	8. -17 $+31$	9. -11 -13	10. $+14$ $+59$

Multiply:

11. -14 $+3$	12. $+16$ $+5$	13. -14 -7	14. $+24$ -6	15. -19 -9

Divide:

16. $\dfrac{+24}{-8}$ 17. $\dfrac{+96}{+16}$ 18. $\dfrac{-52}{-13}$ 19. $\dfrac{-80}{5}$ 20. $\dfrac{+120}{-15}$

21. $\dfrac{+25}{+75}$ 22. $\dfrac{+33}{-99}$ 23. $\dfrac{-14}{98}$ 24. $\dfrac{-3}{-39}$ 25. $\dfrac{+9}{27}$

EVALUATING ALGEBRAIC EXPRESSIONS

Find the value of each of the following if a $= -3$, b $= +2$, *and* c $= -1$:

1. $4ab$

2. $3bc + a$

3. $-5b - c$

4. $ac - b$

5. $\dfrac{5a}{bc}$

6. $\dfrac{a}{b} + c$

7. $ab + ac$

8. $3c - ab$

9. $2b + ac$

10. $-4abc$

11. $\dfrac{+3abc}{-a}$

12. $\dfrac{a + c}{b}$

13. $3a + 2a + 5a$

14. $-4b + 3b$

15. $-2c + 3c + 6c$

16. $a^2 + b^2 + c^2$

17. $4a^2b^2$

18. $-3c^2$

19. $\dfrac{a}{b} + \dfrac{c}{b}$

20. $\dfrac{b}{ac} + \dfrac{b}{ac}$

21. $\dfrac{b}{a} + \dfrac{b}{b}$

22. $\dfrac{3}{a} + \dfrac{2}{b}$

23. $\dfrac{5}{a} + \dfrac{4}{b}$

24. $\dfrac{a + b + c}{abc}$

SOLVING EQUATIONS

Solve for x *and check:*

1. $16x = 14 + 9x$

2. $5x + 8 = 4x - 12$

3. $-4x + 16 = -3x - 6$

4. $14x - x + 1 = 14$

5. $2x + 4 = 0$

6. $3x + 5 = 14$

7. $9 - 2x = 13$

8. $0 = 14 - 2x$

9. $0 = 13 - 3x$

10. $14x - 6 = 20x$

11. $\dfrac{x}{5} = -7$

12. $\dfrac{x}{3} = +7$

13. $\dfrac{x}{2} + 5 = -4$

14. $\dfrac{x}{3} - 6 = 9$

15. $x + \frac{1}{2} = 3x - 3\frac{1}{2}$

16. $\frac{3}{4}x - 4 = 17$

17. $40 = 3x + 52$

18. $x + x - 8 = 13 + x$

WRITING WORD EXPRESSIONS AS ALGEBRAIC EXPRESSIONS

Change the following word expressions into algebraic expressions:

1. The number of days in k weeks.
2. The number of ounces in p pounds.
3. The number of nickels in y dollars.
4. John's age if he is 3 years older than Mary who is x years old.
5. The number of persons who saw the football game this week was $2\frac{1}{2}$ times as many as y persons who saw the game last week.
6. Thirty percent of w workers were women.
7. The sum of two numbers is 42. y stands for one number. What is the other number?
8. One angle of a triangle is three times as large as another which has x degrees.
9. The number of inches in $4k$ yards.

112 *ALGEBRA: ITS BIG IDEAS AND BASIC SKILLS*

BIG IDEAS	EQUATION
	EXPONENT
BASIC SKILLS	Using and interpreting symbols of algebra
	Fundamental operations
	Evaluating algebraic expressions
	Solving equations
	Solving verbal problems
	Using exponents

CHAPTER **5** *Multiplication and Division*

THE FOUR basic operations of algebra are addition, subtraction, multiplication, and division. In Chapter 4 you learned how to add and subtract polynomials. Now you will study the two remaining fundamental operations: multiplication and division.

YOUR AIM

1. To learn how to work with exponents in multiplication and division.

2. To learn how to multiply and divide polynomials.

3. To learn how to remove parentheses and how to enclose quantities in parentheses.

4. To learn how to multiply and divide algebraic fractions.

5. To learn how to solve equations containing parentheses and equations containing fractions.

113

Multiplying Monomials

In Chapter 1 you learned the meaning of whole number exponents. You will work with exponents in multiplying one monomial by another.

An expression like $a^2a^3a^4$ is an indicated product of three monomials, a^2, a^3, and a^4, but this is not the simplest way of writing the product. According to what you learned about exponents in Chapter 1,

$$a^2a^3a^4 = (aa)\,(aaa)\,(aaaa) = aaaaaaaaa = a^9$$

Notice that the exponent 9 is the sum of the exponents 2, 3, and 4.

DO YOU SEE? To simplify the indicated product of powers having the same base, add their exponents.

$$a^2a^6 = a^8$$
$$a^ma^n = a^{m+n}$$

The indicated product of monomials like a^2a^3 can be simplified as a^5, but a product like a^2b^3 cannot be simplified. In the first case a^2 and a^3 are powers having the same base a. In the second case a^2 and b^3 are powers having different bases, a and b.

PROBLEMS

Read off, without writing, the product of each of the following monomials:

1. a^2a^5
2. $b \cdot b^2$
3. a^3a^3
4. dd^2
5. x^4x^4
6. y^8y
7. kkk
8. a^2a^4a
9. m^2m^3nn
10. aab^3b
11. $x^3y^2x^4$
12. xx^4
13. $xxyy$
14. $abab$
15. $a^{15}a^{14}a^{23}$
16. $x^2x^2x^2$
17. y^5y
18. $8 \cdot a \cdot a^2$
19. $9^2 \cdot 9 \cdot 9^5$
20. $(\frac{1}{2})^2 (\frac{1}{2})(\frac{1}{2})^3$

★ 21. $(\frac{1}{3})(\frac{1}{3})$
22. $(0.2)^3(0.2)^4$
23. $5 \cdot x^2 \cdot y^2 \cdot 5^3$
24. $(\frac{3}{10})(\frac{3}{10})(\frac{3}{10})$
25. $5^2 \cdot 5 \cdot 5 \cdot 5^6$
26. $(0.1)^3(0.1)^3$

Dividing Monomials

The expression $\dfrac{a^5}{a^3}$ is an indicated quotient of the monomial a^5 divided by the monomial a^3. This quotient may be simplified as follows:

$$\frac{a^5}{a^3} = \frac{a \cdot a \cdot a \cdot a \cdot a}{a \cdot a \cdot a} = a^2$$

In the same way that you can simplify $\dfrac{3 \cdot 3 \cdot 3 \cdot 3 \cdot 3}{3 \cdot 3 \cdot 3}$ as 3^2, or 9,

you can simplify $\dfrac{a \cdot a \cdot a \cdot a \cdot a}{a \cdot a \cdot a}$ as a^2. Notice that the exponent 2 is the difference of the exponent 3 subtracted from the exponent 5.

114 *ALGEBRA: ITS BIG IDEAS AND BASIC SKILLS*

DO YOU SEE?  To simplify the indicated quotient of powers having the same base, subtract the exponent in the denominator from the exponent in the numerator.

$$\frac{a^7}{a^2} = a^5 \qquad \frac{a^m}{a^n} = a^{m-n} \quad a \text{ is not equal to zero}$$

Monomials like $\dfrac{a^5}{a^3}$ can be simplified as a^2, but those like $\dfrac{a^5}{b^3}$ cannot be simplified. a^5 and a^3 are powers having the same base a. But in a^5 and b^3 the bases, a and b, are not the same. Therefore, the quotient $\dfrac{a^5}{b^3}$ cannot be written in simpler form.

PROBLEMS

Read off, without writing, the quotient of each of the following monomials:

1. $\dfrac{a^5}{a^4}$
2. $\dfrac{x^8}{x^5}$
3. $\dfrac{m^3}{m^2}$
4. $\dfrac{n^9}{n^4}$
5. $\dfrac{k^4}{k}$

6. $\dfrac{h^2}{h}$
7. $\dfrac{x^7}{x}$
8. $\dfrac{m^{10}}{m^8}$
9. $\dfrac{a^{13}}{a^2}$
10. $\dfrac{a^4 b^5}{a^3 b}$

11. $\dfrac{a^6}{a^5}$
12. $\dfrac{n^8}{n^7}$
13. $\dfrac{k^9}{k^2}$
14. $\dfrac{b^4}{b^3}$
15. $\dfrac{a^5 b^6}{a^4 b^2}$

16. $\dfrac{x^4}{x}$
17. $\dfrac{a^{11}}{a^4}$
18. $\dfrac{2^4}{2^2}$
19. $\dfrac{3^4}{3}$
20. $\dfrac{4^3}{4^2}$

21. $\dfrac{(\frac{1}{2})^5}{(\frac{1}{2})^2}$
22. $\dfrac{8a^4}{2a}$
23. $\dfrac{12x^5}{8a^3}$
24. $\dfrac{(0.4)^7}{(0.4)^5}$
25. $\dfrac{(0.32)^7}{(0.32)^6}$

26. $\dfrac{4^2}{8^2}$
27. $\dfrac{8^2 \cdot x^2}{8x}$
28. $\dfrac{(5x)^3}{5x}$
29. $\dfrac{(a+b)^3}{(a+b)^2}$
30. $\dfrac{(2.6)^4}{(2.6)^2}$

Raising Monomials to a Power

The expression $(a^2)^3$ is a power of a power. This expression can be simplified. The cube of any number means that the number is used as a factor three times. Therefore,

$$(a^2)^3 = (a^2)(a^2)(a^2) = (aa)(aa)(aa) = aaaaaa = a^6$$

Notice that $2 \times 3 = 6$; so to get the exponent 6, you could have multiplied the exponents 2 and 3.

DO YOU SEE?  To simplify the indicated power of a power, multiply the two exponents.

$$(a^5)^3 = (a^5)(a^5)(a^5) = a^{15}$$
So $(a^5)^3 = a^{5 \times 3} = a^{15}$
In general, $(a^m)^n = a^{mn}$

MULTIPLICATION AND DIVISION **115**

Examples for Study

1. *Simplify:* $(5 \cdot y^3)^3$

SOLUTION: $(5 \cdot y^3)^3 = 5^3(y^3)^3 = 5^3y^9 = 125y^9$

2. *Simplify:* $(-5a^2b^3)^4$

SOLUTION: $(-5a^2b^3)^4 = (-5)^4(a^2)^4(b^3)^4 = 625a^8b^{12}$

PROBLEMS

Simplify:

1. $(3^4)^2$
2. $(4^3)^2$
3. $(5^2)^4$
4. $(2^2)^5$
5. $(2^5)^2$
6. $(a^3)^4$
7. $(b^5)^4$
8. $(c^3)^8$
9. $(a^5)^5$
10. $(b^9)^3$
11. $(3a^2)^2$
12. $(5b^2)^4$
13. $(-3x^2)^2$
14. $(-1y^5)^2$
15. $(-y^5)$
16. $(\frac{1}{2}k)^2$
17. $(\frac{1}{3}y^5)^4$
18. $(0.3x^2)^3$
19. $(1.2x)^2$
20. $(5y^2)^1$
21. $(a^2b^2)^5$
22. $(3x^2y^4)^2$
23. $(5xy^2)^3$
24. $(-2a^3b^5)^5$
25. $(-8xy)^3$
26. $(\frac{1}{2}x^3y^5)^5$
27. $(3.04xy^2)^3$
28. $(\frac{3}{2}a^5b)^2$

★ 29. $(-6a^5)^4$
30. $(1\frac{1}{2}x^3y^4)^3$
31. $(x^2y^3)^{50}$
32. $(0.1)^{20}$
33. $(10^2)^8$
34. $(\frac{3}{5}x^4)^4$
35. $(0.2a^{50})^2$
36. $(0.01)^5$

Multiplying Fractions

You recall from arithmetic that, to multiply two fractions, you first multiply the two numerators. This product is the numerator of the answer. Then you multiply the two denominators. This product is the denominator of the answer. To simplify the answer, you may divide the numerator and the denominator by the same number, except zero, without changing the value of the fraction. This division may be done before the numerators and denominators are multiplied, as in Examples for Study 1 and 4 below. The method of multiplying algebraic fractions is the same.

Examples for Study

1. *Multiply:* $\dfrac{3}{4}$ by $\dfrac{8}{9}$

SOLUTION: $\dfrac{\overset{1}{3}}{\underset{1}{4}} \cdot \dfrac{\overset{2}{8}}{\underset{3}{9}} = \dfrac{2}{3}$

2. *Multiply:* $\dfrac{a^2}{b^3}$ by $\dfrac{a^4}{b^2}$

SOLUTION: $\dfrac{a^2}{b^3} \cdot \dfrac{a^4}{b^2} = \dfrac{a^6}{b^5}$

3. *Multiply·* $\dfrac{-8k^2}{m^2}$ by $\dfrac{6k^3}{m^3}$

SOLUTION: $\dfrac{-8k^2}{m^2} \cdot \dfrac{6k^3}{m^3} = \dfrac{-48k^5}{m^5}$

4. *Multiply:* $\dfrac{x^2y^2}{z^3}$ by $\dfrac{z^4}{x}$

SOLUTION: $\dfrac{x^2y^2}{\underset{1}{z^3}} \cdot \dfrac{z^4}{\underset{1}{x}} = xy^2z$

PROBLEMS

Multiply:

1. $\dfrac{2}{3} \times \dfrac{3}{4}$ 2. $\dfrac{5}{8} \times \dfrac{3}{4}$ 3. $\dfrac{1}{2} \times \dfrac{4}{5}$ 4. $\dfrac{1}{3} \times \dfrac{5}{8}$

5. $\dfrac{4}{5} \times \dfrac{2}{3}$ 6. $\dfrac{3}{4} \times \dfrac{4}{5}$ 7. $\dfrac{4}{5} \times \dfrac{15}{28}$ 8. $\dfrac{3}{5} \times \dfrac{5}{6}$

9. $\dfrac{3}{a} \cdot \dfrac{a^2}{5}$ 10. $\dfrac{5x}{3} \cdot \dfrac{2x}{y}$ 11. $\dfrac{-7x}{2y} \cdot \dfrac{2}{3}$ 12. $\dfrac{-5}{3a} \cdot \dfrac{2a}{b}$

13. $\dfrac{3a^2}{b^3} \cdot \dfrac{5}{b^2}$ 14. $\dfrac{2x^3}{y} \cdot \dfrac{y^3}{4}$ 15. $\dfrac{-5x^2}{y^2} \cdot \dfrac{2}{x}$ 16. $\dfrac{-2ab}{c} \cdot \dfrac{c}{b}$

17. $\dfrac{3x^2y}{2y} \cdot \dfrac{4z}{5y^2}$ 18. $\dfrac{-5}{2} \cdot \dfrac{3a^2b}{5b^3}$ 19. $\dfrac{5k^2}{-4m} \cdot \dfrac{-4m}{n}$ 20. $\dfrac{(4xy)^2}{7x^2} \cdot \dfrac{(3y)^3}{5y}$

21. $\dfrac{10a^2k^2}{5k} \cdot \dfrac{6k}{5a}$ 22. $\dfrac{6xy}{9k} \cdot \dfrac{15k^2}{16y}$ 23. $\dfrac{3b}{a} \cdot \dfrac{4}{5}$ 24. $\left(\dfrac{5a^2}{3b}\right)^2$

25. $\left(\dfrac{3x^3y^5}{2ab}\right)^2$ 26. $\left(\dfrac{-3a^3}{2b}\right)^2$ 27. $\left(\dfrac{+4x^4}{2y^3}\right)^2$ 28. $\left(\dfrac{7k^2}{3k}\right)^2$

★ 29. $\dfrac{2}{3} \cdot \dfrac{4a}{3b} \cdot \dfrac{5a^2}{6b^3}$ 30. $\dfrac{3}{4} \cdot \dfrac{7}{8} \cdot \dfrac{8x}{9y}$ 31. $\dfrac{5a}{3b}\left(\dfrac{3}{4}\right)^2$ 32. $\left(\dfrac{5x}{2y}\right)^2 \cdot \dfrac{3}{4}$

Dividing Fractions

In dividing a number by a fraction in arithmetic, you inverted the fraction and proceeded as in multiplication. The same method is used in dividing by algebraic fractions.

Examples for Study

1. $\dfrac{1}{a^2} \div \dfrac{1}{a^3} = \underline{\ ?\ }$

SOLUTION: $\dfrac{1}{a^2} \div \dfrac{1}{a^3} = \dfrac{1}{a^2} \cdot a^3 = \dfrac{a^3}{a^2} = a$

2. $\dfrac{5x^3}{3y^2} \div \dfrac{8x}{6y^3} = \underline{\ ?\ }$

SOLUTION: $\dfrac{5x^3}{3y^2} \div \dfrac{8x}{6y^3} = \dfrac{5x^3}{3y^2} \cdot \dfrac{6y^3}{8x} = \dfrac{30x^3y^3}{24xy^2} = \dfrac{5x^2y}{4}$

3. $\dfrac{2}{x} \div x = \underline{\ ?\ }$

SOLUTION: $\dfrac{2}{x} \div x = \dfrac{2}{x} \div \dfrac{x}{1} = \dfrac{2}{x} \cdot \dfrac{1}{x} = \dfrac{2}{x^2}$

4. $\dfrac{c^4}{d^2} \div c^2 = \underline{\ ?\ }$

SOLUTION: $\dfrac{c^4}{d^2} \div c^2 = \dfrac{c^4}{d^2} \div \dfrac{c^2}{1} = \dfrac{c^4}{d^2} \cdot \dfrac{1}{c^2} = \dfrac{c^4}{c^2d^2} = \dfrac{c^2}{d^2}$

PROBLEMS

Divide:

1. $\frac{3}{4} \div \frac{1}{2}$ 2. $\frac{5}{8} \div \frac{3}{4}$ 3. $\frac{7}{8} \div 2$ 4. $8 \div \frac{5}{8}$

5. $3 \div \frac{3}{4}$ 6. $4\frac{1}{2} \div \frac{3}{8}$ 7. $2\frac{2}{3} \div \frac{2}{3}$ 8. $1\frac{1}{2} \div 1\frac{1}{2}$

9. $\frac{a}{b} \div \frac{c}{d}$ 10. $\frac{a^2}{b} \div \frac{a}{b^2}$ 11. $\frac{cd}{a} \div \frac{ef}{a}$ 12. $\frac{x^2y}{y^2} \div \frac{x}{y^2}$

13. $\frac{5x}{3} \div \frac{2y}{3x}$ 14. $\frac{-6x}{5y} \div \frac{3}{2}$ 15. $\frac{-5}{7a} \div \frac{c}{2a}$ 16. $\frac{4a^2}{3b} \div \frac{5a}{6b^3}$

17. $\frac{5ax^2}{2bx} \div \frac{6ax}{b}$ 18. $\frac{x^2y^2}{z} \div \frac{xy}{z}$ 19. $\frac{9a^3b^2}{2} \div \frac{ab}{2}$ 20. $\frac{14}{15} \div \frac{1}{a^2}$

21. $\frac{3a}{7b} \div b$ 22. $\frac{5x^2y}{3} \div 5$ 23. $\frac{10}{7k} \div k$ 24. $\frac{17k^2}{19} \div \frac{17k^2}{19}$

★ 25. $\frac{a}{b} \div b$ 26. $x^2 \div \frac{3}{x}$ 27. $\frac{1}{5} \div 5a$

28. $\frac{(c-d)^2}{a} \div \frac{(c-d)^2}{a^2}$ 29. $m^3 \div \frac{1}{m^3}$ 30. $\frac{1}{ab} \div \frac{1}{ab}$

31. $\frac{10a^2b}{c^3} \div a^3c$ 32. $(x+y)^4 \div \frac{1}{3(x+y)^2}$

Using the Basic Operations

You now know how to add, subtract, multiply, and divide monomials. The problems below will give you a chance to use these four basic operations.

PROBLEMS

Do the operations indicated:

1. $(-2)(-3)$ 2. $6(-2)(-4)$ 3. $(-4)^2$

4. $(-2)^3$ 5. 3^5 6. $(-1)(-1)(-1)$

7. $(-5)(-10)(+6)$ 8. $(-1)^{10}$ 9. $(-1)^7$

10. m^2n^2 11. $a^2 \cdot a^4$ 12. $b^4 \cdot b^6$

13. $(-3a)(+2a)(-5a)$ 14. $(-n^2)(-n^3)n$ 15. $(-2a^3)(-4a^4)$

16. $(-b^2c)bc^5$ 17. $(\frac{1}{3})^2 (\frac{1}{2})^2$ 18. $(+7xy^3)(-5x^2y^4)$

19. $(-0.4x)^2$ 20. $(0.05a^3)^2$ 21. $(1.2y)^2$

22. $(-1.1n)^3$ 23. $(0.3a^4)^3$ 24. $(0.9xy^2)^2$

25. $\frac{a^3b^6}{a^2b^2}$ 26. $\frac{m^6n^3}{m^5n}$ 27. $\frac{14a^5b^2}{7a^3b}$

28. $\frac{-81a^7b^4}{-27a^3b^3}$ 29. $x^6 \div x^5$ 30. $a^{10} \div a^5$

31. $2a^4 \div 8a$
32. $-60xy \div 30x$
33. $-6x \div -6$

34. $12ab \div 6a$
35. $-36a^2x^5y^3 \div 12ax^4y^3$
36. $-a^2 \div a$

37. $\dfrac{a^2}{b} \div \dfrac{a}{b}$
38. $\dfrac{3m^2}{5} \div \dfrac{6m}{5}$
39. $\dfrac{x^4}{y^2} \div \dfrac{x^3}{y^4}$

40. $\dfrac{16}{a^5} \div \dfrac{8}{a^7}$
41. $\dfrac{15m^2}{8n^3} \div \dfrac{5m}{24n^4}$
42. $\dfrac{3mn^2}{8a} \div \dfrac{mn}{16a^2}$

43. $\frac{1}{4}m^2 \div \frac{1}{2}m$
44. $\dfrac{12x^6y^8}{-a^3b^5} \div \dfrac{-24x^5y^7}{7a^3b^6}$
45. $(-10a)(-10a)^2$

46. $(\frac{2}{3}a^2x^3)(6a^5x^7)$
47. $(-1)^3(-1)^2(-1)^5$
48. $(\frac{1}{4}x)^3(-8x)^2$

49. $(a^3)(a^3)(a^2)$
50. $(-6mn^3) \div (-12mn^3)$
51. $(-\frac{1}{2}m^2n)^3$

52. $(-\frac{1}{2}a^3b)(\frac{3}{4}a^4b)(-14ab)$
53. $(0.6a)(-0.8a)^2(ab)$

54. $-mn(3m^2n)(-5mn^4)$
55. $-a(-5a)^3$

56. $(\frac{1}{4}m^4) \div (\frac{1}{2}m^2)$
57. $(-x^2)(-x)^2$

58. $-48ab^5c^4 \div 16abc$
59. $(\frac{1}{2}a^4)(\frac{3}{4}a^2)$

60. $-(-8)^2$
61. $-(-20) + (-15)$

62. $1(+20) - 3(+10)$
63. $-3 - (-5)$

64. $+7(-2) + 6(-2)$
65. $-(-n) - 2n$

66. $-2a(-3a) - (12a^2)$
67. $x(3x^2) \div x(-4x)$

68. $(5abc)(a^2b) \div (-10a^3b)$
69. $(\frac{1}{2}a^2 \div \frac{3}{4})(-2a)$

70. $(-0.01m^3n^5)^2$
71. $(\frac{1}{3}a^2b)(\frac{2}{5}a^3b^4)(-20ab)$

72. $(0.3a^2)^3$
73. $(0.1xy^3)^4$
74. $(-\frac{1}{4}m^2n)^3$

75. $\dfrac{a^3b^4}{5m^5n^2} \times \dfrac{-36a^5b^3}{10m^6n}$
76. $-0.9a^4 \div 9a$
77. $(-0.6x^2)^2\left(\dfrac{10}{x}\right)^2$

78. $(-3)^5 \div (-9)^2$
79. $(-a^4)(-a)^6$
80. $(\frac{1}{10})^2(10a)^3$

81. $\dfrac{8x \cdot 5y}{-20y}$
82. $\dfrac{(3m)(-m)}{-m}$
83. $\dfrac{(-12d)(-5a^2)}{10ad}$

84. $(-\frac{1}{4}x)^3(-16x)$
85. $\dfrac{2m}{-10m^2} \div \dfrac{m}{5}$

86. $(-0.3rs)^3(10r)^2 \div (0.9r^3s^3)$
87. $\dfrac{-5x^4y^6}{-10x^4y^6}$

88. $\frac{1}{5}a^2b^3 \div \dfrac{(-5)^2}{a}$
89. $\dfrac{5x^5}{2y^4} \div \dfrac{10x^3}{3y^6}$

90. $25(-0.2a^3)^2 \div (-\frac{1}{2}a)^2$
91. Subtract $-14x^2$ from $24x^2$.

92. Subtract $+40cd$ from $-60cd$.
93. Add $+30ab$ to $-40ab$.

94. Subtract -50 from -50.

95. Add $+9x^2$ to the product of $3x$ and $-2x$.

96. Add the quotient of $20a^2$ divided by $-5a$ to the sum of $10a$ and $-3a$.

97. Subtract $-m^3n^2$ from the product of $-30mn$ and $2m^2n$.

98. Subtract -81 from -3 raised to the fourth power.

Multiplying a Polynomial by a Monomial

Suppose you want to multiply the polynomial $a + b$ by the monomial 5. You can write the product as $5(a + b)$. You can then use the distributive principle to find another answer. For example,

$$5(a + b) = 5a + 5b$$

Examples for Study

1. *Multiply:* $-x + 4y - 3$ by $-3x$

SOLUTION:

$$-3x(-x + 4y - 3) = (-3x)(-x) + (-3x)(4y) - (-3x)(3) \text{ Why?}$$
$$= 3x^2 - 12xy + 9x \quad \text{Why?}$$

2. *Multiply:* $(a - b)$ by -1

SOLUTION:

$$-1(a - b) = -1(a) - (-1)(b) \quad \text{Why?}$$
$$= -a + b$$

When a quantity is preceded by a negative sign like $-(a - b)$, remember that the coefficient of the quantity is -1. $-(a - b)$ is $-1(a - b)$.

PROBLEMS

In each of the following, multiply the polynomial by the monomial:

1. $2a + 5$, 6
2. $5x - 7$, 8
3. $4b - 8$, 9
4. $-12a - 3$, -4
5. $3x + 9$, $4x$
6. $7ax - b$, $-6x$
7. $-3ab + b$, $-3ab$
8. $14mn - 10$, $-2mn$
9. $-ax + a$, $-a$
10. $6x + 5y - 10$, $+7$
11. $9x^2 - 3xy + y^2$, $5xy$
12. $a^3 + a^2 - a - 1$, $-a$
13. $4(8x + 6)$
14. $3(2a - b)$
15. $-5(2m - 3n)$
16. $-7(10 + 5a)$
17. $2a(6 - a)$
18. $x(2x - 11)$
19. $2n(n^2 + 8n - 9)$
20. $-4x(-x^3 + x^2)$

★ 21. $ab(ab - b)$
22. $-2mn(-11m^2n - n^2)$
23. $-4a^2b(-20a^2b - 9a^4)$
24. $-b(b^2 + b + 1)$
25. $-2x(-1 + y + y^2)$
26. $4y(6x^2 + 3xy + y^2)$
27. $+5ab(2a - 3ab + 2b)$
28. $-k(-4k^2 + 2k + 6)$
29. $\frac{1}{2}x(3 - 2x + 6x^2)$
30. $1.5(7 - 4x + 9x^2)$
31. $141(-2x + 4y - 7)$
32. $875(7x^2 + 5 - 7x^2 - 5)$
33. $95x(18x - 9x - 9x)$
34. $0.1(1 + 0.1 + 0.01)$

The Associative Principle for Addition

Consider the following equation:

$$(a + b) + c = a + (b + c)$$

Suppose $a = -2$, $b = 4$, and $c = -5$. Evaluating this equation gives us:

$$(-2 + 4) + (-5) = (-2) + [4 + (-5)]$$
Adding: $\qquad (+2) + (-5) = (-2) + (-1)$
Adding: $\qquad\qquad -3 = -3$

For the set of values used, the equation becomes a true statement. Try other values for a, b, and c to see whether the equation always gives a true statement. See whether you can find any set of numbers, one replacing a, another b, and a third c, which will not give a true statement.

DO YOU SEE? 👉 **For every value of a, b, and c, $(a + b) + c = a + (b + c)$.**

The equation $(a + b) + c = a + (b + c)$ tells you that the order in which you add terms does not change the sum. The sum is always the same. This equation states a very important relation in mathematics. It is called the **associative principle for addition.**

Examples for Study

1. Find a simpler expression for $4(a - 3b) + (a + b)$.

SOLUTION:
Distributive principle:
$$4(a - 3b) + (a + b) = 4a - 12b + a + b$$
Commutative principle for addition: $\qquad = 4a + a + (-12)b + b$
Distributive principle: $\qquad = a(4 + 1) + b(-12 + 1)$
Adding: $\qquad = a(5) + b(-11)$
Commutative principle for multiplication: $= 5a - 11b$

2. Find a simpler expression for $-3(x^2 - 1) - (x^2 + 2)$.

SOLUTION:
Distributive principle:
$$-3(x^2 - 1) - (x^2 + 2) = -3x^2 + 3 - x^2 - 2$$
Commutative principle for addition: $\qquad = -3x^2 - x^2 + 3 - 2$
Distributive principle: $\qquad = x^2(-3 - 1) + 3 - 2$
Adding: $\qquad = x^2(-4) + 1$
Commutative principle for multiplication: $\; = -4x^2 + 1$

PROBLEMS

Find a simpler expression for each of the following:

1. $5(a + 6) + 4a$
2. $7b + 3(b + 2)$
3. $8(7 - x) + 12$
4. $15 + 9(4 + y)$
5. $4(3k + 2) + k$
6. $7m + 5(3m - 2)$
7. $3(x + 2) + 2(x - 5)$
8. $2(a + 9) - 3(a + 7)$
9. $6(m - 5) + (m - 10)$
10. $16 + (8 - y) - (y + 20)$
11. $r - (r - 11) + 2(3r - 6)$
12. $7(x + 7) - (x - 1)$
13. $20 - (-p - 4) - 12$
14. $-6(s + 6) - 3(-2s)$
15. $-2(5s - 3) + (9s - 8)$
16. $7(2n - 4) - 5(-n - 5)$
17. $12 - (-a + 16) + 4(-a - 12)$
18. $3mn - 2n(m - 4)$
19. $7x^2 + 4x(x - 8) + x(9x + 30)$
20. $a(a + b) - a(a - b)$
21. $-m(m - n) - m(m + n)$
22. $r - (r - s)$
23. $12x(-3x - 5) + x(20x + 40)$
24. $a^2 - (a^2 - b^2) - a(a - b)$
25. $3y + y(-x - y) - x(-x - y)$
26. $ab(a + b) - a(ab + b^2)$
27. $16 - (-2) - (-8)$
28. $-(-x^3) - (-3)^2 + (2x)^3$
29. $(-2a)^5 - 3a(-a)^4$
30. $-3(-2)^3 - (-3)^3 - (-7)^2$
31. $-3ab(-2ab - 8) - ab(ab - 1)$
32. $-2(-2 - x) - 2x$
33. $x(-x + 2) - 2(x - 2)$
34. $(x - y) + (x - y)$
35. $-4 - (8 - m) + 10$
36. $-(a - b) - (a - b)$
37. $ab(1 - ab) + 3ab$
38. $-(m - 3) + (m - 3)$
39. $-3 - 3(3 - b) - 5$
40. $7a - a(7 - 4a) - a^2$
41. $2.5(-x^2 + x - 1) + 7x^2$
42. $\frac{3}{4}a(a - \frac{1}{2}) + \frac{1}{4}a^2$
43. $\frac{2}{3}y(2y - 4) + 1\frac{1}{3}y$
44. $\frac{2}{5}x(\frac{5}{8}x + 10) - 3x$
45. $-5(2 - 3 + 4 - 5)$
46. $3a(2 - 2)$
47. $(x - y)(b + c)$
48. $(c + d)(c - d)$
49. $(p + q)(p + q)$
50. $(2b - 3c)(3b - 2c)$
51. $(x + y)(x^2 - y^2)$
52. $(x - y)(x^2 + xy + y^2)$

SELF TEST

Simplify:

1. $(a^3)^5$
2. $(5x^2)^3$
3. $(2^3)^2$
4. $(\frac{1}{3}x^4)^3$
5. $\frac{5a^2}{b^2} \cdot \frac{3}{b}$
6. $\frac{-3xy}{5x^2} \cdot \frac{2y^2}{3y}$
7. $\frac{5}{8} \cdot \frac{x^2y^2}{5xy}$
8. $\frac{3}{x^2} \cdot \frac{x^3}{4}$
9. $\frac{3x}{5} \div \frac{3}{x^2}$
10. $\frac{5x^2y}{2} \div \frac{4xy}{3}$
11. $\frac{1}{5} \div 5x$
12. $\frac{1}{7a^2} \div \frac{1}{7a^2}$
13. $(-1)^2 (-1)^3$
14. $(-0.3x)^2 \div (\frac{1}{3}x)^2$
15. $(0.1x^2y^3)^5$
16. $\frac{2}{3}a^5 \div \frac{3}{4}a^2$

Multiply:

17. $3x + 7, 8$
18. $2y - 4, 3$
19. $3x^2 - 2x + 4, -3x$

Find a simpler expression for each of the following:

20. $-4y(3y + 2x)$
21. $k(k^2 + 2k + 4)$
22. $-x(x^3 + 2x^2)$
23. $4(y + 3) + 3y$
24. $7(y - 2) - (y - 2)$
25. $-(x + y) + 3(x + y)$
26. $15 + (3 + x) - (15 - 2x)$

122 *ALGEBRA: ITS BIG IDEAS AND BASIC SKILLS*

Multiplying a Polynomial by a Polynomial

To multiply a polynomial by a polynomial, you can use the distributive principle.

Examples for Study

1. *Multiply:* $2x^2 - 4x - 8$ *by* $3x - 5$

SOLUTION:

Distributive principle: $a(b + c + d) = ab + ac + ad$

Using the distributive principle where $a = (3x - 5)$, $b = 2x^2$, $c = 4x$, and $d = 8$:

$(3x - 5)(2x^2 - 4x - 8)$
$$= (3x - 5)(2x^2) - (3x - 5)(4x) - (3x - 5)(8)$$
$$= 6x^3 - 10x^2 - 12x^2 + 20x - 24x + 40 \qquad \text{Why?}$$
$$= 6x^3 - 22x^2 - 4x + 40 \qquad \text{Why?}$$

You may arrange multiplication vertically. For example,

2. $(x + 2)(x - 4) = \underline{\ ?\ }$

SOLUTION:

$$\begin{array}{r} x + 2 \\ x - 4 \\ \hline x^2 + 2x \\ -4x - 8 \\ \hline x^2 - 2x - 8 \end{array}$$

Multiply $x + 2$ by x:
Multiply $x + 2$ by -4:
Add the partial products:

PROBLEMS

Find a simple answer for each of the following products:

1. $(a + 6)(a + 3)$
2. $(x - 4)(x - 2)$
3. $(m + 7)(m - 5)$
4. $(2a - 8)(3a + 4)$
5. $(16m + 3)(3m + 4)$
6. $(12 - 7x)(10 - 5x)$
7. $(x - 2y)(3x + 2y)$
8. $(5x + 4y)(x - y)$
9. $(10m - 5)(10m - 5)$
10. $(4 + ab)(3 - ab)$
11. $(mn - 7)(3mn + 8)$
12. $(10a - 11)(10a + 12)$
13. $(5a + 6)^2$
14. $(2x + 3y + 8)(x - y)$
15. $(5a - 3b + 9)(a + 4b)$
16. $(x^2 + 3x + 1)(x - 1)$
17. $(x^2 - 3x - 1)(x + 1)$
18. $(7x^2 - 10x + 12)(2x - 11)$
19. $(4r + s - 1)(r + 3s)$
20. $(2y^2 - 5y - 4)(y + 6)$
21. $(c^2 + 2c - 1)(c - 1)$
22. $(8 + 3c^2 - c)(10 - 3c)$
23. $(a - 2)(a^2 - 9a - 6)$
24. $(x^2 + xy - y^2)(3x - y)$

★ 25. $(0.5 - 2.5m)(n - 0.7)$
26. $(\frac{2}{3}c - \frac{1}{2})(\frac{1}{4} - d)$
27. $(-2t^2 - s - 3)(\frac{1}{2}t + \frac{1}{3})$
28. $(-0.1u^2 + 2u - 7)(v - 0.1u)$
29. $(1.5v^2 - 1.6h - 1.1)(v - 6)$
30. $(6.5h + 3 - h^2)(10 + 5h)$

Dividing a Polynomial by a Monomial

In dividing a number like 125 by 5, you usually work as follows:

$$\begin{array}{r} 25 \\ 5\overline{)125} \\ \underline{10} \\ 25 \\ \underline{25} \\ 0 \end{array}$$

Let us write the number 125 as the sum of two numbers each one of which is divisible by 5. We will write the division in two different ways:

$$\begin{array}{r} 20 + 5 \\ 5\overline{)100 + 25} \\ \underline{100} \\ 25 \\ \underline{25} \end{array} \qquad \frac{100 + 25}{5} = \frac{100}{5} + \frac{25}{5} = 20 + 5 = 25$$

Notice that each term above, 100 and 25, is divided by 5. Each of the examples below is worked out in two ways.

Examples for Study

1. $(6x^2 + 4x) \div (2x) = \underline{\ ?\ }$

SOLUTION:

$$\begin{array}{r} 3x + 2 \\ 2x\overline{)6x^2 + 4x} \\ \underline{6x^2} \\ 4x \\ \underline{4x} \end{array} \qquad \frac{6x^2 + 4x}{2x} = \frac{6x^2}{2x} + \frac{4x}{2x} = 3x + 2$$

2. $(15x^3 + 10x^2 - 5x) \div (-5x) = \underline{\ ?\ }$

SOLUTION:

$$\begin{array}{r} -3x^2 - 2x + 1 \\ -5x\overline{)15x^3 + 10x^2 - 5x} \\ \underline{15x^3} \\ 10x^2 \\ \underline{10x^2} \\ -5x \\ \underline{-5x} \end{array}$$

$$\frac{15x^3 + 10x^2 - 5x}{-5x} = \frac{15x^3}{-5x} + \frac{10x^2}{-5x} - \frac{5x}{-5x} = -3x^2 - 2x + 1$$

3. $(8a^3x^2 - 4a^2x^3 + 2ax^4) \div (2ax^2) = \underline{\ ?\ }$

SOLUTION:

$$\begin{array}{r} 4a^2 \quad - 2ax \ + \quad x^2 \\ 2ax^2\overline{)8a^3x^2 - 4a^2x^3 + 2ax^4} \\ \underline{8a^3x^2} \\ -4a^2x^3 \\ \underline{-4a^2x^3} \\ 2ax^4 \\ 2ax^4 \end{array}$$

$$\frac{8a^3x^2 - 4a^2x^3 + 2ax^4}{2ax^2} = \frac{8a^3x^2}{2ax^2} - \frac{4a^2x^3}{2ax^2} + \frac{2ax^4}{2ax^2} = 4a^2 - 2ax + x^2$$

CHECK: In checking your work, you can use the fact that division is the inverse of multiplication. Therefore, in Example 3 above, you would have to answer the following question:

$$(4a^2 - 2ax + x^2)(2ax^2) \overset{?}{=} 8a^3x^2 - 4a^2x^3 + 2ax^4$$

Multiplying:

$$(4a^2)(2ax^2) - (2ax)(2ax^2) + x^2(2ax^2) = 8a^3x^2 - 4a^2x^3 + 2ax^4$$

Thus the division is carried out correctly.

PROBLEMS

Divide:

1. $\dfrac{8x + 6}{2}$

2. $\dfrac{12x^3 + 9x^2 + 6x + 6}{3}$

3. $\dfrac{6x^2 + 3x}{3x}$

4. $\dfrac{15x^2 + 12x}{-3x}$

5. $\dfrac{18a^3 + 12a^2 - 9a}{-3a}$

6. $\dfrac{9a^4 + 6a^3}{3a^2}$

7. $\dfrac{10ax^2 + 10ax + 5a}{5a}$

8. $\dfrac{3a^2x^2 + ax^2 + x^2}{x^2}$

9. $\dfrac{6a^2x^3 - 3a^2x^2}{a^2x}$

10. $\dfrac{25a^2b^2 + 15ab^3}{-5ab}$

11. $\dfrac{21a^3b^3 - 28a^4b^5}{7a^2b^3}$

12. $\dfrac{xy + xz}{x}$

★ 13. $\dfrac{mn^4 - mn^3 + mn^2}{-n^2}$

14. $\dfrac{15x^2y^2 + 9x^3y^3 - 21x^5y^2}{-3x^2y^2}$

15. $\dfrac{25x^4 + 10x^3 - 15x^2}{5x}$

16. $\dfrac{6y^7 - 4y^5}{-2y^4}$

17. $\dfrac{ac + ad + ab}{a}$

18. $\dfrac{xt + xt^2 + xt}{xt}$

19. $\dfrac{1.0rst^2 + 1.5rs}{0.5rs}$

20. $\dfrac{a^2(x + y)}{a}$

MULTIPLICATION AND DIVISION **125**

Dividing a Polynomial by a Polynomial

Dividing a polynomial by a polynomial in algebra is very similar to long division in arithmetic.

Example for Study

$$(x^2 + 5x - 24) \div (x - 3) = \underline{\;?\;}$$

STUDY THIS FIRST:

$$
\begin{array}{r}
243 \\
24\overline{)5832} \\
48 \\
\hline
103 \\
96 \\
\hline
72 \\
72 \\
\hline
\end{array}
$$

SOLUTION:

$$
\begin{array}{r}
x + 8 \\
x - 3\overline{)x^2 + 5x - 24} \\
x^2 - 3x \\
\hline
+8x - 24 \\
+8x - 24 \\
\hline
\end{array}
$$

First you divide 58 by 24 and record the quotient 2. Then you multiply 24 by 2, record the product, and subtract, and so on.

First you divide x^2 by x and record the quotient x. Then you multiply $x - 3$ by x, record the product, and subtract, and so on.

NOTE: The terms in the dividend in the example above are arranged in the order of descending powers of x. Before performing division, you should arrange the polynomials in the order of descending powers of x or whatever letter you are using in the polynomial.

PROBLEMS

Divide:

1. $(a^2 + 8a + 15) \div (a + 5)$ 2. $(x^2 - 7x + 12) \div (x - 4)$
3. $(x^2 - 4x - 21) \div (x + 3)$ 4. $(c^2 - c - 20) \div (c - 5)$
5. $(d^2 - 8d + 7) \div (d - 1)$ 6. $(n^2 - 10n - 39) \div (n - 13)$
7. $(6x^2 - 5x - 6) \div (3x + 2)$ 8. $(20m^2 - 13m + 2) \div (4m - 1)$
9. $(42x^2 + 29x - 5) \div (6x + 5)$
10. $(3x^2 + x - 44) \div (x + 4)$
11. $(a^2 + 5ab + 6b^2) \div (a + 2b)$
12. $(2x^2 + 5xy - 3y^2) \div (2x - y)$
13. $(24m^2 - 14mn - 3n^2) \div (4m - 3n)$
14. $(16 + 10x + x^2) \div (2 + x)$
15. $(30 + 13a - 10a^2) \div (5 - 2a)$
16. $(x^2 - 3x - 18) \div (x - 6)$

126 *ALGEBRA: ITS BIG IDEAS AND BASIC SKILLS*

Example for Study

$(x^2 + 4x + 8) \div (x - 2) = \underline{\ ?\ }$

SOLUTION:

$$\begin{array}{r} x + 6 \\ x - 2 \overline{)x^2 + 4x + 8} \\ \underline{x^2 - 2x} \\ +6x + 8 \\ \underline{+6x - 12} \\ +20 \end{array}$$

$+20$ is the remainder.

17. $(x^2 - 2x + 3) \div (x + 5)$ 18. $(x^2 + x - 1) \div (x - 1)$
19. $(a^2 + 3ab - 5b^2) \div (a + b)$
20. $(2a^3 + 3a^2 - 18a - 27) \div (a + 3)$
21. $(12x^3 + 4x^2 - 41x + 140) \div (2x - 5)$
22. $(a^2 - 2ab + b^2) \div (a + b)$
23. $(x^3 + 2x^2 - x - 2) \div (x + 2)$
24. $(x^2 + 2x + 3) \div (x + 1)$
25. $(a^2b^2 + ab - 2) \div (ab - 1)$
26. $(-3m^2 + 13m - 15) \div (-3m + 7)$

Example for Study

$(x^3 - 1) \div (x - 1) = \underline{\ ?\ }$

A polynomial with x^3 in it may also have an x^2 term and an x term. Since $x^3 - 1$ does not, it will be helpful to leave some space between x^3 and -1 or else write $x^3 - 1$ as $x^3 + 0x^2 + 0x - 1$ before dividing.

SOLUTION:

$$\begin{array}{r} x^2 + x + 1 \\ x - 1 \overline{)x^3 + 0x^2 + 0x - 1} \\ \underline{x^3 - x^2} \\ +x^2 + 0x \\ \underline{x^2 - x} \\ +x - 1 \\ \underline{x - 1} \end{array}$$

27. $(a^3 - 1) \div (a - 1)$ 28. $(a^2 - b^2) \div (a - b)$
29. $(a^2 - b^2) \div (a + b)$ 30. $(a^3 + b^3) \div (a + b)$

★ 31. $(a^3 - b^3) \div (a - b)$
32. $(3a^3 + a^2b - 6a - 2b) \div (3a + b)$
33. $(4a^4 + 4a^3b + 2ab + 2b^2) \div (a + b)$
34. $(a^3 - b^3) \div (a^2 + ab + b^2)$
35. $(x^2 - 25) \div (x + 5)$
36. $(x^5 - y^5) \div (x - y)$

Grouping Symbols

The expression "three times the sum of x and $2y$," when written in algebraic symbols, is $3(x + 2y)$. But suppose $y = x - 3$. If you substitute $x - 3$ for y, you need another grouping symbol. This substitution is shown below:

$$3(x + 2y)$$
$$3[x + 2(x - 3)]$$

The symbols [ ] used for enclosing the expression $x + 2(x - 3)$ are called **brackets**. When a third symbol is needed, **braces** $\{\}$ are used.

You can use the distributive and associative principles to simplify the inside or the outside quantity first.

Examples for Study

SIMPLIFYING BY BEGINNING IN-SIDE

$$3[x + 2(x - 3)] =$$
$$3[x + 2x - 6] =$$
$$3[3x - 6] = 9x - 18$$

SIMPLIFYING BY BEGINNING OUT-SIDE

$$3[x + 2(x - 3)] =$$
$$3x + 6(x - 3) =$$
$$3x + 6x - 18 = 9x - 18$$

PROBLEMS

Remove the grouping symbols and combine the like terms:

1. $2[3 + 5(x - 2)]$
2. $2[x - (x - 1)]$
3. $8 + 2[(a - 9) - 1]$
4. $3[-(m - 2) - 4(m + 1)]$
5. $2[xy + x(y - x)]$
6. $-[6 + 3(-1 + m)]$
7. $3[a - 5(a - 5) - 20]$
8. $5x + 7[x - 2(x + 1)]$
9. $4[2x + (x - 5)]$
10. $7 + 3[x + (x - 1)]$
11. $2[4x - 5(x - 1) - 3]$
12. $4[(x + 3) - x]$
13. $-[8 - 3(m - 2)]$
14. $4[x + (3 - x)]$
15. $6[6 - 2(a + 5) - 4]$
16. $2[x - (3 + x)]$
17. $5[3m - 2(m - 5) - 9]$
18. $2[(x - 3) + x]$
19. $-4[-11 - 16x - 3(5x - 2)]$
20. $3x + 9[2(x - 4) + 17]$
21. $-[12 - 7(2 - x)]$
22. $0.02[x - 7(x - 2)]$
23. $3c[9c - 5(2c - 4)]$
24. $0.21[0.3x - (x - 0.2)]$

★ 25. $4[3(x - 2) - (x - 5)] - [2(4x - 8) - 1]$
26. $7a[14 - 2(a + 6) + a] - 13a$
27. $10[3(x - 3)] - [5(6x - 8) + 50]$
28. $-5[-2(x - 7)] - [-(x + 2) + x]$
29. $10a[a - 4(a - 5)] - [-a(6 - 2a)]$
30. $-x[-x(-x - 1) - x] + x\{x + x[x - (x - 1)]\}$

128 *ALGEBRA: ITS BIG IDEAS AND BASIC SKILLS*

Placing Terms Inside Parentheses

To place two or more terms in parentheses, you can use the distributive and associative principles. When working with algebraic expressions, it is frequently necessary to place some of the terms inside parentheses. Placing terms inside parentheses is the inverse of removing parentheses. When you remove parentheses, you multiply; hence, when you place terms inside parentheses, you divide.

If you wish a positive sign in front of the parentheses, simply place the parentheses around the terms. This is the same as dividing each term by $+1$, because dividing by $+1$ does not change the sign of any term.

If you wish a negative sign in front of the parentheses, divide each term by -1 and place the terms inside the parentheses. This, of course, changes the sign of each term that you place inside the parentheses.

Examples for Study

Place the last two terms in each expression inside parentheses preceded by a plus sign:

1. $16 - x - y$

SOLUTION: $16 + (-x - y)$

2. $3a + b + 5$

SOLUTION: $3a + (b + 5)$

Place the last two terms in each expression inside parentheses preceded by a minus sign:

3. $4m - 3n + 7$

SOLUTION: $4m - (3n - 7)$

4. $3x + y - 1$

SOLUTION: $3x - (-y + 1)$

PROBLEMS

Place the last two terms of each of the following expressions inside parentheses preceded by a plus sign. Check your answers by removing parentheses.

1. $x - 5y + 2$
2. $m + n - p$
3. $20 + 3a + 2b$
4. $-x - y - 2$
5. $a - b + c$
6. $m + 5 + y$
7. $6 - x - 2a$
8. $14 + 2m + 2n$
9. $-a - b + c$
10. $15x - 2y + 8$
11. $6 - 2a - 3b$
12. $x^2 - 2x + 8$

13. Place the last two terms in each expression in Problems 1–12 inside parentheses preceded by a minus sign. Check your answers by removing parentheses.

SELF TEST

Divide:

1. $\dfrac{15a^2 + 18a}{3a}$

2. $\dfrac{5a^2y^2 + a^2y^2 + y^2}{y^2}$

3. $\dfrac{21k^2 + 28k}{7k}$

4. $(x^2 + 5x - 24) \div (x - 3)$

5. $(6y^2 + 7y - 5) \div (2y - 1)$

6. $(4x^2 + 6x - 4) \div (2x + 2)$

7. $(8x^3 - y^3) \div (2x - y)$

Remove the grouping symbols and combine like terms:

8. $5[3 + 7(y + 4)]$

9. $2[5 - (x + y) + 7]$

10. $8x[-11 + 4x^2 - 2x(x + 6)]$

11. $-y + 3[4x - 2(y + 1)] + 7$

In each expression enclose the first two terms in parentheses preceded by a minus sign:

12. $3x^2 + 5x + 6$

13. $5y^2 - 8y + 7$

14. $-2xy + 4y + 9$

15. $-8k - 3y - 4z$

Equations Containing Parentheses

Now that you know how to work with parentheses, you will be able to solve equations which have expressions enclosed in parentheses. The example below will show you how it is done.

Example for Study

Solve: $2(3x - 5) - (x - 8) = 3(x + 4)$

SOLUTION: First remove the parentheses; then proceed as usual.

$$6x - 10 - x + 8 = 3x + 12$$
$$5x - 2 = 3x + 12$$
$$2x = 14$$
$$x = 7$$

CHECK:
$$2(3 \cdot 7 - 5) - (7 - 8) \stackrel{?}{=} 3(7 + 4)$$
$$2(21 - 5) - (-1) \stackrel{?}{=} 3(11)$$
$$32 + 1 \stackrel{?}{=} 33$$
$$33 = 33$$

PROBLEMS

Solve and check:

1. $18 + 3(x - 5) = 12$

2. $10(x - 5) + 30 = 20$

3. $5(a - 1) - 15 = 5$

4. $3(y + 1) = 2(y + 4)$

5. $20 - 2(m + 7) = 28$

6. $7d - (d - 10) = 52$

7. $4(x - 3) = 3(x + 2)$

8. $3(2a + 8) = 4(a - 9)$

9. $7(n + 1) = 8(n + 2)$

10. $3(2h + 6) = 4(2h - 1)$

11. $k + (5k + 9) = 3(k + 13)$

12. $16 - (s - 10) = 0$

13. $3 + (6x - 15) = 4(x - 7)$

14. $7(y - 2) - 5(y - 4) = 0$

15. $11(a - 4) - 8(a + 2) = 0$

16. $23 + 9(f + 2) = 4(2f - 10)$

17. $8g - (g + 13) = 2(g + 6)$ 18. $5(3k - 2) - (8k + 10) = 1$
19. $0 = 9(3x - 9) - 3(x - 27)$ 20. $3(2b - 6) = 4(2b + 1)$
21. $\frac{1}{2}(8x - 6) = \frac{1}{4}(4x + 12)$ 22. $4(3x - \frac{3}{4}) = -3(x + 21)$
23. $m - (5m - 12) = 22 + (6m - 30)$
24. $40 - 3(-x - 8) = 16 - (x + 12)$
25. $100 - (c - 70) = 11(c + 10)$
26. $200 - 15(2p + 8) = 5(4p - 34)$

★ 27. $0.3(15y - 20) = 0.7(5y + 60)$
28. $\frac{1}{2}(8a - 20) - \frac{3}{2}(6a - 12) = 23$
29. $16 + 0.1(1.2m + 18) = 0.4(0.8m - 74.5)$
30. $18 - 3(x - 9) = 6(-x + 2)$
31. $20x - (3x + 7) + (6 - x) = (4x - 5)$
32. $5(5y - 1) - 5(1 - 5y) = 5$
33. $3 - 4(x - 2) - (3 - x) = 6 + (2x + 3)$
34. $\frac{1}{2}(2x - 8) + \frac{1}{3}(3x - 6) = 0$
35. $2(3k - 1) - 3(2k + 1) = 2(5k - 2) + 5$
36. $4(5 - b) - 3(b - 5) = 2(3b + 7) - 18$
37. $(16 - x) - (x - 16) = (20 + x) - (10 - x)$
38. $3x(x - 1) - 5(2 - x) - 7 = x(3x - 5) - 38$
39. $10(x - 10) - 5(3 - 2x) - 50 = 4(3 - 5x) - (3 - 10x)$
40. $200 - 5(x - 12) - 10(2x - 9) = 500 + 3(5x + 10)$
41. $0.3(x - 5) - 0.2(2x - 7) - 1 = 0.4(5x - 2) - 6.6$
42. $x(4x - 5) - 2x(x + 4) - 7 = 16 + 2x(x - 5) - 5$
43. $0.5(3 - y) - 0.8(y + 9) = 20 - (y + 1) - 0.6(2y - 7)$
44. $376 - 32(x - 4) = 400 - 16(5x - 8)$
45. $100(x - 2) - 3(20x - 70) - (200 - 90x) = 0$

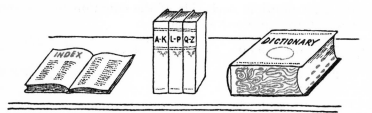

When you read a word in this book that you do not understand:

Use the index. If the word is listed, you will find the number of the page on which the meaning appears.

Find the meaning of the word in a dictionary.

Look up the word in an encyclopedia.

If you are unable to find the meaning of the word, ask your teacher to suggest another source of information.

Equations Containing Fractions

The following examples will show you how you can use your knowledge of fractions in solving equations containing fractions.

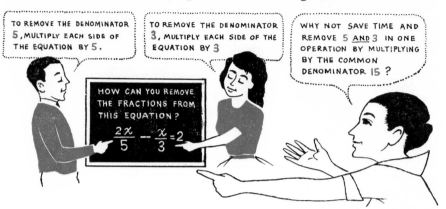

SOLUTION TO PROBLEM PICTURED ABOVE:

$$15\left(\frac{2x}{5} - \frac{x}{3}\right) = 15 \cdot 2$$

$$15 \cdot \frac{2x}{5} - 15 \cdot \frac{x}{3} = 30$$

$$6x - 5x = 30$$

$$x = 30$$

CHECK: $\dfrac{2 \times 30}{5} - \dfrac{30}{3} \overset{?}{=} 2$

$$12 - 10 \overset{?}{=} 2$$

$$2 = 2$$

Examples for Study

1. *Solve:* $\dfrac{-2x}{9} - 6 = 0$

SOLUTION: First multiply each side of the equation by the common denominator 9, then proceed as usual.

$$9\left(\frac{-2x}{9} - 6\right) = 9 \cdot 0$$

$$-2x - 54 = 0$$

$$-2x = 54$$

$$x = -27$$

CHECK: $\dfrac{(-2)(-27)}{9} - 6 \overset{?}{=} 0$

$$6 - 6 \overset{?}{=} 0$$

$$0 = 0$$

2. *Solve:* $\dfrac{3}{4} + \dfrac{6}{x} = 1$

SOLUTION: First multiply each side of the equation by the common denominator $4x$, then proceed as usual.

$$4x\left(\frac{3}{4} + \frac{6}{x}\right) = 4x \cdot 1$$

$$3x + 24 = 4x$$

$$24 = x$$

$$\text{or} \quad x = 24$$

CHECK: $\dfrac{3}{4} + \dfrac{6}{24} \overset{?}{=} 1$

$$\frac{3}{4} + \frac{1}{4} \overset{?}{=} 1$$

$$1 = 1$$

PROBLEMS

Solve and check:

1. $\dfrac{3x}{2} - \dfrac{x}{3} = 14$

2. $\dfrac{x}{2} + \dfrac{11}{2} = 5$

3. $\dfrac{5y}{7} - \dfrac{1}{2} = \dfrac{13}{7}$

4. $\dfrac{-9x}{5} = 36$

5. $\dfrac{a}{4} - \dfrac{3}{2} = 0$

6. $\dfrac{8b}{7} - 8 = 0$

7. $\frac{1}{3}n - 12 = 0$

8. $\dfrac{-x}{5} - 10 = 0$

9. $\dfrac{m}{3} + \dfrac{m}{4} = 7$

10. $\dfrac{c}{4} - \dfrac{c}{5} = 3$

11. $x - \dfrac{x}{6} = 10$

12. $\dfrac{k}{9} - \dfrac{k}{8} = 1$

13. $\frac{1}{2}x + 8 = \frac{1}{4}x$

14. $\dfrac{a}{5} - 1 = \dfrac{a}{2}$

15. $\dfrac{2d}{3} - 8 = 0$

16. $\dfrac{1}{2} - \dfrac{x}{3} = 1$

17. $\dfrac{1}{2} - \dfrac{x}{8} = 2$

18. $3 = \dfrac{6}{a}$

19. $\dfrac{1}{n} = 4$

20. $\dfrac{2}{m} = 2$

21. $\dfrac{5}{y} - \dfrac{1}{4} = 1$

22. $\dfrac{6}{n} + \dfrac{1}{2} = 1$

23. $\dfrac{1}{w} - \dfrac{1}{3} = 2$

24. $\dfrac{3}{a} + \dfrac{3}{4} = 0$

25. $\dfrac{x}{4} - 6 = \dfrac{1}{3}$

26. $\dfrac{2d}{5} - \dfrac{7}{3} = \dfrac{5}{3}$

27. $\dfrac{x}{4} - \dfrac{1}{2} = 4$

28. $\frac{2}{3} = x + 4$

★ 29. $\frac{1}{4}(x + 8) - \frac{1}{2}(x + 2) = 2$

30. $\frac{1}{2}(x + 6) - \frac{3}{4}(x + 12) = 4$

31. $\frac{1}{5}(x + 2) + \frac{1}{2} = 1$

32. $\frac{1}{3}(4x - 2) - \dfrac{x}{2} = 6$

Avoid this burden.

Solving Verbal Problems

Solve each of the following problems by means of equations. Check each answer with the facts given in the problem.

1. The sum of two numbers is 18. The sum of the first number and four times the second number is 39. What are the two numbers?

2. A merchant had 100 books for sale. He planned to sell some of the books at $2 each and the rest at $3 each. How many books must he sell at each price to receive a total of $245?

3. The perimeter of triangle ABC is 30 inches. Side BC of the triangle is 2 inches shorter than side AB. Side CA is twice as long as side BC. How long is each side of the triangle?

4. A man had $20,000 with which to buy some bonds which bring 4% interest and some bonds which bring 5% interest. How much money should he invest in each kind of bond to receive $870 interest in one year?

5. A board was sawed into two pieces. One piece was $\frac{2}{3}$ as long as the whole board and 4 feet longer than the second piece. How long was the board before it was cut?

6. Find two consecutive numbers so that, if the first number were divided by 3 and the second number were divided by 4, the sum of the two quotients would be 23.

7. The sum of one-fifth of a number and two-thirds of the number is 65. What is the number?

8. When $\frac{1}{7}$ of a number is subtracted from $\frac{1}{2}$ of the number, the difference is 20. What is the number?

9. The first of two numbers is three less than the second. The sum of ten times the first number and five times the second number is 285. Find the two numbers.

10. One number is 10 more than another number. The average of the two numbers is $1\frac{1}{2}$. Find the two numbers.

11. The sum of two numbers is 19. Find the two numbers if the sum of $\frac{2}{3}$ of the larger and $\frac{1}{4}$ of the smaller is 11.

12. If n articles cost k cents, what is the cost of 5 articles? Of 100 articles?

★ 13. Find the length of each side of triangle ABC at the right if its perimeter is 41 inches.

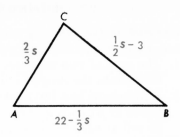

14. In Problem 13, find the perimeter of triangle ABC if this perimeter is represented by $s + 13$ inches.
15. In Problem 13, find the perimeter of triangle ABC if $AB = BC$.
16. When $2x$ is divided by 5, the quotient is $\frac{1}{2}x$ and the remainder is 1. Solve for x.
17. When $6x - 7$ is divided by $x - 1$, the quotient is 6 and the remainder is $\frac{1}{8}x$. Find the dividend, the divisor, and the remainder.

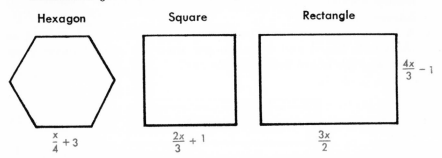

18. A regular hexagon has 6 equal sides. What is the perimeter of the regular hexagon above in terms of x? Of the square above? Of the rectangle above?
19. In Problem 18, if the perimeter of the hexagon equals the perimeter of the square, find the length of the side of each of these two figures.
20. In Problem 18, if the perimeter of the square equals the perimeter of the rectangle, find the length of the sides of each of these two figures.

SELF TEST

Solve and check the following equations:

1. $5(3y - 8) = 2(y + 6)$
2. $15 - (x + 2) = 0$
3. $k - (4k - 10) = 20 + (6k - 28)$
4. $0 = 8[7 + 3(x + 5)]$
5. $\frac{1}{2} - \frac{x}{4} = 1$
6. $\frac{k}{3} + \frac{k}{4} = 28$
7. $\frac{25}{y} = 15$
8. $\frac{6}{x} + \frac{2}{5} = \frac{19}{10}$

9. One-fourth of a number plus three-fifths of the number equals 17. What is the number?
10. A board is cut into two pieces. One piece is $\frac{3}{4}$ as long as the original board and is $13\frac{1}{2}$ feet long. How long was the original board?

SUMMARY OF IMPORTANT THINGS TO REMEMBER

1. Words and expressions

braces equations containing fractions

brackets equations containing parentheses

2. Understandings

The rules for multiplying and dividing fractions in arithmetic are used in multiplying and dividing algebraic fractions.

Parentheses are removed by multiplying each term inside the parentheses by the factor outside the parentheses.

In solving equations containing fractions, each side of the equation is multiplied by the least common denominator of the fractions.

3. Skills

You should be able to:

Multiply and divide polynomials.

Remove parentheses.

Enclose terms in parentheses.

Solve equations containing parentheses.

Multiply and divide algebraic fractions.

Solve equations containing fractions.

PROBLEMS ON YOUR AIMS

YOUR AIM **To learn how to work with exponents in multiplication and division.**

Which number is the base and which is the exponent in each of the following monomials?

1. 3^4 2. 2^5 3. 1^2 4. $(3a)^2$ 5. $(4a)^3$

Which of the following monomials may be simplified? Explain.

6. $d^2 d^4$ 7. $\dfrac{a^6}{a^2}$ 8. $a^2 b^3$ 9. $\dfrac{b^6}{a^4}$

State each of the following formulas in words:

10. $a^m \cdot a^n = a^{m+n}$ 11. $\dfrac{a^m}{a^n} = a^{m-n}$ 12. $(a^m)^n = a^{mn}$

Simplify:

13. $a^2 a$ 14. $b^3 \div b$ 15. $(a^2)^5$ 16. $\dfrac{(6x)^3}{(6x)^2}$ 17. $\dfrac{c^2 d^3}{a^2} \div \dfrac{cd}{a}$

YOUR AIM To learn how to multiply and divide polynomials.

Write the product of each of the following:
1. a and $a + b$ 2. -3 and $4x - 7$ 3. $x + 3$ and $3x - 5$

Write the quotient when $6x - 12$ is divided by each of the following:
4. -3 5. $+3$ 6. -6 7. $+12$

8. If the dividend is $x^2 - 7x + 12$ and the quotient is $x - 3$, what is the divisor?
9. True or false: When $a^2 - 3a - 8$ is divided by $a - 2$, the quotient is $a + 4$? Check your answer by multiplication.

Multiply:
10. $(3x - 4)(x + 3)$ 11. $(x - 2)^3$ 12. $(a - b)(c - d)$

YOUR AIM To learn how to remove parentheses and how to enclose quantities in parentheses.

1. How would you enclose in parentheses a quantity such as $-x + 2y$ when a minus sign is to precede the parentheses? When a plus sign is to precede the parentheses?

Remove parentheses:
2. $-x(x^2 - x - 1)$ 3. $3(a - 1) - (a - 4)$
4. $-(15 - xy)$ 5. $+(b - c)$

YOUR AIM To learn how to multiply and divide algebraic fractions.

Write in words the rule illustrated by each of the following:

1. $\dfrac{a}{b} \cdot \dfrac{c}{d} = \dfrac{ac}{bd}$ 2. $\dfrac{m}{n} \div \dfrac{p}{q} = \dfrac{m}{n} \cdot \dfrac{q}{p}$

Do the indicated operations:

3. $\dfrac{3}{x} \cdot \dfrac{5y}{6}$ 4. $\dfrac{6}{5a} \div \dfrac{8}{25a^2}$ 5. $\dfrac{mn}{3} \cdot \left(\dfrac{-21}{m^2}\right)$

6. $\dfrac{-2x}{3}\left(\dfrac{-1xy}{4}\right)$ 7. $\dfrac{5a^2b}{10c} \div \dfrac{4ab}{15c^2}$ 8. $\dfrac{(-2)^2}{x} \div \dfrac{(-4)^3}{x}$

YOUR AIM To learn how to solve equations containing parentheses and equations containing fractions.

Solve each of the following equations and explain each step:

1. $2(x - 1) = 4 - 2(3x + 1)$ 2. $\dfrac{x}{2} - \dfrac{1}{5} = \dfrac{x}{5} - 3$

3. What is the error most likely to be made in solving the equation $3x - (2 - x) = 4$?

VALUABLE SKILLS PRACTICE

Study the circle graph and answer the following questions:

1. Which continent is the largest? Which is the smallest?
2. Which continent is nearest in size to Europe? Africa? South America?
3. Which two continents taken together are larger than all the other four combined?
4. What percent, rounded to the nearest 1 percent, of the total area shown in the circle graph is occupied by Australia?

Areas of Some Continents of the World

5. Add the columns of numbers on the left to find the values of a, b, and c. Then substitute the values of a, b, and c in the formulas on the right to find the values of A, B, C, D, E, and F. Check your work by using the formula given at the bottom.

Add

2	4	5	$a(c - b) = A$
3	4	7	$c(b - a) = B$
4	5	8	$b(a - c) = C$
1	3	6	
3	1	4	$\dfrac{a}{a - b} + \dfrac{b}{b - a} = D$
7	7	3	
8	2	1	$(c - b)(a - b) = E$
2	6	2	
a	b	c	$\dfrac{c}{a - c} - \dfrac{b}{b - c} = F$

CHECK: $A + B + C + \dfrac{E + F}{D} = -6$

138 *ALGEBRA: ITS BIG IDEAS AND BASIC SKILLS*

Study the bar graph below and answer the following questions:

6. Which city shown in the graph has the largest population?
7. Which three cities of over 5 million population have approximately the same population?
8. Which city shown in the graph is nearest in size to Berlin?
9. Which city shown in the graph has a population between 3 million and 4 million?

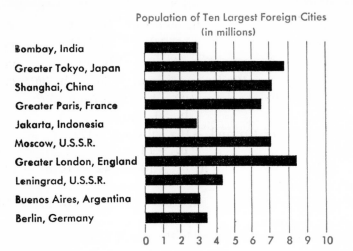

Population of Ten Largest Foreign Cities (in millions)

To answer Questions 10 and 11, use the bar graph above and library sources:

10. How many of the cities shown in the graph are located in the Far East?
11. Find the population of the five largest cities in the United States and compare these figures with the population figures given in the bar graph above.
12. The surface of the earth, which is 197,000,000 square miles, consists of 139,600,000 square miles of water and 57,400,000 square miles of land. Round these numbers to the nearest million and make a circle graph showing this information.
13. Make a bar graph to show the data below:

Some U.S. Territories	Area in Square Miles
American Samoa	76
Guam	206
Panama Canal Zone	648
Virgin Islands	132

CHAPTER TEST

Select the correct answer to each question. Write each question number on a sheet of paper and beside it put the letter of the answer that you choose.

1. Which of the following expressions is a binomial?
   a. $x + y$ **b.** xy **c.** $x + y + 2$

2. How many terms are there in the expression $\frac{1}{2}x^2 - \frac{1}{4}x + 1$?
   a. 1   **b.** 3   **c.** 4

3. $2aaa \cdot 3bb = \underline{\ ?\ }$ **a.** $5a^3b^2$ **b.** $6a^3b^2$ **c.** $2a^3b^2$

4. $(-1)^5 (a^2b^2)^2 = \underline{\ ?\ }$ **a.** $-a^4b$ **b.** $5a^4b^2$ **c.** $-a^4b^4$

5. $(0.2)^2 (10)^3 = \underline{\ ?\ }$ **a.** 4   **b.** 40   **c.** 400

6. $(-5ab)(-6a^2b^3) \div 10a^3b^2 = \underline{\ ?\ }$ **a.** $-3b^2$ **b.** $3b^2$ **c.** $-3b$

7. What is the difference of -100 subtracted from 150?
   a. -50 **b.** 50   **c.** 250

8. From the sum of $10x$ and $-16x$ subtract $-12x$.
   a. $6x$ **b.** $-14x$ **c.** $18x$

9. $(a - 6)(a - 7) = \underline{\ ?\ }$ **a.** $a^2 - 13a - 42$ **b.** $a^2 - 13a + 42$
   c. $a^2 - a + 42$

10. $(3x + 1)(2x - 4) = \underline{\ ?\ }$ **a.** $6x^2 - 10x - 4$ **b.** $6x^2 - 14x - 5$
    c. $6x^2 - 12x + 4$

11. Divide $-18a^4$ by $6a^2$. What is the result of dividing the quotient by $-3a$?   **a.** -1 **b.** 1   **c.** a

12. Which of the following would you do to eliminate the fractions from the equation $\frac{x}{4} - \frac{x}{5} = 1$?
    a. Multiply by 20   **b.** Divide by 20   **c.** Subtract 9

13. What is the value of x in the equation in Problem 12?
    a. -1 **b.** 20   **c.** 9

14. $\frac{6a^3}{7b^3} \div \frac{3a}{14b^5} = \underline{\ ?\ }$ **a.** $\frac{2a^2}{b^2}$ **b.** $\frac{a^2}{b^2}$ **c.** $4a^2b^2$

15. $2(6a - 3) - 4(2a - 5) = \underline{\ ?\ }$ **a.** $2a - 16$ **b.** $4a + 14$ **c.** $4a - 36$

16. $3[2(a - 4) - (a - 7)] = \underline{\ ?\ }$ **a.** $5a - 14$ **b.** $3a - 3$ **c.** $3a - 45$

17. $5(2x - 3) - (x + 1) = 11$. What is the value of x?
    a. 1   **b.** 2   **c.** 3

18. $11 - (9x - 1) = 119 + 4(3x - 11)$. What is the value of x?
    a. 2   **b.** -3 **c.** -4

19. $25 is 5% of what amount?   **a.** $50   **b.** $200   **c.** $500

20. One number is 15 less than 3 times another number. If their sum is 85, find the two numbers. What is the equation for solving this problem?
    a. $3x - 15 = 85$ **b.** $4x - 15 = 85$ **c.** $15 - 3x = 85$

CUMULATIVE REVIEW PROBLEMS

WORKING WITH ALGEBRAIC EXPRESSIONS

Do the indicated operations and reduce each answer to the simplest form:

1. $m \cdot m \cdot m \cdot m$
2. $3a \cdot 3a \cdot 3a$
3. $x^2 \cdot x^3$
4. $2 \cdot 2 \cdot 2 \cdot 2 \cdot 2$
5. $a^2 \cdot a^3 \cdot a^4$
6. $(-a)^3 (3a)^2$
7. 3^4
8. 2^6
9. $3a(a + 6)$
10. $-5(-x - 2)$
11. $(-2a)^2 (a - 3)$
12. $4(x - 2) - 3(x - 3)$
13. $\frac{1}{2}(6x - 8) - \frac{1}{2}(9x - 12)$
14. $\frac{3}{4}(8a - 16) - \frac{1}{4}(12a - 24)$
15. $(-2ab)(-3ab)(-4ab)$
16. $16xy^2 \div -4xy$
17. $(-3m)^4 \div (-9m^3)$
18. $3^3 - 2^4$
19. $10^3 - 5^3$
20. $(a + 2)(a + 4)$
21. $(-1)^6 (-1)^5$
22. $(0.5x^2)^2$
23. $(\frac{1}{2})^3$
24. $(\frac{1}{4})^3$
25. $m^4 \cdot m^4$
26. $(\frac{3}{4})^2 \div (\frac{1}{4})^2$
27. $\dfrac{16a^2b}{9} \div \dfrac{8ab}{27}$
28. $\dfrac{x^3}{4} \div \dfrac{x^3}{2}$
29. $(-4ax)^2 \div (-8ax^2)$
30. $\frac{3}{4}c^2d \div \frac{1}{4}cd$
31. $3ab \cdot 4a^2b^2 \cdot 5a^3b^3$
32. $-7mn\left(\dfrac{-mn}{7} - \dfrac{1}{mn}\right)$
33. $(-4x^2y)^3 \div (-8x^3y)^2$
34. $-a(-a - 1) - (a - 1)$
35. $6(2x - 5) + 2(4x + 14)$
36. $4am(am - 2) - 2a^2(2m^2 - 1)$
37. $(3x - 1)(2x + 1)$
38. $(a + 6)(a - 5)$
39. $(2a - 1)(a - 1)$
40. $(7x - 2)(6x - 5)$
41. $(x - 7)(x - 7)$
42. $(a + b)(2a + b)$
43. $(x - 2y)(x + 3y)$
44. $(a + 3)(a^2 + a + 1)$
45. $(x - 1)(x^2 - x - 1)$
46. $(x^2 - 12x + 35) \div (x - 5)$
47. $(10a^2 + 29a + 21) \div (5a + 7)$
48. $(60x^2 + 80x - 55) \div (10x - 5)$
49. $(2m^2 - mn - n^2) \div (m - n)$
50. $(x - 4)(x^2 + 5x - 6) \div (x - 1)$

Find the value of x *if* a $= 2$, b $= 3$, c $= -1$, *and* d $= 0$:

51. $ax + b = c$
52. $bx + cx = ab$
53. $a^2x + 4bc = d$
54. $bx = ac + c$
55. $ax - a^2 = b^2 + c^2$
56. $a^2x + c^2 = bx$
57. $abx - 10d = 10b$
58. $a^3 - b^3 - 5cx = 0$
59. $bcx - ad = bd$
60. $\dfrac{ax}{b} + \dfrac{bx}{a} = c$
61. $ab^2 - cx = ax$
62. $a(x - b) + c(x - d) = 0$

MULTIPLICATION AND DIVISION **141**

Write each of the following using algebraic symbols:

63. Five times the sum of x and y.

64. Five times the quotient of x divided by y.

65. Five times the sum of x and y, divided by the product of x and y.

66. The product of 2, x, and $-5x$.

67. The sum of 2, x, and $-5x$.

68. Nine more than one-fourth of a^2.

69. The next consecutive odd number after $2n + 1$.

70. The first consecutive number preceding $2n + 1$.

71. The area of a rectangle whose sides are $4a$ and $5b$.

72. The perimeter of the rectangle in Problem 71.

73. The area of a rectangle whose sides are a and $3a$.

74. The perimeter of the rectangle in Problem 73.

75. The area of a triangle whose base is $5m$ and whose altitude is $8m$.

SOLVING EQUATIONS

Solve and check:

1. $2x + 9 = x + 10$

2. $18 = 7x - 24 - 14x$

3. $3x + 1 = 25 - x$

4. $\frac{1}{3}x + 2 = 7$

5. $10(x - 3) - 7x = 0$

6. $1 - 3(2x - 4) = 4x - 9$

7. $7x - 2 = 11x - 1 + 15$

8. $\frac{4x}{3} - \frac{x}{3} = 5$

9. $3(x - 4) - 2(x - 8) = 1$

10. $\frac{12x}{5} = 48$

11. $100 + 17x = 240 - 18x$

12. $37 - (x + 12) = 20 + 4x$

13. $\frac{8x}{5} - 2 = \frac{4x}{3} - 4$

14. $2(x + 6) + 32 = 5(x - 2)$

15. $\frac{10}{x} = 2$

16. $\frac{5x}{7} - 30 = \frac{5x}{3}$

17. $\frac{1}{x} + \frac{1}{2} = \frac{1}{3}$

18. $5(2x - 9) = 7(x - 6)$

19. $\frac{1}{3}(6x - 9) = \frac{1}{2}(8x + 2)$

20. $\frac{3x}{4} - \frac{x}{5} = 11$

21. $16 - 3(x - 4) = 1$

22. $28 - 8(\frac{1}{2}x - \frac{3}{4}) = x + 1$

23. $18 - (2x - 18) = 5x + 2(3x - 8)$

24. $2x(x - 1) + 12 = x(2x - 3)$

142 *ALGEBRA: ITS BIG IDEAS AND BASIC SKILLS*

1. Tom works at his father's store on Saturdays. He earns $2 for the day plus 10% of sales. On one of his better days he earned $16. What was the total amount of his sales for that day?

2. $1200 is invested, part at 6% and the rest at 3%. If the first year's income is $42, how much money was invested at each rate?

3. Sharon is twice as old as her brother Davey. Eight years from now she will be $1\frac{1}{3}$ times as old. Find the present ages of Sharon and Davey.

4. A number increased by 20% of itself is 48. Find the number.

5. One side of a rectangle is 12 centimeters less than its adjacent side. Find the length and the width of the rectangle if its perimeter is 148 centimeters.

6. Mr. Patrick and Mr. Drozney have a partnership. Mr. Patrick receives two-thirds as much of the profits as Mr. Drozney. The profits are $12,600. How much profit does each man receive?

7. The sum of the angles of a triangle is 180°. The second angle is twice the first. The third angle is 20° less than the second. How many degrees are there in each angle?

8. The length of a rectangle is 4 centimeters more than the width. If the length were decreased 5 centimeters and the width were decreased 2 centimeters, the perimeter would be 18 centimeters. Find the length and the width of the rectangle.

9. A store marked the selling prices of one lot of its goods so as to make a profit of 40% of the cost. If the selling price of an article is $39.95, what was its cost?

10. The power output of a motor is 8.2 horsepower. This is 80% of its rated horsepower. What is its rated horsepower?

11. A real estate agent received $156.25 for selling a building lot. His commission was $2\frac{1}{2}$% of the purchase price. What was the purchase price?

12. The length of a rectangle is 3 inches less than twice the width. Write a formula for the area A of the rectangle in terms of its width w.

13. The length of rectangle is $l - 1$ units. Its width is 6 units less than the length. Find the length and the width of the rectangle if its perimeter is 30 units.

14. The width of a rectangle is $w - 5$ units. Its length is 3 units longer than its width. Write a formula for the perimeter p of the rectangle in terms of w.

15. The standard meter stick is 39.37 inches in length. Write a formula for the number of inches i in m meters.

16. Joe lives $d - 3$ blocks from the school. After he has walked 3 blocks, how many blocks away from the school is he?

17. If 3 pencils cost x cents, what is the cost of n pencils?

18. If the length of a rectangle is k units more than its width w, what is its perimeter?

19. A cargo plane, flying 220 miles per hour, left an airport. A jet plane took off 2 hours later and flew in the same direction as the cargo plane. The jet flew at an average speed of 460 miles per hour. How long after the take-off did the jet overtake the cargo plane?

20. An airplane pilot has a 6.2-hour supply of fuel. How far from his base can he fly if his average speed out is 160 miles per hour and his average speed back is 150 miles per hour?

21. Eight minutes were required for a plane to take off and reach flying altitude after a starting signal was given. Forty-four minutes after the starting signal was given, the plane was 289.2 miles from the base. What was the average speed of the plane after it reached flying altitude at a point above its take-off position?

22. Tom bought a secondhand camera for $24. This was 40% of the cost when new. What was the cost of the camera when new?

23. When a packaging machine operates at 90% efficiency, its output is 45 packages an hour. Find the output when the machine operates at 100% efficiency.

24. One of the large diesel locomotives on our railroads produces 4480 horsepower when operating at 80% capacity. What horsepower will the diesel produce when operating at 100% capacity?

25. The sum of three consecutive even numbers is 132. Find the three numbers.

26. Find the sum of money invested at $5\frac{1}{2}\%$ simple interest that will earn $86.25 at the end of a year.

27. A jet plane flew from Houston, Texas, to Cleveland, Ohio—a distance of 1405 miles. The plane spent 20 minutes on the ground in Cleveland. It then took off and flew 460 miles to New York. The plane's average speed while in the air was 504 miles per hour. Find the number of hours that elapsed between the take-off in Houston and the landing in New York.

28. Sixty more than 6 times a certain number is 9. Find the number.

29. A manufacturer sold some dresses to a wholesaler and made a profit of 8% on his selling price. The wholesaler sold the dresses to a retailer at a profit of 10% of the price he received from the retailer. The retailer sold the dresses at a profit of 12% on the retail selling price. The manufacturer's cost of making each dress was $23. What was the final retail price received on each dress?

30. How much money must be loaned out at 5% interest to amount to a total (principal plus interest) of $5000 in a year?

BUSINESSMEN USE ALGEBRA

At the end of a day a store owner counted his total income for the day. The total amount of money in his cash registers was $5346.28. This amount of money included both the amount charged for the goods sold and the 3% sales tax collected on the sales. To find how much tax he owed, he used algebra. He wrote:

Let P = the amount of money charged for the goods sold
then $0.03P$ = the amount of the sales tax

The amount of money in the cash registers was $5346.28, so:

$$5346.28 = P + 0.03P$$
$$5346.28 = 1.03P$$
$$5190.56 = P$$

So the sales amounted to $5190.56, and the sales tax collected was $155.72.

BIG IDEAS	LETTERS FOR NUMBERS
	EQUATION
	FUNCTION
BASIC SKILLS	Using and interpreting symbols of algebra
	Evaluating algebraic expressions
	Solving equations
	Solving verbal problems
	Using exponents

CHAPTER **6** *Functions*

REVIEWING the first five chapters of this book, you will find that you have used the following basic skills: using and interpreting symbols of algebra, evaluating algebraic expressions, solving equations, solving verbal problems, and using exponents. You have also studied three big ideas of algebra: the use of letters to represent numbers, the use of equations in solving problems and in finding unknown quantities, and the use of signed numbers to indicate opposite directions.

In this chapter you will continue to use all the basic skills listed above, and you will study another big idea of algebra—the idea of function.

YOUR AIM  1. To learn what function is and to learn ways of expressing functions.

2. To learn to use algebraic symbols in expressing various mathematical relations.

3. To learn the meaning of direct variation and of inverse variation.

146

Expressing Relations in Algebra

You live in a world of relations, in which one thing depends upon another. To illustrate, consider the price of the last movie ticket you bought. How many factors determined the price of that ticket? The rent the theater owner paid for the film, the wages he paid to his employees, and the taxes you paid on the price of the ticket are some factors. How many other factors can you think of?

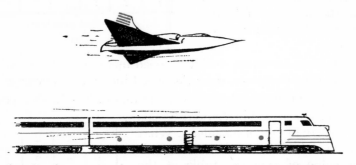

The time it takes to travel a certain distance depends upon the speed.

The time it takes you to walk or ride to school depends upon the distance you walk or ride and upon how fast you walk or ride.

The factors in the above examples are related and interdependent. As one factor changes, other factors change also. For example, if you travel faster in going to school, it takes you less time to get there. Or if you move to a house farther from the school, it probably takes you more time to get there.

Algebra provides you with tools for expressing relations between various factors accurately and briefly. Algebraic symbols make it easier to understand involved relations.

PROBLEMS

Here are a few examples of relations that were discovered long ago. Study these carefully and notice in each case how the values of one quantity depend upon the values of another quantity.

1. $C = \pi d$. The circumference C of a circle depends on the length d of the diameter. Copy the table at the right and fill in the correct values of C for each value of d. Use $\pi = 3\frac{1}{7}$.

d	$3\frac{1}{2}$	7	14	21	28
C	?	?	?	?	?

2. As the diameter of a circle increases, does the circumference increase or decrease?

3. How does the circumference of a circle change when the diameter is doubled?

4. $r = \dfrac{d}{t}$. The speed r at which you travel a certain distance d depends upon the time t. Find the speed r at which you must travel to go 12 miles in each time t shown in the table at the right. t is the number of hours, and r is the speed in miles an hour.

t	2	3	4	6	12	24
r	?	?	?	?	?	?

5. As the time increases, does the speed increase or decrease?

6. As the time decreases, does the speed increase or decrease?

7. If the time is doubled, what change takes place in the speed?

8. $A = s^2$. The area A of a square equals the square of one of its sides s. What is the value of A for each corresponding value of s in the table at the right?

s	1	2	3	4
A	?	?	?	?

9. Does the area A of a square depend upon the length of the side? Explain.

10. How does the area of a square change as the length of the side increases?

11. When the length of the side s is tripled, what change takes place in the area of a square?

12. Which changes at a greater rate, s or A?

★ 13. $A = \frac{1}{2}ab$. The area A of a triangle equals one-half the product of the base b and the altitude a. Find the value of A for each pair of corresponding values of a and b in the table at the right.

a	5	10	10	20
b	10	10	20	50
A	?	?	?	?

14. How does the area of a triangle A change as the base b and the altitude a increase?

15. If b is not changed and a is doubled, what effect does this change have on the area A of a triangle?

16. If a is not changed and b is doubled, what effect does this have on the area A of a triangle?

17. If both a and b are doubled, what is the effect of this change on the area A of a triangle?

18. Does the value of the area of a triangle A depend upon the lengths of the base b and the altitude a? Explain.

148 *ALGEBRA: ITS BIG IDEAS AND BASIC SKILLS*

19. $A = \pi r^2$. The area A of a circle equals the product of π and the square of the radius, r^2. Copy the table at the right and find the value of A for each value of r. Use $\pi = 3.14$.

r	1	2	3	4	5	6
A	?	?	?	?	?	?

20. As the radius of a circle increases, how does the area change?
21. How many times is the area of a circle increased as the radius is doubled?
22. How many times is the area of a circle increased as the radius is tripled?
23. Which changes at a greater rate, r or A?

Variables and Constants

Suppose a laborer is paid $1.50 per hour. If you let w represent his wages and h the number of hours he works, then the following formula expresses the relation between the wages in dollars and time in hours:

$$w = 1.50h$$

In this formula you can replace h by any positive number. For each value of h, a value of w is determined. For example, if you replace h by 8, then w is found to be 1.50 × 8, or 12. This means that for 8 hours of work, the laborer earns $12. If h is replaced by 10, then w is 15.

The value of w in the formula $w = 1.50h$, then, depends on the value of h. The letters w and h in this formula are called **variables**. A variable is a symbol, usually a letter, that can be replaced by any one of a set of numbers. For example, in the algebraic expression $2x + 3$, if x can be replaced by any number, then x is a variable.

When in a given situation a symbol represents only one number, then the symbol is called a **constant**. For example, in the equation $w = 80h$, the symbol 80 is a constant. It stands for only one number, namely, 80. In the formula for the circumference of a circle, $C = \pi d$, π is a symbol which stands for only one number, namely, pi (approximately 3.1416). π is a constant. C and d are variables because each one of them can be replaced by any positive number.

PROBLEMS

In each of the following formulas, equations, or algebraic expressions name the variables and the constants:

1. $5y + 7$ 2. $y + 4$ 3. $3x = 12$ 4. $A = lw$
5. $C = 2\pi r$ 6. $A = \frac{1}{2}bh$ 7. $d = rt$ 8. $A = \pi r^2$
9. $A = s^2$ 10. $3k + 6$ 11. $7S$ 12. $\dfrac{x}{17}$
13. $p = 2(w + l)$ 14. $A = \frac{1}{2}h(b + B)$ 15. $p = 4s$ 16. $V = \frac{4}{3}\pi r^3$

The Meaning of Function

The cost of 5 dozen oranges depends upon the price per dozen. At 20 cents per dozen the cost of 5 dozen is $1. At 30 cents per dozen, 5 dozen cost $1.50, and at 50 cents per dozen, 5 dozen cost $2.50. It is easy to list this information by a set of ordered pairs of numbers as follows:

$$(0.20, 1.00), (0.30, 1.50), \text{ and } (0.50, 2.50)$$

In every pair above, the second number is five times as great as the first number. If the first number of the pair represents the price per dozen of oranges, then the second number represents the cost of 5 dozen oranges. Of course, there is no limit to the number of such pairs. Some other pairs of numbers in which the second number is five times as great as the first number are: $(0.40, 2.00), (0.42, 2.10), (0.48, 2.40), (0.515, 2.575), (1.34, 6.70)$.

Since it is not possible to list all pairs of numbers such that the second number is five times as great as the first number, we can use another method for describing this set of number pairs. We could say, "All the ordered pairs of numbers (p, c) which make the equation $c = 5p$ a true statement." This set is an example of an *infinite set* of ordered pairs of numbers.

Consider the relation between the area of a square and the length of a side of the square. Here again we could think of the set of the ordered pairs of numbers (s, A) which satisfy the equation $A = s^2$. Some of the number pairs which belong to this set, without naming the unit of measure, are:

$$(1, 1), (\tfrac{1}{2}, \tfrac{1}{4}), (3, 9), (7, 49), (14.5, 210.25), (100, 10{,}000)$$

In the above pairs the second number is always the square of the first. If we think about only the area of squares, then the first number of the pair will always be a positive number. It is meaningless to talk about a square with a negative number as the length of a side. If we were not thinking about a square, but simply thinking of the equation $A = s^2$, we could also find A for negative values of s. For example, if $s = -5, A = 25$.

Since we are thinking about the areas of squares, we will not permit negative values for s. Thus every value of s will have a different value of A. In the set of ordered pairs of numbers (s, A) it is also impossible to get two different numbers for A from the same number s. In other words, for a given first number in the pair there is one and only one second number.

We can list ordered pairs of numbers in many ways—in a table, for example. The set of ordered pairs of numbers for $A = s^2$, listed above in parentheses, is listed in a table on page 151.

s	1	$\frac{1}{2}$	3	7	14.5	100
A	1	$\frac{1}{4}$	9	49	210.25	10,000

Any given set of ordered pairs of numbers such that for every first number in a pair there is one and only one second number is called a **function**. A function, thus, is a set of ordered pairs of numbers.

The second number of an ordered pair in the function is called the **value of the function** for the given first number of the pair. For example, one number pair in the function $A = s^2$ is (4, 16). Hence, 16 is the value of the function for $s = 4$. Where $s = 7$, the number pair in $A = s^2$ is (7, 49), and the value of the function is 49.

Domain and Range of a Function

For any set of ordered pairs (x, y) the set of number replacements for the first variable x is called the **domain** of the function, and the set of number replacements for the second variable y is called the **range** of the function.

For the function described by the equation $C = \pi d$ the set of ordered pairs of numbers is represented by (d, C). The first variable in the pair whose number replacements are in the domain is called the **independent variable**. The second variable in the pair whose number replacements are in the range is called the **dependent variable**. For circles we say that the circumference depends upon the diameter. Of course, we could also think of the diameter as depending upon the circumference. In this case the variable d would be the second variable in the ordered pair (C, d) and would thus be the dependent variable.

EXAMPLES:

1. When you think of the set of pairs of numbers (x, y) which make the equation $y = 3x + 2$ a true statement, you are thinking of a function. There is one and only one value of y for every different x.

2. When you think of the pairs of numbers in which the first number represents the number of cars in a given parking lot for each of the seven days of one week and the second number represents the number of cars' wheels on the ground, then you are thinking of a function.

3. $s = \pm\sqrt{A}$ does not describe a function because for each value of A there is not one and only one s. For example, if $A = 25$, then s could be either $+5$ or -5.

4. The set (5, 3) is a function even though there is only one number pair in this set. The domain of this function is the single number 5. The range of the function is the single number 3.

Using Tables to Express Functions

The equation $y = 2x + 10$ describes a function. The set of all (x, y) that make this become a true statement is the function. It is possible to list some of the (x, y) in a table.

When $x =$	1	2	3	4	5
$y =$	12	14	16	18	20

Note that the difference between the successive values of x is 1, whereas the difference between the successive values of y is 2. In other words, as x increases by 1, y increases by 2. As the values of the variable x increase, the values of the function y increase twice as much.

PROBLEMS

1. Make a table of values of the function described by $y = 6x - 1$ as x is replaced by the numbers given in the following table:

When $x =$	1	2	3	4	5
$y =$	?	?	?	?	?

2. In Problem 1, what is the difference between the successive values of x? What is the difference between the successive values of y?
3. How does the change in the values of y compare with the change in the values of x?
4. Make a table of values for the function $y = 2x^2 + 3$ as x is replaced by the numbers given in the following table.

When $x =$	0	1	2	3	4	5
$y =$	?	?	?	?	?	?

Complete the tables of values for each of the following functions:

5. $y = 24 - 6x$

x	-4	-3	-2	-1	0	$+1$	$+2$	$+3$
y	?	?	?	?	?	?	?	?

6. $y = 2x^2 - 3x + 1$

x	-4	-3	-2	-1	0	$+1$	$+2$	$+3$	$+4$
y	?	?	?	?	?	?	?	?	?

★ 7. $\dfrac{16}{x} = y$

y	?	?	?	?	?
x	-16	-8	-4	-2	-1

8. In Problem 7 can x be replaced by any number? Explain.

9. $F = \frac{9}{5}C + 32$

C	-20	-10	0	10	50	100
F	?	?	?	?	?	?

10. $V = \frac{4}{3}\pi r^3$; use $\pi = 3.14$

r	1	2	3	4
V	?	?	?	?

Changing the Subject of Formulas

In the formula $d = rt$, d is the subject of the formula. It is the dependent variable, and r and t are the independent variables. You can change the subject of a formula by using the four laws of equations you learned in Chapter 2.

Suppose in the formula $d = rt$, d represents distance, r represents rate, and t represents time. If you know the distance and the time and you want to find the rate, you would change the subject of the formula as follows:

$$\frac{d}{t} = \frac{rt}{t} \quad \text{or} \quad r = \frac{d}{t}$$

In the formula $r = \frac{d}{t}$, r is the subject of the formula. r is the dependent variable, and d and t are the independent variables.

Now if you know the distance and the rate and you want to find the time, you would change the subject of the formula as follows:

$$\frac{d}{r} = \frac{rt}{r} \quad \text{or} \quad t = \frac{d}{r}$$

In the formula $t = \frac{d}{r}$, t is the subject of the formula. t is the dependent variable, and d and r are the independent variables.

Examples for Study

1. Rewrite $p = 2(l + w)$ so that w is the dependent variable.

SOLUTION: Multiplying $(l + w)$ by 2: $p = 2l + 2w$
Subtracting $2l$ from both sides: $p - 2l = 2w$

Dividing both sides by 2: $w = \dfrac{p - 2l}{2}$

2. Rewrite $m - b = ax + b$ so that x is the dependent variable.

SOLUTION:
$$m - b = ax + b$$
$$m - 2b = ax$$
$$x = \frac{m - 2b}{a}$$

PROBLEMS

Rewrite each of the following so that the variable enclosed in parentheses is the dependent variable:

1. $p = 4s$ (s)
2. $C = 2\pi r$ (r)
3. $p = s - c$ (c)
4. $A = ab$ (a)
5. $V = lwh$ (w)
6. $V = \frac{1}{3}Bh$ (B)
7. $v = at$ (t)
8. $p = a + b + c$ (b)
9. $ax - b = c$ (x)
10. $3ax - 6 = 12$ (x)
11. $14m - 2y = 4m$ (y)
12. $mx - am = 0$ (x)
13. $i = prt$ (r)
14. $d + m = m - 2y$ (y)
15. $5x - 10z = 25x$ (z)
16. $2ax - 3a = 1$ (x)
17. $6y - 10n = y + 10n$ (y)
18. $2x - a = x - 3a$ (x)

★
19. $4x - m = 2x + 7m$ (x)
20. $5y - 2p = 3p - 5q$ (y)
21. $7k + 16 - m = -4m$ (m)
22. $3y - 2\frac{1}{2}x = -4x + 6y$ (x)
23. $\frac{2}{3}a - 15b = \frac{5}{6}a - 17b$ (a)
24. $2.6c + 2.4b + 7.2c = 0$ (c)
25. $3\frac{1}{8}xyz = 15$ (y)
26. $3\frac{1}{3}xyz + 18 = 0$ (x)
27. $x + y + z + 15 = 0$ (y)
28. $\dfrac{3xyz}{k} = 1$ (k)
29. $3k - 1\frac{2}{3}k + 4\frac{1}{2}k = 0$ (k)
30. $9\frac{5}{8}k = 9\frac{5}{8}$ (k)

Formulas Describe Change

You use the formula $A = lw$ to find the area of a rectangle. Now consider the following question: If the width of a rectangle is doubled, how is the area changed?

To answer this question, you might make drawings like the following.

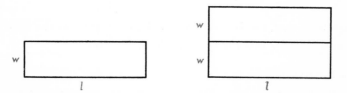

The width of the rectangle at the right above is twice the width of the rectangle at the left. You can also see that the area of the rectangle at the right is twice the area of the rectangle at the left.

You can reach the same conclusion on the basis of the formula $A = lw$. Since the width is doubled, substitute $2w$ for w in this formula. Using A' to represent the area of the rectangle with the doubled width, we have:

$$A' = l(2w) = 2lw$$

Since $A = lw$, we have $A' = 2A$, or the area of the rectangle is doubled.

Example for Study

If each side of a square is doubled, how is the area changed?

SOLUTION: The formula for the area of a square is $A = s^2$. Doubling the length of each side means that the length s becomes $2s$. You can substitute $2s$ for s in the formula $A = s^2$.

$$A' = (2s)^2$$
$$A' = 4s^2 \quad \text{or} \quad A' = 4A$$

Hence, doubling the sides of a square will make the area four times as large.

PROBLEMS

Answer the questions in the following problems. Check each answer by using a numerical example.

1. The formula for the perimeter p of a square in terms of the side s is $p = 4s$. If the side of a square is doubled, how is the perimeter changed?
2. The formula for the circumference C of a circle in terms of the radius r is $C = 2\pi r$. If the radius of a circle is doubled, how is the circumference changed?

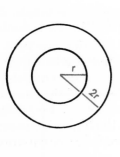 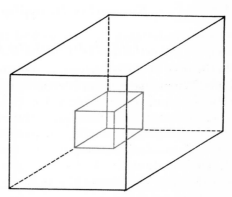

3. The formula for the volume V of a cube in terms of the edge e is $V = e^3$. If the side of a cube is tripled, how is the volume changed?
4. The formula for the volume V of a rectangular solid in terms of the length l, the width w, and the height h is $V = lwh$. If both the length and the width are doubled while the height remains the same, how is the volume changed?
5. The formula for the area A of a circle in terms of the radius r is $A = \pi r^2$. If the radius of a circle is doubled, how is the area changed?
6. The formula for the area A of a square in terms of the side s is $A = s^2$. If each side of a square is tripled, how is the area changed?

What is the perimeter of a square one of whose sides is the following?
7. a **8.** $2a$ **9.** $3a$

What is the area of a square one of whose sides is the following?
10. a **11.** $2a$ **12.** $3a$

What is the area of a circle whose radius is the following?
13. a **14.** $2a$ **15.** $3a$

SELF TEST

1. In the expression $3 \cdot x$, where x can be replaced by any number you wish, the letter x is called a ___?___.
2. When for every number you use to replace x you can find the particular corresponding number for y, then y is said to be a ___?___ of x.
3. When a symbol, such as a letter, represents only one number, then the symbol is called a ___?___.

Change the subject of the following formulas so that the letter in parentheses becomes the dependent variable:

4. $p = 2l + 2w$ (w) **5.** $C = 2\pi r$ (r)

6. $p = a + b + c$ (a) **7.** $A = P + Prt$ (r)

8. $ky - t = 7m$ (y) **9.** $5m + 7t = 3t - rm$ (m)

10. $\dfrac{4rst}{y} = 3$ (y) **11.** $V = \frac{1}{3}\pi r^2 h$ (h)

★   ## *The Degree of an Equation*

The **degree of an equation** is determined by the exponent of a variable. When an equation is expressed in the independent variable x and the independent variable x does not occur in a denominator of a fraction or under the radical sign, then the degree of the equation is the highest exponent of the independent variable x. For example, $y = 3x + 1$ is a first-degree equation because the highest exponent of x is 1. The equation $y = 4x^2 - 2x - 9$ is a second-degree equation because the highest exponent of x is 2.

Examples for Study

Study the following tables of values of x *and* y *for each of the three equations. Then see how the differences between successive values of* x *and* y *tell you the degree of an equation.*

1. $y = 3x + 2$ is a first-degree equation.

		1	1	1		1	
x	0	1	2	3		4	
y	2	5	8	11		14	
		3	3	3		3	

The differences between the successive values of x are equal to 1. The differences between the successive values of y are constant. This is typical of first-degree equations.

★ See page vii for explanation of use of starred material.

2. $y = 2x^2 + 1$ is a second-degree equation.

x	0	1	2	3	4
y	1	3	9	19	33

The differences between the successive values of y are not constant. The differences between the differences are constant, however.

3. $y = x^3 - 1$ is a third-degree equation.

x	0	1	2	3	4
y	-1	0	7	26	63

The differences between the successive values of y are not constant. The differences between the differences of the differences are constant, however.

PROBLEMS

Examine the following tables and determine the degree of each equation. Then, from the group of three equations under each table, select the equation which describes the function given in the table. Check the equation by substituting the values appearing in the table.

1.

a	0	1	2	3	4
b	1	5	9	13	17

a. $b = 4a + 1$
b. $b = a^2 + 1$
c. $b = a^3 - 1$

2.

n	1	2	3	4	5
m	4	7	12	19	28

a. $m = 3n + 1$
b. $m = n^2 + 3$
c. $m = n^3 - 1$

3.

a	0	1	2	3	4
p	1	7	13	19	25

a. $p = 6a + 1$
b. $p = a^2 + 1$
c. $p = a^3 - 1$

4.

c	0	3	6	9	12
d	3	5	7	9	11

a. $d = \frac{2}{3}c + 3$
b. $d = 2c^2 + 3$
c. $d = 2c^3 + 3$

5.

s	0	1	2	3	4
r	-1	1	15	53	127

a. $r = 2s - 1$
b. $r = 2s^2 - 1$
c. $r = 2s^3 - 1$

6.

x	0	1	2	3	4
y	4	5	12	31	68

a. $y = x + 4$
b. $y = 2x^2 + 4$
c. $y = x^3 + 4$

7.

x	0	2	4	6	8
y	8	10	16	26	40

a. $y = x + 8$
b. $y = \frac{1}{2}x^2 + 8$
c. $y = \frac{1}{2}x^3 + 8$

8.

x	0	2	4	6	8
y	-7	-1	5	11	17

a. $y = 3x - 7$
b. $y = 3x^2 - 7$
c. $y = 2x^3 - 7$

9.

x	0	4	8	12	16
y	-1	2	5	8	11

a. $y = \frac{3}{4}x - 1$
b. $y = \frac{3}{4}x^2 - 1$
c. $y = \frac{1}{4}x^3 - 1$

10.

x	0	1	2	3	4
y	0	0	4	18	48

a. $y = x - 1$
b. $y = x^2 - 1$
c. $y = x^3 - x^2$

11.

x	0	1	2	3	4
y	1	0	-1	-2	-3

a. $y = -x + 1$
b. $y = -x^2 + 1$
c. $y = -x^3 + 1$

12.

x	0	2	4	6	8
y	3	5	11	21	35

a. $y = x^2 + 3$
b. $y = \frac{1}{2}x^2 + 3$
c. $y = \frac{1}{2}x^3 + 3$

★ 13.

x	2	4	6	8	10
y	$\frac{1}{2}$	$1\frac{1}{2}$	$2\frac{1}{2}$	$3\frac{1}{2}$	$4\frac{1}{2}$

a. $y = \frac{1}{2}x - \frac{1}{2}$
b. $y = \frac{1}{2}x^2 + x$
c. $y = \frac{1}{8}x^3 - 1$

14.

x	0	1	2	3	4
y	$3\frac{1}{5}$	$4\frac{7}{10}$	$6\frac{7}{10}$	$9\frac{1}{5}$	$12\frac{1}{5}$

a. $y = 2x + 2\frac{7}{10}$
b. $y = \frac{1}{4}x^2 + \frac{5}{4}x + 3\frac{1}{5}$
c. $y = \frac{1}{3}x^3 + 7x + 4$

15.

x	0	1	2	3	4
y	1	5	31	109	269

a. $y = 15x + 1$
b. $y = x^2 + 100$
c. $y = 5x^3 - 4x^2 + 3x + 1$

16.

x	0.5	1.0	1.5	2.0	2.5
y	1.65	2.00	2.35	2.70	3.05

a. $y = 0.7x + 1.30$
b. $y = 0.6x^2 + 1.50$
c. $y = 0.2x^3 + 0.35$

158 *ALGEBRA: ITS BIG IDEAS AND BASIC SKILLS*

★ ## *Discovering Equations from Tables*

Now you are ready to study methods of discovering equations from the values of two related variables given in the form of a table. First you must try to determine the degree of an equation which describes the function. Then you will try to write the equation.

Examples for Study

1.

		1	1	1	1	
a	0	1	2	3	4	
b	2	7	12	17	22	
		5	5	5	5	

The differences between the successive values of b are the same. Therefore, this function may be described by a first-degree equation.

As a increases by 1, b increases by five times as much. Suppose you guess that the equation is

$$b = 5a$$

But when $a = 0$, $b = 2$. Thus, the value of b is 2 more than $5a$. It would appear, then, that the equation may be

$$b = 5a + 2$$

To see if this can be correct, substitute each of the values for a that appear in the table and compare the results obtained with the corresponding values for b. For example, if $a = 2$, $b = 5 \cdot 2 + 2$, or 12. This value checks with the one in the table. Check the remaining values.

2.

		3	3	3	
x	0	3	6	9	
y	4	6	8	10	
		2	2	2	

This function may be described by a first-degree equation.

As x increases by 3, y increases by 2. Therefore, y increases by $\frac{2}{3}$ as much as x. Consequently, you may guess that the equation is

$$y = \tfrac{2}{3}x$$

But when $x = 0$, $y = 4$. Therefore, the value of y is apparently 4 more than $\frac{2}{3}x$, or

$$y = \tfrac{2}{3}x + 4$$

Check this by substituting in this equation each value given for x in the table and by comparing the values you obtain for y with the values given in the table.

3.

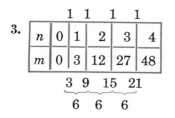

n	0	1	2	3	4
m	0	3	12	27	48

3 9 15 21

6   6   6

This function may be described by a second-degree equation.

You may write as your guess:

$$m = n^2$$

Then, when $n = 0$, $m = 0$. These values agree with those in the table. But when $n = 1$, $m = 1$. This does not agree with the table, for m should equal 3. Apparently, then, m is three times n^2, or

$$m = 3n^2$$

Check this equation by substituting each value of m given in the table.

PROBLEMS

For each of the following, write an equation which may describe the function:

1.

a	0	1	2	3	4
b	1	3	5	7	9

2.

x	0	1	2	3	4
y	4	6	8	10	12

3.

s	0	1	2	3	4
A	0	1	4	9	16

4.

e	0	1	2	3	4	5
V	0	1	8	27	64	125

5.

x	0	4	8	12	16	20
y	1	4	7	10	13	16

6.

x	0	1	2	3	4	5
y	6	7	8	9	10	11

7.

t	1	2	3	4	5
d	40	80	120	160	200

8.

x	0	1	2	3	4	5
y	0	5	20	45	80	125

Galileo, an Italian philosopher and scientist, discovered the laws of falling bodies by allowing balls to roll down an inclined plank. He collected data on the distance the balls traveled and the time they required for descending the distance. Then from the data similar to those given in the two tables for Problems 9 and 10, he formulated the laws of freely falling bodies.

Examine the tables and see if you can write these laws in the form of equations. v stands for the velocity in feet per second, t for the time in seconds, and s for the total distance in feet.

9.

t	0	1	2	3	4
v	0	32	64	96	128

10.

t	0	1	2	3	4
s	0	16	64	144	256

Ratio and Proportion

There are two ways of comparing two numbers. You can say by how much one number is greater than another, or you can say how many times as great one number is as another.

In answer to the question "By how much is one number greater than another?" you find the difference between the two numbers. In answer to the question "How many times as great is one number as another?" you find the quotient.

A new car owner generally wishes to check his gasoline mileage as soon as possible. If one owner finds that he gets 20 miles to the gallon, while his neighbor gets 16 miles to the gallon, the comparison between the distances traveled for each gallon of gasoline used is 20 to 16. For every 5 miles that he travels, his neighbor can travel 4 miles on the same amount of gasoline.

If during the summer vacation George earned twice as much as Joe —that is, if for every $2 earned by George, Joe earned $1—the comparison is 2 to 1.

Comparison made by division, like the comparisons above, is called a "ratio." The **ratio of two quantities** is the quotient of their two measures when the measures are in the same unit. The **ratio of two numbers** is their quotient.

FUNCTIONS **161**

The ratio of a to b can be written in three different ways:

$$a : b \qquad a \div b \qquad \frac{a}{b}$$

Each of the expressions above means the same thing. A ratio is most commonly written in the form of a fraction.

In writing ratios, it is important to remember that the numerator and the denominator of the fraction must be expressed in the same unit. For example, you would write the ratio of 2 feet to 6 inches as $\frac{24}{6}$.

A ratio, as stated above, is the quotient of two numbers. A **proportion** is an expression that two ratios are equal. Thus, $\frac{3}{4}$ and $\frac{6}{8}$ are ratios, and $\frac{3}{4} = \frac{6}{8}$ is a proportion. $\frac{3}{5} = \frac{x}{10}$ is also a proportion.

Examples for Study

1. Find two numbers whose sum is 35 and whose ratio is 3 to 4.

SOLUTION: Let $3x = $ the smaller number

Then $4x = $ the larger number, because $\frac{3x}{4x} = \frac{3}{4}$

The sum of the two numbers is 35.
Therefore, the equation is: $\quad 3x + 4x = 35$
Solving: $\qquad\qquad\qquad\qquad 7x = 35$
$\qquad\qquad\qquad\qquad\qquad\quad x = 5$
Thus, the smaller number is 15 and the larger number is 20.

CHECK: $15 + 20 = 35 \quad$ and $\quad \frac{15}{20} = \frac{3}{4}$

2. One of the United States Air Force patrol bombers has a range of 6000 miles. If on a test flight it flew 1240 miles in 2.3 hours, how long would it take the bomber to travel 6000 miles at the same speed?

SOLUTION: Writing as a proportion:

$$\frac{\text{Miles in the first case}}{\text{Miles in the second case}} = \frac{\text{time in the first case}}{\text{time in the second case}}$$

Let $t = $ number of hours required for the flight of 6000 miles. Then,

$$\frac{1240}{6000} = \frac{2.3}{t}$$

Multiplying both sides by $6000t$: $\quad 1240t = 13,800$
Dividing both sides by 1240: $\qquad\quad t = 11.13$ hours

PROBLEMS

Write each of the following as a fraction reduced to the lowest terms:

1. 9 to 12   2. 18 to 15   3. $45 : 55$
4. $14m : 21m$ 5. $24a : 36a^2$ 6. $x : x^2$

Express each of the following as a ratio written in the simplest form:
7. 26 weeks to 1 year   8. 2 dimes to 1 dollar
9. 3 yards to 2 feet   10. 6 months to 9 days

11. In each picture above, the ratio tells you the scale of the drawing. Using a ruler, find the real height of each of the birds and animals.
12. Study the following table and explain how the standing of a baseball team—that is, the ratio of games won—is determined.

Baseball Standing

Team	Games won	Games lost	Standing
St. Louis	36	27	0.571
Milwaukee	35	27	0.565
Brooklyn	33	26	0.559
Chicago	33	31	0.516
New York	32	31	0.508

13. Two numbers are in the ratio 7 to 3. Their difference is 40. Find the two numbers.
14. Three numbers have the ratio 3 : 4 : 5. This means that the ratio between the first two numbers is $\frac{3}{4}$ and the ratio between the second and third numbers is $\frac{4}{5}$. Their sum is 96. Find the three numbers.
15. The three angles of a triangle are in the ratio 1 : 3 : 5. The sum of the angles of a triangle is 180°. Find the number of degrees in each angle.
16. Common glass is composed of three ingredients: sand, soda ash, and borax in the ratio of 17 : 4 : 2. Find the number of pounds of sand in a 10-pound glass windowpane.
17. A tourist in estimating his gasoline cost for a trip found that he averaged 55 miles for each 3 gallons of gasoline consumed. On the same basis, how many gallons would he need for a trip of 2200 miles?

★ 18. On a certain farm a 40-acre plot of ground yielded 625 bushels of corn. After conservation measures were taken, the same plot yielded 1000 bushels. On the same basis, how many bushels of corn would 70 acres of soil yield before conservation measures were taken? After conservation measures were taken?

19. A plot of ground yielded 14 bushels of wheat per acre before conservation steps were taken and 22 bushels per acre 5 years after conservation work began. If a similar plot of ground is now producing 16 bushels per acre, about how many bushels per acre might be expected after proper care of the land for 5 years?

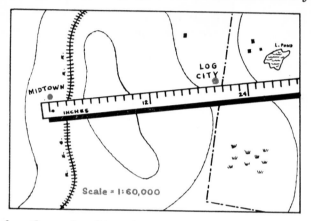

20. A map has the scale of 1 to 60,000. This means that 1 inch between two points on the map represents 60,000 inches between the actual two points on the earth. How far apart are two cities that are 20 inches apart on the map?

21. A cow feed mixture is made of 120 pounds of soybean-oil meal, 200 pounds of ground corn, 170 pounds of ground oats, 7 pounds of salt, and 3 pounds of bonemeal. How many pounds of each ingregredient would be needed to make 2800 pounds of the mixture?

SELF TEST

Solve and check:

1. $\dfrac{3}{x} = \dfrac{5}{8}$

2. $\dfrac{y}{7} = \dfrac{15}{19}$

3. $\dfrac{5}{8} = \dfrac{20}{x}$

Write each of the following as ratios:

4. 1 yard to 1 foot
5. 18 inches to 1 yard
6. 18 inches to 1 foot
7. 1 inch to 25 inches
8. 3 pounds to 4 ounces
9. 15 ounces to 1 pound

10. To make some candy, Mary used 2 cups of sugar to $\frac{1}{2}$ cup of water. How much water would she need for 5 cups of sugar?

11. A recipe calls for 5 tablespoons of flour to 2 tablespoons of butter. How much flour should be used with $3\frac{1}{2}$ tablespoons of butter?

164 *ALGEBRA: ITS BIG IDEAS AND BASIC SKILLS*

Direct and Inverse Variation

Suppose you are going to buy some candy bars at 5 cents each. Below is a table showing the relation between the number of candy bars you buy and the cost of the candy bars. Does the cost of the candy bars depend upon the number of bars you buy? If so, the cost of the candy bars is a function of the number of bars you buy.

Cost of candy in cents	5	10	15	20	25
Number of bars	1	2	3	4	5

Find the ratio of the cost of the candy bars to the number of bars in each case in the table. Do this by dividing the cost of the candy by the number of bars. Did you find this ratio to be constant, that is, always the same?

A **direct variation** between two variables x and y is one in which the ratio of one variable to the other is a constant. One variable is said to *vary directly as* or be *directly proportional to* the other. In the language of algebra, $\frac{x}{y} = c$ where c is called the **constant of variation.**

Now suppose you went into the candy store with exactly 50 cents. You have to choose among several kinds of candy bars. The table below shows the relation between the number of candy bars you can buy and the cost per bar.

Cost per bar in cents	1	2	5	10
Number of bars	50	25	10	5

Notice that the product of the two numbers in each case in the table is a constant, namely, 50.

An **inverse variation** between two variables x and y is one in which the product of x and y is a constant. One variable is said to *vary inversely as* or be *inversely proportional to* the other. In the language of algebra, $xy = c$ where c is the *constant of variation.*

Examples for Study

Write each of the following as an algebraic expression:

1. At a constant speed, the distance d an automobile travels is directly proportional to the time t it travels.

SOLUTION: The form of direct variation is $\frac{y}{x} = c$. So in the case of the automobile, $\frac{d}{t} = c$ or $d = ct$; c in this case is the constant speed of travel.

2. The time t it takes to do a certain job varies inversely as the number of men n working on the job.

SOLUTION: The form of inverse variation is $xy = c$. So in this case $tn = c$ or $t = \dfrac{c}{n}$.

3. The lift L of an airplane wing varies directly as the square of the speed s of the plane.

SOLUTION: $\dfrac{L}{s^2} = c$ or $L = cs^2$

4. The force of gravitation f between the sun and the earth varies inversely as the square of the distance d between their centers.

SOLUTION: $fd^2 = c$ or $f = \dfrac{c}{d^2}$

5. The price P of an article varies directly as the demand D for the article and inversely as the supply S of the article.

SOLUTION: $\dfrac{PS}{D} = c$ or $P = c \cdot \dfrac{D}{S}$

PROBLEMS

Write the following statements as algebraic expressions, using in each case c as the constant of variation:

1. The pressure P of the air in a tire pump varies inversely as the volume V of the air, provided the temperature remains constant.
2. The amount of stretch e of a spring varies directly as the stretching force f.
3. The pressure p on your body under the water varies directly with the depth d.
4. The distance s through which a freely falling body passes varies directly as the square of the time t.
5. The volume V of a cube is directly proportional to the third power of the length of the edge e.
6. The number of revolutions N of a gear is inversely proportional to the radius r of the gear.
7. The distance d necessary to stop a car once the brakes have been applied varies directly as the square of the speed s of the car.

★ 8. The strength s of a wooden rectangular beam varies directly as the cross-sectional area A and inversely as the distance d between its points of support.
9. The illumination I on the page of a book under an electric light varies directly as the wattage w of the light bulb and inversely as the square of the distance d between the book and the bulb.

Examples for Study

Change the following algebraic expressions of variation into word expressions:

1. $RI = c$

SOLUTION: R varies inversely as I. c is the constant of variation.

2. $d = \dfrac{m}{v}$

SOLUTION: d varies directly as m and inversely as v.

Change the following algebraic expressions of variation into word expressions:

10. $C = \pi d$ 11. $V = \frac{4}{3}\pi r^3$ 12. $I = \dfrac{c}{d^2}$

13. $pr = c$ 14. $\dfrac{R}{E} = c$ 15. $M = 25.4i$

SUMMARY OF IMPORTANT THINGS TO REMEMBER

1. Words and Expressions

constant	independent variable
constant of variation	inverse variation
degree of an equation	proportion
dependent variable	range
direct variation	ratio of two numbers
domain	ratio of two quantities
function	variable

2. Understandings

A variable is a symbol, usually a letter, that can be replaced by any one of a set of numbers.

A function is a set of ordered pairs of numbers such that for every first number in an ordered pair there is one and only one second number.

Functions can be described by means of equations, tables, or verbal rules.

Ratio and proportion are very useful in solving problems.

3. Skills

You should be able to:

Tell from a table or formula how a change in the independent variable affects the dependent variable.

Change the subject of a formula.

Set up and solve a proportion.

PROBLEMS ON YOUR AIMS

YOUR AIM ☞ **To learn what a function is and to learn ways of expressing functions.**

Which of the following situations describe a function?
1. A formula that shows how to find the number of ounces a book weighs, given the number of pages in the book.
2. Two sets of numbers: one set consisting of numbers of desks in each room in the school; the other set consisting of numbers of problems in arithmetic each pupil works one day.
3. A table that shows how much it costs to mail a parcel-post package if you know its weight.
4. A table that shows the temperature for every hour of the day.

In each of the following, identify the numbers which would be represented by a variable and the numbers which would be represented by a constant:
5. The number of pages in a certain book
6. The number of pages in the books of a library
7. The number of people in a classroom at a certain time

Make a table of values for each of the following functions:
8. The value of $2x - 5$ when x takes on whole-numbered values from $x = -3$ to $x = +3$.
9. The value of $x^2 - x + 3$ when x takes on whole-numbered values from $x = 0$ to $x = 5$.

Rewrite each of the following so that x is the dependent variable:

10. $y = 3x - 6$ 11. $y = \dfrac{2x}{3} + 8$ 12. $y = \frac{1}{2}x$

YOUR AIM ☞ **To learn to use algebraic symbols in expressing various mathematical relationships.**

a. The area of a square equals the square of one side.

b. $A = s^2$

c.

s	$\frac{1}{2}$	1	$1\frac{1}{2}$	2	$2\frac{1}{2}$	3	$3\frac{1}{2}$	4
A	$\frac{1}{4}$	1	$2\frac{1}{4}$	4	$6\frac{1}{4}$	9	$12\frac{1}{4}$	16

1. Between what two quantities do **a**, **b**, and **c** above express a relationship?

168 *ALGEBRA: ITS BIG IDEAS AND BASIC SKILLS*

2. Which of **a**, **b**, and **c**, on page 168, is the easiest and simplest to write?
3. When would table **c** be convenient to use?
4. When would table **c** be inconvenient to use?
5. Would it be practical to make a table large enough to contain areas of squares with sides of all possible lengths? Explain.
6. Name some tables of related numbers that are of practical value.
7. Rewrite the following in its simplest and most useful form: The volume of a cubical block is equal to the cube of the length of one of its edges.

YOUR AIM 👉 **To learn the meaning of direct variation and inverse variation.**

Read each of the following statements and tell whether it describes (1) direct variation, (2) inverse variation, (3) either direct or inverse variation, or (4) undetermined variation:
1. The variation is an expression of relationship between two variables.
2. The indicated product of two variables is a constant.
3. The variation is defined in terms of a constant.
4. The indicated ratio of two variables is a constant.
5. One variable is equal to the other.

In the following equations x and y are variables and other letters are constants. For each equation state whether it describes (1) direct variation, (2) inverse variation, (3) both direct and inverse variation, or (4) neither direct nor inverse variation.

6. $xy = a$ 7. $x = y$ 8. $xy = 4$

9. $x = \dfrac{1}{y}$ 10. $2xy = 5$ 11. $4x = 3y$

12. $x + 5 = 7$ 13. $x^2 + 2x = 15$ 14. $\dfrac{x}{y} = 15a$

15. Which of the following tables expresses a direct variation? An inverse variation? Neither a direct nor an inverse variation?

a.

x	2	4	6	8	10
y	4	8	12	16	20

b.

x	3	4	8	12	24
y	8	6	3	2	1

c.

x	5	9	6	7	4	3
y	9	8	7	6	5	4

VALUABLE SKILLS PRACTICE

1. Copy the following table. Do the operations indicated at the top of each column for the different values of a and b listed in the first two columns. Write the answers in the proper spaces of your table. The sum of your answers in the last column should be 19.9.

a	b	$M = a + b$	$N = a - b$	$P = ab$	$Q = \dfrac{a}{b}$	$M + N + PQ$
-3	-4	?	?	?	?	?
2	$-1\frac{1}{2}$	?	?	?	?	?
-4	2.5	?	?	?	?	?
0.1	-0.1	?	?	?	?	?
0.3	0.3	?	?	?	?	?
					Total	19.9

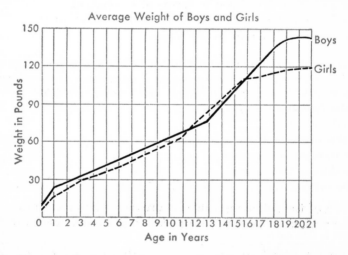

Average Weight of Boys and Girls

Study the line graph above and answer the following questions:

2. Is the average weight for boys under ten years of age more or less than the average weight for girls under ten years of age?
3. During which years is the average weight of girls higher than the average weight of boys?
4. What is the average weight of sixteen-year-old girls?
5. During which years does the average weight of boys exceed the average weight of girls?

170 *ALGEBRA: ITS BIG IDEAS AND BASIC SKILLS*

Define each of the following terms:
6. Numerator
7. Subtrahend
8. Quotient
9. Mixed number
10. Multiplier
11. Minuend
12. Denominator
13. Product
14. Addend
15. Dividend
16. Multiplicand
17. Improper fraction
18. The number 3 in $\frac{2}{3}$ is called the ___?___.
19. In $16 \div 8 = 2$, 2 is called the ___?___.
20. In $10 \times 5 = 50$, 50 is called the ___?___.
21. A number such as $3\frac{1}{2}$ is called a ___?___.
22. In $144 - 36 = 108$, 36 is called the ___?___.
23. In $9 + 4 = 13$, 4 and 9 are called ___?___.

Write the following in arabic numerals:
24. Nine thousand five
25. Three million sixty thousand thirty-one
26. Ten thousand four hundred thirty
27. One million one thousand one hundred

Do the operations required:
28. Add \$14.37, \$101.64, \$29.73, \$4.03.
29. Find the product of $4\frac{1}{2}$ and $6\frac{1}{4}$.
30. Subtract $2\frac{1}{2}$ from $3\frac{1}{3}$.
31. $\frac{1}{2} \div 2 = $ ___?___
32. $\frac{1}{3} - \frac{1}{5} = $ ___?___
33. $3 \div \frac{1}{3} = $ ___?___

CHAPTER TEST

1. The set of all (x, y) such that $y = 7x + 1$ is true is a ___?___.
2. In the formula $C = \pi d$, since π does not change in value, it is referred to as a ___?___.
3. In the formula $C = \pi d$, which letter is the dependent variable? The independent variable?
4. The sides of two squares are m and $4m$. What are their areas? What is the ratio of the area of the larger square to the area of the smaller square?
5. The sides of two cubes are n and $4n$. What are their volumes? What is the ratio of the volume of the larger cube to the volume of the smaller cube?

Rewrite each of the following so that x is the dependent variable:
6. $m = \dfrac{x}{n}$
7. $t = px$
8. $f = x + d$
9. $b = ax - c$
10. $d = \dfrac{1}{2}mx$
11. $q = \dfrac{p}{x}$
12. $g = \dfrac{3abx}{4}$
13. $k = \dfrac{mx + b}{a}$
14. $w = r(x - r)$

Solve:

15. A 5-ounce bottle of tincture of iodine contains 0.25 ounces of iodine. How much iodine is there in a bottle containing 12 ounces of the tincture?

16. A car consumes about 6 gallons of gasoline in traveling 115 miles. At the same rate, how many gallons will be needed for a 245-mile trip?

17. A jet plane traveled 1200 miles in $2\frac{1}{2}$ hours. At this rate of speed, how far would the plane travel in $3\frac{1}{2}$ hours?

18. 250 grams of potassium chlorate produce 98 grams of oxygen. On the same basis, how many grams of oxygen, to the nearest tenth of a gram, could be obtained from 80 grams of the chemical potassium chlorate?

19. A piece of wrought iron 14 feet long was bent to form a rectangle whose length and width are in the ratio of 3 to 2. What are the length and the width of the rectangle?

20. Divide 150 into two numbers so that the ratio of the smaller number to the larger number is 3 to 7.

21. The lengths of the adjacent sides of a rectangle are in the ratio of 5 to 6. Find the dimensions of the rectangle if its perimeter is 66 inches.

22. A girl scout troop hiked 6 miles in $2\frac{1}{4}$ hours. At this rate, how long will it take the troop to hike $9\frac{1}{2}$ miles?

23. It took 8 men 6 hours to do a piece of work. At this rate, how long would it take 10 men to do the job?

24. The lengths of the sides of a triangle are in the ratio $1\frac{1}{2} : 2\frac{1}{2} : 3$. Find the sides of the triangle if its perimeter is 42 inches.

25. The side of a square and the length of a rectangle are in the ratio $2 : 3$. The width of the rectangle is 6 inches. The perimeters of the square and the rectangle are equal. Find the side of the square and the length of the rectangle.

26. The number of revolutions a wheel makes in rolling a given distance varies inversely as the diameter of the wheel. If a wheel 3 feet in diameter makes 42 revolutions in rolling a certain distance, how many revolutions will a wheel 4 feet in diameter make in rolling the same distance?

27. A wheel 6 inches in diameter makes 84 revolutions in rolling a certain distance. How many revolutions will a wheel 9 inches in diameter make in rolling the same distance?

28. A wheel 10 centimeters in diameter makes 28 revolutions in rolling a given distance. Find the diameter of a wheel that makes twice as many revolutions in rolling the same distance.

CUMULATIVE REVIEW PROBLEMS

WORKING WITH ALGEBRAIC EXPRESSIONS

Write each of the following expressions in the simplest form:

1. $b + b + b$
2. bbb
3. $2a + 3a - a$
4. $w - y + y - 2w$
5. $(-2a)(-3ab)(-b)$
6. $aaa + bbb$
7. $16 - x - 8 - xy + 3x$
8. $3a + 2ab - 2a - ab$
9. $a^2 \cdot a^3 \cdot a^4$
10. $2(a - 3) - 3(a - 2)$
11. $4a + a^2 + 3a$
12. $xxxyy$
13. $4(m + n) + m + n$
14. $(-3x)(-3x)$
15. $3b + 4b - b$
16. $6a^2 \div 3a$

Change each of the following into an algebraic expression:

17. a raised to the b power.
18. x diminished by y.
19. The sum of $2a$ and $3b$.
20. ab times the quantity a plus b.
21. The number of cents in $5d$ dimes.
22. The number of days in $2w$ weeks.
23. Eight times m added to the product of $3a$ and $2a$.
24. x increased by x square.
25. The number of inches in $2f$ feet and $3y$ yards.
26. The number of ounces in m pounds.
27. The number of quarters in c cents.
28. The number of cents in q quarters.
29. Five less than twice John's age.
30. Three added to the quotient of a and b.

Do the indicated operations and express each answer in the simplest form:

31. $(-3a)^2 (-2a)^3$
32. $\dfrac{12x^4}{5} \div \dfrac{6x^2}{10}$
33. $(-1)^4 (a - 8)$
34. $5(x - 3) - 3(x - 5)$
35. $5^5 - 5^3$
36. $(x - 4)(x + 5)$
37. $(a - 3)(2a - 7)$
38. $(4x - 5)(3x - 1)$
39. $(-\frac{1}{4}a)^3(-8a)^2$
40. $-2x(x - 3) - 5x(-x + 1)$
41. $(6x - 1)^2$
42. $(a + 2)(a^2 - 2a + 4)$
43. $(2x - 3)(3x^2 + x - 4)$
44. $(x^2 - 11x + 30) \div (x - 5)$
45. $(2a^2 - a - 1) \div (a - 1)$
46. $(42x^2 + 23x - 10) \div (6x + 5)$
47. $10am(am - 2) - a^2m(5m - 2)$
48. $\frac{3}{2}(6x - 8) + \frac{5}{4}(8x - 4)$
49. $-4[8a - 5(2 - a)]$
50. $6[2(x - 2)] - [9(x - 3)]$
51. $-8[5x - (3 + 2x)]$
52. $3[(x - y) + y]$
53. $-[-3(x - 5) + 16]$
54. $6[4 - 3(-x)]$

FUNCTIONS **173**

PERFORMING THE FUNDAMENTAL OPERATIONS

Do the indicated operations:

1. $(-16) - (-8)$
2. $(-5) + (-10)$
3. $(-12) - (-12)$
4. $(20) \div (-15)$
5. $(9)(-4) - (10)(2)$
6. $(-6)(-2) - (-3)$
7. $(-1)(25) \div (-5)$
8. $(-1 - 4)(-8 - 2)$
9. $(-3)(-8) \div (-12)$
10. $(16 - 8)(-5) \div (7 - 5)$

11. Find the average of $-18, 16, -12, -6, 10$.
12. Divide the sum of -15 and $+45$ by -6.
13. From $+2$ subtract -22 and divide the result by 6.
14. Divide the product of -10 and -6 by the sum of -18 and $+24$.
15. What is the sum of 5 and 5? The difference? The product? The quotient?
16. What is the sum of a and a? The difference? The product? The quotient?
17. Name two factors whose product is -10.
18. If -3 is one factor of 12, what is the other factor?
19. If -7 is one factor of -21, what is the other factor?
20. From $+15$ subtract the sum of -8 and -7.

SOLVING EQUATIONS

Solve and check:

1. $4x - 10 = x - 7$
2. $38 - x - 11 = 2x + 3$
3. $0 = 4x - 15$
4. $-8 = -3x - 6 + x$
5. $4 + 3(2x - 1) = 17$
6. $9 = 9x$
7. $\frac{3}{4}x - 15 = 5$
8. $1.5x = 6$
9. $5(x - 3) = 25$
10. $-3(x - 6) = 12$
11. $3x - 40 = 8x + 40$
12. $\frac{2}{5}x - 9 = 21$
13. $\frac{1}{2} - \frac{1}{4}x = \frac{3}{4} - \frac{1}{2}x$
14. $50 - 2(x - 8) = 40 + (x + 5)$
15. $\frac{11x}{6} = 121$
16. $\frac{5x}{3} - \frac{9x}{2} = 17$
17. $\frac{13}{4} - \frac{2x}{3} = 1$
18. $16 - (2x - 6) = 14 - 6x$
19. $3.2x + 3.8 - x = 25.8$
20. $160 - 12(4x - 10) = 2(50 + x)$
21. $\frac{18}{x} + \frac{1}{4} = 1$
22. $\frac{4 - x}{5} - \frac{x}{2} = \frac{2x - 5}{5}$
23. $\frac{15 - x}{3} - \frac{x}{2} = \frac{-5}{3}$
24. $\frac{5}{x} + \frac{1}{4} = 1\frac{1}{2}$
25. $\frac{3}{x} - \frac{2}{x} = \frac{1}{8}$
26. $\frac{x}{8} + \frac{x}{6} = \frac{14}{3}$
27. $14.5 - 1.1(x - 5) = 2.5(4 - 0.4x)$

174 *ALGEBRA: ITS BIG IDEAS AND BASIC SKILLS*

SOLVING VERBAL PROBLEMS

1. If $2a - 3$ is the side of a square, find the perimeter and the area of the square.
2. If w is the width of a rectangle in inches and the length is 5 inches less than twice the width, find the perimeter and the area.
3. If the side of the smaller of two squares is $x - 1$ units in length and the side of the larger square is $x + 1$ units, by how much does the perimeter of the larger square exceed the perimeter of the smaller? By how much does the area of the larger square exceed the area of the smaller?
4. If the expressions $2a + 5$, $3a - 11$, and $a - 6$ stand for three numbers, find the average of the numbers.
5. The formula for showing the relation between Fahrenheit and centigrade thermometer scales is $F = \frac{9}{5}C + 32$. Find the temperature that would read the same on either scale.
6. Ray and Bob earned $54. They agreed to divide the money on a 3-to-2 ratio with Ray getting the larger portion. How much did each receive?
7. The sizes of the angles of a triangle are in the ratio $2 : 3 : 4$. How many degrees has each angle?
8. A piece of lumber 70 inches in length was cut into two parts in the ratio of 5 to 9. Find the lengths of each part.
9. One inch on a map used by pilots stands for 15.9 miles on the ground. The distance between two cities on this map is $9\frac{1}{2}$ inches. How far apart are the cities?
10. The resistance of a piece of wire to the passage of an electric current varies directly as the length of the wire. If a wire 420 feet long has a resistance of 1.1 units, what will be the resistance of 1000 feet of the same wire?
11. A car dealer has 50 cars in his used-car lot. In the past he sold, on the average, 3 new cars for every 7 used cars. On this basis, how many new cars can he expect to sell by the time he has sold the 50 used cars?
12. During his first semester of school, Jim spent 7.7 times as much for lunches as for books. The total expense for both was $92.28. How much did he spend for each?
13. Mr. Burrows' car used 6 gallons of gasoline in going 115 miles. At this rate, how many gallons will be needed to go 245 miles?
14. In $8\frac{1}{2}$ weeks the Shaws used 293 gallons of oil to heat their home. At this rate, how many gallons will the Shaws use in 20 weeks?
15. One meter is equal to 39.37 inches. A distance of 20.5 inches is equal to how many meters?
16. An antifreeze solution for the radiator of an automobile is made by adding 6 quarts of antifreeze to 14 quarts of water. How much antifreeze should be added to 21 quarts of water?

AGRICULTURAL SPECIALISTS USE ALGEBRA

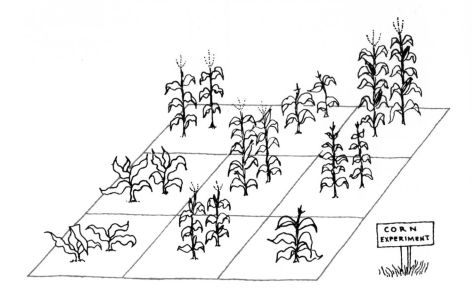

A visitor to a state agricultural experiment station saw a plot of ground similar to that shown in the above drawing. A research worker was trying to find which variety of corn will give the best yields. In analyzing results, research workers often use algebra. For example, the following table might be prepared in connection with the statistical study of the experiment shown in the drawing.

Source	Degrees of freedom
Varieties	$r - 1$
Rows	$r - 1$
Columns	$r - 1$
Residual	$(r - 1)(r - 2)$
Total	$r^2 - 1$

Check the sum of the expressions in the second column to see if the sum is $r^2 - 1$.

176 *ALGEBRA: ITS BIG IDEAS AND BASIC SKILLS*

BIG IDEAS	EQUATION
	FUNCTION
	GRAPH
BASIC SKILLS	Using and interpreting symbols of algebra
	Evaluating algebraic expressions
	Drawing and reading graphs

CHAPTER **7** *Graphical Representation of Algebraic Functions*

IN CHAPTER 6 you learned the meaning of function. It is often convenient to represent a function in the form of a graph. In your previous courses in mathematics you have worked with circle graphs, bar graphs, and line graphs. You know that graphs are widely used in magazines and newspapers. The phrase **to graph** means "to write," "to paint," or "to draw." All types of graphs are used to show a picture. In this chapter you will learn to "draw a picture" of algebraic functions.

YOUR AIM

1. **To learn how to locate in a plane a point which corresponds to a given pair of numbers.**

2. **To learn how to graph an algebraic function.**

3. **To learn what is meant by the slope of a line.**

4. **To learn how to find the equation of a line.**

177

Locating Points

Pupils in a mathematics class at Franklin High School made a study of the automobile accidents that took place in Franklin during a certain period. They made a street map of the city, like the one below, on which they showed the location of each accident.

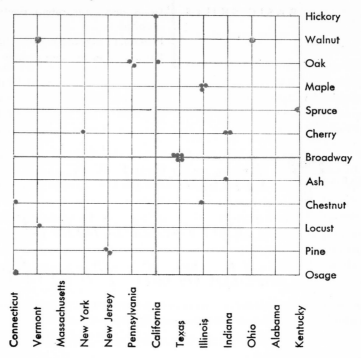

To make the job of locating the accidents on the map easier, Cathy, one of the pupils, suggested using Broadway and California Street as reference lines and locating the accidents from those streets. She said, "We could call the location of the accident that happened yesterday at Indiana and Cherry Streets (3, 1), because Cherry Street is three blocks east of California and one block north of Broadway."

"But how will we know that (3, 1) means Indiana and Cherry?" asked Harry. "Those numbers could also stand for the point where Indiana crosses Ash or where New York crosses Cherry or Ash."

To solve the problem that Harry brought up, the pupils decided to:

(1) Let the first number—for example, the 3 in (3, 1)—mean the distance east or west of California Street and to use the letter E or W to show direction.

(2) Let the second number—that is, the 1 in (3, 1)—mean the distance north or south of Broadway and to use the letter N or S to show direction. For example, ($E3$, $N1$) would be the corner of Indiana and Cherry Streets.

178 *ALGEBRA: ITS BIG IDEAS AND BASIC SKILLS*

Examples for Study

1. The accident at Indiana and Cherry was labeled $(E3, N1)$.
2. The accident at New Jersey and Pine was labeled $(W2, S4)$.
3. The accident at California and Oak was labeled $(0, N4)$.

PROBLEMS

Use the system the class worked out and label the following points where accidents occurred:

1. Ohio and Walnut
2. Kentucky and Spruce
3. Indiana and Ash
4. Vermont and Walnut
5. Illinois and Chestnut
6. Pennsylvania and Oak
7. Connecticut and Osage
8. New York and Cherry
9. California and Hickory
10. Texas and Broadway

After trying their new system, the pupils decided that it would be better to use signed numbers rather than E, W, N, and S to show direction. They used *positive numbers* to show distances *east* of California Street and *negative numbers* to show distances *west* of California Street. Distances *north* of Broadway were shown by *positive numbers* and distances *south* of Broadway by *negative numbers*. So they now labeled the accident at Indiana and Cherry Streets $(+3, +1)$ rather than $(E3, N1)$. The accident at New Jersey and Pine was labeled $(-2, -4)$ rather than $(W2, (S4)$.

11. Use positive and negative numbers to label the points where the accidents in Problems 1–10 happened.

Use positive and negative numbers to label the following street intersections:

12. Illinois and Spruce
13. Alabama and Oak
14. New York and Hickory
15. New Jersey and Maple
16. Vermont and Chestnut
17. Kentucky and Walnut
18. Ohio and Locust
19. Texas and Ash
20. California and Pine
21. Indiana and Broadway

What are the street intersections for each of the following pairs of numbers?

22. $(3, 5)$
23. $(6, 2)$
24. $(1, -4)$
25. $(-1, -1)$
26. $(-5, 3)$
27. $(-4, -4)$
28. $(1, 1)$
29. $(-4, 0)$
30. $(2, 0)$
31. $(0, 4)$
32. $(0, 0)$
33. $(0, 1)$

★ 34. Draw a street map for the neighborhood around your school. Choose two intersecting streets near your school as the reference streets. Label that intersection $(0, 0)$. Consider north and east as positive directions, and south and west as negative directions. Locate some places on your map and label them by the same system you used in Problems 12–21.

Coordinate Axes

The method for locating points used in mathematics is like the method the pupils used in locating street intersections. Instead of main streets, mathematicians use a pair of perpendicular lines called **coordinate axes.** The horizontal line is called the *x*-**axis** and the vertical line is called the *y*-**axis.** The point of intersection of the two lines is called the **origin.**

Notice that the two axes divide the plane into four parts called

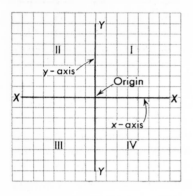

quadrants. The upper right-hand quadrant is considered the *first quadrant;* the upper left-hand quadrant is considered the *second quadrant;* the lower left-hand quadrant is considered the *third quadrant;* and the lower right-hand quadrant is considered the *fourth quadrant* as marked in the drawing at the left.

Distances to the right of the y-axis and upward from the x-axis are considered positive. Distances to the left of the y-axis and downward from the x-axis are considered negative.

The distance of any point from the y-axis along or parallel to the x-axis is called its x-**distance** or **abscissa.** The distance of any point from the x-axis along or parallel to the y-axis is called its y-**distance** or **ordinate.** These two distances for any point are called its **coordinates.**

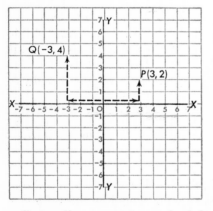

In the graph at the left, the coordinates of point P are $+3$ and $+2$. Therefore, the point is labeled (3,2). Note that the first number is the abscissa, or the x-distance, and that the second number is the ordinate, or the y-distance. The point Q has the x-distance -3 and the y-distance $+4$. Therefore, it is labeled $(-3, 4)$. It is agreed that the first number always denotes the x-distance and that the second number always denotes the y-distance.

Generally, a point may be labeled (x, y). The numbers represented by x and y are called the "coordinates of the point." The point representing the number pair (x, y) is called the "graph of (x, y)." For example, in the number pair $(-3, 4)$ the numbers -3 and 4 are the

180 *ALGEBRA: ITS BIG IDEAS AND BASIC SKILLS*

coordinates of the point, and the point corresponding to the number pair $(-3, 4)$ is called the "graph of $(-3, 4)$." Locating a point on the coordinate axes is called "plotting the point."

PROBLEMS

1. Using positive and negative numbers, give the coordinates of points A, B, C, D, E, and F in the graph at the right.

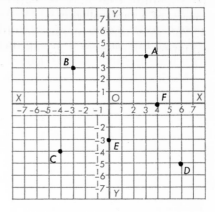

Draw a pair of coordinate axes and graph each of the following:

2. $(-4, 0)$ 3. $(6, 2)$
4. $(4, 0)$ 5. $(-6, 2)$
6. $(6, -2)$ 7. $(2, 6)$
8. $(-6, -2)$ 9. $(-2, -6)$
10. $(-2, 6)$ 11. $(0, 4)$
12. $(2, -6)$ 13. $(0, -4)$

In which quadrant does each of the following points fall?
14. $(-6, 1)$ 15. $(1, 2)$ 16. $(-4, -4)$ 17. $(6, -3)$
18. $(-5, +5)$ 19. $(17, 1)$ 20. $(38, -365)$ 21. $(16, -16)$

22. What is true of the graph of each of the following pairs of numbers: $(0, 1)$, $(0, 7)$, $(0, -5)$, $(0, +2)$?
23. If a point is on the y-axis, what is its x-distance, or abscissa?
24. If a point is on the x-axis, what is its y-distance, or ordinate?
25. What are the coordinates of the vertices of triangle ABC in the graph at the right?

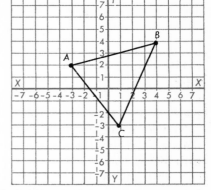

26. On graph paper draw rectangle $ABCD$ whose vertices are: A $(6, 3)$, B $(6, -3)$, C $(-4, 3)$, D $(-4, -3)$.
27. What are the coordinates of the origin on the coordinate axes?
28. What are the coordinates of a point on the x-axis four units to the right of the origin?
29. Draw a pair of axes and locate the points whose coordinates are given in the following table.

Point	A	B	C	D	E	F	G	H
x-distance	0	2	-2	-4	0	5	-5	3
y-distance	-3	1	-7	5	4	0	0	-4

Drawing a Graph from a Table of Values

In Chapter 6 you learned that a function which is formed according to a definite rule may be expressed by means of an equation or by means of a table of values. For example, if the sum of two numbers is 4, you may represent one number as x and the other as y. Then the equation expressing the relationship between the two numbers is:

$$x + y = 4$$

Or, as a table:

x	0	1	2	3	4
y	4	3	2	1	0

Graph A

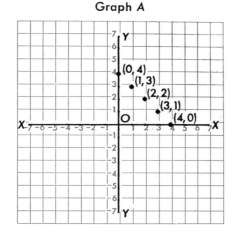

The points whose coordinates are given in the above table are shown on Graph A. When $x = 0$, $y = 4$, the point is (0, 4); when $x = 1$, $y = 3$, the point is (1, 3); and so on. Do the five points on the graph appear to be in a straight line?

Now let us make a table containing more than five pairs of numbers that satisfy the equation $x + y = 4$. We shall choose values for x with differences of $\frac{1}{2}$ from $x = 0$ to $x = 5$. We shall also choose values of x with differences of $\frac{1}{2}$ from $x = 0$ to $x = -3$. For each of these values of x the corresponding value of y is computed. The pairs of numbers that result from this computation are recorded in the table below.

x	0	$\frac{1}{2}$	1	$1\frac{1}{2}$	2	$2\frac{1}{2}$	3	$3\frac{1}{2}$	4	$4\frac{1}{2}$	5	$-\frac{1}{2}$	-1	$-1\frac{1}{2}$	-2	$-2\frac{1}{2}$	-3
y	4	$3\frac{1}{2}$	3	$2\frac{1}{2}$	2	$1\frac{1}{2}$	1	$\frac{1}{2}$	0	$-\frac{1}{2}$	-1	$4\frac{1}{2}$	5	$5\frac{1}{2}$	6	$6\frac{1}{2}$	7

The points whose coordinates are given in the larger table are plotted on Graph B. How does this graph compare with Graph A? In Graph B there are more points, and they are closer together.

If you were to make a still larger table of values by decreasing the interval between successive values of x and y, you would get a graph something like Graph C. The graph of all possible number pairs (x, y) when $x + y = 4$ is a straight line as shown in Graph D.

Graph B

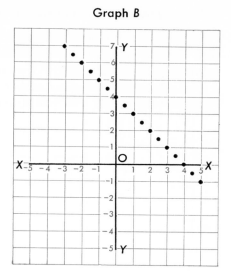

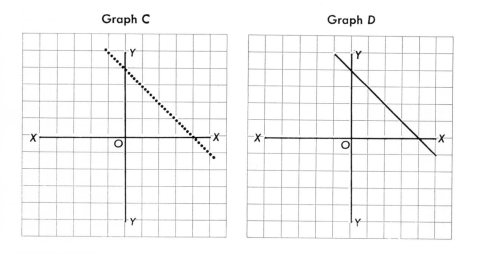

Graph C

Graph D

The equation $x + y = 4$ is a first-degree equation. If it were physically possible to draw the graph of every possible pair of numbers that satisfies this equation, you would find that the points graphed would form a straight line. For example, the pair of numbers $x = 1.8, y = 2.2$ satisfies the equation. The point $(1.8, 2.2)$ is also on the same line as shown in the above graph. So also is the point $(8\frac{1}{3}, -4\frac{1}{3})$.

The graphs of all first-degree equations are straight lines. For this reason, first-degree equations are often called **linear equations.**

PROBLEMS

Draw a pair of coordinate axes for each of the following tables of values and locate the points listed. Connect the points with a straight line.

1.

x	y
0	1
1	3
2	5
3	7
4	9

2.

x	y
-2	8
-1	6
0	4
1	2
2	0

3.

x	y
-4	10
-2	5
0	0
$+2$	-5
$+4$	-10

4.

x	y
-20	-11
-10	-7
0	-3
$+10$	$+1$
$+20$	$+5$

5.

x	y
0	0
-1	-1
-2	-2
1	1
4	4

6.

x	y
-2	6
-1	4
0	2
1	0
2	-2

7.

x	y
0	0
-1	3
-2	6
1	-3
2	-6

8.

x	y
0	1
2	2
-4	-1
-8	-3
6	4

★ *Copy and complete the table of values for each of the following equations and draw the graph of each equation:*

9. $y = 3x + 12$

x	y
0	?
-1	?
-2	?
3	?
2	?

10. $y = x + 8$

x	y
0	?
-2	?
3	?
6	?
8	?

11. $x + 2y = 8$

x	y
?	0
0	?
?	2
2	?
-2	?

12. $3x - 2y = 4$

x	y
0	?
?	0
2	?
?	4
-2	?

The Meaning of the Graph of an Equation

Copy and complete the table of values at the right for the equation $2x + y = 4$ whose graph is shown below.

x	0	2	3	-1
y	?	?	?	?

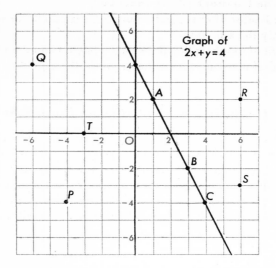

Graph of $2x+y=4$

PROBLEMS

1. What are the coordinates of points A, B, and C in the graph above?
2. Substitute each of the pairs of numbers in your table in the equation $2x + y = 4$. Does each pair of numbers satisfy the equation?
3. Select any other point on the graph, determine its coordinates, and substitute them in the equation. What conclusion can you draw concerning the coordinates of any point that lies on the graph of the equation $2x + y = 4$?
4. Find the coordinates of points P, Q, R, S, and T which are not on the graph of the equation $2x + y = 4$. Substitute these coordinates in the equation and see if they satisfy the equation. What conclusion can you draw about the coordinates of points which are not on the graph of the equation $2x + y = 4$? Check your conclusion.
5. Find four or more pairs of numbers, such as $(2, 1)$, $(-3, -2)$, and so on, that do not satisfy the equation $2x + y = 4$. See if the points which are graphs of these pairs of numbers fall on the graph of this equation. What conclusion can you draw about the graphs of pairs of numbers which do not satisfy the equation $2x + y = 4$? Check your conclusion.

GRAPHICAL REPRESENTATION **185**

We can summarize some important ideas about the graphs of equations as follows:

1. **The coordinates of every point on the graph of an equation satisfy the equation.**
2. **Every pair of numbers that satisfies an equation determines a point that lies on the graph of the equation.**
3. **The coordinates of every point not on the graph of an equation do not satisfy the equation.**
4. **Every pair of numbers that does not satisfy an equation determines a point that does not lie on the graph of the equation.**

Graphing a First-degree Equation

It is easy to see that, given two points, there is only one line going through these two points. Therefore, only two points are needed to graph a first-degree equation. Your graph is more apt to be accurate if the two points chosen are as far apart as convenient. It is a good idea to use a third point as a check. If the third point does not fall on the line determined by the two other points, you will know that you have made an error.

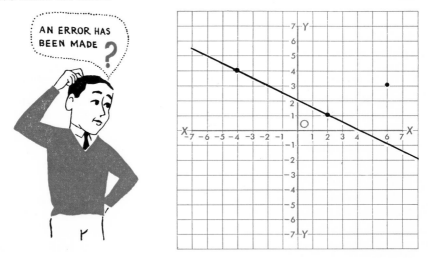

PROBLEMS

Plot at least three points in graphing each of the following equations. Before plotting the points, make a table like the tables on page 182.

1. $y = 4x - 8$
2. $y = \frac{1}{2}x + 1$
3. $y = -2x + 6$
4. $x + y = 2$
5. $x - y = 2$
6. $x + 3y = 6$

7. $2x + y = 6$ 8. $x + 3y = 0$
9. $2x - 3y = 12$ 10. $\frac{1}{4}x - \frac{1}{2}y = 0$
11. $x = 3y - 6$ 12. $2x = 3y$
13. $5x + y = 0$ 14. $5x - y = 0$
15. $x + 2y = 2$ 16. $x + 2y = -4$

17. What is the ordinate, or the y-distance, for any point on line AB in the graph at the right? The equation for this line is $y = 5$.

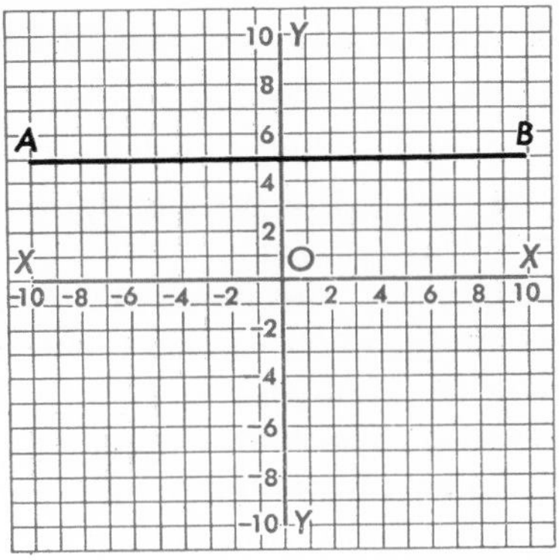

DO YOU SEE? The equation for any line parallel to the x-axis is $y = b$, where b is the y-intercept.

Draw the graph of each of the following equations:

18. $y = 6$ 19. $y = -5$
20. $y = 8$ 21. $y = -3$
22. $y = 10$ 23. $y = 0$

24. What is the abscissa, or the x-distance, for any point on the line CD in the graph at the right? The equation for this line is $x = 4$.

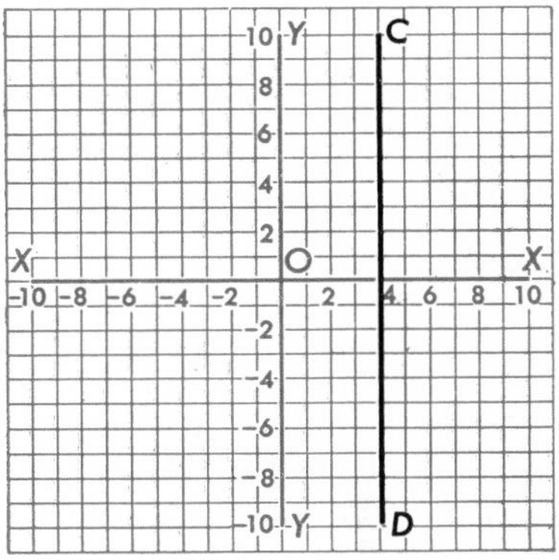

DO YOU SEE? The equation for any line parallel to the y-axis is $x = c$, where c is the x-intercept.

Draw a graph of each of the following equations:
25. $x = 10$ 26. $x = 4$ 27. $x = -3$
28. $x = 7$ 29. $x = -6$ 30. $x = 0$

Graph each of the following equations:
31. $\frac{3}{4}x - y = 0$ 32. $\frac{3}{4}x + y = 0$ 33. $3x - 2y = 6$
34. $3x - 2y = -6$ 35. $0.6y = 1.8x + 2.5$ 36. $y = 0.15$

37. If x stands for any length measured in feet and y stands for the same length measured in yards, then $y = \dfrac{x}{3}$. Draw the graph of this equation.

GRAPHICAL REPRESENTATION **187**

★ *Graphing Inequations*

A sentence which contains one or more variables and an inequality symbol is called an **inequation**. For example, $x > y - 3$, $1 + x < 7$, and $x + y > 4$ are inequations.

When numbers are substituted for the variable or variables in an inequation, the resulting statement may be either true or false. For example, when $(3, 9)$ is substituted for x and y in $x + y > 4$, the resulting statement is true. When $(2, 1)$ is substituted, however, the resulting statement is false.

To graph the inequation $x + y > 4$, we would need to draw on the graph paper all the points whose coordinates would make $x + y > 4$ a true statement.

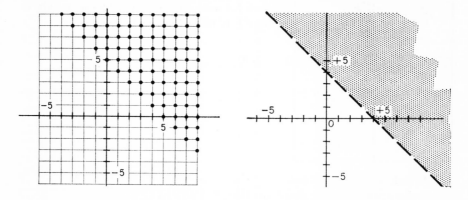

Several points whose coordinates satisfy (make true) the inequation $x + y > 4$ are graphed in the drawing on the left. Check to see that they do. The points so plotted have pairs of integers for coordinates, but fractions or decimals could also be used. For example, the coordinates $(4.1, 0.2)$ would also make $x + y > 4$ a true statement. To plot all possible points whose coordinates make $x + y > 4$ true, we would have to shade in the entire surface above the line through the points $(0, 4)$ and $(4, 0)$, as shown in the drawing on the right. The drawing on the right then is the graph of $x + y > 4$.

PROBLEMS

1. Would the exact point $x = 6$ be on the graph of $1 + x > 7$?
2. Would the point $x = 6.00000001$ be on the graph of $1 + x > 7$?
3. Would the points $(0, 4)$ and $(4, 0)$ be on the graph of $x + y > 4$?

Draw a graph of each of the following inequations:

4. $x + y > 1$ 5. $x + y > -5$ 6. $y > x + 4$
7. $x > y - 3$ 8. $2x + y > 4$ 9. $y - x > -3$
10. $x < y$ 11. $|x| + |y| > 4$ 12. $|x| > |y|$

188 *ALGEBRA: ITS BIG IDEAS AND BASIC SKILLS*

Graphs Picture Functions

In Chapter 6 you studied the idea of function. You learned that a table, a formula, and a verbal statement can be used to show a relation between two variables.

A graph can also be used to describe functions. The graph has the advantage over the other means of describing functions in that it gives you the general idea of the function at a glance.

When diving into the water, you feel pressure on your eardrums. The deeper you go, the greater is the pressure. Some of the depths and corresponding pressures are listed in the table below.

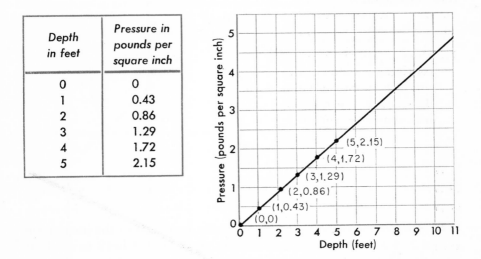

Depth in feet	Pressure in pounds per square inch
0	0
1	0.43
2	0.86
3	1.29
4	1.72
5	2.15

You can also picture this function between the pressure and the depth by means of a graph as shown above. Notice that you can find some of the ordered pairs belonging to this function by reading the graph. For example, suppose you wish to know the pressure 10 feet under the surface. To find this, place your finger on the depth axis (x-axis) where 10 feet is indicated. Now follow this line vertically until your finger reaches the graph. From this point move your finger horizontally until it reaches the pressure axis (y-axis). The reading at this point is the pressure at 10 feet: about 4.3 pounds per square inch. The resulting pair is (10, 4.3).

DO YOU SEE? A graph represents a function because the coordinates of the set of points on the graph are the members (ordered pairs of numbers) of the function.

PROBLEMS

Find on the graph at the right the Fahrenheit temperature corresponding to each of the following centigrade temperatures:

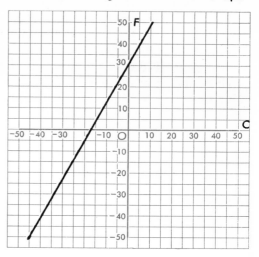

Fahrenheit-Centigrade Conversion Graph

1. $0°$ 2. $5°$ 3. $10°$
4. $-10°$ 5. $-40°$

Find on this graph the centigrade temperatures which correspond to the following Fahrenheit temperatures:

6. $0°$ 7. $50°$ 8. $5°$
9. $-4°$ 10. $-45°$

11. Does an increase in the centigrade temperature produce an increase or a decrease in the Fahrenheit temperature?

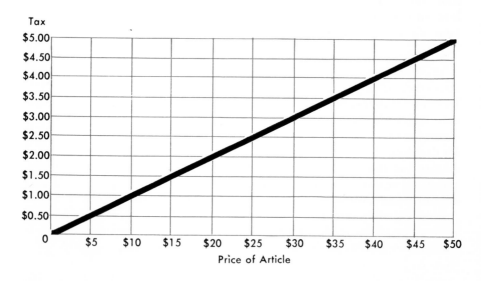

Use the graph above. Find the special tax on taxable articles whose prices are:

12. $5 13. $12 14. $32 15. $43

16. How can you tell from the graph what effect an increase in the price of an article has on the amount of the special tax on the article?

190 *ALGEBRA: ITS BIG IDEAS AND BASIC SKILLS*

Slope of a Line

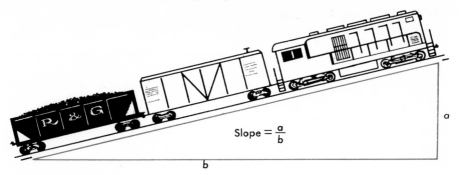

Slope $= \dfrac{a}{b}$

The slope, or grade, of the road is the ratio of the vertical distance, a, to the horizontal distance, b.

To find the slope of any straight line:

(1) Take any point on the graph and count to the right any convenient number of units. In the illustration 4 units are counted off to the right.

(2) Now count up or down as necessary until you meet the graph. In the illustration 3 units are counted up for line AB and 3 units down for line CD. The slope is found by dividing the number of units you counted in the vertical direction by the number of units you counted in the horizontal direction.

Up and *right* are *positive. Down* is *negative.* The slope of line AB, then, is $+\frac{3}{4}$. The slope of line CD is $-\frac{3}{2}$.

Positive slope

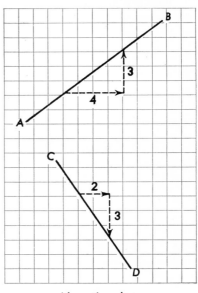

Negative slope

DO YOU SEE? 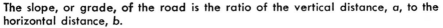 A line that rises to the right is said to have positive slope.

A line that falls to the right is said to have negative slope.

PROBLEMS

1. Find the slope of each of the lines in the graph below.

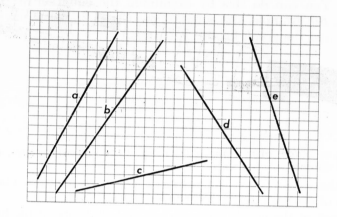

Draw on graph paper lines that have the following slopes:

2. $+\frac{1}{2}$ 3. $-\frac{1}{2}$ 4. $+3$

5. -2 6. $+\frac{1}{4}$ 7. $-\frac{1}{4}$

8. -3 9. $\frac{2}{3}$ 10. $\frac{5}{2}$

11. -1 12. 1 13. 0

14. -4 15. 2 16. $\frac{3}{4}$

17. $+4$ 18. $-\frac{1}{3}$ 19. $\frac{1}{3}$

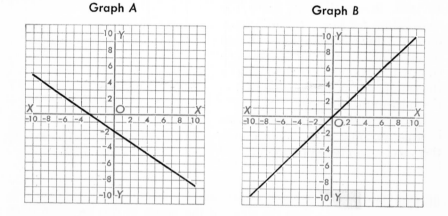

Graph A   Graph B

20. Study the graphs above. What is the slope of each line? From the following equations choose the two which are the equations of the lines in the graphs above:

a. $y = -\frac{2}{3}x - 2$ **b.** $y = x$ **c.** $y = 2x$ **d.** $y = \frac{1}{2}x - 1$

192 *ALGEBRA: ITS BIG IDEAS AND BASIC SKILLS*

The Slope-intercept Form of a Linear Equation

You can learn some important facts about a line without drawing the line. You can do this by examining the equation of the line. Examine, for example, the equation $y = 3x + 2$. Below are a table of values and the graph for this equation.

x	0	1	2	3	4
y	2	5	8	11	14

(across top: 1, 1, 1, 1; across bottom: 3, 3, 3, 3)

Note in the table that, as x increases by 1, y increases by 3. Therefore, the ratio of change in y to the change in x is 3 to 1, or $\frac{3}{1}$.

Now look at the graph. You can see that the slope of the line is $\frac{3}{1}$.

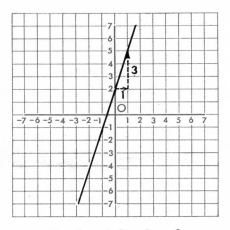

The slope is 3 to 1, or $\frac{3}{1}$.

Now see what is the coefficient of x in the equation $y = 3x + 2$. It is 3, which is the same as $\frac{3}{1}$.

DO YOU SEE? When a linear equation is in the form $y = mx + b$, then the slope of the graph of this equation is m.

Now examine the graphs of the equations on page 194. Since the coefficient of x in each equation is $\frac{1}{3}$, the slopes of these lines are equal. Each line has a slope equal to $\frac{1}{3}$.

GRAPHICAL REPRESENTATION **193**

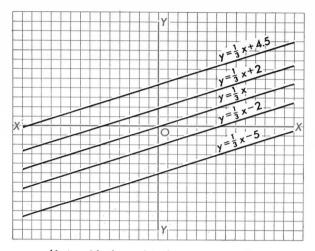

Lines with the same slope are parallel.

How do these lines differ from each other? You can see that each line crosses the y-axis at a different point. The y-coordinate of the point where the graph of an equation crosses the y-axis is called the **y-intercept.** See whether you can find the y-intercept of each line above simply by looking at the equation of the line.

Find from the graph the y-intercept of each line. Now see what the constant term is in each of the equations. Compare the constant term of each equation with the y-intercept of its graph.

DO YOU SEE? When a linear equation is in the form $y = mx + b$, the y-intercept of the graph of this equation is b.

When a linear equation is written in the form $y = mx + b$, we say that it is in the **slope-intercept form.**

Example for Study

Find the slope and y-intercept of the graph of $3x - y = -2$.

SOLUTION:
Change the equation to the form $y = mx + b$:
$$3x - y = -2$$
$$-y = -3x - 2$$
$$y = +3x + 2$$

m, the coefficient of x, is the slope:
$$m = +3$$

b, the constant term, is the y-intercept:
$$b = +2$$

Hence, the slope is $+3$ and the y-intercept $+2$.

194 *ALGEBRA: ITS BIG IDEAS AND BASIC SKILLS*

PROBLEMS

Change each of the following equations to the form y = mx + b. *Then determine by inspection the slope and the y-intercept of the graph of each of the equations:*

1. $2x - y = 7$

2. $8x - 2y = 1$

3. $5x + 10y = 60$

4. $x + \frac{1}{2}y = 1$

5. $x + \frac{1}{4}y = 3$

6. $7x + 21y = 84$

7. $\frac{3}{4}x = y - 8$

8. $8x - 4y = 6$

9. $2x + 5y = 11$

10. $\frac{2}{3}x - \frac{3}{5}y = 3$

11. $6x = -y + 12$

12. $2x - 3y = 9$

13. $2x - \frac{1}{2}y = 1$

14. $3x - 4y = 12$

15. $x - 4y = 8$

16. $5x - 6y = 24$

★ 17. $5(x + y) = -3$

18. $3(x + 1) = 2y$

19. $\frac{1}{2}(x + y + 4) = 0$

20. $x - (y - 1) + 8 = 0$

21. $3(y - 2) - (y - 4) = 8x$

22. $0.04x + 0.1y = 1.1$

23. $0.9x - 0.3y = 3$

24. $3y = 150x - 21$

The Slope-intercept Method of Graphing

It is easy to graph a first-degree equation once you know the slope and the y-intercept of the graph. What you learned in the last section will enable you to graph a line very quickly.

Examples for Study

On graph paper draw the graphs of each of the following two equations without making a table of values:

1. $y = \frac{3}{2}x + 2$

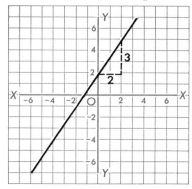

SOLUTION: Since this equation is in the form $y = mx + b$, you know that:

(1) The graph crosses the y-axis at $y = 2$.

(2) The slope is positive.

(3) The slope is $\frac{3}{2}$.

From the y-intercept, $+2$, measure two units to the right. Then measure up 3 units. This point and the y-intercept determine the line.

GRAPHICAL REPRESENTATION **195**

2. $3x + 5y = -20$

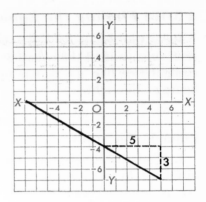

SOLUTION: Change the equation to the form $y = mx + b$; that is, solve for y:

$$y = -\tfrac{3}{5}x - 4$$

You know that:

(1) The y-intercept is -4.
(2) The slope is negative.
(3) The slope is $-\tfrac{3}{5}$.

From the y-intercept, -4, measure 5 units to the right. Then measure down 3 units. This point and the y-intercept determine the line.

PROBLEMS

Use the slope-intercept method of graphing to graph each of the following linear equations. Place the graphs for Problems 1, 2, and 3 on one pair of coordinate axes, the graphs for Problems 4, 5, and 6 on one pair of coordinate axes, the graphs for Problems 7, 8, and 9 on one pair of coordinate axes, and the graphs for Problems 10, 11, and 12 on one pair of coordinate axes.

1. $y = 3x - 1$ 2. $y = 3x + 4$ 3. $y = 3x$
4. $y = -\tfrac{1}{2}x + 6$ 5. $y = -\tfrac{1}{2}x - 5$ 6. $y = -\tfrac{1}{2}x$
7. $y = 2x - 5$ 8. $y = 3x - 5$ 9. $y = \tfrac{1}{2}x - 5$
10. $y = \tfrac{1}{4}x$ 11. $y = -2x$ 12. $y = x$

On graph paper draw a pair of coordinate axes and graph the following equations without making a table of values:

13. $3y = x + 9$ 14. $2x = y + 3$
15. $4y + x = 12$ 16. $3\tfrac{1}{2}x = 3\tfrac{1}{2}y + 1\tfrac{1}{2}$
17. $4x + 3y = 0$ 18. $3x - 4y - 3 = 0$

★ 19. $\tfrac{3}{4}y - \tfrac{2}{3}x + 6 = 0$ 20. $1.5x + 3.2y - 6.4 = 0$
21. $3x = \tfrac{5}{6}y$ 22. $2y = 0.4x + 1.6$
23. $x = 3y + 6$ 24. $3(x + y) = 6$

25. A set of straight lines is described by the equations $y = 3x + 2$, $y = 5x + 2$, and $y = x + 2$. What one thing is true of the graph of each one of these equations?
26. A set of straight lines is described by the equations $y = 4x + 3$, $y = 4x - 4$, and $y = 4x + 10$. What one thing is true of the graph of each one of these equations?
27. The points $(-3, -2)$, $(4, -2)$, and $(1, 4)$ are the vertices of a triangle. Plot these points on a pair of coordinate axes and draw the triangle. Find the area of the triangle.

Finding the Equation of a Straight Line

By using the slope and y-intercept, you can find the equation of a straight line like AB or CD in the figure at the right.

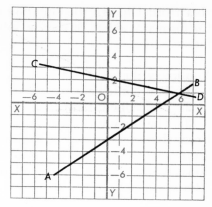

Examples for Study

1. Find the equation of line AB in the figure at the right.

SOLUTION: The slope of AB is $\frac{2}{3}$ and its y-intercept is -3. Check these values for yourself. You know that, in the equation of a straight line $y = mx + b$, m represents the slope of the line and b represents the y-intercept. Substituting the values for the slope and the y-intercept:

$$m = \tfrac{2}{3} \text{ and } b = -3$$

$$y = mx + b$$
$$y = \tfrac{2}{3}x - 3 \quad \text{or} \quad 3y = 2x - 9$$

The equation of line AB is $3y = 2x - 9$.

2. Find the equation of line CD in the figure above.

SOLUTION: The slope of CD is $-\frac{1}{5}$ and the y-intercept is $+1.7$. Check these values for yourself. Substituting these values in $y = mx + b$:

$$m = -\tfrac{1}{5} \text{ and } b = +1.7$$

$$y = mx + b$$
$$y = -\tfrac{1}{5}x + 1.7 \quad \text{or} \quad 5y = -x + 8.5$$

The equation of line CD is $5y = -x + 8.5$.

PROBLEMS

Write the first-degree equations whose graphs have the following slopes and y-intercepts:
1. Slope is 3 and y-intercept is 2.
2. Slope is $\frac{1}{2}$ and y-intercept is -6.
3. Slope is -5 and y-intercept is 8.
4. Slope is 2 and y-intercept is 0.
5. Slope is a and y-intercept is k.
6. Slope is 0 and y-intercept is c.

*What is the slope and the **y**-intercept of each of the lines shown below?*

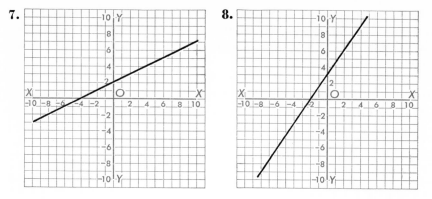

7. 8.

9. Write the equations of the lines in Problems 7 and 8 by substituting the proper values for m and b in $y = mx + b$.

Draw the lines determined by the values given in the following tables. Write the equations of these lines.

10.

x	0	1	2	3	4
y	6	8	10	12	14

11.

x	0	1	2	3	4
y	1	0	-1	-2	-3

12.

x	0	2	4	6	8
y	5	8	11	14	17

13.

x	0	1	2	3	4
y	-6	-3	0	3	6

14.

x	0	3	6	9	12
y	-2	-1	0	1	2

15.

x	-4	0	4	8	12
y	3	0	-3	-6	-9

★ 16. Analyze this graph. Write the equation for P in terms of A.

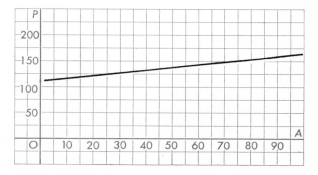

Curved-line Graphs

You have seen that an equation of a straight line is a first-degree equation. You have also seen that a graph of a first-degree equation is a straight line. What kind of a graph would you get by graphing a second-degree equation?

Example for Study

Make a table of values and graph the equation $y = \frac{1}{4}x^2$.

SOLUTION:

x	0	1	2	3	4	5	6	-1	-2	-3	-4	-5	-6
y	0	$\frac{1}{4}$	1	$2\frac{1}{4}$	4	$6\frac{1}{4}$	9	$\frac{1}{4}$	1	$2\frac{1}{4}$	4	$6\frac{1}{4}$	9

Now if you plot these points and draw a smooth curve through them, you will get a curved line like the one in the graph below. Curved lines are typical of second-degree equations.

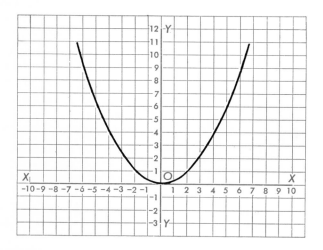

PROBLEMS

Make a table of values for each of the following equations. Plot the points and draw a curve through them.

1. $y = \frac{1}{2}x^2$
2. $y = \frac{1}{10}x^2$
3. $y = \frac{3}{4}x^2$
4. $y = 2x^2$
5. $y = x^2 + 4$
6. $y = x^2 + 2$
7. $y = x^2 - 2$
8. $y = x^2 - 4$

9. Examine your graph for Problem 1. As x increases, what change takes place in y? As x decreases, what change takes place in y?
10. Examine your graph for Problem 3. Describe the change in y as x changes from positive numbers to negative numbers. What is the value of y when x is 0?

Graphing Algebraic Functions

You have graphed functions described by equations, for example, $y = \frac{1}{2}x + 3$. This function could also be described as the set of ordered pairs $(x, \frac{1}{2}x + 3)$ for all replacements of x. For example, when x is replaced by 8, then $\frac{1}{2}x + 3$ equals 7, so the ordered pair is $(8, 7)$. We could replace x by any number and there would be determined one and only one second number. Some of these pairs are shown in the tables below.

Table 1. Values for the Equation $y = \frac{1}{2}x + 3$

x	0	2	6	-4	-8
y	3	4	6	1	-1

Table 2. Values for the Function $(x, \frac{1}{2}x + 3)$

x	0	2	6	-4	-8
$\frac{1}{2}x + 3$	3	4	6	1	-1

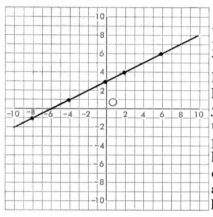

Graph of the Function $(x, \frac{1}{2}x + 3)$

The only difference between the two tables is that y is used in Table 1 and $\frac{1}{2}x + 3$ is used in Table 2. When using Table 1, you would locate the values of x along the horizontal axis and the values of y along the vertical axis. You would use Table 2 in the same way, plotting the values of x on the horizontal axis and plotting the corresponding values of $\frac{1}{2}x + 3$ along the vertical axis, as shown here.

Since the graph of any first-degree equation is a straight line and the graph of any equation higher than the first degree is a curved line, what conclusion can you make about the graphs of $(x, 10x + 8)$ and $(x, 16x - 20)$? About the graphs of $(x, 3x^2 - 4)$ and $(x, 5x^2 + 3x - 4)$?

PROBLEMS

Examine the following functions and tell whether their graphs are straight lines or curved lines:

1. $(x, 8x - 40)$
2. $(x, 3 + x - x^2)$
3. $(x, \frac{3}{4}x - 17)$
4. $(x, x^3 - x + 9)$
5. $(x, 18 + 2x - x^2)$
6. $(x, 2x^2 + 6x)$

Copy the following tables and fill in the values of each function for each value of **x**. *Then draw the graph of each function.*

7.

x	0	2	8	-1
$x + 8$	?	?	?	?

8.

x	-1	-2	-3	0	1	2	3
$x^2 - 4$	?	?	?	?	?	?	?

9.

x	0	3	-1	-3
$2x + 1$	?	?	?	?

10.

x	-1	-2	-3	-4	0	1	2	3
$\frac{1}{2}x^2 - 8$	?	?	?	?	?	?	?	?

Make a table of values for each of the following functions and graph each function.

11. $(x, \frac{3}{4}x + 6)$
12. $(x, 7 - \frac{1}{2}x)$
13. $(x, 1 + x)$
14. $(x, 2x - 5)$
15. $(x, x^2 - 9)$
16. $(x, x^2 + 4)$
17. $(x, 4 - \frac{1}{4}x)$
18. $(x, x^2 - x - 8)$
19. $(x, 3x)$

20. $(x, \frac{1}{4}x)$
21. $\left(x, \dfrac{4x}{5} - 7\right)$
22. $\left(x, \dfrac{3x - 5}{2}\right)$

★ 23. $(x, x^3 - 2)$
24. $(x, -3x^2 + 1)$
25. $\left(x, \dfrac{1}{x}\right)$

26. $\left(x, \dfrac{1}{x + 2}\right)$
27. $(x, |\, x\,|)$
28. $(x, 1)$

29. $(x, -x^2)$
30. $(x, -3)$
31. $(x, |\, x + 4\,|)$

SELF TEST

Tell the slope and the y-intercept of the graph of each of the following equations:

1. $y = 2x + 6$
2. $y = \frac{1}{2}x - 3$
3. $y = -\frac{1}{3}x + 7$
4. $4y + x = 16$
5. $\frac{1}{4}y + 2x = 5$
6. $4(x + 2) = 2y$

Write the equations of the straight lines that have the following characteristics:

7. Slope is 4 and y-intercept is $+2$.
8. Passes through the origin and has the slope of 3.
9. Is parallel to the x-axis and has the y-intercept of -5.

10. Find the slope and the y-intercept of the line determined by the following table of values.

x	-2	-1	0	$+1$	$+2$	$+3$
y	-1	2	5	8	11	14

11. Graph the equation $xy = 4$. What kind of variation is this?
12. In Problem 11, describe the change in y as x changes from a very small number to a very large number.

Four Ways of Expressing Functions

You have now studied four ways of stating the relationship between two variables: (1) a verbal statement, (2) a formula or equation, (3) a table of values, (4) a graph.

Example for Study

If the cost of preparing fruit punch for a school dance is 30 cents per quart, then the total cost is a function of, or depends upon, the number of quarts prepared. Express this relationship in four ways.

SOLUTION:

(1) As a verbal statement: The cost of the punch in cents equals 30 multiplied by the number of quarts prepared.

(2) As a formula: $C = 30n$

(3) As a table of values:

n	1	2	3	4	5	6
C	30	60	90	120	150	180

(4) As a graph:

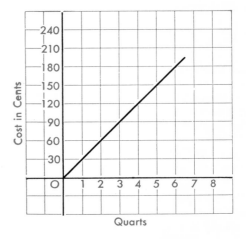

PROBLEMS

1. If the price of gasoline is 31 cents per gallon, the cost of gasoline is a function of the number of gallons bought. Express this relationship in four ways.

2. If w stands for any number of weeks and d stands for the number of days in w weeks, express in four ways the relationship between w and d. Begin your verbal statement with "The number of days in any number of weeks may be found by multiplying . . ."

3. If a laborer makes $1.20 per hour, his weekly wage w is a function of the number of hours h per week that he works. Express this relationship in four ways. From your graph read off the weekly wage for a 30-hour week, a 36-hour week, a 40-hour week.

Because of the curvature of the earth, there is a limit to the distance that ships may be seen at sea. The approximate height h in feet to which it is necessary for the average person to rise in order to see a ship at a certain distance is found by taking two-thirds of the square of the distance d in miles. Express this relationship as a formula, a table of values, and a graph.

SOLUTION:

(1) As a formula: $h = \frac{2}{3}d^2$

(2) As a table:

d	0	1	2	3	4	5	6	7	8	9
h	0	$\frac{2}{3}$	$2\frac{2}{3}$	6	$10\frac{2}{3}$	$16\frac{2}{3}$	24	$32\frac{2}{3}$	$42\frac{2}{3}$	54

(3) As a graph:

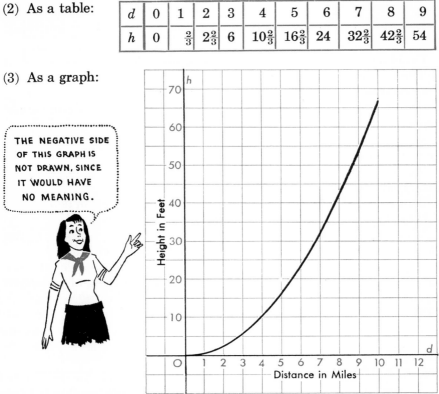

THE NEGATIVE SIDE OF THIS GRAPH IS NOT DRAWN, SINCE IT WOULD HAVE NO MEANING.

4. Read from the graph above the approximate height above sea level at which the average person can see a ship at a distance of 3 miles, 6 miles, 10 miles.

5. From the graph above read the distance that the average person can see a ship from a height of 15 feet, 20 feet, 25 feet.

GRAPHICAL REPRESENTATION **203**

SUMMARY OF IMPORTANT THINGS TO REMEMBER

1. Words and Expressions

abscissa, or x-distance   quadrant

coordinate axes   slope

coordinates   slope-intercept form of a linear equation

curved-line graph   straight-line graph

graph x-axis

linear equation y-axis

ordinate, or y-distance y-intercept

origin

2. Understandings

Functions can be expressed by means of graphs, tables, equations, and verbal statements.

Graphs of first-degree equations are straight lines.

The equation of a straight line is a first-degree equation.

Graphs of second-degree equations are curved lines.

The coordinates of every point on the graph of an equation satisfy the equation.

Every pair of numbers that satisfies an equation determines a point that lies on the graph of the equation.

The coordinates of every point not on the graph of an equation do not satisfy the equation.

Every pair of numbers that does not satisfy an equation determines a point that does not lie on the graph of the equation.

When a linear equation is written in the form $y = mx + b$, the slope of its graph is m and the y-intercept of its graph is b.

A graph represents a function because the coordinates of the set of points on the graph are the members (ordered pairs of numbers) of the function.

3. Skills

You should be able to:

Locate a point in a plane by using coordinate axes.

Graph an algebraic function.

Graph a linear equation using the slope and y-intercept.

Express a function in two or more ways.

Draw a graph of a function given by a table of related values.

204 *ALGEBRA: ITS BIG IDEAS AND BASIC SKILLS*

PROBLEMS ON YOUR AIMS

YOUR AIM To learn how to locate in a plane a point which corresponds to a given pair of numbers.

1. When two numbers are used in locating a point, what does the first number stand for? The second?
2. What pair of numbers corresponds to a point on the x-axis two units to the right of the origin?
3. What pair of numbers corresponds to a point on the y-axis two units below the origin?
4. What are the coordinates of a point 5 units above the x-axis and 4 units to the left of the y-axis?
5. What are the coordinates of the origin?
6. Graph these points: $A(3, 4)$, $B(-1, 2)$, $C(4, -2)$, $D(0, 5)$.

YOUR AIM To learn how to graph an algebraic function.

1. Describe how you would graph $3x - 2y = 6$ by the use of a table of values.
2. How many points are necessary for graphing a straight line?
3. How many points are necessary for graphing a curved line?

Tell which of the following functions have straight-line graphs and which have curved-line graphs.
4. $(x, 2x - 4)$ 5. $(x, \frac{1}{2}x + 2)$ 6. $(x, 3x^2 - 10)$ 7. $(x, x^3 - 5)$

YOUR AIM To learn what is meant by the slope of a line.

1. In engineering, a slope or grade of 0.1% means 0.1 foot vertical rise (as of a road) to 100 feet of horizontal distance. How does this compare with meaning of the slope of a line?
2. How can you tell, without graphing, the slopes of the lines given by $y = 4x - 1$ and $y - 3x = 8$?
3. What is true about the slopes of parallel straight lines?

YOUR AIM To learn how to find the equation of a line.

1. What is the general equation whose graph is a straight line?
2. If a straight line passes through the origin and has a slope of $\frac{2}{3}$, what is its equation?
3. If the y-intercept of a straight line is -4 and its slope is 5, what is the equation of the line?
4. What is the equation of a straight line that passes through the point $(2, 0)$ and is parallel to the y-axis?

GRAPHICAL REPRESENTATION **205**

VALUABLE SKILLS PRACTICE

1. First find the values of a, b, c, and d. Next substitute the values of a, b, c, and d in the equations that follow to find the values of X and Y. Then, as a check, substitute the values of X and Y in the equation $X - Y = 2$.

$$a = (5 \times 6) + [8 \div (-2)] - (3 \times 7)$$
$$b = 12 - (18 \div 9) \times 3 - (25 \div 5)$$
$$c = 8 - (3 \times 16) \div 6(12 - 8)$$
$$d = (4.8 \div 12) - (3 \times 1.8) + (24 \div 4.8)$$

$a - b = \underline{\ ?\ }$	$\dfrac{a}{b} + \dfrac{d}{c} = \underline{\ ?\ }$
$a^2 + b^2 = \underline{\ ?\ }$	$abc + bcd = \underline{\ ?\ }$
$a + b + c + d = \underline{\ ?\ }$	$a^b - b^b = \underline{\ ?\ }$
$(a - b)(a + b) = \underline{\ ?\ }$	$\dfrac{d}{a} + \dfrac{b}{c} + \dfrac{a}{c} = \underline{\ ?\ }$
$(c - a)(b - c) = \underline{\ ?\ }$	$a^2 + a - ab - bc = \underline{\ ?\ }$
Total $\quad\overline{X}$	Total $\quad\overline{Y}$

CHECK: $X - Y = 2$

Find the area of each of the following:

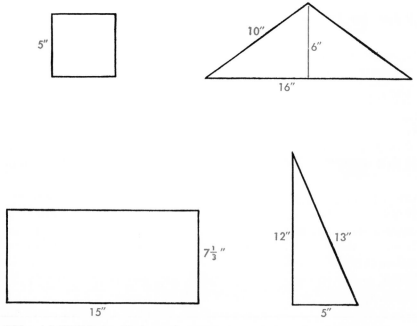

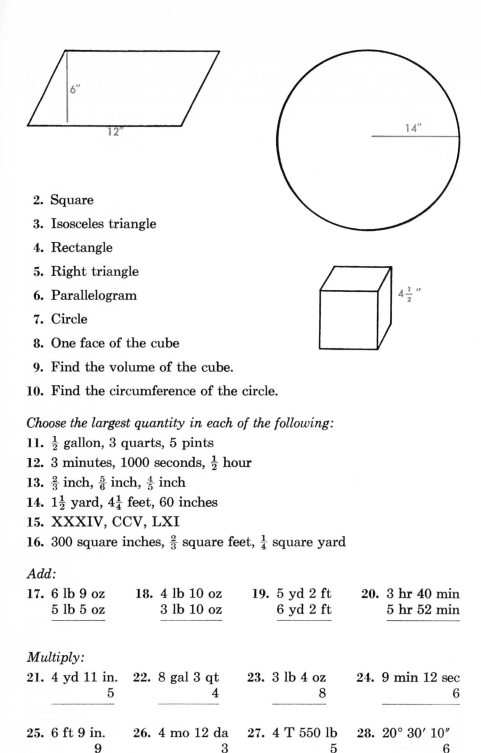

2. Square

3. Isosceles triangle

4. Rectangle

5. Right triangle

6. Parallelogram

7. Circle

8. One face of the cube

9. Find the volume of the cube.

10. Find the circumference of the circle.

Choose the largest quantity in each of the following:

11. $\frac{1}{2}$ gallon, 3 quarts, 5 pints

12. 3 minutes, 1000 seconds, $\frac{1}{2}$ hour

13. $\frac{2}{3}$ inch, $\frac{5}{6}$ inch, $\frac{4}{5}$ inch

14. $1\frac{1}{2}$ yard, $4\frac{1}{4}$ feet, 60 inches

15. XXXIV, CCV, LXI

16. 300 square inches, $\frac{2}{3}$ square feet, $\frac{1}{4}$ square yard

Add:

17. 6 lb 9 oz	18. 4 lb 10 oz	19. 5 yd 2 ft	20. 3 hr 40 min
5 lb 5 oz	3 lb 10 oz	6 yd 2 ft	5 hr 52 min

Multiply:

21. 4 yd 11 in.	22. 8 gal 3 qt	23. 3 lb 4 oz	24. 9 min 12 sec
5	4	8	6

25. 6 ft 9 in.	26. 4 mo 12 da	27. 4 T 550 lb	28. 20° 30′ 10″
9	3	5	6

CHAPTER TEST

1. Copy this table and fill in the values for x and y so that they satisfy the equation $3x - 5y = 15$. Graph the equation.

x	0	-5	-10	?
y	?	?	?	0

In which quadrant does each of the following points belong?
2. $(-1, 4)$ 3. $(7, -3)$ 4. $(-1, -3)$ 5. $(5, 6)$

Draw a pair of coordinate axes and plot the following points:
6. $(-4, 2)$ 7. $(6, -1)$ 8. $(0, 4)$ 9. $(7, -8)$
10. $(-5, 0)$ 11. $(-5, -5)$ 12. $(4, 3)$ 13. $(0, 0)$

The slopes of the graphs of which of the following pairs of equations are equal?

14. $y = 2x - 5$
    $y = 3x - 5$

15. $y = \frac{1}{2}x - 1$
    $y = \frac{1}{2}x + 4$

16. $x + 4y = 9$
    $y = \frac{1}{4}x - 3$

Rewrite the following equations so that y is the dependent variable. What is the slope and y-intercept of the graph of each equation?
17. $x + y = 6$ 18. $2x - y = 3$ 19. $x - 2y = 4$

20. In the graph shown below, what are the coordinates of points A, B, and C?

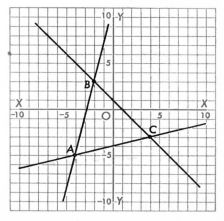

By inspection tell which equation determines line AB, *which* BC, *and which* AC:
21. $y = -x + 1$ 22. $y = \frac{1}{4}x - 4$ 23. $y = 4x + 11$

24. Write a first-degree equation whose graph has the slope 3 and the y-intercept -2.
25. The points $(0, 0)$, $(0, -3)$, $(-4, 0)$, and $(-4, -3)$ are the vertices of a rectangle. Plot these points and draw the rectangle. Find the perimeter and the area of the rectangle.
26. State four ways of expressing functions.

208 *ALGEBRA: ITS BIG IDEAS AND BASIC SKILLS*

CUMULATIVE REVIEW PROBLEMS

WORKING WITH ALGEBRAIC EXPRESSIONS

If a $= 2,$ b $= -3,$ c $= 1,$ *and* d $= 0,$ *find the value of* w, x, y, *and* z:

1. $w = bd + b(c - a)$
2. $y = a(b + c) + a$
3. $x = abc + a^5 + (ab)^2$
4. $z = ad - c^4 - a(a + b)$

5. Check your results in Problems 1–4 by substituting them in the formula $w + x + y + z = 64$.

If A $=$ x $- 1,$ B $=$ x $- 2,$ *and* C $= 2$x $+ 1,$ *find the value of each of the following in terms of* x:

6. $A + B + C$
7. AB
8. $(A + B)(B + C)$
9. $(A - B)(C - A)$

10. Add the results you obtained in Problems 6–9. The sum of the correct answers is $7x^2 - 9x + 5$.

Find the values of a, b, c, *and* d:

11. $a = (\frac{1}{4})^2 (-8)^2 + (-2)^3$
12. $b = (-3)^3 (\frac{1}{3})^2$
13. $c = (-1)^4 (-5)^3 + (-10)^2 - (\frac{1}{2})^3 (-4)^3 (\frac{5}{2})$
14. $d = (-2)(-1)$

15. Check your results in Problems 11–14 by substituting them in the formula $abd + 1 = c^2$.

Express each of the following in the simplest terms:

16. $8(2a - 2b) - 3(3a - 6b)$
17. $7(2a + b) - \frac{3}{2}(16a + 8b)$
18. $\frac{1}{2}(18a - 2b) + \frac{3}{4}(-4a - 12b)$
19. $-(4a - 11b) - (-4a - b)$

20. Add your results in Problems 16–19. You should obtain the sum $3a - b$.

Find the value of each of the following expressions when x *is replaced by* -2:

21. $3x + 2$
22. $x - x^3$
23. $6x^2 - x - 1$
24. $\frac{1}{2}x^5 - \frac{1}{4}x^4 - \frac{1}{8}x^3$

25. Add your results in Problems 21–24. The sum of the results should be equal to the root of the equation $3(x - 2) = \frac{1}{2}(x + 10) + 9$.

Do the indicated operations and express each answer in simplest form:

26. $(+2x)^3 (-3y)^2$
27. $(-1)^7 (x + 5)$
28. $4(a + b) + 3(a + b)$
29. $5(x - y) + 5(y - x)$
30. $(3a - b)(3a + 2b)$
31. $(7x - y)(3x - 3x)$
32. $(-a)^2 (a^2 + 2a - 6)$
33. $aaa + bb$
34. $a + a + a + b + b$
35. $4[7x - 3(x - y)]$
36. $(18x^2 - 6x + 5) \div (3x + 2)$
37. $(x^3 - y^3) \div (x + y)$
38. $\dfrac{3x^4}{4} \div \dfrac{6x^2}{8}$
39. $\dfrac{15x^3}{2} \div \dfrac{5x}{6}$

Solve each of the following equations:

1. $3a - 6 = 15$
2. $\frac{1}{2}b + 1 = b$
3. $2c - 6 = \dfrac{c - 3}{2}$
4. $10\frac{1}{2} - 3d = 16\frac{1}{2} - 9d$

5. Check the roots you obtained in Problems 1–4 by substituting them in the formula $a^b - b^c - d^d = 40$.

Solve each of the following equations:

6. $m - 3(2m + 4) = 8$
7. $n - (-n + 1) = 1$
8. $\frac{1}{2}p + \frac{3}{4}(p + 8) = 6$
9. $\frac{1}{3}q - \frac{1}{6} = \frac{5}{6}$

10. Check the roots you obtained in Problems 6–9 by substituting them in the formula $m^2 + mn + pq = 12$.

Solve each of the following equations:

11. $1 = \frac{1}{2}x$
12. $3y = 2$
13. $0.01z = 1$
14. $5y = 2y + 2$

15. Check the roots you obtained in Problems 11–14 by substituting them in the formula $\left(\dfrac{x}{y}\right)^2 + 1 = \sqrt{z}$.

Solve each of the following equations:

16. $3x - 6 = x + 4$
17. $41 - x - 8 = 2x$
18. $5x - 8 = 3x + 20$
19. $\frac{2}{3}x - 6 = \frac{1}{3}x + 4$
20. $\dfrac{8x}{5} - \dfrac{6x}{5} = 11$
21. $\dfrac{3x}{5} + \dfrac{8x}{3} - \dfrac{4}{15} = 3$
22. $\dfrac{9x}{2} + 4 = 7$
23. $\dfrac{3}{x} - \dfrac{8}{5} = 1$
24. $4[7 - 3(x + 1)] = 8$
25. $-[(3x - 2) + 4] = -14$
26. $2.5x + 6.1 = 7.8$
27. $3.2(14 - 5x) = 16.7$
28. $\dfrac{5 - x}{3} - \dfrac{x}{2} = 0$
29. $\frac{4}{5}(x + \frac{2}{3}) = \frac{1}{5}(x + 6)$

To remember what you have learned:

Do each day's lesson thoroughly.
Do the Self Tests.
Study the Summary of Important Things to Remember.
Do the Problems on Your Aims.
Do the Valuable Skills Practice.
Do the Chapter Test.
Do the Cumulative Review Problems.

BIG IDEAS	EQUATION
	GRAPH

BASIC SKILLS	Using and interpreting symbols of algebra
	Solving equations
	Solving verbal problems
	Drawing and reading graphs

CHAPTER **8** *Systems of Linear Equations with Two Variables*

THE MOST important skill in algebra is that of solving problems by the use of equations. You have learned how to solve first-degree equations with one variable, such as $3x + 4 = 14$. In Chapter 7 you graphed equations with two variables, such as $x - 2y = 12$. In this chapter you will learn how to use two variables in solving problems. It is often much easier to solve a problem by using two variables instead of one. However, you will learn that, in order to find a solution to a problem by using two variables, you will have to use two equations. Rather than finding the solution to one equation, you will be finding the solution to a system of two equations.

YOUR AIM

1. To learn how to solve a system of two linear equations with two variables.

2. To improve your ability to use variables in writing equations for solving verbal problems.

211

Graphical Solution of Systems of Equations

Suppose that you wish to find two numbers whose sum is 23 and whose difference is 7. By using a letter to represent each number, you can write the equations quickly and easily. If you let x = the larger number, and y = the smaller number; then

$$x + y = 23$$
$$x - y = 7$$

The graph of the first equation $x + y = 23$ is a straight line. One pair of numbers that satisfies this equation is $x = 0, y = 23$. Another pair of numbers that satisfies this equation is $x = 15, y = 8$. There are many pairs of numbers (x, y) that satisfy the equation. Likewise you can find many pairs of numbers that will satisfy the equation $x - y = 7$. For example, $x = 15, y = 8$ will satisfy the equation. So will $x = 0, y = -7$. In fact, any pair of numbers that describes a point on the graph of $x - y = 7$ will satisfy the equation.

Two straight lines can intersect in only one point. You learned in Chapter 7 that the coordinates of any point on the graph satisfy the

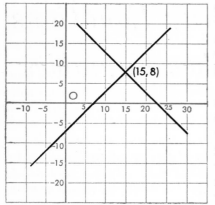

equation of that graph. This means that the coordinates of any point common to two graphs—that is, their point of intersection—will satisfy the equations of *both* graphs.

The graphs of these two equations are shown at the left. Their point of intersection is (15, 8). This means that the solution for both equations is $x = 15$ and $y = 8$. It is, therefore, their *common solution*. Does this result check with the conditions of the problem?

CHECK: $x + y = 23$
$15 + 8 \overset{?}{=} 23$ The sum of the two numbers is 23.
$23 = 23$

$x = 15, y = 8$ satisfies the first equation.

$x - y = 7$
$15 - 8 \overset{?}{=} 7$ The difference between the two numbers is 7.
$7 = 7$

$x = 15, y = 8$ also satisfies the second equation.

If two or more equations have a common solution, they are called a **system of simultaneous equations.**

Examples for Study

1. *Find the common solution:*
$$x - 2y = 2$$
$$x + y = 8$$

2. *Find the common solution:*
$$x + y = 4$$
$$x + y = 1$$

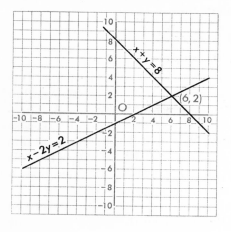

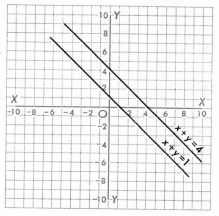

SOLUTION: Look at the graphs of $x - 2y = 2$ and $x + y = 8$ shown above. These graphs intersect at the point $(6, 2)$.

Hence, $\quad\quad x = 6$
$\quad\quad\quad\quad\quad y = 2$

CHECK: $\quad\quad x - 2y = 2$
$\quad\quad\quad 6 - 2 \cdot 2 \overset{?}{=} 2$
$\quad\quad\quad\quad\quad\quad 2 = 2$

$\quad\quad\quad\quad x + y = 8$
$\quad\quad\quad\quad 6 + 2 \overset{?}{=} 8$
$\quad\quad\quad\quad\quad\quad 8 = 8$

In checking the solution, why should you substitute the values obtained for x and y in both equations?

No solution! The equations $x + y = 4$ and $x + y = 1$ have no common solution since their graphs are parallel and, hence, do not intersect. You could have guessed there would be no solution by examining the equations. It would be absurd to assume that the sum of two numbers could be both 4 and 1. It is for this reason that a system of such equations is called a **system of inconsistent equations.**

PROBLEMS

By graphing, find the common solution of each of the following systems of equations. Check your results. If a system has no common solution, explain why.

1. $x + y = 5$
   $2x - 3y = 0$

2. $x - 2y = -6$
   $2x - y = 3$

3. $3x - y = -10$
   $x + 2y = 6$

4. $x - y = 7$
   $x - y = 1$

5. $x - 4y = 9$
   $x - 2y = 3$

6. $2x - y = 9$
   $3x + 4y = 8$

7. $x - 2y = 1$
   $x - 3y = 4$

8. $y = x + 6$
   $y = \frac{1}{2}x + 5$

9. $2y = x - 1$
   $x - 2y = 4$

10. $y = x$
    $y = \frac{1}{4}x + 3$

11. $x = 5$
    $y = \frac{3}{5}x - 3$

12. $x = -2y$
    $y = 3x$

13. $x + y = 6$
    $x - y = -1$

14. $2x + y = 4$
    $2x - y = 10$

15. $3x - y = 2$
    $5x + y = 10$

16. $x + 2y = -4$
    $-2y - 4y = 8$

17. $y = \frac{1}{2}x + 4$
    $y = -\frac{3}{2}x - 2$

18. $y = -2x + 2$
    $y = \frac{3}{2}x - 5$

19. $y = \frac{1}{3}x - 6$
    $y = -\frac{2}{3}x$

20. $y = \frac{x}{5} + 2$
    $y = -\frac{3}{5}x + 6$

21. $y = x$
    $y = -x$

22. $y = 3x$
    $y = -3x + 4$

★ 23. $y = \frac{3}{4}x - 6$
    $y = \frac{3}{4}x + 6$

24. $y = \frac{2}{3}x - 4$
    $y = x - 2$

25. $\frac{1}{2}y + 3x = 5$
    $\frac{1}{2}y + 3x = -5$

26. $x + y = a$
    $2x - y = 5a$

27. $4x - 3y = 1$
    $2x + 3y = 3$

28. $3x - y = 4a$
    $x + 2y = -a$

29. $\dfrac{1}{x} - \dfrac{1}{y} = \dfrac{1}{2}$
    $\dfrac{2}{x} + \dfrac{1}{y} = 1$

30. $\dfrac{1}{x} + \dfrac{1}{y} = 0$
    $\dfrac{3}{x} - \dfrac{4}{y} = \dfrac{2}{y}$

31. $\frac{1}{2}x - y = a$
    $x - 2y = -3a$

32. $5x + 9y = 8$
    $15x + 27y = 24$

DO YOU SEE? ☞ **Finding the solution to a system of equations by graphing the equations is time consuming and usually results in only approximate answers.**

214 *ALGEBRA: ITS BIG IDEAS AND BASIC SKILLS*

Solution by Addition or Subtraction

In solving systems of equations, the graphical method helps you understand what it means to solve a system of equations. It is not a practical method, however. It is time consuming, requires precise graphing, and usually gives only an approximate answer.

It is much better to use algebraic methods which enable you to find the solution to a system of equations in a direct, concise way. Algebraic methods also have the advantage of giving the exact solution rather than an approximate solution. One algebraic method of finding the solution to a system of equations is that of either adding or subtracting the two equations to obtain one equation in one variable. After solving this one equation for the one variable, you solve for the second variable. Study the following explanation and the examples on page 216.

To solve the set of equations

$$2x + 5y = 9$$
$$3x - 2y = 4$$

multiply each side of the first equation by 2 and each side of the second equation by 5. When you do this, you get:

$$4x + 10y = 18$$
$$15x - 10y = 20$$

Now add the two equations—left side to left side and right side to right side—and thus eliminate one variable:

$$4x + 10y = 18$$
$$\underline{15x - 10y = 20}$$
$$19x \qquad\quad = 38$$

Solve this last equation for x:

$$x = 2$$

Substitute 2 for x in either of the original equations and solve for y:

$$2x + 5y = 9$$
$$2(2) + 5y = 9$$
$$4 + 5y = 9$$
$$5y = 5$$
$$y = 1$$

Now check in both original equations:

$$2x + 5y = 9 \qquad\qquad 3x - 2y = 4$$
$$2(2) + 5(1) \stackrel{?}{=} 9 \qquad\qquad 3(2) - 2(1) \stackrel{?}{=} 4$$
$$4 + 5 \stackrel{?}{=} 9 \qquad\qquad 6 - 2 \stackrel{?}{=} 4$$
$$9 = 9 \qquad\qquad\qquad 4 = 4$$

Examples for Study

1. *Solve for* x *and* y: $3x - y = 7$
$$x + y = 5$$

SOLUTION:

Add to eliminate one variable:

$$3x - y = 7$$
$$x + y = 5$$
$$4x = 12$$

Solve for x: $x = 3$

Substitute 3 for x in either of the original equations and solve for y:

$$x + y = 5$$
$$3 + y = 5$$
$$y = 2$$

CHECK: $3x - y = 7$ $x + y = 5$
$3 \cdot 3 - 2 \overset{?}{=} 7$ $3 + 2 \overset{?}{=} 5$
$9 - 2 \overset{?}{=} 7$ $5 = 5$
$7 = 7$

2. *Solve for* m *and* n: $m + n = 1$
$$m - 5n = 7$$

SOLUTION:

Subtract to eliminate one variable:
$$m + n = 1$$
$$m - 5n = 7$$
$$6n = -6$$

Solve for n: $n = -1$

Substitute -1 for n in either of the original equations and solve for m:
$$m + n = 1$$
$$m - 1 = 1$$
$$m = 2$$

CHECK: $m + n = 1$ $m - 5n = 7$
$2 + (-1) \overset{?}{=} 1$ $2 - 5(-1) \overset{?}{=} 7$
$2 - 1 \overset{?}{=} 1$ $2 + 5 \overset{?}{=} 7$
$1 = 1$ $7 = 7$

3. *Solve for* a *and* b: $2a - 3b = 8$
$$3a - 2b = 17$$

SOLUTION:

To eliminate one variable, a, multiply the first equation by 3 and the second equation by 2 and subtract:

$$6a - 9b = 24$$
$$6a - 4b = 34$$
$$-5b = -10$$
$$b = 2$$

Substitute 2 for b in either of the original equations and solve for a:

$$2a - 3b = 8$$
$$2a - 3 \cdot 2 = 8$$
$$2a - 6 = 8$$
$$2a = 14$$
$$a = 7$$

CHECK:
$$2a - 3b = 8 \qquad 3a - 2b = 17$$
$$2 \cdot 7 - 3 \cdot 2 \stackrel{?}{=} 8 \qquad 3 \cdot 7 - 2 \cdot 2 \stackrel{?}{=} 17$$
$$14 - 6 \stackrel{?}{=} 8 \qquad 21 - 4 \stackrel{?}{=} 17$$
$$8 = 8 \qquad 17 = 17$$

PROBLEMS

Solve the following equations by addition or subtraction and check your results:

1. $x + y = 6$
   $x - y = 4$

2. $2x - y = 3$
   $x + y = 9$

3. $3x - 2y = 12$
   $2x + 2y = 13$

4. $x + y = 15$
   $2x + y = 3$

5. $3x - y = 4$
   $2x - y = 2$

6. $x - y = 16$
   $x - 3y = 2$

7. $3x - y = -2$
   $3x + 4y = -17$

8. $5x - 4y = 26$
   $2x + 4y = 16$

9. $x + 5y = 0$
   $x - 5y = 20$

10. $x + 2y = 36$
    $3x - y = 27$

11. $2x - 7y = 5$
    $2x + y = 20$

12. $2x - 5y = 14$
    $x + 2y = 11$

13. $6x - 3y = -3$
    $5x - 2y = 2$

14. $7x - 3y = -2$
    $2x - 5y = -13$

15. $6x - y = 3$
    $x - 2y = 6$

16. $x - 6y = 11$
    $x - y = 1$

17. $15x - 13y = 2$
    $3x + 7y = 10$

18. $x - y = 4$
    $x + y = -8$

19. $x - y = -12$
    $\frac{1}{2}x + y = 6$

20. $x - 4y = 15$
    $x - 5y = 20$

21. $9x - 7y = 41$
    $x - 5y = 13$

22. $x - 8y = 10$
    $2x - 12y = 40$

23. $40x - 33y = 9$
    $20x - 21y = 3$

24. $27x - 40y = 1$
    $13x - 8y = 23$

25. $80x - 50y = 0$
    $24x - 35y = -4$

26. $26x + 20y = -4$
    $16x - 10y = 31$

27. $2x - 5y = 1$
    $9x - 10y = 7$

28. $6x + 8y = 9$
    $2x - 4y = -1$

29. $x + 7 = 5y$
    $2x - y = 13$

30. $y = 3x - 12$
    $x = 10y + 4$

31. $x - 4y = 2$
    $3x - 5y = 20$

32. $6x + 5y = 11$
    $3x - 7y = -4$

33. $14x - 2y = 30$
    $3x + 3y = 24$

34. $10x - y = 1$
    $6x - y = -3$

★ 35. $x = y - 7$
$2x + y = 29$

36. $3x - 5y = 8$
$2x - 23y = -34$

37. $x - \frac{1}{2}y = 1$
$\frac{1}{2}x - \frac{3}{4}y = \frac{-5}{2}$

38. $x - 4y = 8$
$y = 4 - x$

39. $8a - 4b = 4$
$3a + b = 9$

40. $3a - 3b = 3$
$a + b = 3$

41. $\frac{1}{2}x - \frac{1}{3}y = 7$
$x - \frac{1}{2}y = 13$

42. $10x - 12y = -1$
$15x - 28y = -4$

43. $\frac{3}{4}x + y = 8$
$\frac{1}{4}x = y - 8$

44. $0.2a - 0.3b = 0.1$
$0.5a - 0.2b = 3$

45. $12a + 7b = 4.5$
$a - 3b = -0.7$

46. $c = 3.9 - 0.5d$
$c - 5d = 5$

47. $0.01m + 0.03n = 0$
$0.04m - 3n = 6.24$

48. $\frac{x}{3} - \frac{2y}{5} = 10$
$\frac{x}{6} - y = 17$

49. $0.07a - 0.08b = -0.07$
$0.04a - 0.09b = -0.35$

50. $1.1c - 2.3d = -0.35$
$2.4c - 2.3d = -0.22$

51. $\frac{x}{5} - \frac{3y}{2} = -\frac{71}{10}$
$\frac{2x}{5} + \frac{2y}{3} = \frac{62}{15}$

52. $\frac{x}{8} + y = 3\frac{1}{16}$
$\frac{1}{x} + \frac{1}{y} = \frac{5}{x}$

Don't be discouraged if you fail to solve a problem. Keep trying. A problem, like a puzzle, can be fun to solve.

The work of examining the given facts, deciding how to solve the problem, and actually solving the problem helps you learn to think in an orderly way.

You will find the habit of orderly thinking developed in this algebra course helpful in dealing with problems in everyday life.

Thinking a problem through to solution is sometimes hard work. But there is a reward: you feel that you have done a job well.

218 *ALGEBRA: ITS BIG IDEAS AND BASIC SKILLS*

Solution by Substitution

Elimination by substitution is the second algebraic method of solving pairs of equations. The idea is basically the same as the first method; namely, reduce the two equations with two variables to one equation with one variable.

Here are the steps to follow:

Step 1. Solve either equation for one of the variables.

Step 2. Substitute the value found in Step 1 in the remaining equation, thereby obtaining one equation with one variable.

Step 3. Solve this equation for the variable.

Step 4. Substitute the value obtained in Step 3 in the original equation used in Step 1 and solve for the other variable.

Step 5. Check by substituting the values of the variables in both original equations.

Example for Study

Solve for x *and* y: $\quad x - 2y = 4$
$$3x - y = 17$$

SOLUTION:

Solve the first equation for x in terms of y: $\quad x - 2y = 4$
$$x = 2y + 4$$

NOTE: You may solve either equation for one of the variables. Always select the equation and the variable that are easier to work with.

Substitute $2y + 4$ for x in the second equation and solve for y:
$$3x - y = 17$$
$$3(2y + 4) - y = 17$$
$$6y + 12 - y = 17$$
$$5y + 12 = 17$$
$$5y = 5$$
$$y = 1$$

Substitute 1 for y in the first equation and solve for x:
$$x - 2y = 4$$
$$x - 2 \cdot 1 = 4$$
$$x - 2 = 4$$
$$x = 6$$

CHECK: $\quad x - 2y = 4 \qquad\qquad 3x - y = 17$
$\quad 6 - 2 \cdot 1 \overset{?}{=} 4 \qquad\quad 3 \cdot 6 - 1 \overset{?}{=} 17$
$\quad\quad 6 - 2 \overset{?}{=} 4 \qquad\qquad 18 - 1 \overset{?}{=} 17$
$\quad\quad\quad 4 = 4 \qquad\qquad\quad 17 = 17$

PROBLEMS

Solve by substitution and check your answers:

1. $x = 2y$
   $x + 3y = 10$

2. $x = 4y$
   $x - y = 9$

3. $2x = y$
   $5x - 2y = 3$

4. $x - y = 2$
   $2x - 3y = 2$

5. $3x + y = 8$
   $4x - 3y = -11$

6. $x = 3y + 7$
   $2x - 5y = 13$

7. $x = y$
   $6x - y = 30$

8. $x - y = 7$
   $5x - 3y = 5$

9. $2x - 7y = 2$
   $x - 2y = 4$

10. $x - 6 = y$
    $2x + 3y = 27$

11. $x - 2y = -4$
    $10x - 3y = 28$

12. $x - y = 2$
    $9x - y = 10$

13. $x - y = 0$
    $13x - 15y = 16$

14. $\frac{1}{2}x + y = 3$
    $3x - 2y = 12$

15. $2x = 3y + 1$
    $4x - 3y = 11$

16. $2x - y = 1$
    $7x + 4y = -19$

17. $3x - 5y = 7$
    $2x + 3y = -8$

18. $2x - 4y = 10$
    $9x - 2y = 29$

19. $10x - 30y = 0$
    $x + 3y = 1$

20. $x = \dfrac{2y}{3} - 5$
    $6x + 7y = 3$

21. $\frac{1}{2}x = \frac{1}{2}y + 1$
    $x + y = 10$

22. $\dfrac{x}{3} = 2y - 14$
    $3x - 4y = 0$

23. $\dfrac{x}{9} = y$
    $x - 10y = 1$

24. $\dfrac{x}{3} = 2y$
    $x - y = 10$

25. $4x = 2y + 12$
    $2x - 3y = 8$

26. $x - y = 25$
    $x - \frac{1}{2}y = 19$

27. $x = \frac{3}{4}y$
    $x - y = 2$

28. $\frac{1}{2}x = 3y + 5$
    $x - 8y = 12$

29. $2y = 3x$
    $6x - 5y = 3$

30. $x - y = 11$
    $\frac{1}{3}x + \frac{1}{2}y = 2$

31. $x = 10y$
    $\frac{1}{2}x = 3y + 2$

32. $0.01x - 0.02y = 0$
    $x - 10y = 8$

Solve for x *and* y *by any method and check your answers:*

33. $x - \frac{1}{2}y = -2$
$2x + y = 0$

34. $2x - y = 5$
$x - \frac{1}{2}y = 2$

35. $x - 3 = y$
$\frac{1}{4}x - 1 = y$

36. $6x + y = 4$
$3x + 4y = 2$

37. $\frac{x}{8} - \frac{y}{3} = 0$
$\frac{x}{6} - \frac{y}{9} = 3$

38. $\frac{2x}{5} - \frac{y}{4} = -2$
$\frac{3x}{5} + \frac{y}{2} = -10$

39. $x + y = a$
$x - y = 5a$

40. $3x - y = b$
$x - 2y = 7b$

41. $x = 6$
$\frac{1}{2}x - y = 0$

42. $y - 10 = 0$
$y - 10x = 1$

43. $1.2y = 6x$
$2x + 7y = 37$

44. $0.5x = 0.2y + 4$
$y - x = -11$

★ 45. $\frac{x}{a} - \frac{y}{b} = 2$
$\frac{x}{a} + \frac{y}{b} = 0$

46. $ax - y = a$
$x + ay = 1$

47. $\frac{x}{2} - \frac{y}{3} = \frac{5}{9}$
$\frac{x}{5} - \frac{y}{2} = \frac{7}{15}$

48. $3ax = y$
$2x + \frac{y}{3a} = \frac{5}{a}$

49. $\frac{x}{3} - \frac{y}{4} = 1$
$\frac{3x}{2} - y = 4$

50. $\frac{4x}{5} - \frac{y}{4} = \frac{1}{2}$
$x - \frac{1}{3}y = 1$

SELF TEST

Solve and check each of the following systems of equations by the addition or subtraction method:

1. $x + y = 7$
$2x - 3y = -6$

2. $3x - y = -5$
$3x + y = 11$

3. $3x + 5y = 14$
$2x + 3y = 8$

4. $x + y = 8$
$2x + 2y = 8$

Solve and check each of the following systems of equations by the substitution method:

5. $y = x$
$3x + 5y = 32$

6. $x + y = 19$
$2x - 3y = -12$

7. $\frac{1}{2}y = 4x$
$5x + 3y = 29$

8. $x - y = 4$
$\frac{1}{3}x + \frac{1}{5}y = 4$

SYSTEMS OF LINEAR EQUATIONS **221**

The Algebraic Method of Solving Verbal Problems

A real test of your skill in algebra is solving verbal problems. If you are a good problem solver, you have three abilities:

(1) You can read and understand what you read.

(2) You can write what you read in the form of an equation or equations.

(3) You can solve the equation or the system of equations.

In solving word problems by the algebraic method, you use the three abilities above in the order in which they are listed. In the pages that follow you will have practice in reading problems, writing the facts contained in the problems as equations, and solving the equations that you have written.

Example for Study

The sum of two numbers is 21 and their difference is 9. Using one variable, write the facts in this statement as one equation. Then, using two variables, write the facts in the form of a system of two equations.

SOLUTION:

AS ONE EQUATION	AS TWO EQUATIONS
Let $x =$ the larger number; then,	Let $x =$ the larger number and
$21 - x =$ the smaller number	$y =$ the smaller number
Hence, $x - (21 - x) = 9$	Hence, $x + y = 21$
	$x - y = 9$

PROBLEMS

Read the following statements and write the facts in the form of equations. First use one variable and write one equation. Then use two variables and write the facts in the form of a system of two equations with two variables. Do not solve the equations you have written.

1. The sum of two numbers is 63 and the difference between the larger number and one-half of the smaller number is 30.
2. The sum of two numbers is 27. The larger number is twice the smaller number.
3. The sum of two numbers is 26. Twice the larger number is 19 more than the smaller number.
4. Joe and Roy have 95 cents between them. Roy has 7 cents more than Joe.
5. A man made two investments, the first at 4% and the second at 6%. He received a yearly income from them of $200. If the total investment was $4000, how much did he invest at each rate?
6. The sum of Mary's and Richard's ages is 14. In 2 years Mary will be twice as old as Richard. What are their present ages?

Solving Verbal Problems Using Two Variables

When solving word problems, you will find it helpful to follow these steps:

Step 1. Read the problem and decide which quantities are unknown. Represent these unknown quantities by variables.

Step 2. Study the stated facts until you understand their meaning. Then write these facts in the form of a system of two equations with two variables.

Step 3. Solve the system of equations.

Step 4. Check by comparing your solution with the facts stated in the word problem.

Example for Study

The sum of two numbers is 84 and the difference between them is 18. Find the two numbers.

SOLUTION:

Represent the unknown quantities by variables:

$$x = \text{the larger number}$$
$$y = \text{the smaller number}$$

Write the stated facts as a system of equations:

$$x + y = 84$$
$$x - y = 18$$

Solve the system of equations:

$$x = 51$$
$$y = 33$$

Check by comparing your solution with the facts stated in the word problem:

The sum of the two numbers is 84: $51 + 33 = 84$
The difference of the two numbers is 18: $51 - 33 = 18$

NOTE: It is important that you check the answers with the facts in the word problem, because you may have made an error in setting up your equations.

PROBLEMS

1. Find two numbers whose sum is 108 and whose difference is 36.
2. If three times the smaller of two numbers is increased by five times the larger number, the result is 128. The sum of the numbers is 30. Find the two numbers.
3. If the larger of two numbers is diminished by one-half of the smaller number, the result is 67. The difference between the two numbers is 45. Find the two numbers.
4. The sum of two numbers is 49. The larger number is 7 more than the smaller number. Find the two numbers.
5. The first of two numbers is 16 more than the second number. If the first number is added to twice the second number, the result is 139. Find the two numbers.
6. One number is five times another number, and their difference is 44. Find the two numbers.
7. The smaller of two numbers is three-fourths of the larger number. What are the two numbers if their difference is 6?
8. Separate 124 into two numbers so that two-thirds of the smaller number equals one-fourth of the larger number.
9. Find two consecutive numbers whose sum is 57.
10. Find two consecutive odd numbers so that twice the first number increased by three times the second number is 121.
11. The sum of two numbers is 45. If the larger number is divided by the smaller number, the quotient is 4 and the remainder is 5. Find the two numbers.
12. Separate 85 into two numbers so that the first number divided by the second number gives a quotient of 2 and a remainder of 10.
13. Judy is 6 years older than her brother Paul. Four years ago she was twice as old as Paul. Find the present ages of Judy and Paul.
14. Oscar is 8 years older than Oswald. Five years ago Oscar was three times as old as Oswald. Find the present ages of Oscar and Oswald.
15. Pauline is 2 years younger than Shirley. Four years from now the sum of their ages will be 36. Find the present ages of Pauline and Shirley.
16. George Jordan has two sons. If the sum of their ages is 19 and the difference between their ages is 3, what are the ages of the two sons?
17. Harry is three times as old as Dick. Find the age of each if the sum of their ages is 24.
18. A man is four times as old as his son. Eighteen years from now he will be only twice as old as his son. Find the present ages of the man and his son.
19. Ann is 6 years younger than Rose. One-half of Ann's age is equal to one-third of Rose's age. How old are they now?

20. A candy-shop owner wished to mix candy selling for 75 cents per pound with another grade of candy selling for 50 cents per pound to get a mixture to be sold for 60 cents per pound. How many pounds of each grade of candy must he use to get 50 pounds of the 60-cent mixture?

SOLUTION: Let x = number of pounds of 75¢ candy
and y = number of pounds of 50¢ candy

Basis for each equation:

Number of pounds of 75¢ candy	+	number of pounds of 50¢ candy	=	number of pounds of mixture
x	+	y	=	50

Value of 75¢ candy	+	value of 50¢ candy	=	value of mixture
$75x$	+	$50y$	=	$60 \cdot 50$

Hence, the equations are:
$$x + y = 50$$
$$75x + 50y = 3000$$

Complete the solution and check.

21. How many pounds each of 95-cent and 90-cent coffee must be mixed to get a mixture of 90 pounds to be sold for 92 cents per pound?

22. A fruit dealer mixed apples that sold for 8 cents per pound with apples that sold for 11 cents per pound and sold the mixture at 10 cents per pound. How many pounds of each did he use if the total sale from the mixture was $30?

23. A dealer mixed oranges selling for 30 cents per dozen with oranges selling for 39 cents per dozen and sold the mixture at 35 cents per dozen. If he sold 90 dozen in all, how many dozen of each grade did he sell?

24. A store owner wishes to mix two grades of nuts selling for 48 cents and 60 cents per pound to make a mixture to sell for 55 cents per pound. How many pounds of each grade of nuts must he use in order to get 20 pounds of the mixture?

25. Thompson's stand collected $67.50 in one day's sale of single- and double-dip ice cream cones. The single-dip cones sold for 7 cents each and the double-dip cones sold for 12 cents each. If 3 single-dip cones were sold for every 2 of the double-dip cones, how many of each kind of cone were sold?

26. The gate receipts at a Crockett High School basketball game amounted to $288.60. The price of an adult ticket was 55 cents, and the price of a student ticket was 25 cents. If three student tickets were sold for every adult ticket, how many of each kind of ticket were sold?

27. A piggy bank contains 25 coins, consisting of nickels and dimes. If the total value of the money is $2.10, find the number of nickels and the number of dimes in the bank.

NOTE: The bases for the two equations are:

Number of nickels	+	number of dimes	=	total number of coins
Value of nickels	+	value of dimes	=	total value of coins

28. Mr. Shaw saves quarters and half dollars. If the total value of his collection is $62.50 and the number of quarters is 10 more than the number of half dollars, how many coins of each kind has he?

29. Joe has 85 cents in nickels and dimes, 14 coins in all. How many of each kind of coin has he?

30. Linda has $4.95 in dimes and quarters. She has 3 more quarters than dimes. How many coins of each kind has she?

31. Kathleen gave a $5 bill in paying for a season basketball ticket which cost $1 and received the change in dimes and quarters, 19 coins in all. How many coins of each kind did she receive?

32. The class dues for each pupil in a certain freshman class was 25 cents per semester. One morning 13 freshmen paid their dues, all in quarters and half dollars. After the proper change was made, there were 10 coins left for the treasurer. How many coins of each kind were there?

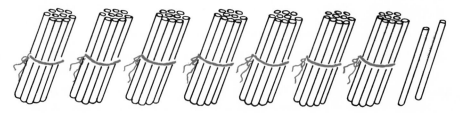

The number 72 is the same as 70 + 2; that is, the tens' digit 7 stands for 7 tens and the units' digit 2 stands for 2 ones. Hence, let u = the units' digit of a number and t = the tens' digit; then the number is $10t + u$.

226 *ALGEBRA: ITS BIG IDEAS AND BASIC SKILLS*

33. The sum of the digits of a two-digit number is 13. Find the number if the tens' digit is 5 less than the units' digit.
34. Find a two-digit number in which the units' digit is twice the tens' digit and the difference between the digits is 3.
35. The tens' digit of a two-digit number is twice the units' digit. One-half of the sum of the digits is equal to 2 less than the tens' digit. Find the number.
36. The units' digit of a two-digit number is 5 less than the tens' digit, and the number itself is the same as eight times the sum of the digits. What is the number?
37. The units' digit and the tens' digit of a two-digit number are consecutive numbers. The tens' digit is the smaller of the two. The number is 3 more than five times the sum of its digits. Find the number.

The number 52 means:

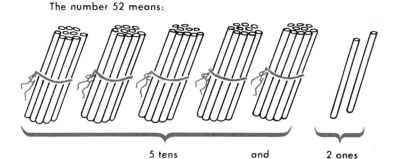

5 tens   and   2 ones

When the digits are reversed, there are:

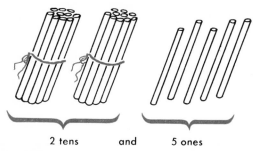

2 tens   and   5 ones

38. The units' digit of a two-digit number is 4 more than the tens' digit. If the digits were reversed, the new number would be 1 less than twice the number. Find the number.
39. In a certain number, the units' digit is 5 more than the tens' digit. If the digits were reversed, the new number would exceed twice the number by 7. Find the number.

40. The units' digit of a two-digit number is four times the tens' digit. If the digits were reversed, the new number would be 2 less than three times the original. Find the original number.

41. In any parallelogram the sum of any two adjacent angles is 180°. If angle y is $3\frac{1}{2}$ times as large as angle x, how many degrees are there in each angle?

42. If angle A of parallelogram $ABCD$ is 37° less than angle B, find the number of degrees in each angle.

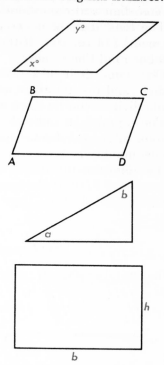

43. The acute angles of any right triangle are complementary; that is, their sum equals 90°. If angle a equals one-half of angle b, how many degrees has each angle?

44. The sides of a rectangle are b and h; b exceeds h by 10 inches. Find the length and the width of the rectangle if the perimeter is 102 inches.

45. The length of a rectangle exceeds twice its width by 7 inches. The perimeter is 44 inches. Find the length and the width.

46. During the Junior Red Cross drive, a class gave $4.60, all in dimes and quarters. If there were 37 coins in all, how many of each kind of coin were there?

47. An automobile sales company one week sold 6 standard-model cars and 4 custom-built models. The following week the same number of cars were sold but in reverse order. The sales for the first week totaled $18,493.40 and for the second week, $18,991.10. Find the price of each model.

★ 48. A and B are two pieces of lumber, each 1 rod in length. A is cut into an equal number of parts, of which each has the length a. B is also cut into an equal number of parts of length b each. Three parts of a and 2 parts of b total 54 inches, while 5 parts of a and 3 parts of b total 84 inches. Find the number of parts into which each piece of lumber is cut.

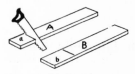

49. Mr. Day invested $15,000, a part at 3% and the rest at 4%. If his yearly income from these investments is $464, how much did he invest at each rate?

50. A contractor employed 100 men. The daily payroll was $1040. The unskilled laborers earned $8 per day, and the skilled laborers earned $14 per day. How many unskilled and how many skilled laborers did he employ?

51. On a two-day trip Mr. Allen drove 1240 miles. If during the first day he drove 80 miles more than during the second day, how many miles did he drive each day?

52. Peter rowed 18 miles downstream in 2 hours. The return trip took 4 hours. Find his speed in still water and the speed of the current.

53. Two investments, one at 4% and the other at 5%, yield a yearly income of $740. If the amount invested at 4% is $5000 more than that invested at 5%, how much money is invested at each rate?

★ *Systems of Inequations*

What number pairs (x, y) will satisfy each of the following inequations?

$$x + y > 2$$
$$x - y > 2$$
$$x < 7$$

To find the answer graphically, we will graph each of the inequations. Those points on the graphs of all three inequations will have coordinates that satisfy all three inequations. The graphs are shown here. Check to see that they are correct.

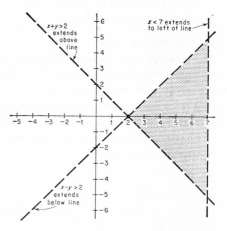

All points enclosed in the triangle are points whose coordinates will satisfy each of the three inequations. For example, the point (4.50, 0.25) is in the triangle. This pair of numbers will satisfy each of the three inequations as shown here.

$x + y > 2$	$4.50 + 0.25 > 2$
$x - y > 2$	$4.50 - 0.25 > 2$
$x < 7$	$4.50 < 7$

SYSTEMS OF LINEAR EQUATIONS **229**

PROBLEMS

For each of the following inequations, plot the graph of all pairs of (x, y) *that satisfy all the inequations in the set:*

1. $x > -2$
   $y > +2$

2. $x + y > -5$
   $x + y < -3$

3. $y + \frac{1}{2}x < 2$
   $x > -2$
   $y > +2$

4. $x > 4$
   $x < 3$

5. $x > 7$
   $y > -2$
   $y < -\frac{1}{2}x + 10$

6. $x + y < 2$
   $x > 0$
   $y > 0$

7. $5x > y$
   $y < 10$
   $x > 0$

8. $y > -x - 4$
   $y < -\frac{1}{2}x - 2$
   $x < 1$

9. $3x - y > 0$
   $2x + y > 0$
   $y < 7$

10. $2x + 7 < 15$
    $5y > 6$
    $y < x + \frac{1}{2}$

11. $y < |x|$
    $y > -2$
    $x < 6$
    $x > 2$

12. $x > 1$
    $x < 2$
    $y < 3$
    $y > 2$

SUMMARY OF IMPORTANT THINGS TO REMEMBER

1. *Words and Expressions*
   graphical solution
   solution by addition or subtraction
   solution by substitution
   system of inconsistent equations
   system of simultaneous equations
   systems of equations

2. *Understandings*
   To solve a system of two equations in x and y means to find the number for x and the number for y which when substituted in each equation will make the equations true statements.
   The solutions of a system of equations with two variables may be found by graphing or by algebraic methods.
   Using two equations with two variables is a useful method of solving many problems.

3. *Skills*
   You should be able to:
   Solve a system of two first-degree equations with two variables by graphing.
   Solve a system of two first-degree equations with two variables by addition or subtraction.
   Solve a system of two first-degree equations with two variables by substitution.
   Use the algebraic method of solving word problems.

PROBLEMS ON YOUR AIMS

YOUR AIM  To learn how to solve a system of two linear equations with two variables.

$x - 2y = -2$

x	?	?	?	?	?
y	2	3	4	5	6

$2x + 3y = 17$

x	-2	1	4	7	10	13
y	?	?	?	?	?	?

1. Copy and complete the table of values for each equation above.
2. How many solutions does each equation above have?
3. How many pairs of values for x and y did you find to be the same for the two equations? Can you find more?
4. If the graphs of the above equations were drawn on the same coordinate axes, would the lines intersect? If so, where?
5. What is meant when we say that equations such as $x - 2y = -2$ and $2x + 3y = 17$ have a common solution?
6. Why is the graphical method of solving systems of equations with two variables not considered to be a practical method?

Solve the following systems of equations by addition or subtraction:
7. $2x - y = 4$
   $3x + y = 6$
8. $x - 2y = 4$
   $2x + 3y = -13$

Solve the following systems of equations by substitution:
9. $x - y = 3$
   $3x + 2y = 14$
10. $2x + 3y = 5$
    $3x + 2y = 0$

YOUR AIM To improve your ability to use variables in writing equations for solving verbal problems.

1. If two variables are used in representing unknowns in a word problem, how many equations must you form to solve the problem?
2. If x stands for the units' digit and y stands for the tens' digit in a two-digit number, write the number in terms of x and y.
3. If x stands for the units' digit, $2x$ stands for the tens' digit, and $3x$ stands for hundreds' digit in a three-digit number, write the number in terms of x.
4. If x articles are bought at 10 cents each and y articles at 20 cents each, what is the total cost of the articles?
5. If n represents the largest of three consecutive odd numbers, what represents the smallest number?
6. A grocer sells 4 oranges and 3 bananas for 45 cents or 3 oranges and 4 bananas for 40 cents. If x stands for the price of the oranges and y for the price of the bananas, find the price of each.

SYSTEMS OF LINEAR EQUATIONS **231**

VALUABLE SKILLS PRACTICE

Reduce each of the following to the simplest form:

1. $-(-6) - (-3) - (-1)$
2. $(5)(-2)^3 - (-1)^3(-1)^3$
3. $(\frac{1}{4})^3 (8)^2 - (-16)(-\frac{1}{2})^4$
4. $4(-2 + 5)^2 \div \frac{3}{4}$
5. $10 + (+8) - (-12) - (+40)$
6. $(-1)^4 - (-2)^3 + (-3)^2(-4)$

7. Do each of the problems in the table below. Check your work by substituting the values of a and b in the formula given at the bottom of the table.

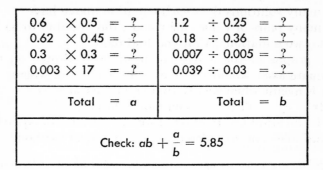

$0.6 \times 0.5 = \underline{?}$	$1.2 \div 0.25 = \underline{?}$
$0.62 \times 0.45 = \underline{?}$	$0.18 \div 0.36 = \underline{?}$
$0.3 \times 0.3 = \underline{?}$	$0.007 \div 0.005 = \underline{?}$
$0.003 \times 17 = \underline{?}$	$0.039 \div 0.03 = \underline{?}$
Total $= a$	Total $= b$

$$\text{Check: } ab + \frac{a}{b} = 5.85$$

$V = lwh$
$V = e^3$
$V = \frac{4}{3}\pi r^3$
$V = \frac{1}{3}\pi r^2 h$
$V = \pi r^2 h$

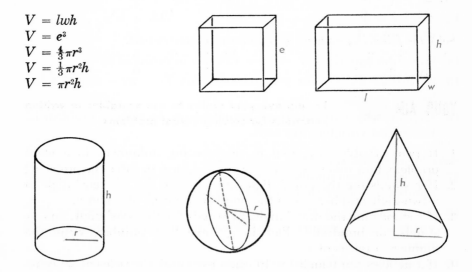

Examine the formulas and figures above. Then select the formula for finding the volume of each of the following.

8. Cylinder
9. Cube
10. Rectangular solid
11. Sphere
12. Cone

232 *ALGEBRA: ITS BIG IDEAS AND BASIC SKILLS*

CHAPTER TEST

Solve the following systems of equations graphically:

1. $x - 2y = 5$
   $2x + y = 5$

2. $2x - y = 0$
   $3x + 2y = 14$

3. Do the equations $3x - y = 16$ and $3x - y = 18$ have a common solution? Explain.

4. If the equations $5x - y = 8$ and $2x + y = 6$ were graphed, what would be the coordinates of their point of intersection?

5. At what point do the graphs of the equations $y = 5$ and $2x - 3y = 5$ intersect?

Solve the following systems of equations by addition or subtraction:

6. $15a - 2b = 5$
   $15a + 8b = 55$

7. $3m - 7n = -41$
   $8m + 5n = 9$

8. $\frac{1}{5}x - \frac{2}{3}y = 8$
   $x - 3y = 37$

9. $0.2x - 0.3y = 0.1$
   $x + y = 13$

Solve the following systems of equations by substitution:

10. $3x = y$
    $6x - y = 6$

11. $x - 4y = 0$
    $\frac{1}{3}x - \frac{2}{3}y = 2$

12. $x - 2y = 3$
    $5x = 6y - 1$

13. $x = y$
    $\frac{2}{3}x - \frac{1}{6}y = 6$

14. Solve the equation $3x - 2y = 12$ for y in terms of x.

15. Substitute $4x - 1$ for y in the equation $7x - 2y = 5$ and solve for x.

16. Explain why two equations are necessary to solve a problem in which two variables are used.

Solve by using two variables:

17. The sum of two numbers is 96. Find the two numbers if the larger number is 3 more than twice the smaller number.

18. An investment of $2400, part at 3% and the remainder at 4%, yields a yearly income of $81. Find the amount invested at each rate.

19. A two-digit number is 1 more than five times the sum of its digits. If the digits were reversed, the new number would exceed the number by 9. Find the number.

20. Steel and nickel when combined in the right proportion form a strong nickel-steel alloy. If three times as much steel as nickel is used in the process, how many pounds of each metal must be used in making 1 ton of this alloy?

Solve by using one variable or two variables, whichever is easier:

21. If three-sevenths of a number is decreased by 5, the result is 16. Find the number.
22. If a number is increased by two-fifths of itself, the result is 50. Find the number.
23. Find the altitude of a triangle whose base is 4.2 inches and whose area is 35.7 square inches.
24. Each leg of an isosceles triangle is twice the length of its base. Its perimeter is 56.5 inches. Find the base.
25. Harry is 6 years older than George. Six years ago Harry was twice as old as George. Find their present ages.
26. On opening day a school bookstore sold 320 notebooks, some at 25 cents each and the rest at 80 cents each. How many notebooks of each kind were sold if the total sale was $190.55?
27. A man left a will dividing $50,000 as follows: "Of the $50,000, my wife gets $10,000 less than three times the amount left to the public library." How much did his wife get?
28. It takes Tom 3 hours to drive a certain distance. By increasing his speed 8 miles per hour, he can drive this distance in three-quarters of an hour less time. Find his rate of travel at the faster speed.
29. A man invests equal amounts of money in two businesses. From one he receives interest at 6.5% and from the other he receives interest at 8.25%. During the first year he received $11.76 more from the 8.25% investment than from the 6.5% investment. How much did he invest in each business?
30. The tens' digit of a two-digit number is larger by 1 than three times the units' digit. The number is eight times the sum of the digits. What is the number?
31. Eight pencils and 10 tablets cost $1.90. Twelve pencils and 9 tablets cost $1.95. Find the cost of 1 pencil and 1 tablet.
32. The difference between the highest and the lowest temperature readings on a certain day was 27°. The reading of the highest temperature was three times as large as that of the lowest temperature. Find the two readings.
33. Mr. George invested a total of $10,500. Part of this money was invested at 2% interest and the rest at 3% interest. The total interest received was $270. How much money did Mr. George invest at each rate of interest?
34. Sally has $2.15 in nickels and dimes. She has one more nickel than she has dimes. How many nickels and dimes has she?
35. An airplane flew 330 miles with the wind in 2 hours. The return trip, against the wind, took 2 hours and 16 minutes. Find the plane's speed in still air and the speed of the wind.

CUMULATIVE REVIEW PROBLEMS

WORKING WITH ALGEBRAIC EXPRESSIONS

Find the value of the following expressions if $a = 3, b = -3, c = 1$, *and* $m = 0$:

1. $ab - c(a + b)$
2. $a^a + b^c$
3. $m^a + b^c + c^a$
4. $\left(\dfrac{a}{b}\right)^a + c^c$
5. $abc - (ab)(mc)$
6. $\dfrac{am + bc}{c - b}$

7. How many cents are there in $3n$ nickels and $2d$ dimes?
8. Five years ago Bob was a years old. What will be his age 10 years from now?
9. If n is an even number, what is the second consecutive even number following n?
10. If a rocket plane can fly d miles in h hours, how far can it fly in 10 hours? In t hours?
11. Multiply $a^2 - y - a$ by $16 + 2a^2 - 3a$.
12. Simplify $18 - a(a - 6) - 10(6 - a) - (a - a^2)$.
13. If $a = \frac{1}{2}b$ and $b = \frac{1}{2}c$, what is the value of a in terms of c?
14. If $x = 0.1y$ and $y = 0.1z$, find x in terms of z.
15. If a is 6 more than b and b is 3 less than c, find c in terms of a.

In the formula $W = fd$, *what change takes place in* W *if*:
16. f is constant but d increases?
17. d is constant but f decreases?
18. Both f and d increase?
19. f and d are each doubled?

In the formula $S = 16t^2$, *what change takes place in* S *if*:
20. t increases?
21. t decreases?
22. t is doubled?
23. t is halved?

SOLVING EQUATIONS

Solve for x:

1. $7x - 1 = x + 2$
2. $1.5 = 3x - 1.2$
3. $\frac{1}{2}x - 16 = 2x - 10$
4. $100 - 2x = x + 40$
5. $2(x - 1) - 3(-4x + 1) = 1$
6. $\frac{3}{5} - x = \frac{1}{3}x$
7. $x - \frac{1}{2} = \frac{1}{2}x$
8. $2 = x + 2$
9. $5x - 1.5 = 1.5$
10. $\dfrac{x}{2} = \dfrac{1}{2} - x$
11. $ax = b$
12. $\dfrac{x}{a} = b$
13. $ax = \dfrac{1}{a}$
14. $ax - b = c$
15. $ax - a = 0$
16. $\dfrac{2x}{m} - m = 1$

SYSTEMS OF LINEAR EQUATIONS **235**

Solve for x *and* y:

17. $x = 2y + 11$
    $5x - 3y = 34$

18. $x + 2y = 6$
    $3x - 2y = 14$

19. $3x = 4y$
    $6x - 2y = 6$

20. $0.2x - 3y = 5$
    $x + 3y = 7$

21. $3x = 8y - 34$
    $5x + 8y = -14$

22. $4x - y = -2$
    $2x - y = -1$

23. $x = -25y$
    $x + 5y = 10$

24. $2y = 3x + 2$
    $4y = x + 24$

25. $16 - x = y$
    $3x + 57 = 4y$

26. $14x + y = 0$
    $8x - y = 11$

27. $x = 5$
    $2x - \frac{1}{2}y = 0$

28. $y + 4 = 0$
    $7x - 5y = 6$

29. $2x = 5y$
    $x = 2y + 2$

30. $0.04x + 0.5y = 5.08$
    $x = 2y - 18$

31. $x + y = 0$
    $\frac{1}{3}x = \frac{1}{2}y + 10$

32. $x - 2y = 45$
    $\frac{1}{5}x - y = 15$

33. $x + y = 3a$
    $x - y = a$

34. $2x - 3y = 5a$
    $x - 2y = 3a$

35. $ax + by = 2$
    $2ax - by = 1$

36. $0.5x = 1 + y$
    $2x - y = 4$

37. If a divided by 3 equals $6a$ decreased by 18, find a.
38. Is $x = -5$ a root of the equation $3x - 15 = 0$?
39. What degree is the equation $x + 3y = 10$? How many solutions has this equation? Is $x = 2$, $y = 3$ a solution?
40. What degree is the equation $y = 2x^2 + 1$? Is $x = 0$, $y = 1$ a solution to this equation?
41. If $a = -4$, what is the value of x in the equation $4ax + a^2 = 24$?
42. $a^2 - ax = 12$. Find x if $a = \frac{1}{2}$.

WORKING WITH GRAPHS

1. Does the point $(3, -5)$ fall on the graph of $3x + y = -6$?
2. What is the slope of the graph of $x - 3y = 12$?
3. Find, by graphing, the common solution to: $x - y = 8$
$$x - 2y = 6$$
4. If the slope of the graph of a first-degree equation is 2 and the y-intercept is -10, write the equation of the graph.
5. What is the slope of the graph of $y = 6x - 3$?
6. What is the slope of the graph of $y = 6x + 2$?
7. What important geometric fact do you know about the graphs of the two equations given in Problems 5 and 6?
8. Without drawing the graphs, tell where the graphs of the equations $y = 4x - 3$ and $y = 2x - 3$ intersect.

236 *ALGEBRA: ITS BIG IDEAS AND BASIC SKILLS*

SOLVING VERBAL PROBLEMS

1. Two planes took off from an airport and flew in opposite directions. One plane traveled 140 miles per hour faster than the other. At the end of $2\frac{1}{2}$ hours, the planes were 1750 miles apart. Find the average speed of each plane.

2. Two bicycle riders left a point at the same time and rode in opposite directions. One rider traveled 2 miles per hour faster than the other. At the end of 3 hours and 10 minutes, the two riders were 50 miles apart. What was the speed of each rider?

3. Find two consecutive even numbers whose sum is 626.

4. The sum of one number and twice another number is 102. The difference between the numbers is 9. Find the numbers. Can you find two pairs of numbers which satisfy these conditions?

5. The ratio of two numbers is five-eighths. The difference of three times the smaller number subtracted from the larger number is -21. Find the two numbers.

6. A gasoline station has 62 quarts of oil, consisting of two grades. One grade sells for 45 cents a quart and the other for 35 cents a quart. When all the oil is sold, the amount received will be $25.10. How many quarts of each kind of oil does the station have?

7. The sum of the digits of a two-digit number is 10. The number is sixteen times the units' digit. Find the number.

8. The ratio of the tens' and units' digits of a certain two-digit number is 2. The difference between the number and the number obtained by reversing the digits is 36. Find the number.

9. The sum of the two acute angles of a right triangle is $90°$. One of these angles is $18°$ more than three times the other. Find each of the acute angles.

10. If the length of a certain rectangle is decreased by 3 inches and the width is increased by 2 inches, the area remains unchanged. Also, if the length is increased by 3 inches and the width is decreased by 1 inch, the area is unchanged. Find the length and the width of the rectangle.

11. Ted has 280 stamps. His collection consists of British and United States stamps and is valued at $33.60. The average value of each kind of stamp is the same, namely, 12 cents. How many stamps of each kind has Ted if he has three times as many British stamps as he has United States stamps?

12. Bill and Steve walked 8 miles. They walked part of the distance at the rate of 3 miles per hour and part at the rate of 4 miles per hour. If they had walked at 3 miles per hour the distance that they covered at 4 miles per hour and if they had walked at 4 miles per hour the distance that they covered at 3 miles per hour, their trip would have taken one-third of an hour less time. Find the distance the boys walked at each rate.

SYSTEMS OF LINEAR EQUATIONS **237**

SOME HIGHLIGHTS IN THE DEVELOPMENT OF MATHEMATICS

EGYPTIANS BECOME SKILLED IN PRACTICAL GEOMETRY

2000 B.C.

Before 2000 B.C. the ancient Egyptians developed practical geometry. Each spring the Nile River flooded their lands, making it necessary to relocate the boundaries. As a result of this necessity, their surveyors, who were called "rope stretchers," became skilled in practical geometry. They learned, for example, that if they made the sides of a triangle 3, 4, and 5 units in length, a right triangle would be formed.

GREEKS MASTER GEOMETRY

The ancient Greeks made great advances in the study of geometry. About 300 B.C. Euclid wrote his *Elements*, which is still the basis of modern geometry. In their study the early Greeks used sand and a stick for making diagrams.

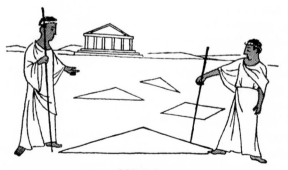

300 B.C.

HINDUS INVENT NUMBER SYSTEM

We are indebted to the Hindus for the invention of zero and our number system. This invention dates back to about A.D. 400. The Arabs borrowed the idea from the Hindus and later passed it on to the European peoples. This is why we refer to the system as Hindu-Arabic numbers.

A.D. 400

ARABS DEVELOP ALGEBRA

The Arabs are generally given credit for developing algebra, although they borrowed much from the Hindus. However, to one Arab, by the name of Muhammad ibn musa Al-Khowarizmi, much credit must be given, for he wrote the first algebra book. He called his book *Al-jabr w-al-muqabalah*. This lengthy title in use became *al-jabr*, from which eventually our present word *algebra* evolved.

A.D. 800

ANALYTIC GEOMETRY

René Descartes, a French philosopher, developed analytic geometry (his work was published in 1637) by selecting a pair of perpendicular lines, or coordinate axes, for locating points in a plane. This scheme enabled mathematicians to represent and to apply algebraic equations to geometric figures. And this use proved, indeed, to be a big idea. It led to great advances in mathematics and contributed much to-

René Descartes

ward the progress of civilization. Calculus, in all probability, would never have developed without it. Today, in honor of Descartes' great work, the coordinates of a point are often referred to as "Cartesian coordinates."

HIGHLIGHTS IN MATHEMATICS **239**

BIG IDEA	EQUATION
BASIC SKILLS	Using and interpreting symbols of algebra
	Fundamental operations
	Evaluating algebraic expressions
	Solving equations
	Factoring
	Solving verbal problems

CHAPTER **9** *Special Products and Factoring*

THE PURPOSE of this chapter is to help you to become more skillful in working with algebraic expressions. You will learn how to find products of certain algebraic expressions in a short way. You will also learn how to find factors of algebraic expressions. You will need these skills in solving a new kind of equation, called "quadratic equation." Quadratic equations, in turn, are very helpful in solving word problems, just as linear equations are helpful in solving some word problems.

YOUR AIM

1. To learn how to multiply certain algebraic expressions using short-cut methods.

2. To learn how to recognize quickly the factors of an algebraic expression.

3. To learn how to use factoring in solving second-degree equations.

240

Products and Factors

You remember the meaning of *product* and the meaning of *factor*. A product is the result of multiplying two or more numbers. A factor is one of the numbers multiplied to obtain a product.

$$3 \cdot 7 = 21 \qquad\qquad a \cdot b = ab$$

21 is the product $\qquad ab$ is the product

3 and 7 are factors $\qquad a$ and b are factors

There are special cases in multiplication in which you may use quick and easy methods of finding the products. You will learn these methods to become more skillful in using algebra.

Finding the factors of a number or of an algebraic expression involves, in a sense, reversing the multiplication.

$$5 \cdot 3 = 15 \qquad 15 \div 3 = 5 \qquad 15 = 5 \cdot 3$$

Multiplying $\qquad$ Dividing $\qquad$ Factoring

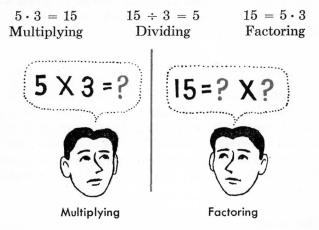

Multiplying $\qquad\qquad$ Factoring

If you were asked to name two factors of 15, undoubtedly you could state readily that 5 and 3 are factors of 15. However, if you were asked to give two factors of 51, you might not have a ready answer. How could you go about finding the factors? There are two methods that you might employ:

(1) *Trial and error:* In this method you try several combinations of numbers until you find the right one. Of course, you should use judgment as to which numbers to try.

$$8 \cdot 7 = 56$$
$$9 \cdot 5 = 45$$
$$2 \cdot 25 = 50$$
$$7 \cdot 7 = 49$$
$$3 \cdot 16 = 48$$
$$3 \cdot 17 = 51$$

Hence, 3 and 17 are factors of 51.

(2) *Division combined with trial and error:* In this method the trial and error is in selecting the trial numbers for dividing. Perhaps you will realize at once that 2 is not a factor, since 51 is an odd number. Thus you will try only odd numbers. The division shows that 2 and 25 are *not* factors and that 3 and 17 *are* factors of 51.

$$\begin{array}{r} 25 \\ 2\overline{)51} \\ \underline{4} \\ 11 \\ \underline{10} \\ 1 \end{array} \quad \text{remainder} \qquad \begin{array}{r} 17 \\ 3\overline{)51} \\ \underline{3} \\ 21 \\ \underline{21} \\ \end{array}$$

Factors of a number do not have to be whole numbers. For example, $7 = 3 \times 2\frac{1}{3}$. Therefore, 3 and $2\frac{1}{3}$ are factors of 7. When we speak of *factors of a number,* however, we will mean *whole-number factors.* You will find that usually there are more ways than one of factoring a number.

FOR EXAMPLE: $12 = 1 \cdot 12$ or $12 = 2 \cdot 6$ or $12 = 3 \cdot 4$

When a number is separated into all the factors possible, these factors are spoken of as **prime factors** of the number. The prime factors of 6 are 2 and 3. The prime factors of 12 are 2, 2, and 3, since $2 \cdot 2 \cdot 3 = 12$. The prime factors of 10 are 2 and 5, because $2 \cdot 5 = 10$ and 2 and 5 cannot be factored except into themselves times 1. Prime factors, then, are factors that are not divisible by another number except themselves and 1.

Example for Study

Find the prime factors of 75.

SOLUTION: Try 5: $75 \div 5 = 15$ and $15 = 3 \cdot 5$

So $75 = 3 \cdot 5 \cdot 5$

The prime factors of 75 are 3, 5, and 5.

PROBLEMS

Find all the possible whole-number pairs of factors of each of the following numbers:

1. 10	2. 15	3. 21	4. 28	5. 36
6. 30	7. 20	8. 27	9. 60	10. 88

Find all the prime factors of each of the following numbers:

11. 18	12. 24	13. 25	14. 33	15. 45
16. 39	17. 32	18. 81	19. 56	20. 6
21. 112	22. 124	23. 58	24. 16	25. 132
26. 128	27. 374	28. 143	29. 819	30. 714

Using the Distributive Principle

Suppose you want to multiply a polynomial by a monomial, for example, $3x + 2y$ by $4x$. You can write the product as $4x(3x + 2y)$. Sometimes you will want to write the product in different form. To do this, you can use the distributive principle. This principle may be stated: For every value of a, b, and c,

$$a(b + c) = ab + ac$$

Example for Study

Change the form of the product: $4x(3x + 2y)$

SOLUTION:
In the distributive principle, a corresponds to $4x$, b to $3x$, and c to $2y$. Hence:

$$4x(3x + 2y) = (4x)(3x) + (4x)(2y)$$
$$= 12x^2 + 8xy$$

Notice that the factor $4x$ is distributed to both terms of the quantity.

PROBLEMS

Using the distributive principle, change the form of the following products:

1. $2(2x + 3)$
2. $6(a - b)$
3. $2a(m - 3n)$
4. $3x(2x - 1)$
5. $4b(3b - 2c)$
6. $x(x^2 - x)$
7. $-m(-m + mn)$
8. $-cd(cd + 1)$
9. $a^2(a^2 + b^2)$
10. $xy(xy - y)$
11. $\frac{1}{2}a^3b(4a^2b^2 - 2ab^3)$
12. $\frac{1}{3}m^3n(12m^3n^4 + 15m)$
13. $0.1a(10a - 20)$
14. $0.01k(120k - 0.1)$
15. $\frac{4}{3}d(\frac{1}{2}d^2 - \frac{1}{4})$
16. $7a^2b^3(3ab^3c + ab^4 - 3a^2c)$

Examples for Study

1. $x^m \cdot x^n = x^{m+n}$ 2. $x^a \cdot x = x^{a+1}$ 3. $x^{4a} \cdot x^{3a} = x^{7a}$

Whenever a letter is used as an exponent in this chapter, the only numbers that can be substituted for it are positive whole numbers.

Change the form of the following products:

17. $x^a(x^a + 1)$
18. $x^{2a}(x^{3a} - 3)$
19. $a^x(a^x + a^y)$
20. $e^x(e^{2x} - e^x)$
21. $2a^m(3a^{4m} - 2a)$
22. $m^n(m^n - m)$
23. $a(a^a + a)$
24. $(x^a)^5$
25. $(a^5)^b$
26. $3x^a(x^b + x^c)$
27. $-c^5(b^4 - c^a)$
28. $4n^{2b}(3b + n^b)$
29. $-3v(-6v - v^v)$
30. $m^a n^b(-mn + m^a n^b)$
31. $a^{2y}(a^{3y} - b^{2y})$

32. $(a + b)(c + d)$
33. $(m - n)(p + q)$
34. $(x + y)(x + y)$
35. $(z - y)(z - y)$
36. $(a + b)(a - b)$
37. $(c + 4)(c - 4)$

SPECIAL PRODUCTS AND FACTORING **243**

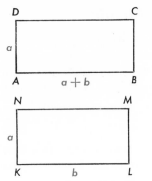

38. What is the area of rectangle $ABCD$?

39. What is the perimeter of rectangle $ABCD$?

40. What is the area of the rectangle $KLMN$?

41. Find the area of rectangle $KLMN$ if the length b is increased 3 units.

42. $A = lw$ is the formula for finding the area of a rectangle. Write the expression for the area of a rectangle in which $l = 2w + 3$.

43. $C = 2\pi r$. Find C if $r = x + \frac{1}{2}$.

44. Write the expression for $\frac{1}{2}ax$ if $x = a - \frac{1}{2}$.

Factoring Polynomials Having Common Factors

The distributive principle tells us that for every value of a, b, and c, $a(b + c) = ab + ac$. Notice that the factor a appears in each term on the right side of the equation. A factor which appears in each term of an algebraic expression is called a **common factor.** The distributive principle enables us to remove a common factor from terms having such a factor. The expression we get is a product having two or more factors. For example,

$$2rx + 2ry = 2r(x + y)$$ by the distributive principle where a corresponds to $2r$, b to x, and c to y

$$14mn - 7mn^2 = 7mn(2 - n)$$ by the distributive principle where a corresponds to $7mn$, b to 2, and c to n

In selecting common factors, it is important that you discover the **greatest common factor.** In $4a^2 + 12a$, 4 is common to both terms. If you write:

$$4a^2 + 12a = 4(a^2 + 3a)$$

notice that $(a^2 + 3a)$ still has a common factor remaining, that is, a. Hence, the greatest common factor is $4a$.

$$4a^2 + 12a = 4a(a + 3)$$

Study the following steps in factoring a polynomial.

$$ax + bx + cx = x(a + b + c)$$

Step 1. Determine by inspection the greatest common factor.

Step 2. Write the greatest common factor outside a set of parentheses.

Step 3. Fill in the quantity within the parentheses by dividing each term of the polynomial by the greatest common factor.

Example for Study

$Factor: 6a^2b - 15ab^2$

SOLUTION: $6a^2b - 15ab^2 = 3ab(2a - 5b)$

CHECK: If the two factors are multiplied, they should give the original expression. Observe, however, if $3a$ had been selected as a factor, then the factors would have been:

$$6a^2b - 15ab^2 = 3a(2ab - 5b^2)$$

When multiplied, these factors give the original polynomial. But this is not the solution you were seeking, for you wanted the greatest common factor $3ab$.

PROBLEMS

Factor each of the following:

1. $ax + ay$
2. $2a - 2b$
3. $4x - 8$
4. $6m + 6n$
5. $2ab - 2ac$
6. $x^2 - xy$
7. $14m^2 + 42m$
8. $ab + a$
9. $16y - 8$
10. $18r - 12rs$
11. $51mn + 9mn^2$
12. $36pq - 18q$
13. $9 - 6b$
14. $ca - 3c$
15. $3y - 2y$
16. $5x + 7x + 6x$
17. $2\pi r - 2\pi R$
18. $\frac{1}{2}hb + \frac{1}{2}hb$
19. $3b^2y + by^2$
20. $8nk - 12n$
21. $k^2m - mk^2$
22. $x^3 + x^2 + x$
23. $ax^2 + ax + a$
24. $3a^2 + 3a$
25. $5x^2 + 5x + 5$
26. $\frac{1}{2}abc - \frac{1}{2}a^2b^2c^2$
27. $3x^6 - 4x^3$
28. $a^4 - a^3$
29. $x^8 + x^3$
30. $\frac{1}{3}\pi r^2h - \frac{1}{3}\pi R^2h$

★ 31. $5 - 10x - 20y$
32. $10x^2y + 15xy - 5y$
33. $2a + 4ab + 2ac$
34. $24ax^2 - 16a$
35. $9x - 6y + 12z$
36. $102xy - 6xy^2$
37. $72a^7b^5 - 48a^3b^3$
38. $\frac{1}{2}a^2 + \frac{1}{2}$
39. $\frac{3}{4}x - \frac{1}{4}y + \frac{1}{4}$
40. $0.4a^2 - 0.8a - 0.4$
41. $1.6w - 0.8w^2$
42. $a^{2x} + a^x$

Example for Study

$Factor: m^{x+y} + m^x$

SOLUTION: Notice that m^{x+y} is the same as $m^x \cdot m^y$.
$$m^x m^y + m^x = m^x(m^y + 1)$$

Factor each of the following:

43. $a^{3m} + 3a^{2m}$
44. $e^x - 2e^{2x}$
45. $x^{m+2} + x^2$
46. $a^x b + a^{3x} b$
47. $a^{2a} - a^a$
48. $x^5 \cdot x^3 - x^3$

49. If $b = a + 5$, rewrite $ab + 2b = b(a + 2)$.
50. If $m = a - 2$, rewrite $3am - m = m(3a - 1)$.

Example for Study

Factor: $a(m + n) + b(m + n)$

SOLUTION: To understand this problem, rewrite this expression replacing $m + n$ by x:

$$ax + bx$$

In this form it is clear that x is a common factor and may be divided out:

$$ax + bx = x(a + b)$$

Now replace x by $m + n$:

$$a(m + n) + b(m + n) = (m + n)(a + b)$$

Notice that the quantity $m + n$ is a common factor, just as x is a common factor.

Factor each of the following:

51. $x(a + 1) + y(a + 1)$

52. $3m(2a - b) - 4n(2a - b)$

53. $ax + ay + cx + cy$

54. $10m - 10 + am - a$

55. $ax^2 + x + a^2x + a$

56. $2x - 4 - ax + 2a$

57. $a(x + y + z) - b(x + y + z)$

58. $p(a - b) - r(a - b)$

59. If R is the radius of one circle and r is the radius of another circle, write a formula in factored form to show the sum of the areas of the two circles.

60. If the area of $ABCD$ is $ab - 2b$, what is the length of side AB?

61. How many inches are there in f feet and y yards? Write the result in factored form.

62. In the figure at the right what are the coordinates of point P? Of point T?

63. What is the length of side PR? Of RS?

64. What is the perimeter of $PRST$?

65. What is the area of $PRST$? Write the result in factored form.

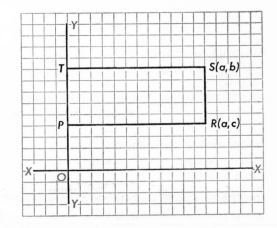

246 *ALGEBRA: ITS BIG IDEAS AND BASIC SKILLS*

Multiplying Two Binomials

Suppose in the distributive principle, $a(b + c) = ab + ac$, a is replaced by a binomial such as $(2b - 3c)$. Then,

$$(2b - 3c)(b + c) = (2b - 3c)b + (2b - 3c)c$$
$$= 2b^2 - 3bc + 2bc - 3c^2$$
$$= 2b^2 - bc - 3c^2$$

Study the following examples. In the first example the product is found by a long method and then by a shorter method.

Examples for Study

1. *Find the product:* $x + 4$ *and* $x + 3$.

SOLUTION:

LONG METHOD

$x + 4$
$x + 3$
$\overline{x^2 + 4x}$
$ + 3x + 12$
$\overline{x^2 + 7x + 12}$

SHORT METHOD

$+x^2 \quad +12$
$(x + 4)(x + 3) = x^2 + 7x + 12$
$+4x$
$+3x$

You do the following steps mentally in the short method:

Step 1. Find the product of the first terms:

$$x \cdot x = x^2$$

Step 2. Find the sum of the products of the inside and the outside terms:

$$(4 \cdot x) + (x \cdot 3) = 4x + 3x = 7x$$

Step 3. Find the product of the last terms:

$$4 \cdot 3 = 12$$

2. *Find the product:* $(2x - 3)(3x + 1)$

SOLUTION:

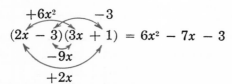

$+6x^2 \qquad -3$
$(2x - 3)(3x + 1) = 6x^2 - 7x - 3$
$-9x$
$+2x$

Practice until you can do all these steps mentally, using your pencil only to write down the answers.

SPECIAL PRODUCTS AND FACTORING **247**

PROBLEMS

Write the first terms only for each of the products in Problems 1–6:

1. $(x + 6)(x + 5)$
2. $(2a + 1)(a + 3)$
3. $(7m + 2)(6m + 5)$
4. $(x^2 - 8)(3x^2 - 7)$
5. $(\frac{1}{2}x + 3)(\frac{1}{3}x + 2)$
6. $(0.2x + 5)(0.3x - 1)$

Write the middle terms only for each of the products in Problems 7–12:

7. $(a + 3)(a + 2)$
8. $(m + 2)(m + 6)$
9. $(3x - 2)(2x - 3)$
10. $(x + 8)(x - 5)$
11. $(2y - 10)(y + 3)$
12. $(0.5a + 8)(0.1a - 2)$

Write the last terms only for each of the products in Problems 13–18:

13. $(m + 8)(m + 3)$
14. $(x - 6)(x - 7)$
15. $(y - 10)(y + 2)$
16. $(a - b)(a - b)$
17. $(x - 2y)(x + 3y)$
18. $(x - 0.01)(x + 0.02)$

19. Read off mentally the entire products in Problems 1–18.

Find the products of the following binomials:

20. $(a + 7)(a + 2)$
21. $(a + 3)(a + 5)$
22. $(b - 4)(b - 3)$
23. $(m - 10)(m - 4)$
24. $(x + 1)(x + 2)$
25. $(x - 12)(x - 2)$
26. $(y - 6)(y - 6)$
27. $(5 + x)(4 + x)$
28. $(2 - m)(3 - m)$
29. $(10 + x)(10 + x)$
30. $(2x - 1)(3x - 4)$
31. $(6x - 1)(5x - 1)$
32. $(x + 7)(x - 5)$
33. $(y - 2)(y + 3)$
34. $(2x - 3)(x + 1)$
35. $(10x - 1)(x - 1)$
36. $(y - 10)(2y + 11)$
37. $(m - 13)(m + 2)$
38. $(8 - a)(5 + a)$
39. $(t - 11)(3t + 1)$
40. $(x - 4)(x + 5)$
41. $(y - 7)(y + 4)$
42. $(m - 8)(m - 7)$
43. $(2a - 3)(4a + 1)$
44. $(10b + 3)(5b - 2)$
45. $(9x - 4)(3x + 7)$
46. $(h - 10)(h + 11)$
47. $(16x - 1)(10x - 1)$
48. $(4 - 3y)(5 + 3y)$
49. $(12 - a)(12 + a)$
50. $(3x + 4)(2x - 5)$
51. $(a - 12)(a + 11)$
52. $(x + y)(x + 2y)$
53. $(a - 3b)(a - 2b)$
54. $(m + 4n)(2m - n)$
55. $(6r - t)(6r - t)$
56. $(11k - p)(5k + p)$
57. $(ab + 1)(ab + 2)$
58. $(xy - 3)(xy - 4)$
59. $(ad + 4)(2ad - 3)$
60. $(x^2 - 2)(x^2 - 2)$
61. $(a^3 - 3)(a^3 + 5)$

★
62. $(m^2 + n^2)(m^2 + 2n^2)$
63. $(a^2b^2 - 3)(2a^2b^2 - 1)$
64. $(\frac{1}{2}a - 4)(\frac{1}{2}a - 6)$
65. $(\frac{1}{3}x - 2)(\frac{1}{2}x + 6)$
66. $(\frac{3}{5}y - 2)(\frac{2}{5}y - 7)$
67. $(\frac{1}{4}m + \frac{1}{2})(\frac{3}{4}m - \frac{1}{2})$
68. $(0.1x - 0.2y)(0.01x - 0.3y)$
69. $(0.05a - 0.05)(a + 1)$
70. $(a^x + 1)(a^x + 2)$
71. $(e^x - 3)(e^x + 5)$
72. $(a^{2x} + 5)(a^{2x} + 3)$
73. $(2a^m - 3)(3a^m + 7)$
74. $(a^n - b)(a^n + b)$
75. $(a^{5x} - 7)(a^{5x} - 5)$

Factoring Trinomials

Since $(x + 2)(x + 3) = x^2 + 5x + 6$, the factors of $x^2 + 5x + 6$ are $(x + 2)$ and $(x + 3)$. Your problem now is to begin with a trinomial, such as $x^2 + 5x + 6$, and discover how to find its binomial factors. You must not assume, however, that every trinomial has binomial factors. But any trinomial that is produced as a result of multiplying two binomials may be changed back to two binomial factors.

The method of factoring a trinomial of the type $ax^2 + bx + c$ is systematic trial and error; that is, it is the method of examining the possible combinations until the correct combination is discovered.

Assume that you do not know the factors of $x^2 + 5x + 6$. Begin by writing the two sets of parentheses for the two factors:
$$x^2 + 5x + 6 = (\qquad)(\qquad)$$
Now, thinking in reverse from the process of multiplying two binomials, note three facts:

(1) x^2 was produced as a result of multiplying the first terms of the binomials. Therefore, you may write:
$$(x \qquad)(x \qquad)$$
(2) $+6$ was produced as a result of multiplying the last terms of the binomials. This allows two possibilities for these terms: 1 and 6 or 2 and 3. Thus you now know that the factors are either:
$$(x + 1)(x + 6) \quad \text{or} \quad (x + 2)(x + 3)$$
(3) $+5x$, the middle term, is the algebraic sum of the product of the inside terms and the product of the outside terms. A quick mental check shows you that the correct combination is:
$$(x + 2)(x + 3)$$

Examples for Study

1. *Factor:* $8x^2 + 6x - 5$

SOLUTION: $8x^2 + 6x - 5 = (\qquad)(\qquad)$

Note these facts:

(1) The first terms of the binomials must be factors of $8x^2$, that is, $4x \cdot 2x$ or $8x \cdot 1x$.

(2) The last terms of the binomials must be factors of -5. Since the sign of 5 is minus, its factors must have unlike signs, that is, one positive and the other negative, as $(-5)(+1)$ or $(+5)(-1)$.

(3) The sum of the products of the inside terms and the outside terms must be $+6x$. Begin by writing possible factors until you find the right combination:
$$(4x - 1)(2x + 5)$$
$$(4x - 5)(2x + 1)$$
$$(4x + 5)(2x - 1)$$
The third trial is correct.
$$8x^2 + 6x - 5 = (4x + 5)(2x - 1)$$

2. *Factor:* $4x^2 - 7x + 3$

SOLUTION: $4x^2 - 7x + 3 = ($ $)($ $)$

Note these facts:

(1) The first terms of the binomials are either $4x$ and x or $2x$ and $2x$.

(2) The last terms of the binomials may be either $+3$ and $+1$ or -3 and -1, since $(+3)(+1) = +3$ and $(-3)(-1) = +3$.

(3) The middle term is negative. Therefore, the sign between both sets of terms is negative. So, the possibilities are:

$$(2x - 1)(2x - 3)$$
$$(4x - 1)(x - 3)$$
$$(4x - 3)(x - 1)$$

The last of these trials is correct.

$$4x^2 - 7x + 3 = (4x - 3)(x - 1)$$

PROBLEMS

Factor the following trinomials:

1. $a^2 + 5a + 6$ 　　　 2. $x^2 + 8x + 15$ 　　　 3. $x^2 + 3x + 2$

4. $m^2 + 7m + 10$ 　　 5. $b^2 + 6b + 8$ 　　　 6. $x^2 + 7x + 12$

$x^2 + 6x - 7 = (x + 7)(x - 1)$

If the constant term of a trinomial is negative, the signs between the terms of the binomial factors will be unlike.

---

7. $x^2 - 9x + 20$ 　　　　　　 8. $m^2 - 10m + 21$

9. $a^2 - 8a + 12$ 　　　　　 10. $b^2 - 7b + 6$

11. $x^2 - 2x - 15$ 　　　　 12. $y^2 - y - 12$

13. $d^2 + 4d - 12$ 　　　　 14. $n^2 + 2n - 24$

15. $m^2 + 3m - 28$ 　　　 16. $x^2 - 12x + 36$

$x^2 - 10x + 24 = (x - 6)(x - 4)$

If the constant term of a trinomial is positive, the signs between the terms of the binomial factors will be alike. The sign of the first-powered term of the trinomial determines whether the signs are both positive or both negative.

---

17. $x^2 - 6x - 40$ 　　　　 18. $r^2 + 4r - 32$

19. $a^2 + 9a + 8$ 　　　　 20. $c^2 + 10c - 11$

21. $6a^2 - 7a + 2$ 　　　　 22. $2x^2 - 3x + 1$

23. $10x^2 - 23x - 5$ 　　 24. $12m^2 + 32m + 5$

25. $5x^2 + 14x - 3$ 　　　 26. $8y^2 + 11y + 3$

27. $6d^2 - 25d + 4$ 　　　 28. $10p^2 - 49p - 5$

SELF TEST

Find the prime factors of each of the following numbers:
1. 25   2. 30   3. 84   4. 45
5. 264   6. 80   7. 405   8. 250

Multiply:
9. $3(5x + 6)$ 10. $-xy(x^2 + 3y)$ 11. $\frac{2}{3}k(15k + 9)$
12. $(x + 5)(x - 7)$ 13. $(y - 3)(y + 2)$ 14. $(3a + 2b)(a - b)$

Factor each of the following:
15. $5x - 5y$ 16. $a^2 + ab$ 17. $9x^2y - 6xy + 12y$
18. $y^2 - 10y + 21$ 19. $r^2 + 3r - 18$ 20. $8x^2 - 18x - 18$

Factoring Completely

One of the first things you should do in factoring is to look at each term of the polynomial to see if there is a common factor present. This common factor should be factored out first. For example, to factor $4x^2 + 12x + 8$, first factor out 4.
$$4x^2 + 12x + 8 = 4(x^2 + 3x + 2)$$
Now the trinomial in the parentheses can be factored.
$$4(x^2 + 3x + 2) = 4(x + 2)(x + 1)$$
If the common factor 4 had not first been factored out, you would have factored as follows:
$$4x^2 + 12x + 8 = (4x + 8)(x + 1)$$
$$= 4(x + 2)(x + 1)$$
$$\text{or} \quad 4x^2 + 12x + 8 = (x + 2)(4x + 4)$$
$$= 4(x + 2)(x + 1)$$

PROBLEMS

Factor completely:
1. $2x^2 + 8x + 6$ 2. $5x^2 + 5x - 30$
3. $6x^2 + 33x + 36$ 4. $ax^2 - 5ax + 6a$
5. $x^3 + x^2 - 20x$ 6. $3x^3 - 6x^2 - 24x$
7. $4x^2 - 28x + 40$ 8. $6bx^3 + 11bx^2 - 2bx$
9. $48 + 30x + 3x^2$ 10. $120x^4 - 10x^3 - 350x^2$
11. $5x + 10x^2 - 15x^3$ 12. $2x^3 - 16x^2 - 18x$
13. $6x - 54xy + 84xy^2$ 14. $a^3b^3 + 2a^2b^2 + ab$
15. $a + 2ax + ax^2$ 16. $m^4n^4 - m^3n^3 - 2m^2n^2$
17. $12x^2 - 12x - 144$ 18. $5x^3 - 4x^2 - x$
19. $\frac{3}{4}x^2 + \frac{1}{4}x - \frac{1}{2}$ 20. $4.5x^2 + 2.4x + 0.3$
21. $2x^2 + 2$ 22. $x^2 + 2x + 2$
23. $a^2b + ab$ 24. $m^3 - m$
25. $3a^2 + 10ab + 3b^2$ 26. $18 - 18y^2$
27. $k - k^5$ 28. $\frac{1}{2} - \frac{1}{4}x$

SPECIAL PRODUCTS AND FACTORING **251**

Squaring a Binomial

"To square a number" means "to multiply the number by itself." For example, 3^2 means $3 \cdot 3$, or 9. Similarly, x^2 means $x \cdot x$. $(x + y)^2$ means $(x + y)(x + y)$.

Example for Study

Find the square of the binomial $x + 3$.

SOLUTION: $(x + 3)^2 = (x + 3)(x + 3)$
$$= x^2 + 6x + 9$$

PROBLEMS

Find the square of each of the following binomials:

1. $x + 1$
2. $x + 2$
3. $a + 5$
4. $x - 10$
5. $a - 5$
6. $x - 7$
7. $2n + 1$
8. $2a + 1$
9. $4m - 3$
10. $5y - 6$
11. $2 - \frac{1}{2}a$
12. $1 - \frac{1}{4}x$

Try to discover a rule for squaring a binomial. Begin by representing any binomial, as $a + b$. If you square $a + b$, you get:
$$(a + b)^2 = a^2 + 2ab + b^2$$
Check this rule on several binomials whose squares you have found by ordinary multiplication.

Will your rule work for $(a - b)^2$?
$$(a - b)^2 = a^2 - 2ab + b^2$$
What change will you have to make in your rule?

DO YOU SEE? To square a binomial:

Square the first term | plus or minus | twice the product of the two terms | plus | the square of the last term

Find the answer to each of the following:

13. $(a + 5)^2$
14. $(x + 6)^2$
15. $(b + 1)^2$
16. $(d + 8)^2$
17. $(y + 10)^2$
18. $(m - 2)^2$
19. $(p - 11)^2$
20. $(t - 20)^2$
21. $(w - 15)^2$
22. $(1 - x)^2$
23. $(3x - 5)^2$
24. $(6y + 8)^2$
25. $(10d + 9)^2$
26. $(7m - 5)^2$
27. $(8n - 3)^2$
28. $(x + y)^2$
29. $(4x + 5y)^2$
30. $(x - 3y)^2$
31. $(9a + 7b)^2$
32. $(10c - 11d)^2$
33. $(4m + 5)^2$
34. $(5y + k)^2$
35. $(8 - x)^2$
36. $(3y - 7)^2$
37. $(2x + a)^2$
38. $(x - y)^2$
39. $(10x + 1)^2$
40. $(10x - 1)^2$
41. $(20 - k)^2$
42. $(20 + k)^2$
43. $(2x - y)^2$
44. $(x - 7y)^2$
45. $(5xy + 3x)^2$
46. $(8a^2b + 4a^2c)^2$
47. $(x - \frac{1}{2})^2$
48. $(y - \frac{2}{3})^2$

★ Applying the Rule for Squaring a Binomial

The rule for squaring a binomial is broad in its application. You may use it, for example, to find the square of a trinomial, as $(a + b + 3)^2$, or the square of any number, as 43^2.

Examples for Study

1. Find $(a + b + 3)^2$ by applying the rule for squaring a binomial.

SOLUTION: First group two of the terms and consider this grouping as one term. Then proceed as in squaring a binomial.
$$[(a + b) + 3]^2 = (a + b)^2 + 2 \cdot 3(a + b) + 3^2$$
$$= a^2 + 2ab + b^2 + 6a + 6b + 9$$

2. Find $(x + y - 5)^2$ by applying the rule for squaring a binomial.

SOLUTION: $[(x + y) - 5]^2 = (x + y)^2 - 2 \cdot 5(x + y) + 5^2$
$$= x^2 + 2xy + y^2 - 10x - 10y + 25$$

3. Find 43^2 by applying the rule for squaring a binomial.

SOLUTION: $43^2 = (40 + 3)^2 = 40^2 + 2 \cdot 120 + 3^2$
$$= 1600 + 240 + 9 = 1849$$

PROBLEMS

Do the operations indicated by applying the rule for squaring a binomial:

1. $(x + a + 6)^2$
2. $(2a + b + 5)^2$
3. $(x - 3y + 4)^2$
4. $(m - n - 7)^2$
5. $(a + b + c)^2$
6. $(2x - y + z)^2$
7. $(m - n - \frac{1}{2})^2$
8. $(2a + b - 1)^2$
9. $(\frac{1}{2}m + n - \frac{1}{2}p)^2$

The diagram on the left below is a geometric representation of the square of a binomial. Study this before doing Problem 10. Observe that the diagram is a square and that the length of each side is $a + b$.

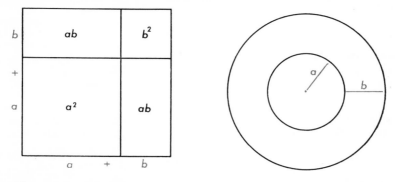

10. Show by a diagram similar to the one at the left above that $(2a + b)^2 = 4a^2 + 4ab + b^2$.
11. In $5x^2 - 6x + 8$ replace x by $2a - 1$. Write the result in the simplest form.
12. In the figure at the right above find the area of the larger circle.

Factoring Perfect-square Trinomials

You know that, by squaring a binomial like $a + b$, you get a trinomial $a^2 + 2ab + b^2$. The square of $a + b$ is written $(a + b)^2$.

Now if the trinomial $a^2 + 2ab + b^2$ is factored, two identical factors are obtained:

$$a^2 + 2ab + b^2 = (a + b)(a + b) \quad \text{or} \quad (a + b)^2$$

A trinomial which can be factored into two identical factors is called a **perfect-square trinomial**.

PROBLEMS

Factor each of the following perfect-square trinomials:

1. $x^2 + 6x + 9$
2. $x^2 + 4x + 4$
3. $m^2 + 10m + 25$
4. $x^2 - 12x + 36$
5. $a^2 + 2a + 1$
6. $4x^2 - 12x + 9$
7. $49y^2 - 70y + 25$
8. $121h^2 - 198h + 81$
9. $81 + 18m + m^2$
10. $121 - 22n + n^2$
11. $25p^2 + 60pq + 36q^2$
12. $400 - 40b + b^2$
13. $16x^2 - 4x + \frac{1}{4}$
14. $169d^2 - 260d + 100$
15. $y^2 + y + \frac{1}{4}$
16. $m^2 - \frac{2}{3}m + \frac{1}{9}$
17. $144 - 24y + y^2$
18. $\frac{1}{16}x^2 - \frac{1}{6}x + \frac{1}{9}$
19. $a^2 + 49b^2 + 14ab$
20. $x^2 + 64 - 16x$
21. $4a^2 - 12ab + 9b^2$
22. $\frac{1}{25}x^2 + \frac{8}{5}x + 16$
23. $r^2 + 36s^2 + 12rs$
24. $4k^2 - 2k + \frac{1}{4}$
25. $9k^2 + 2k + \frac{1}{9}$
26. $\frac{1}{16}x^2 + \frac{1}{4}x + \frac{1}{4}$

★

27. $y^2 + 0.4y + 0.04$
28. $\frac{1}{4} - \frac{1}{2}x + \frac{1}{4}x^2$
29. $\frac{1}{x^2} - \frac{2}{x} + 1$
30. $0.09 - 0.12y + 0.04y^2$
31. $\frac{a^2}{b^2} - \frac{2ac}{bd} + \frac{c^2}{d^2}$
32. $0.0025x^2 - 0.0005xy + 0.0001y^2$
33. $\frac{4}{a^2} - \frac{16}{3a} + \frac{16}{9}$
34. $\frac{9}{m^2} - \frac{n}{m} + \frac{n^2}{36}$
35. $\frac{0.01}{a^2} - 1 + \frac{a^2}{0.04}$
36. $\frac{m^2}{0.16} + 1 + \frac{0.04}{m^2}$
37. $\frac{0.25}{k^2} + 2mk + \frac{m^2}{0.25}$
38. $\frac{10.24}{x^2} + \frac{6.4y}{x} + y^2$

Factor each of the following trinomials by removing the common factor first:

39. $3a^2 + 6a + 3$
40. $x^3 + 4x^2 + 4x$
41. $bx^2 + 8bx + 16b$
42. $-x^2 - 2x - 1$
43. $2x^2 - 2x + \frac{1}{2}$
44. $-0.001 + 0.004a - 0.004a^2$
45. $\frac{1}{8}a^2 - \frac{1}{6}ab + \frac{1}{18}b^2$
46. $\frac{x^2}{2a} - \frac{xy}{a} + \frac{y^2}{2a}$

254 *ALGEBRA: ITS BIG IDEAS AND BASIC SKILLS*

How to Identify Perfect-square Trinomials

The following trinomials are perfect squares:
$$x^2 + 6x + 9$$
$$x^2 - 6x + 9$$

In a perfect-square trinomial:
1. Two terms of the trinomial must be positive and must be perfect squares, as x^2 and 9.
2. The remaining term may be either positive or negative but must be twice the product of the square roots of the other two terms, as

$$6x = 2\sqrt{x^2} \cdot \sqrt{9}$$
$$= 2 \cdot x \cdot 3$$
$$= 6x$$

The order in which the terms in a trinomial are written does not matter, because $x^2 + 9 + 6x$ is the same as $x^2 + 6x + 9$.

Example for Study

Find the term which when added to $x^2 + 18x$ will make it a perfect-square trinomial.

SOLUTION: Since the coefficient of $18x$ must be twice the product of the square roots of the other two terms, then $\frac{1}{2}$ of 18 should be the square root of the desired term. So the term is 9^2 or 81. The perfect-square trinomial is $x^2 + 18x + 81$.

PROBLEMS

Find the term which will make each expression a perfect-square trinomial:

1. $a^2 + 4a + \underline{\ ?\ }$
2. $a^2 + 10a + \underline{\ ?\ }$
3. $x^2 - 12x + \underline{\ ?\ }$
4. $b^2 - \underline{\ ?\ } + c^2$
5. $d^2 - \underline{\ ?\ } + 64$
6. $4a^2 - \underline{\ ?\ } + 9b^2$
7. $\underline{\ ?\ } + 8a + 16$
8. $\underline{\ ?\ } - 6b + 9$
9. $\underline{\ ?\ } - 10x + 25x^2$
10. $\underline{\ ?\ } - 48x + 64$
11. $x^2 + y^2 - \underline{\ ?\ }$
12. $14m + 49 + \underline{\ ?\ }$
13. $9y^2 + 1 - \underline{\ ?\ }$
14. $20n + n^2 + \underline{\ ?\ }$
15. $x^2 - \frac{1}{2}x + \underline{\ ?\ }$
16. $4a^2 + \underline{\ ?\ } + 9$

Tell which of the following are perfect-square trinomials:

17. $a^2 + 8a + 16$
18. $x^2 - 4x - 4$
19. $1 + y^2 + 2y$
20. $p^2 + 8p + 9$
21. $36 - 18a + 9a^2$
22. $q^2 + 10q + 25$
23. $a^2 + 2ab - b^2$
24. $x^2 + x + 1$
25. $m^2 - \frac{1}{2}m + \frac{1}{4}$
26. $\frac{1}{4}x^2 + \frac{1}{16} + \frac{1}{8}x$

SPECIAL PRODUCTS AND FACTORING **255**

Squares and Square Roots

The square root of any number is one of its two equal factors. 2 is a square root of 4, since $2 \cdot 2 = 4$. x is a square root of x^2, since $x \cdot x = x^2$. $a + 1$ is a square root of $a^2 + 2a + 1$, since $(a + 1)^2 = a^2 + 2a + 1$.

Since $3^2 = 9$ and $(-3)^2 = 9$, $+3$ and -3 are square roots of 9. The positive root $+3$ is called the "principal root" and is written $\sqrt{9}$. The negative square root of 9 is -3 and is written $-\sqrt{9}$.

$\sqrt{n}$ is understood to be $+\sqrt{n}$. Thus, the symbol $\sqrt{n}$ when not prefixed by a positive or a negative symbol is understood to indicate a positive number.

An important point to remember is that the square root of any positive number has one positive root and one negative root. When the square root of a number is written by means of the radical sign without a sign in front of it, only the positive, or principal, root is meant.

The Product of the Sum and the Difference

Let $a + b$ represent the sum of two numbers and $a - b$ represent the difference between the same two numbers. Then $(a + b)(a - b)$ represents the product of the sum of two numbers and the difference between the same two numbers.

Ordinarily, when you multiply two binomials, you get a trinomial. Thus, $(a + 3)(a + 4) = a^2 + 7a + 12$. But when you multiply the sum of two numbers by the difference between the same two numbers, the middle term is zero and the product is a binomial.

FOR EXAMPLE:
$$\overset{\displaystyle -5x}{\underset{\displaystyle +5x}{(x + 5)(x - 5)}} = x^2 - 25$$

The middle term is $-5x + 5x$, which is equal to zero.

DO YOU SEE? The product of the sum of two numbers and the difference between the same two numbers is the difference between the squares of the two numbers.

Examples for Study

1. $(y + 10)(y - 10) = y^2 - 100$
2. $(2a + 1)(2a - 1) = (2a)^2 - 1^2 = 4a^2 - 1$
3. $(x^2y^2 - \frac{2}{3})(x^2y^2 + \frac{2}{3}) = (x^2y^2)^2 - (\frac{2}{3})^2 = x^4y^4 - \frac{4}{9}$

256 *ALGEBRA: ITS BIG IDEAS AND BASIC SKILLS*

PROBLEMS

Examine the following and write their indicated products:

1. $(x + 4)(x - 4)$
2. $(x + 1)(x - 1)$
3. $(x + 3)(x - 3)$
4. $(a + 2)(a - 2)$
5. $(d - 10)(d + 10)$
6. $(x - 9)(x + 9)$
7. $(2x + 5)(2x - 5)$
8. $(3m - 8)(3m + 8)$
9. $(7n - 2)(7n + 2)$
10. $(10p + 6)(10p - 6)$
11. $(a - 2b)(a + 2b)$
12. $(c - 5d)(c + 5d)$
13. $(ab - 1)(ab + 1)$
14. $(xy + 12)(xy - 12)$
15. $(3a + 5b)(3a - 5b)$
16. $(x^2 - y^2)(x^2 + y^2)$
17. $(m^4 - n^4)(m^4 + n^4)$
18. $(c^2d^2 + 4)(c^2d^2 - 4)$
19. $(a^6 - 1)(a^6 + 1)$
20. $(a^3 + a^2)(a^3 - a^2)$
21. $(1 + 5m^2)(1 - 5m^2)$
22. $(20 - 11x)(20 + 11x)$
23. $\left(\dfrac{2x}{3} - 1\right)\left(\dfrac{2x}{3} + 1\right)$
24. $(\frac{1}{4}a + \frac{1}{2})(\frac{1}{4}a - \frac{1}{2})$
25. $\left(\dfrac{5a}{6} + 2\right)\left(\dfrac{5a}{6} - 2\right)$
26. $\left(2 - \dfrac{3x}{4}\right)\left(2 + \dfrac{3x}{4}\right)$
27. $\left(\dfrac{3}{x} + 5\right)\left(\dfrac{3}{x} - 5\right)$
28. $\left(\dfrac{2}{y} - \dfrac{x}{3}\right)\left(\dfrac{2}{y} + \dfrac{x}{3}\right)$

★ 29. $\left(\dfrac{2x^2}{5} + \dfrac{5}{9}\right)\left(\dfrac{2x^2}{5} - \dfrac{5}{9}\right)$
30. $(0.1m - 0.2n)(0.1m + 0.2n)$
31. $(0.09a - 8)(0.09a + 8)$
32. $(\frac{1}{3}x^3 - \frac{1}{5}y^5)(\frac{1}{3}x^3 + \frac{1}{5}y^5)$
33. $(x^4 + x)(x^4 - x)$
34. $(y^n + 1)(y^n - 1)$
35. $(a^z + 1)(a^z - 1)$
36. $(a^{2z} - b^y)(a^{2z} + b^y)$
37. $(a^m - b^n)(a^m + b^n)$
38. $(5x^{2a} + y^3)(5x^{2a} - y^3)$
39. $(a^a - b^b)(a^a + b^b)$
40. $(a - 2)(a + 2)(a^2 + 4)$
41. $(x + 3)(x - 3)(x^2 + 9)$
42. $(b^2 + 1)(b + 1)(b - 1)$
43. $(2x + 3)(2x - 3)(4x^2 + 9)$
44. $(\frac{1}{2}y - \frac{1}{3})(\frac{1}{2}y + \frac{1}{3})(\frac{1}{4}y^2 + \frac{1}{9})$
45. $[(x + y) + z][(x + y) - z]$
46. $[a + (b - c)][a - (b - c)]$

47. Mr. Walker decided to make a vegetable garden. He first laid it off in the form of a square, but later found that it would be more convenient if he increased the length by 6 feet and decreased the width by the same amount. Was the area of the new plot the same as the area of the square? Less than that of the original plot? Greater than that of the original plot? Support your answers with facts.

48. Mr. Wilson was making a metal box from some sheet metal. The plans called for a square base and a height of 5 inches. Mr. Wilson decided that he would change the plans and make the length 3 inches longer and the width 3 inches shorter. When he did this, the box had a volume of 200 cubic inches. What were the original dimensions of the box which were called for in the plans?

SPECIAL PRODUCTS AND FACTORING **257**

Factoring the Difference between Two Squares

Since $(a + b)(a - b) = a^2 - b^2$, $a + b$ and $a - b$ are factors of $a^2 - b^2$. Therefore, any binomial which is a difference between two squares can be factored. Also if a binomial can be reduced to a difference between two squares, it is factorable.

Examples for Study

1. *Factor:* $x^2 - \frac{1}{16}$

SOLUTION: $x^2 - \frac{1}{16} = (x + \frac{1}{4})(x - \frac{1}{4})$

2. *Factor:* $x^4 - y^4$

SOLUTION: $x^4 - y^4 = (x^2 + y^2)(x^2 - y^2)$
$$= (x^2 + y^2)(x + y)(x - y)$$

PROBLEMS

Factor:

1. $a^2 - 25$	2. $m^2 - 49$	3. $x^2 - 1$
4. $16 - 81a^2$	5. $100 - p^2$	6. $m^2 - n^2$
7. $x^2 - 9y^2$	8. $16 - a^2b^2$	9. $100p^2 - 1$
10. $144 - t^2$	11. $121 - w^4$	12. $m^2n^2 - p^2$
13. $1 - 169x^2y^4$	14. $625 - a^4$	15. $2a^2 - 2$
16. $3x^4 - 48$	17. $m^2n - n$	18. $\frac{1}{25}y^2 - \frac{1}{36}$
19. $p^4 - 256$	20. $3y^5 - 81y$	21. $m^2n^2 - 121$
22. $a^xb^2 - a^xc^2$	23. $0.09m^2 - 0.25$	24. $0.0081x^2 - 0.01$

★ 25. In $x^2 - b^2$, replace x by $m + n$ and factor.
26. In $a^2 - b^2$, replace b by $m + n$ and factor.

Factor:

27. $(x + y)^2 - 16$	28. $(m - 2n)^2 - 9$
29. $a^2 - (b + c)^2$	30. $9a^2 - (x - 3)^2$
31. $a^2 + 2ab + b^2 - c^2$	32. $(x + y)^2 - (a + b)^2$
33. $25 - x^2 - 2xy - y^2$	34. $1 - 2xy - x^2 - y^2$

Short Cuts in Arithmetic Derived from Algebra

You will now see how some of the rules for working with algebraic expressions can be used to simplify your work in arithmetic.

In multiplying two numbers like 19×21, you can think of 19 as $20 - 1$ and of 21 as $20 + 1$. Then,

$$19 \times 21 = (20 - 1)(20 + 1) = 20^2 - 1^2 = 399$$

258 *ALGEBRA: ITS BIG IDEAS AND BASIC SKILLS*

PROBLEMS

Multiply using the short cut explained on page 258:

1. $(29)(31)$ 2. $(39)(41)$ 3. $(49)(51)$ 4. $(59)(61)$
5. $(69)(71)$ 6. $(18)(22)$ 7. $(28)(32)$ 8. $(38)(42)$
9. $(48)(52)$ 10. $(58)(62)$ 11. $(17)(23)$ 12. $(27)(33)$
13. $(37)(43)$ 14. $(47)(53)$ 15. $(16)(24)$ 16. $(36)(44)$
17. $(15)(25)$ 18. $(25)(35)$ 19. $(45)(55)$ 20. $(24)(36)$

In squaring some numbers, it is convenient to think of the number as a sum of two numbers. Then you can use the rule for squaring a binomial.

FOR EXAMPLE:

$$21^2 = (20 + 1)^2 = 20^2 + 2 \cdot 20 \cdot 1 + 1^2 = 400 + 40 + 1 = 441$$

Find the square of each using the rule for squaring a binomial:

21. $(12)^2$ 22. $(22)^2$ 23. $(31)^2$ 24. $(32)^2$
25. $(41)^2$ 26. $(19)^2$ 27. $(29)^2$ 28. $(28)^2$

You can use the following short cut to multiply numbers that are slightly less than 100, 1000, 10,000, or slightly less than any other power of 10.

To multiply 98×97, write the difference between each number and 100 to the right of the number as shown. Then multiply the differences, 2×3, and write the product 6 in the units' place in the answer. Next subtract either 2 from 97 or 3 from 98. Write the difference 95 in hundreds' place. So the answer is 95 hundred plus 6, or 9506.

$$\begin{array}{rr} 98 & +2 \\ \times 97 & +3 \\ \hline 9506 & \end{array}$$

Here is the algebraic explanation of why this short cut works:

$$(100 - a)(100 - b) = 100 \cdot 100 - 100a - 100b + ab$$

Factoring 100 out of the first three terms, you get:

$$100(100 - a - b) + ab$$

This expression explains the steps used in the short cut.

29. In the example 98×97 what is a? What is b?
30. In the example 98×97 what is ab?
31. In the example 98×97 what is $100 - a$? What is $100 - a - b$?
32. Why do you write $100 - a - b$ in hundreds' place?

Use the short cut explained above to find the following products:

33. 99×98 34. 99×97 35. 96×98 36. 97×96
37. 95×98 38. 95×99 39. 96×95 40. 94×98
41. 93×96 42. 94×97 43. 93×97 44. 92×98
45. 92×99 46. 93×98 47. 91×96 48. 91×97

49. By algebra show that the above short cut works for numbers slightly less than 1000, like 998×997.

SPECIAL PRODUCTS AND FACTORING **259**

Use the short cut to find the following products:

50. 998×997 **51.** 996×999 **52.** 998×995 **53.** 993×999
54. 992×998 **55.** 993×996 **56.** 995×995 **57.** 992×991

58. Do you think you can multiply $99,999,997 \times 99,999,995$ by a short-cut method? Try it.

Numbers which are slightly larger than some power of 10, like 102×103, can also be multiplied using a short cut.

To multiply 102×103 by the short-cut method, write 2 and 3 to the right of the numbers 102 and 103, as shown. Multiply 2×3 and write the product 6 in the units' place in the answer. Next either add 2 to 103 or 3 to 102. Write the sum 105 in hundreds' place. The answer is 105 hundred plus 6, or 10,506.

$$
\begin{array}{r r}
102 & 2 \\
\underline{103} & 3 \\
10506 &
\end{array}
$$

An algebraic explanation for this short cut is as follows:

$$(100 + a)(100 + b) = 100 \cdot 100 + 100a + 100b + ab$$
$$= 100(100 + a + b) + ab$$

Use the short-cut method shown above to find the following products:

59. 101×103 **60.** 103×104 **61.** 105×102 **62.** 101×106
63. 105×105 **64.** 106×106 **65.** 104×108 **66.** 109×101
67. 108×102 **68.** 103×112 **69.** 105×101 **70.** 102×102

71. Can you solve $100,005 \times 100,006$ by a short-cut method? Try it.

Factoring out a common monomial factor will often save work.

Example for Study

Find the area of the shaded ring in the figure shown here. The radius of the inside circle is 8 inches and the radius of the outside circle is 9 inches.

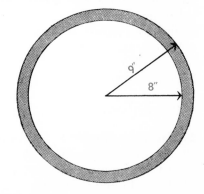

SOLUTION:

Area of ring = area of outside circle — area of inside circle

$$A = (3.14) \times 9^2 - (3.14) \times 8^2$$
$$= 3.14(9^2 - 8^2)$$
$$= 3.14(81 - 64)$$
$$= 3.14(17)$$
$$= 53.4 \text{ square inches}$$

260 *ALGEBRA: ITS BIG IDEAS AND BASIC SKILLS*

Find the answers to the following using factoring:

72. $8 \times 3 \times 4 - 8 \times 3 \times 3$ 73. $3.14(63) + 3.14(37)$

74. $4 \times 9(12)^2 + 3 \times 9(12)^2 - 5 \times 9(12)^2$

75. $3\frac{1}{2} \times 15 + 3\frac{1}{2} \times 17$

76. $4 \times 3 \times 7 \times 5 + 6 \times 2 \times 7 \times 5$

77. $\frac{1}{2} \times 7 \times 16 - \frac{1}{2} \times 7 \times 13$

78. $8^2 \times 6^2 \times 3 + 8 \times 6^3 \times 3^2$ 79. $25(17) + 25(3) + 25(30)$

80. $3.1416 \times 12^2 - 3.1416 \times 10^2$ 81. $98(3)(15^2) + 4(15) - 2(15^2)$

SELF TEST

Find the product of each of the following:

1. $(a + b)^2$ 2. $(3a - 5)^2$ 3. $(a + 2)(a - 2)$

4. $(2x - 3)(2x + 3)$ 5. $(ab + 2)(ab - 2)$ 6. $(2xy + 3)^2$

7. $(4x - 2y)^2$ 8. $(a^2 + b^2)(a^2 - b^2)$

Factor:

9. $z^2 - 25$ 10. $36 - y^2$ 11. $x^2 + 6x + 9$

12. $y^2 - 8y + 16$ 13. $49x^2 - 84x + 36$ 14. $z^2 + z + \frac{1}{4}$

15. $(x + y)^2 - 25$ 16. $z^4 - y^4$

Use a short-cut method to find the answer to each of the following:

17. $(39)(41)$ 18. $(31)^2$ 19. $(96)(95)$ 20. $(103)(105)$

★   ### Two Special Products

Find the products:

1. $(x + y)(x^2 - xy + y^2)$ 2. $(x - y)(x^2 + xy + y^2)$

3. $(a + b)(a^2 - ab + b^2)$ 4. $(a - b)(a^2 + ab + b^2)$

5. $(a + 1)(a^2 - a + 1)$ 6. $(a - 1)(a^2 + a + 1)$

7. $(1 + b)(1 - b + b^2)$ 8. $(1 - b)(1 + b + b^2)$

9. $(y + 3)(y^2 - 3y + 9)$ 10. $(y^2 - 3)(y^4 + 3y^2 + 9)$

DO YOU SEE? ☞ **1. The product of a binomial and trinomial of the form $(x + y)(x^2 - xy + y^2)$ is the sum of two cubes $x^3 + y^3$.**

2. The product of a binomial and a trinomial of the form $(x - y)(x^2 + xy + y^2)$ is the difference of two cubes $x^3 - y^3$.

Find the product of each of the following by inspection:

11. $(a + 2c)(a^2 - 2ac + 4c^2)$ 12. $(x + 3)(x^2 - 3x + 9)$

13. $(4y - 5)(16y^2 + 20y + 25)$ 14. $(4y + 5)(16y^2 - 20y + 25)$

15. $(a + \frac{1}{2})(a^2 - \frac{1}{2}a + \frac{1}{4})$ 16. $(y - \frac{1}{3})(y^2 + \frac{1}{3}y + \frac{1}{9})$

17. $(x + 0.3)(x^2 - 0.3x + 0.09)$ 18. $(1 - y + y^2)(1 + y)$

★ *Factoring the Sum of or the Difference between Two Cubes*

You have learned that:
$$(x + y)(x^2 - xy + y^2) = x^3 + y^3$$
$$(x - y)(x^2 + xy + y^2) = x^3 - y^3$$

You can use these facts to factor the sum of or the difference between two cubes.

Examples for Study

1. $x^3 - 1$ factors into $(x - 1)(x^2 + x + 1)$.
2. $8b^3 + c^3$ factors into $(2b + c)(4b^2 - 2bc + c^2)$.

PROBLEMS

Factor each of the following:

1. $a^3 + b^3$
2. $x^3 - y^3$
3. $x^3 - 8y^3$
4. $8x^3 + y^3$
5. $1 + 27a^3$
6. $125x^3 - y^3$
7. $x^6 + y^6$
8. $x^6 - y^6$
9. $125 - a^3$
10. $64r^3 - 27s^3$
11. $\frac{1}{8} - x^3$
12. $y^3 + \frac{1}{64}$
13. $0.001 - a^3$
14. $b^3 + 0.008$
15. $x^6 - y^3$
16. $125 - 27$
17. $125c^9 - b^6$
18. $3a^3 - 24b^3$
19. $5a^3 + 40b^3$
20. $2.7x^3 - 6.4y^3$
21. $1000x^3 + 125y^3$

★ *Factoring by Grouping*

You can factor some polynomials by grouping. For example, in the polynomial $ax + by + ay + bx$ you can group the terms having a in them and those having b in them:
$$ax + ay + bx + by$$

Next factor out a and b:
$$a(x + y) + b(x + y)$$
$(x + y)$ can now be factored out:
$$(x + y)(a + b)$$
Thus, $\qquad ax + by + ay + bx = (x + y)(a + b)$

Check this factoring by multiplying the two binomials.

PROBLEMS

Factor each of the following:

1. $ay + ax - by - bx$
2. $2y^2 - ay + 2xy - ax$
3. $6xy - 12ay + 9ax - 18a^2$
4. $4ax - 4bx - 3ac + 3bc$
5. $10ax - 12bx + 5ay - 6by$
6. $5ay - a - 15yc + 3c$
7. $4ak + a + 4bk + b$
8. $5ax - 5bx - 2ay + 2by$
9. $x + 1 + x^5 + x^4$
10. $3a^2x - 2b^2y + 2a^2y - 3b^2x$
11. $5ab + 5ac + 5bx + 5cx$
12. $kb^2 - 7abc + 7ac^2 - kbc$

262 *ALGEBRA: ITS BIG IDEAS AND BASIC SKILLS*

Solving Literal Equations

Equations like $ax + b = c$ are called **literal equations.** In equations of this kind there are several variables. Solving a literal equation means "expressing one of the variables in terms of the others." For example, the method of solving the literal equation $ax + b = c$ is the same as the method you used for solving the equation $2x + 6 = 10$.

Examples for Study

Solve the following equations for x:

1. $2x + 6 = 10$

SOLUTION: $2x = 10 - 6$

$$x = \frac{10 - 6}{2}$$

2. $ax + b = c$

SOLUTION: $ax = c - b$

$$x = \frac{c - b}{a}$$

3. $px - d = qx$

SOLUTION:

$$px - qx = d$$
$$x(p - q) = d$$
$$x = \frac{d}{p - q}$$

4. $ax - a^2 = bx - b^2$

SOLUTION:

$$ax - bx = a^2 - b^2$$
$$x(a - b) = (a + b)(a - b)$$
$$x = \frac{(a + b)(a - b)}{(a - b)}$$
$$x = a + b$$

PROBLEMS

Solve each of the following equations for x:

1. $ax + bx = c$
2. $mx = nx + p$
3. $bx - b^2 = x - 1$
4. $ax + 2x - b = 0$
5. $5x = 10a + 5$
6. $2x + 6 = 12s - x + 3$
7. $ax = an - a$
8. $mx + px = m^2 + 2mp + p^2$
9. $2px = px + a$
10. $3abx - a = abx$
11. $cx - dx = c^2 - d^2$
12. $ax - a^2 - 9 = 6a - 3x$
13. $mx - 2x = m^2 + m - 6$
14. $16 + ax - a = x + 15$
15. $x - ax = 1 - 2a + a^2$
16. $6x + ax = 1$
17. $4a + 3x = 2ax + 6$
18. $x - 1 = a - ax$
19. $\dfrac{ax}{b} = x + 1$
20. $bx - b^2 - 2bc = c^2 - cx$

★ 21. $c^2x - c + d = d^2x$

22. $\dfrac{ax}{b} = bx + 2$

23. $\dfrac{3 + x}{y} = \dfrac{5 + x}{y}$

24. $\dfrac{a}{k + x} = \dfrac{b}{m + x}$

25. $\dfrac{5}{x} + \dfrac{b}{2} + \dfrac{c}{d} = k$

26. $arx^2 = r$

27. $\dfrac{ax}{b} + \dfrac{ax}{c} = d$

28. $\dfrac{b}{ax} + \dfrac{c}{ax} = d$

Using Factoring to Solve Second-degree Equations

In solving any equation, you try to get the variable, such as x, by itself on one side of the equation; that is, you reduce the equation to the form:

$$x = \underline{\ ?\ }$$

You cannot easily change many second-degree equations to this form. You must first reduce them to two first-degree equations. The reason for this will be clear after you study the explanation and examples given below.

The method for reducing many second-degree equations to two first-degree equations depends upon this principle:

If the product of two factors equals zero, then at least one of these factors must equal zero.

1. If $a \cdot b = 0$, then before this can be a true statement, either $a = 0$ or $b = 0$ or both $a = 0$ and $b = 0$.
2. If $(x - 5)(x - 6) = 0$, then either $x - 5 = 0$ or $x - 6 = 0$ or both $x - 5 = 0$ and $x - 6 = 0$.

The equation in the second example is a second-degree equation. If you multiply the factors $(x - 5)$ and $(x - 6)$ in the equation $(x - 5)(x - 6) = 0$, you get $x^2 - 11x + 30 = 0$. This equation is called a "second-degree equation" or a **quadratic equation** because the highest power of the variable is 2.

You can reverse this procedure by first factoring the left side of the equation. Thus,

$$x^2 - 11x + 30 = 0$$
$$(x - 5)(x - 6) = 0$$

Since this product is equal to zero if either of the two factors is zero, set each factor equal to zero, thus getting two first-degree equations:

$$x - 5 = 0 \qquad x - 6 = 0$$
$$x = 5 \qquad x = 6$$

You may check whether these numbers are the roots of the equation by substituting them in the original equation:

$$
\begin{array}{ll}
x^2 - 11x + 30 = 0 & x^2 - 11x + 30 = 0 \\
5^2 - 11 \times 5 + 30 \overset{?}{=} 0 & 6^2 - 11 \times 6 + 30 \overset{?}{=} 0 \\
25 - 55 + 30 \overset{?}{=} 0 & 36 - 66 + 30 \overset{?}{=} 0 \\
0 = 0 & 0 = 0
\end{array}
$$

Since both numbers, 5 and 6, satisfy the original equation, you know that the quadratic equation $x^2 - 11x + 30 = 0$ has the roots 5 and 6.

Later you will learn a method of solving second-degree equations which cannot be factored.

Examples for Study

1. *Solve:* $x^2 - 10x = -21$

SOLUTION:

Rewrite the equation so that the right side is zero:

$$x^2 - 10x + 21 = 0$$

Factor:

$$(x - 7)(x - 3) = 0$$

Set each factor equal to zero and solve these first-degree equations:

$$x - 7 = 0 \qquad x - 3 = 0$$
$$x = 7 \qquad x = 3$$

CHECK: $x^2 - 10x = -21$ $\qquad$ $x^2 - 10x = -21$
$7^2 - 10 \times 7 \overset{?}{=} -21$ $\qquad$ $3^2 - 10 \times 3 \overset{?}{=} -21$
$-21 = -21$ $\qquad$ $-21 = -21$

2. *Solve:* $x^2 + 8 = 8 - 2x$

SOLUTION:

Rewrite the equation so that the right side becomes zero:

$$x^2 + 2x = 0$$

Factor:

$$x(x + 2) = 0$$

Set each factor equal to zero and solve each first-degree equation:

$$x = 0 \qquad x + 2 = 0$$
$$x = 0 \qquad x = -2$$

CHECK: $x^2 + 8 = 8 - 2x$ $\qquad$ $x^2 + 8 = 8 - 2x$
$0 + 8 \overset{?}{=} 8 - 0$ $\qquad$ $(-2)^2 + 8 \overset{?}{=} 8 - 2(-2)$
$8 = 8$ $\qquad$ $12 = 12$

PROBLEMS

Solve and check:

1. $x^2 + 15 = 8x$
2. $x^2 + 6x = 27$
3. $x^2 = 9x - 8$
4. $x^2 + 9x + 20 = 0$
5. $5x^2 = 4x$
6. $2x^2 - x = 0$
7. $x^2 - 12x = -32$
8. $x^2 - 100 = 0$
9. $x^2 - 13x + 42 = 0$
10. $x^2 - 5x = 6$
11. $25x^2 - 9 = 0$
12. $8x^2 = 14x + 15$
13. $2x^2 + 9 = 9x$
14. $6x^2 + 7x = 3$
15. $2x^2 + 6x = 2x - x^2 + 4$
16. $x^2 + 11x = -30$
17. $x^2 - 8x = 0$
18. $x^2 - 2x = 3$
19. $4x^2 = 1$
20. $x^2 - \frac{1}{4} = 0$
21. $x^2 - x = 56$
22. $x^2 - 9x = 10$
23. $3x^2 + 15x = x - 8$
24. $15x^2 + x = 2x + 2$

25. Three times the square of a number is 45 more than six times the number. What is the number?

SOLUTION: Let $x =$ the number

Write the equation: $\qquad$ $3x^2 = 6x + 45$

Divide by 3 to reduce the equation: $\qquad$ $x^2 = 2x + 15$

Rewrite the equation to make the
right side zero: $\qquad$ $x^2 - 2x - 15 = 0$

Factor: $\qquad$ $(x - 5)(x + 3) = 0$

Complete the solution and check.

26. The square of a number is 20 more than eight times the number. Find the number.

27. The square of a number increased by five times the number is 24. Find the number.

28. The product of two consecutive numbers is 21 more than five times the first number. What are the two numbers?

29. The area of a rectangle is 40 square inches. The length is 3 inches more than the width. Find the length and the width.

30. If one side of a square were increased by 5 feet and another side were decreased by 2 feet, the new area would be 44 square feet. Find a side of the square.

31. The product of two consecutive odd numbers is 143. Find the two numbers.

32. The length of a rectangle is four times the width. The area of the rectangle is 9 square feet. Find the length and the width.

DO YOU SEE? By learning how to factor algebraic expressions, you were able to learn a method of solving second-degree equations.

★ **Example for Study**

Find an equation whose roots are 3 and 5.

SOLUTION: If an equation has two roots, it is a quadratic equation. To find an equation, reverse the process used in solving it:

$$x = 3 \qquad\qquad x = 5$$
$$x - 3 = 0 \qquad x - 5 = 0$$

$$(x - 3)(x - 5) = 0$$
$$x^2 - 8x + 15 = 0$$

★ *For each of the following pairs of numbers find a quadratic equation of which the two given numbers are roots:*

33. 4, 7 $\qquad$ **34.** 6, 8 $\qquad$ **35.** $\frac{1}{2}, \frac{1}{4}$ $\qquad$ **36.** 0.2, 0.08

37. 5, 5 $\qquad$ **38.** $-3, 2$ $\qquad$ **39.** $-\frac{2}{3}, 1$ $\qquad$ **40.** 1.5, 2.5

SUMMARY OF IMPORTANT THINGS TO REMEMBER

1. *Words and Expressions*

common factors
factoring; factoring completely
greatest common factor
literal equation

perfect-square trinomial
prime factors
quadratic equation
square of a binomial

2. *Understandings*

By being able to recognize certain types of algebraic expressions, you can quickly determine factors of these expressions.

A product is zero if any of its factors is zero.

3. *Skills*

You should be able to:

Find special products by inspection.
Factor algebraic expressions.
Solve quadratic equations by factoring.

PROBLEMS ON YOUR AIMS

YOUR AIM **To learn how to multiply certain algebraic expressions using short-cut methods.**

1. What is the product of $3x$ and $4x^2 + 7x + 15$?

How many terms will there be in the product of each of the following?
2. $(3a - b)(4a + b)$ 3. $(x - 4)(x + 4)$ 4. $(2a - 1)(2b + 1)$

Describe short-cut methods for:
5. Squaring the binomial $a + b$.

6. Finding the product of the sum of and the difference between two numbers.

7. Finding the product of two binomials, such as $(2x - 3)(x + 5)$.

YOUR AIM **To learn how to recognize quickly the factors of an algebraic expression.**

Find the common factor or factors in each of the following expressions:
   1. $3x + 3y + 6$ 2. $ax^2 - a^2x$ 3. $-x - y - 4$

Which of the following are perfect-square trinomials?
   4. $x^2 - x + 1$ 5. $4a^2 + 4a + 1$ 6. $8xy + x^2 + y^2$

Which of the following have two factors, one representing the sum of two numbers and the other the difference between two numbers?
   7. $1 - x^2$ 8. $x^3 - 4$ 9. $ab^2 - a^3$

Find the binomial factors of:
10. $x^2 - 3x - 4$ 11. $x^4 - y^4$ 12. $6a^2m + am - 2m$

SPECIAL PRODUCTS AND FACTORING **267**

YOUR AIM

To learn how to use factoring in solving second-degree equations.

1. If the product of two factors is zero, as $m \cdot n = 0$, what must be true of at least one of the factors?
2. What use is made of the fact given in Problem 1 in solving second-degree equations?

Solve:

3. $2x^2 - x = 1$ 　　　　 4. $2x^2 - 3x = 0$ 　　　　 5. $x^2 - \frac{1}{9} = 0$

VALUABLE SKILLS PRACTICE

1. Add each column of numbers in the following table to find the values of a, b, c, and d. Check your answers by substituting them in the formula given at the bottom of the table.

8762	2101	9471	5847
1208	3889	2882	2618
3165	6763	6936	7821
7881	9001	8011	9678
6927	2817	2587	4829
5152	8523	7634	6732
a	b	c	d

CHECK: $(a - b)(d - c) = +4$

$A = lw$
$A = ab$
$A = \frac{1}{2}bh$
$A = \pi r^2$
$A = \frac{1}{2}h(a + b)$
$A = s^2$

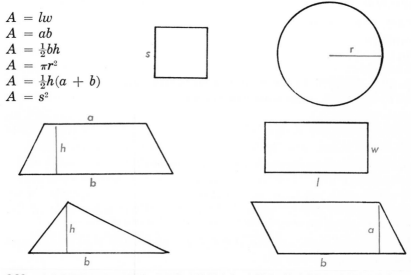

Examine the formulas and the figures on page 268. Then select the formula for finding the area of each of the following.

2. Square
4. Circle
6. Rectangle
3. Parallelogram
5. Triangle
7. Trapezoid

Find the value of $A = ab$ *when:*

8. $a = 1\frac{1}{5}$ inches and $b = 2\frac{1}{4}$ inches
9. $a = \frac{1}{3}$ yard and $b = 1\frac{1}{2}$ yards
10. $a = 7\frac{1}{4}$ feet and $b = 3\frac{1}{8}$ feet
11. $a = 6\frac{1}{2}$ rods and $b = 10\frac{1}{2}$ rods

Find the value of $A = \frac{1}{2}h(a + b)$ *in square inches when:*

12. $a = 1\frac{1}{2}$ inches, $b = 2\frac{1}{2}$ inches, $h = 3\frac{1}{2}$ inches
13. $a = \frac{3}{4}$ foot, $b = \frac{5}{8}$ foot, $h = \frac{3}{16}$ foot
14. $a = \frac{1}{3}$ yard, $b = \frac{2}{3}$ yard, $h = \frac{3}{8}$ yard
15. $a = 1$ foot 2 inches, $b = 2$ feet 6 inches, $h = 18$ inches

16. Find the area of a square one of whose sides is $1\frac{1}{3}$ inches.
17. Find the area of a triangle whose base is $2\frac{1}{4}$ inches and whose altitude is $3\frac{1}{2}$ inches.
18. Find the area of a circle whose radius is $3\frac{1}{2}$ inches. Use $\pi = 3\frac{1}{7}$.
19. Find the area of a trapezoid whose bases are $3\frac{1}{2}$ and $5\frac{1}{3}$ inches and whose altitude is $4\frac{1}{2}$ inches.

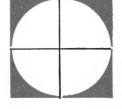

20. In the figure at the right, the side of the square and the diameter of the circle each are 12 inches in length. Which has the greater area, the square or the circle? How much greater?
21. How many square feet are there in a rectangular sheet of metal $9\frac{1}{4}$ by $15\frac{3}{4}$ inches?
22. The width of the flight deck of an airplane carrier is 0.11 of its length. Find the width if its length is 1056 feet.
23. In Problem 22, what would be the length of the carrier if its width were 102 feet.
24. Plywood usually comes in sheets 48 by 72 inches. If the price is $6.40 per sheet, what is the cost of 1 square foot of plywood?
25. A triangle and a rectangle have equal bases, but the altitude of the triangle is three times that of the rectangle. Compare their areas.
26. A circle with a radius of 8 inches is cut out of a circular sheet of metal that has a radius of 14 inches. What is the area of the piece of metal that is left?
27. What is the total area in the 6 faces of a cube that is 3 inches on each edge?

CHAPTER TEST

If $A = x + 4$, $B = x - 5$, $C = x - 4$, *and* $D = 2x - 1$, *find:*

1. AB
2. AC
3. CD
4. AD
5. BD
6. BC
7. $A^2 + B^2$
8. $A^2 + C^2$
9. $B^2 - C^2$
10. $D^2 - A^2$
11. $(A + B)(A - B)$
12. $(A + C)^2 (A - 2B)^2$

Factor completely:

13. $am - a$
14. $a^2 - 1$
15. $a^2 - 5ab - 6b^2$
16. $2a^3 - 2a$
17. $m^4 - 81$
18. $1 - 2x + x^2$
19. $48m^2 - 2m - 35$
20. $ax^2 - x^2 - ax$
21. $8mx^2 + 28mx - 60m$
22. $a(x - y) + b(x - y)$

Solve for x:

23. $x^2 - 11x = -24$
24. $x^2 = 60 + 4x$
25. $3x - 6(x - 1) = 15 - 2(2x - 3)$
26. $x^2 - 10x = 0$
27. $12 - 10x = 0$
28. $x^2 - 144 = 0$
29. $\dfrac{1}{x} - a = 0$
30. $121 - x^2 = 0$
31. $2 - x = x^2$
32. $x^2 - x = 0$
33. $ax - x = 1$
34. $\dfrac{x}{a} - \dfrac{a}{x} = 0$

35. x stands for the second of three consecutive numbers. Find the numbers if the product of the first and the third numbers is 99.
36. Write a quadratic equation whose roots are -6 and 2.
37. Find the difference between $(a + b)^2$ and $a^2 + b^2$ if $a = 6$ and $b = 7$.
38. Find a square root of $4a^2 + 36a + 81$.
39. x stands for the last of three consecutive numbers. Find the numbers if the product of the first two is 110.
40. The length of a rectangle is 4 inches more than the width. Its area is 117 square inches. Find the length and width of the rectangle.
41. The length of a rectangle is twice the width. If the length were increased by 3 units and the width by 2 units, the area would be increased by 34 square units. Find the length and the width of the rectangle.
42. A rectangular flower plot measures 20 by 12 feet. It is surrounded by a brick walk of uniform width. Find the width of the walk if the entire area, walk and flower plot, is 468 square feet.
43. The altitude of a triangle is 3 feet shorter than the base. The area is 20 square feet. Find the base and the altitude of the triangle.

CUMULATIVE REVIEW PROBLEMS

WORKING WITH ALGEBRAIC EXPRESSIONS

Find the following products:

1. $(2a - 1)(3a + 2)$
2. $(x - 8)(x - 7)$
3. $(y + 3)^2$
4. $4a(x - 5)$
5. $(m - 6)(m + 6)$
6. $(y + 10)(y - 9)$
7. $2a(x - 4)(x + 4)$
8. $(2m - n)(3m - n)$
9. $(x - \frac{1}{2})(x + \frac{1}{2})$
10. $(1 + a)(1 + 2a)$
11. $(6 - b)(6 + b)$
12. $3n(n + 9)^2$
13. $(7 - 4b)^2$
14. $(\frac{1}{2} + \frac{1}{4}x)^2$
15. $(a - 4b)^2$
16. $a^2(a + 3)(a - 3)$
17. $5(a + 4)^2$
18. $(a - 3b)(a - 4b)$
19. $(x - 8)(x + 8)$
20. $\frac{1}{2}(4 - 3b)^2$
21. $(x - 5)(x + 5)(x^2 + 25)$
22. $(mn - 6)(mn - 8)$
23. $(ab - 10)(ab + 3)$
24. $(13 + x^2)(3 - x^2)$
25. $10ab(a + b)^2$
26. $(a - b)^2(a + b)^2$
27. $(x + 1)^2 (x - 1)^2$
28. $8(a - 10)(a + 10)$
29. $ab(a + b)^2$
30. $(4x)^2 (x - 10)^2$
31. $(a^2b + \frac{1}{2})(a^2b - \frac{1}{4})$
32. $(a^3 + b^3)(a^3 - b^3)$
33. $(2 + m)(2 + m)$
34. $(x - 5)^2 (x + 5)^2$
35. $(3 + b)^2 (3 - b)^2$
36. $(\frac{1}{3}x - 6)(\frac{1}{4}x - 9)$
37. $[3 + (x + y)][3 - (x + y)]$
38. $(a + b - 6)(a + b + 6)$
39. $(m - n + 5)(m - n - 5)$
40. $(5 - 3a - x)(5 + 3a + x)$
41. $(a - b + c)^2$
42. $(m + 2n - 3)^2$

★ 43. $a^x(a^x - 1)$
44. $3a^a(a^a + a)$
45. $(a^2 + b^2)(a - b)(a + b)$
46. $(a^x - b^x)(a^x + b^x)$
47. $x^n(x^n + x^ny)$
48. $(x^m + x)^2$
49. $(e^x - 2)(e^x - 3)$
50. $x(x^x + x)(x^x - x)$

51. Draw a rectangle and label it $ABCD$. Mark side AD as w. If AB is 5 more than AD, find the area in terms of w. If AB is decreased by 2 units and AD is increased by 2 units, find the area in terms of w.

52. If n is the first of three consecutive numbers, find the product of the three numbers.

53. Find the area of the inner circle at the right in terms of a and b.

54. In the product a^2b^2, replace a by $x - y$ and b by $x + y$ and find the result.

55. In $3x^2 - 2x - 10$, replace x by $2a - 1$ and rewrite in the simplest form.

SPECIAL PRODUCTS AND FACTORING **271**

56. If the side s of a square is increased by 5 units, by how much is the area increased?

57. The length of a rectangle is 4 more than three times the width w. Find the area in terms of w.

58. A room is $y + 3$ yards long and $y - 3$ feet wide. Find its area in square feet in terms of y.

59. Find the circumference of a circle in terms of x if its radius is $7x + 14$ feet.

60. If $3x$ stands for the second of three consecutive numbers, find the product of the first and third numbers in terms of x.

Factor completely each of the following:

61. $2x^2 - 18$
62. $ax - a^2x$
63. $x^2 - 3x + 2$
64. $y^2 - 5y + 4$
65. $a^2 + ax + 6a$
66. $3h^2 - 5h + 2$
67. $x^2 + 10x + 25$
68. $2m^2 + 16m + 24$
69. $x^2 - \frac{1}{4}$
70. $m^2 - 6m + 8$
71. $10y^2 + y - 2$
72. $ax^2 + 7ax + 12a$
73. $1 - 6p + 9p^2$
74. $x^2 + 2xy - 15y^2$
75. $3am - 6a^2m^2$
76. $25d^2 - 26d + 1$
77. $5 + 5a + 5b$
78. $m^4 - n^4$
79. $28d^3 - 7d$
80. $ax^2 - axy - 2ay^2$
81. $y^2 - y - 132$
82. $10 - 100a$
83. $36y^2 + 41y + 8$
84. $72x^2 + 25x - 63$
85. $2k^2 - 2$
86. $16p^2 - 8p + 1$
87. $4k + 2kx - 2kx^2$
88. $d^2 - 0.36$
89. $ax + a^2x^2$
90. $5m^2 + 13m + 6$
91. $100 - 100x^4$
92. $60y^2 - 140y + 40$
93. $a^5 - ab^4$
94. $m^2 - 4m + 4$

SOLVING EQUATIONS

Solve each of the following equations for x. *Before you begin, decide whether each is a first-degree or a second-degree equation.*

1. $3x - 6 = 2x + 4$
2. $x^2 - 7x = 30$
3. $\frac{3}{4}x + 8 = x + 5$
4. $7x + 9 - 9x = 1$
5. $2x^2 - 3x = 0$
6. $11x - 12 = 6x - 9 - 2x^2$
7. $6 - 5x = 0$
8. $-2x - 3(x - 1) = 13$
9. $8x - 3 = 5x + 9$
10. $3x - 9 + 5x = 2x + 15$
11. $x^2 - 9x = -14$
12. $2x^2 + 15x + 7 = 0$
13. $5 + 2x = 0$
14. $12x - 7 - 5x = 6x - 8$
15. $x^2 - 9 = 0$
16. $\frac{3}{5}(x - 2) - 2 = 0$
17. $x^2 - 5x = 24$
18. $3x^2 + 4x + 1 = 9x + 2x^2 + 37$
19. $x + 2 = x^2$
20. $2 - 5x = 11 - 4x$
21. $cx + dx = a$
22. $16 - \frac{2}{3}(x + 1) = 14$
23. $\frac{1}{2} - x = \frac{1}{4} + x$
24. $5(x - 2) - 4(x - 3) = 2$

272 *ALGEBRA: ITS BIG IDEAS AND BASIC SKILLS*

BIG IDEA	NUMBER
BASIC SKILLS	Using and interpreting symbols of algebra Fundamental operations Evaluating algebraic expressions Factoring Using exponents

CHAPTER **10** *Algebraic Fractions*

IN CHAPTER 9 you increased your knowledge of algebra through the study of products and factoring. In this chapter you will learn some new things about algebraic fractions, that is, fractions which have variables in them.

You will find that the study of algebraic fractions will increase your understanding of fractions you worked with in arithmetic. Thus by studying fractions in algebra you will know more about the fractions of arithmetic. You will also find that to understand fractions in algebra you will often use fractions of arithmetic to get help in working with algebraic fractions. Thus it works both ways. The arithmetic helps the algebra, and the algebra helps the arithmetic.

YOUR AIM 👉 **1. To get a better understanding of fractions.**

2. To learn how to change fractions to equivalent fractions.

3. To learn how to add, subtract, multiply, and divide algebraic fractions.

What Are Algebraic Fractions?

In arithmetic you studied several kinds of fractions:

(1) Common fractions, those which indicate the division of two whole numbers, such as $\frac{1}{2}$ and $\frac{3}{4}$.

(2) Decimal fractions, those whose denominators are 10, 100, and so forth, but which are expressed by means of a decimal point, as 0.1 and 0.01.

(3) Complex fractions, those whose numerators or denominators or both are fractions, as

$$\frac{\frac{1}{2}}{\frac{1}{4}} \quad \text{and} \quad \frac{\frac{11}{7}}{5}$$

Algebraic fractions have a variable in either or in both the numerator and the denominator.

$$\frac{a}{b} \qquad \frac{x+y}{10} \qquad \frac{x^2-1}{x+2}$$

The methods of algebra provide a way of writing all kinds of fractions using a simple symbol like $\frac{a}{b}$. a and b may stand for any number or expression except that b cannot be zero.

FOR EXAMPLE: If $a = 2$ and $b = 5$, then $\frac{a}{b} = \frac{2}{5}$.

If $a = \frac{1}{2}$ and $b = \frac{3}{4}$, then $\frac{a}{b} = \frac{\frac{1}{2}}{\frac{3}{4}}$.

If $a = x - 6$ and $b = y + 10$, then $\frac{a}{b} = \frac{x-6}{y+10}$.

You may think of a fraction according to the original meaning of the word, that is, as a fractional part of the whole. A dime is $\frac{1}{10}$ of a (whole) dollar. A quarter is $\frac{1}{4}$ of a dollar. Or you may think of a fraction as an indicated division.

$$\frac{a}{b} \text{ means } a \div b \qquad \frac{17}{5} \text{ means } 17 \div 5$$

The word "fraction" has two meanings:

1. $\frac{1}{4}$ means "one of the four equal parts of the whole."

2. The line separating the denominator from the numerator means "divide."

$$\frac{1}{4} \text{ means } 1 \div 4$$

274 *ALGEBRA: ITS BIG IDEAS AND BASIC SKILLS*

PROBLEMS

Write fractions by replacing a *and* b *in* $\frac{a}{b}$ *by the values given:*

1. $a = 2, b = 3$
2. $a = 6, b = m - 5$
3. $a = 7, b = 4$
4. $a = x - 2, b = x + 6$
5. $a = 12, b = 1$
6. $a = \dfrac{2x + 1}{3}, b = \dfrac{6}{x - 1}$

7. If AB has the length a and the points C, D, and E divide AB into four equal parts, how long is AC? AD? AE?

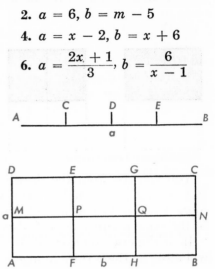

The six small divisions of rectangle ABCD *have equal areas. If the length of the rectangle* ABCD *is* b *and the width is* a, *find the area of each of the following:*

8. $ABCD$
9. $ABNM$
10. $AHQM$
11. $AFPM$
12. $ABNQGD$
13. $FBCE$

14. What is the area of the circle at the right?
15. What is the area of sector I? Of sector II? Of sector III?
16. Find the cost of one orange if the cost of a dozen oranges is 54 cents. If the cost of a dozen is x cents.

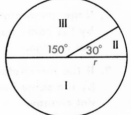

17. If a jet-propelled plane can travel 600 miles per hour, how long will it take for it to travel 1000 miles? x miles? If it travels d miles in h hours, what is its rate of travel?
18. How many apples at p cents each can be bought for c cents?
19. If Bob can do a piece of work in 10 hours, what part of that piece of work can he do in 1 hour? In 2 hours? In x hours?
20. If Barbara can do a piece of work in h hours, what part of that piece of work can she do in 1 hour? In 2 hours? In x hours?
21. If eggs cost p cents per dozen, how many dozen can be bought for $1.25?
22. What part of a month is 15 days? 10 days? x days?

Do the indicated division:

23. $\dfrac{2}{5}$
24. $\dfrac{3}{4}$
25. $\dfrac{3}{8}$
26. $\dfrac{15a}{3}$
27. $\dfrac{5a - 10}{5}$
28. $\dfrac{a^2 - 2a}{a}$
29. $\dfrac{2x - 3y}{0.1}$
30. $\dfrac{6m - 9m^2}{3m}$

ALGEBRAIC FRACTIONS **275**

Equivalent Fractions

One of the most important and interesting facts about fractions is that many different fractions can be equal to the same number.

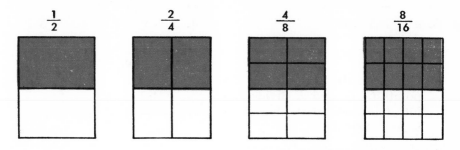

$$\frac{1}{2} \qquad \frac{2}{4} \qquad \frac{4}{8} \qquad \frac{8}{16}$$

You can see from the drawings above that each of the fractions $\frac{1}{2}$, $\frac{2}{4}$, $\frac{4}{8}$, and $\frac{8}{16}$ is equal to the same number, namely, $\frac{1}{2}$. In how many more ways could you write the number $\frac{1}{2}$? Fractions which are equal to the same number are called **equivalent fractions.**

In arithmetic you learned two important rules about fractions. You will also use these rules in algebra.

1. **If the numerator and the denominator of a fraction are multiplied by the same number, except zero, the value of the fraction does not change.**

2. **If the numerator and the denominator of a fraction are divided by the same number, except zero, the value of the fraction does not change.**

PROBLEMS

Study the following and explain what operation has been performed on the fraction on the left side in order to produce the equivalent fraction on the right side.

1. $\dfrac{1}{3} = \dfrac{3}{9}$

2. $\dfrac{2}{5} = \dfrac{10}{25}$

3. $\dfrac{am}{an} = \dfrac{m}{n}$

4. $\dfrac{x^2}{ax} = \dfrac{x}{a}$

5. $\dfrac{6k}{12k} = \dfrac{1}{2}$

6. $\dfrac{3m}{5} = \dfrac{15mn}{25n}$

7. $\dfrac{24a^3}{16a^4} = \dfrac{3}{2a}$

8. $\dfrac{m+n}{m-n} = \dfrac{3m+3n}{3m-3n}$

276 *ALGEBRA: ITS BIG IDEAS AND BASIC SKILLS*

9. $\dfrac{a(x+1)}{(x+1)^2} = \dfrac{a}{x+1}$

10. $\dfrac{5x}{6y} = \dfrac{5x^2 + 10x}{6xy + 12y}$

11. $\dfrac{2m-1}{p} = \dfrac{4m^2-1}{2pm+p}$

12. $\dfrac{x+y}{x-y} = \dfrac{x^2-y^2}{x^2-2xy+y^2}$

★ 13. $\dfrac{x^4-y^4}{(x^2+y^2)(x^2+y^2)} = \dfrac{x^2-y^2}{x^2+y^2}$

14. $\dfrac{x^2+5x-24}{x^2-7x+12} = \dfrac{x+8}{x-4}$

15. $\dfrac{15x^3(x^2-y^2)}{3(x-y)} = \dfrac{5x^3(x+y)}{1}$

16. $\dfrac{64-b^3}{16+4b+b^2} = \dfrac{4-b}{1}$

17. $\dfrac{2a+1}{2a-1} = \dfrac{4a^2-1}{4a^2-4a+1}$

18. $\dfrac{5xyz+5z}{3xyz+3z} = \dfrac{5}{3}$

19. $\dfrac{a+b}{a+b} = 1$

20. $\dfrac{56x^2y+24z}{24x^2y+56z} = \dfrac{7x^2y+3z}{3x^2y+7z}$

Use the first rule on page 276 to find the missing numerator or denominator in each of the following problems:

21. $\dfrac{3}{4} = \dfrac{?}{8}$

22. $\dfrac{5}{6} = \dfrac{?}{18}$

23. $\dfrac{3}{8} = \dfrac{?}{16}$

24. $\dfrac{7}{9} = \dfrac{?}{27}$

25. $\dfrac{4}{5} = \dfrac{12}{?}$

26. $\dfrac{2}{3} = \dfrac{16}{?}$

27. $\dfrac{5}{9} = \dfrac{25}{?}$

28. $\dfrac{11}{3} = \dfrac{33}{?}$

29. $\dfrac{5}{8} = \dfrac{?}{8 \cdot 3}$

30. $\dfrac{4}{5} = \dfrac{4 \cdot 7}{?}$

31. $\dfrac{5}{6} = \dfrac{4 \cdot 5}{?}$

32. $\dfrac{2}{3} = \dfrac{?}{100 \cdot 3}$

33. $\dfrac{?}{8} = \dfrac{3 \cdot 5}{3 \cdot 8}$

34. $\dfrac{6}{?} = \dfrac{7 \cdot 6}{7 \cdot 5}$

35. $\dfrac{5}{3 \cdot 4} = \dfrac{5 \cdot 6}{?}$

36. $\dfrac{2}{3 \cdot 7} = \dfrac{2 \cdot 7}{?}$

★ 37. $\dfrac{1}{2} = \dfrac{?}{2 \cdot 5 \cdot 7}$

38. $\dfrac{3}{5} = \dfrac{?}{5 \cdot 5 \cdot 6}$

39. $\dfrac{5}{8} = \dfrac{?}{3 \cdot 2 \cdot 8 \cdot 5}$

40. $\dfrac{7}{5} = \dfrac{?}{(1 \cdot 5)5}$

41. $\dfrac{5}{21} = \dfrac{21 \cdot 5 \cdot 4}{?}$

42. $\dfrac{7}{12} = \dfrac{3 \cdot 7^2}{?}$

43. $\dfrac{9}{16} = \dfrac{?}{3^2 \cdot 16 \cdot 5}$

44. $\dfrac{2}{11} = \dfrac{?}{3 \cdot 11^2}$

45. $\dfrac{22}{6} = \dfrac{2^2 \cdot 11}{?}$

46. $\dfrac{7x}{8x} = \dfrac{?}{8x^2}$

47. $\dfrac{5xy}{6xy} = \dfrac{?}{18x^2y^2}$

48. $\dfrac{4a^2}{3m} = \dfrac{?}{6am}$

49. $\dfrac{6k}{12k} = \dfrac{1}{?}$

50. $\dfrac{3(x+y)}{4(x+y)} = \dfrac{3}{?}$

51. $\dfrac{y^2}{ax} = \dfrac{?}{a^2x^2}$

52. $\dfrac{7}{?} = \dfrac{7x^2}{x^2y^2}$

53. $\dfrac{4}{5y^2} = \dfrac{4x^2}{?}$

54. $\dfrac{9x^2-1}{6x-2} = \dfrac{3x+1}{?}$

55. $\dfrac{5a-10b}{5 \cdot x} = \dfrac{?}{x}$

56. $\dfrac{3a^2-2}{4x^2} = \dfrac{15a^2-10}{?}$

57. $\dfrac{(x+4)}{?} = \dfrac{5(x+4)}{10x+40}$

ALGEBRAIC FRACTIONS **277**

Reducing Fractions

You can use the second rule in the preceding section to reduce fractions to equivalent fractions in lower terms.

Examples for Study

1. $\dfrac{10}{25}$

SOLUTION: $\dfrac{10}{25} = \dfrac{\frac{10}{5}}{\frac{25}{5}} = \dfrac{2}{5}$

2. $\dfrac{20x^2}{12x}$

SOLUTION: Divide both the numerator and the denominator by $4x$, which is the greatest common factor.

$$\frac{20x^2}{12x} = \frac{\frac{20x^2}{4x}}{\frac{12x}{4x}} = \frac{5x}{3}$$

3. $\dfrac{x^2 - 5x + 6}{x^2 - 4}$

SOLUTION: First factor both the numerator and the denominator. Then divide both the numerator and the denominator by the common factor $x - 2$.

$$\frac{x - 5x + 6}{x^2 - 4} = \frac{(x - 3)(x - 2)}{(x + 2)(x - 2)}$$

$$= \frac{x - 3}{x + 2}$$

PROBLEMS

Reduce the following fractions using the second rule on page 276:

1. $\dfrac{4}{8}$ 2. $\dfrac{6}{8}$ 3. $\dfrac{5}{15}$ 4. $\dfrac{12}{16}$

5. $\dfrac{20}{25}$ 6. $\dfrac{18}{27}$ 7. $\dfrac{24}{36}$ 8. $\dfrac{45}{60}$

9. $\dfrac{3 \cdot 5}{4 \cdot 5}$ 10. $\dfrac{4 \cdot 9}{17 \cdot 4}$ 11. $\dfrac{8 \cdot 6}{96}$ 12. $\dfrac{3 \cdot a}{5 \cdot a}$

13. $\dfrac{36}{72}$ 14. $\dfrac{3 \cdot 5}{4 \cdot 5}$ 15. $\dfrac{5 \cdot 9}{4 \cdot 9}$ 16. $\dfrac{7x}{7y}$

17. $\dfrac{7x}{8x}$ 18. $\dfrac{5a^2}{9a^2}$ 19. $\dfrac{3r^2}{2r}$ 20. $\dfrac{5xy}{25x}$

21. $\dfrac{24}{56}$ 22. $\dfrac{32a^2}{16a}$ 23. $\dfrac{100mn}{10m}$ 24. $\dfrac{50a^2b^3}{35a^3b^2}$

25. $\dfrac{ax}{bx}$ 26. $\dfrac{45x^3y}{15y^2}$ 27. $\dfrac{d}{d^2}$ 28. $\dfrac{a^2m}{am}$

29. $\dfrac{x^2 + 7x + 12}{(x + 4)}$

30. $\dfrac{5(x + 7)}{8(x + 7)}$

31. $\dfrac{3(a + b)^2}{10(a + b)}$

32. $\dfrac{3(a + b)}{(a + b)^2}$

33. $\dfrac{(a - 1)}{b(a + 1)}$

34. $\dfrac{x(a - b)}{xy(a - b)}$

35. $\dfrac{ax - 5a}{a}$

36. $\dfrac{x^2 - 9}{x^2 - 5x + 6}$

37. $\dfrac{x^2 - 7x + 12}{x^2 - 16}$

38. $\dfrac{2x^2 + 4x}{3ax + 6a}$

39. $\dfrac{m^2 - mn}{am - an}$

40. $\dfrac{15x^2 - xy - 2y^2}{3x^2 + 4xy + y^2}$

★ 41. $\dfrac{x^2 - 9x - 22}{3x - 33}$

42. $\dfrac{5m - 10}{m^2 + m - 6}$

43. $\dfrac{x^4 - 16}{x^4 + x^2 - 20}$

44. $\dfrac{3x - 21}{3x^2 - 15x - 42}$

45. $\dfrac{2x^2 + 11x + 5}{4x^2 + 4x + 1}$

46. $\dfrac{9x^2 - 12x + 4}{9x^2 - 4}$

47. $\dfrac{x^2 - 5x - 5y + xy}{(x - 5)(x^2 - y^2)}$

48. $\dfrac{1 - 216y^3}{1 - 36y^2}$

49. $\dfrac{x^4 - y^4}{(x^2 + 2xy + y^2)(x^2 - 2xy + y^2)}$

50. $\dfrac{(a^2 - 1)(5a^2 + 5)}{5(a^4 - 1)}$

51. $\dfrac{(4k^2 + 4ky + y^2)(k^2 - y^2)}{(k + y)(4k^2 - 4ky + y^2)}$

52. $\dfrac{6a^3b^2 - 23ab^2 + 20ab^2}{3a^2b^2 - 4ab^2}$

Common Errors in Algebra

Write the fraction $\frac{2}{3}$. Now add 1 to both the numerator and the denominator. You now have 3 in the numerator and 4 in the denominator. Does $\frac{2}{3} = \frac{3}{4}$?

Write $\frac{4}{6}$. Now subtract 2 from both the numerator and the denominator. You now have 2 in the numerator and 4 in the denominator. Does $\frac{4}{6} = \frac{2}{4}$?

Try adding or subtracting the same number to or from both the numerator and the denominator of several fractions. Does the value of the fraction change?

DO YOU SEE? Adding or subtracting the same number, other than zero, to or from both the numerator and the denominator of a fraction changes the value of a fraction, except fractions of the form $\frac{a}{a}$.

The important principle of arithmetic and algebra that you have been using to reduce fractions is sometimes not well understood by pupils, and errors result. Rather than always thinking "I can divide the numerator of a fraction by some number provided I also divide the denominator by the same number," some pupils get the bad habit of just marking lines through numbers without thinking.

ALGEBRAIC FRACTIONS **279**

PROBLEMS

1. May wanted to reduce the fraction $\frac{2+3}{2+4}$ to lowest terms. After crossing out the 2 in the numerator and marking a 1 above it, as shown at the right, she had $1+3$, or 4. What operation did she use on $2+3$ to get 4?

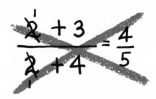

2. May also crossed out the 2 in the denominator and marked a 1 below it. What operation did she do to get $1+4$, or 5, from $2+4$?

3. Why was May's work wrong?

Tell why each of the following methods of reducing fractions is wrong:

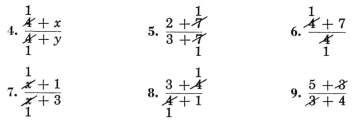

4. $\dfrac{\overset{1}{\cancel{4}}+x}{\underset{1}{\cancel{4}}+y}$

5. $\dfrac{2+\overset{1}{\cancel{7}}}{3+\underset{1}{\cancel{7}}}$

6. $\dfrac{\overset{1}{\cancel{4}}+7}{\underset{1}{\cancel{4}}}$

7. $\dfrac{\overset{1}{\cancel{x}}+1}{\underset{1}{\cancel{x}}+3}$

8. $\dfrac{3+\overset{1}{\cancel{4}}}{\underset{1}{\cancel{4}}+1}$

9. $\dfrac{5+\cancel{8}}{\cancel{8}+4}$

10. Why is the first problem shown below solved correctly? Why is the second solution incorrect?

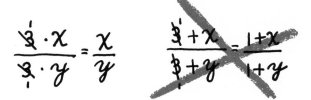

11. Mary's teacher said, "Mary, you have the right answer, but your problem is wrong." Mary's problem is shown at the right. Explain why it is wrong.

$$\dfrac{\overset{1}{\cancel{2}}+x}{\underset{1}{\cancel{2}}+x}=\dfrac{x}{x}=1$$

DO YOU SEE? ☞ 1. You can multiply or divide the numerator and the denominator of a fraction by the same number, except zero, without changing the value of the fraction.

2. You change the value of a fraction when you add or subtract the same number, other than zero, to or from both the numerator and the denominator, unless the fraction is of the form $\dfrac{a}{a}$.

SELF TEST

Reduce to lowest terms:

1. $\dfrac{15}{45}$

2. $\dfrac{3 \cdot 9}{4 \cdot 9}$

3. $\dfrac{k}{k^2}$

4. $\dfrac{25x^2y}{5xy}$

5. $\dfrac{a^2 - 16}{a^2 + 8a + 16}$

6. $\dfrac{y^2 + 6y + 9}{y^2 + 5y + 6}$

7. $\dfrac{(x + y)8}{(x + y)9}$

8. $\dfrac{t^2 + ts}{rt + rs}$

Find the missing numerator in each of the following problems:

9. $\dfrac{3}{4} = \dfrac{?}{16}$

10. $\dfrac{7}{8} = \dfrac{?}{5 \cdot 8}$

11. $\dfrac{5}{8x} = \dfrac{?}{8x^2}$

12. $\dfrac{x}{7} = \dfrac{?}{21}$

13. $\dfrac{(a + b)}{(x + y)} = \dfrac{?}{3(x + y)}$

14. $\dfrac{6}{8a} = \dfrac{?}{2a}$

15. $\dfrac{1}{2} = \dfrac{?}{8x}$

16. $\dfrac{k^2}{ky} = \dfrac{?}{y}$

Multiplication of Algebraic Fractions

You know that, in multiplying two fractions, you multiply the numerators to find the numerator of the product and that you multiply the denominators to find the denominator of the product.

FOR EXAMPLE: $\qquad \dfrac{2}{3} \times \dfrac{5}{7} = \dfrac{2 \times 5}{3 \times 7} = \dfrac{10}{21}$

The same method of multiplying is used in algebra.

FOR EXAMPLE: $\qquad \dfrac{a}{b} \times \dfrac{c}{d} = \dfrac{ac}{bd}$

Often you can multiply fractions more simply. Consider this example:

$$\dfrac{5}{8} \times \dfrac{24}{25} = \underline{\;?\;}$$

You could solve this by following the usual method:

$$\dfrac{5}{8} \times \dfrac{24}{25} = \dfrac{5 \times 24}{8 \times 25} = \dfrac{120}{200} = \dfrac{3}{5}$$

The simplified way to do this is to divide both the numerator and the denominator by the common factors before multiplying:

$$\dfrac{5}{8} \times \dfrac{24}{25} = \dfrac{\overset{1}{\cancel{5}} \times \overset{3}{\cancel{24}}}{\underset{1}{\cancel{8}} \times \underset{5}{\cancel{25}}} = \dfrac{3}{5}$$

You can also simplify the multiplication of algebraic fractions whenever common factors are present. First factor, when possible, the numerators and the denominators and divide both the numerators and the denominators by the common factors. Then multiply the factors that are left in the numerators and divide their product by the product of the factors that are left in the denominators.

ALGEBRAIC FRACTIONS **281**

Examples for Study

1. *Multiply:* $\dfrac{2a}{a - 2} \cdot \dfrac{a^2 - 4}{6a^2}$

SOLUTION: $\dfrac{2a}{a - 2} \cdot \dfrac{a^2 - 4}{6a^2} = \underline{\ ?\ }$

Factor: $\dfrac{2a}{a - 2} \cdot \dfrac{(a - 2)(a + 2)}{6a^2} = \underline{\ ?\ }$

Divide by the common factors:

$$\dfrac{\overset{1}{\cancel{2a}}}{\underset{1}{\cancel{(a - 2)}}} \cdot \dfrac{\cancel{(a - 2)}(a + 2)}{\underset{3a}{\cancel{6a^2}}} = \dfrac{a + 2}{3a}$$

2. *Multiply:* $\dfrac{x^2 - 3x}{16y} \cdot \dfrac{18y^2}{x^2 + x - 12}$

SOLUTION: $\dfrac{x^2 - 3x}{16y} \cdot \dfrac{18y^2}{x^2 + x - 12} = \underline{\ ?\ }$

Factor: $\dfrac{x(x - 3)}{16y} \cdot \dfrac{18y^2}{(x - 3)(x + 4)} = \underline{\ ?\ }$

Divide by the common factors:

$$\dfrac{x\cancel{(x - 3)}}{\underset{8}{\cancel{16y}}} \cdot \dfrac{\overset{9y}{\cancel{18y^2}}}{\underset{1}{\cancel{(x - 3)}}(x + 4)}$$

Divide the product of the factors left in the numerators by the product of the factors left in the denominators:

$$\dfrac{x(1)}{8} \cdot \dfrac{9y}{1(x + 4)} = \dfrac{9xy}{8x + 32}$$

PROBLEMS

Multiply:

1. $\dfrac{2}{3} \times \dfrac{1}{2}$

2. $\dfrac{3}{4} \times \dfrac{1}{2}$

3. $\dfrac{2}{3} \times \dfrac{3}{4}$

4. $\dfrac{3}{7} \times \dfrac{4}{5}$

5. $\dfrac{5}{8} \times \dfrac{3}{4}$

6. $\dfrac{3}{5} \times \dfrac{7}{10}$

7. $11 \times \dfrac{1}{2}$

8. $2 \times \dfrac{5}{7}$

9. $a \cdot \dfrac{b}{c}$

10. $a \cdot \dfrac{a^2}{c}$

11. $\dfrac{1}{2} \times \dfrac{1}{5}$

12. $\dfrac{2}{3} \times \dfrac{10}{7}$

13. $\dfrac{a}{b} \cdot \dfrac{1}{c}$

14. $\dfrac{a}{b} \cdot \dfrac{a}{b}$

15. $\dfrac{x}{y} \cdot \dfrac{x^2}{y^2}$

16. $\dfrac{1}{x^2} \cdot \dfrac{x^2}{y}$

17. $\dfrac{10ab}{11xy} \cdot \dfrac{22x}{30ab}$

18. $\dfrac{m^2}{n^2} \cdot \dfrac{n}{m^2}$

19. $\dfrac{2a}{15b} \cdot \dfrac{5b^2}{3a}$

20. $\dfrac{(x+6)}{(x+5)} \cdot \dfrac{(x+5)^2}{x(x+6)}$

21. $\dfrac{x^2-9}{y^2} \cdot \dfrac{y}{x+3}$

22. $\dfrac{x^2-100}{28ax} \cdot \dfrac{42a^2}{x+10}$

23. $\dfrac{3xy}{a-b} \cdot \dfrac{a^2-b^2}{6xy^2}$

24. $\dfrac{x+1}{x-1} \cdot \dfrac{x+1}{x-1}$

25. $\dfrac{ax}{x+a} \cdot \dfrac{x+a}{xa}$

26. $\dfrac{ax}{a+x} \cdot \dfrac{ax}{a-x}$

27. $x \cdot \dfrac{y}{z}$

28. $\dfrac{x}{9} \cdot \dfrac{3}{x(y+z)}$

29. $\dfrac{8^2 \cdot 5^3}{3^2 \cdot 2^5} \cdot \dfrac{3^5}{5^2}$

30. $\dfrac{3 \cdot 7^2 \cdot 4}{2 \cdot 3 \cdot 7} \cdot \dfrac{7 \cdot 5 \cdot 3^2}{2 \cdot 3}$

31. $\dfrac{3^2 \cdot 5 \cdot 7}{3 \cdot 11} \cdot \dfrac{11^2 \cdot 4}{7 \cdot 5}$

32. $\dfrac{5x^2y}{7k} \cdot \dfrac{14k^2}{z}$

33. $\dfrac{(x+1)^2(x+y)}{(x-y)} \cdot \dfrac{(x-y)^2}{(x+y)}$

34. $\dfrac{5x^2a}{a(x+5)} \cdot \dfrac{(x^2-5)}{5x}$

35. $\dfrac{3\pi r^2}{4} \cdot \dfrac{2\pi r^2}{5}$

36. $\dfrac{x(x-y)}{x^2-y^2} \cdot \dfrac{(x+y)}{x}$

37. $\dfrac{3a}{5(a+b)} \cdot \dfrac{3a}{5(a+b)}$

38. $\dfrac{5^2 \cdot k^2 \cdot a}{4} \cdot \dfrac{k}{3ab^2}$

⭐ 39. $\dfrac{(x+y)^2}{(x+3)} \cdot \dfrac{(x+3)(x+2)}{(x+y)}$

40. $\dfrac{5}{8} \cdot \dfrac{x^2-y^2}{x-y} \cdot \dfrac{8}{5}$

41. $\dfrac{7y(y-x)}{3x(y+x)} \cdot \dfrac{9(y+x)^2}{14(y^2-x^2)}$

42. $\dfrac{3a^2-5ab-2b^2}{15a^2-4ab-3b^2} \cdot \dfrac{5a^2+7a-6}{a^2-4b^2}$

43. $\dfrac{m-4}{12} \cdot \dfrac{18}{m^2-4m}$

44. $\dfrac{4\pi r}{2\pi r + 2\pi r^2} \cdot \dfrac{1+2r+r^2}{2}$

45. $\dfrac{(x-5)^3}{x} \cdot \dfrac{x+5}{(x-5)^2}$

46. $\dfrac{a^4-81}{a^3} \cdot \dfrac{5a}{a^2-9}$

47. $\dfrac{16a^2b}{3x^3-27x} \cdot \dfrac{12x+36}{32ab}$

48. $\dfrac{16-m^2}{5m-1} \cdot \dfrac{5m^2-m}{16-8m+m^2}$

49. $\dfrac{(x^4-y^4)}{x^2} \cdot \dfrac{(x^2-y^2)}{x^2}$

50. $\dfrac{5^2(a^2+b^2)}{(a-b)} \cdot \dfrac{3^2 \cdot 5^3}{(a+b)}$

51. $\dfrac{x^6-y^6}{(x^3-y^3)} \cdot \dfrac{3x}{(x^3+y^3)}$

52. $\dfrac{\frac{4}{3}\pi r^3}{\pi r^2} \cdot \dfrac{3a}{4a^2}$

53. $\dfrac{(a^4-b^4)}{3a^2} \cdot \dfrac{(a^2+b^2)}{(a^2-b^2)}$

54. $\dfrac{(x^6-y^6)}{(x^3-y^3)} \cdot \dfrac{15rs}{(3r^2s^2)}$

Division of Algebraic Fractions

When studying arithmetic, you undoubtedly memorized the rule for dividing fractions: Invert the divisor and multiply. Algebraic fractions provide an explanation of this rule. For example, the statement y divided by x may be expressed algebraically as $y \div x = \dfrac{y}{x}$. Let $y = \dfrac{a}{b}$ and $x = \dfrac{c}{d}$; then:

$$\frac{a}{b} \div \frac{c}{d} = \frac{\dfrac{a}{b}}{\dfrac{c}{d}}$$

If you multiply the numerator and the denominator of a fraction by the same number, the value of the fraction is not changed. When you multiply the numerator and the denominator of the fraction above by $\dfrac{d}{c}$, you get:

$$\frac{\dfrac{a}{b} \cdot \dfrac{d}{c}}{\dfrac{c}{d} \cdot \dfrac{d}{c}} = \frac{\dfrac{ad}{bc}}{\dfrac{cd}{dc}} = \frac{\dfrac{ad}{bc}}{1} = \frac{a \cdot d}{b \cdot c}$$

Now compare $\dfrac{a}{b} \div \dfrac{c}{d}$ with $\dfrac{a \cdot d}{b \cdot c}$. Note that $\dfrac{d}{c}$ in the quotient is the divisor $\dfrac{c}{d}$ inverted.

DO YOU SEE? To divide one fraction by another, invert the divisor and multiply.

The word "reciprocal" is often used in mathematics. The *reciprocal of any number*, except zero, is defined as 1 divided by the number. Thus,
1. The reciprocal of 10 is $1 \div 10$, or $\frac{1}{10}$.
2. The reciprocal of $\frac{2}{3}$ is $1 \div \frac{2}{3}$, or $\frac{3}{2}$.
3. The reciprocal of x is $1 \div x$, or $\frac{1}{x}$.

Examples for Study

1. *Divide:* $\dfrac{x^2 + xy}{xy} \div \dfrac{x^2 - y^2}{x^2 y^2}$

SOLUTION: Write the reciprocal of the divisor and indicate multiplication:

$$\frac{x^2 + xy}{xy} \cdot \frac{x^2 y^2}{x^2 - y^2}$$

Factor and divide by the common factors:

$$\frac{\overset{1}{x\cancel{(x+y)}}}{\underset{1}{\cancel{xy}}} \cdot \frac{\overset{xy}{\cancel{x^2y^2}}}{\underset{1}{\cancel{(x+y)}}(x-y)}$$

Multiply the factors remaining in the numerators and the factors remaining in the denominators:

$$\frac{x(1)}{1} \cdot \frac{xy}{1(x-y)} = \frac{x^2y}{x-y}$$

CHECK: Substitute numerical values for the letters in the original problem and in your answer. If your answer is correct, you will get the same results. Avoid using zero for the value of a letter or any combination of values which will make any denominator equal to zero.

$$\text{Let } x = 2 \text{ and } y = 3$$

Substituting in the original problem:

$$\frac{2^2 + 2 \cdot 3}{2 \cdot 3} \div \frac{2^2 - 3^2}{2^2 \cdot 3^2} = \frac{4+6}{6} \div \frac{4-9}{4 \cdot 9}$$

$$= \frac{10}{6} \div \frac{-5}{36}$$

$$= \frac{10}{6} \times \frac{36}{-5}$$

$$= -12$$

Substituting in the answer:

$$\frac{2^2 \cdot 3}{2-3} = \frac{4 \cdot 3}{-1} = -12$$

Since the number -12 was obtained by substituting in the original problem and also was obtained by substituting in the answer, the answer checks.

2. *Divide:* $\dfrac{3}{5} \div 4$

SOLUTION:

$$\frac{3}{5} \div \frac{4}{1} = \frac{3}{5} \cdot \frac{1}{4}$$

$$= \frac{3}{20}$$

3. *Divide:* $\dfrac{7a^2}{b} \div a^3$

SOLUTION:

$$\frac{7a^2}{b} \div \frac{a^3}{1} = \frac{\overset{7}{\cancel{7a^2}}}{b} \cdot \frac{1}{\underset{a}{\cancel{a^3}}}$$

$$= \frac{7}{ab}$$

PROBLEMS

Divide:

1. $\dfrac{1}{2} \div 3$

2. $\dfrac{1}{4} \div 2$

3. $2 \div \dfrac{1}{4}$

4. $3 \div \dfrac{1}{2}$

5. $\dfrac{1}{4} \div \dfrac{3}{4}$

6. $\dfrac{3}{4} \div \dfrac{1}{4}$

7. $6 \div \dfrac{3}{5}$

8. $\dfrac{3}{5} \div 6$

9. $a \div \dfrac{a}{b}$

10. $\dfrac{a}{b} \div a$

11. $\dfrac{a}{b} \div \dfrac{a}{b}$

12. $\dfrac{1}{m} \div \dfrac{1}{n}$

13. $a \div ab$

14. $\dfrac{x}{2} \div \dfrac{3x^2}{8}$

15. $\dfrac{a+b}{a} \div \dfrac{b}{a}$

16. $\dfrac{m+n}{m} \div m$

17. $\dfrac{x}{x-y} \div \dfrac{x}{y}$

18. $5xy \div \dfrac{10x}{y}$

19. $\dfrac{a}{a-b} \div \dfrac{2a}{a^2-b^2}$

20. $\dfrac{5x+10}{x^2} \div \dfrac{5}{x}$

21. $\dfrac{a^2}{x^2-1} \div \dfrac{a^2}{x-1}$

22. $\dfrac{xy-x}{y} \div \dfrac{ay-a}{y^2}$

23. $\dfrac{x^2-5x+6}{x+2} \div \dfrac{2x-6}{x^2+4}$

24. $\dfrac{3x^2-3y^2}{5(x-y)} \div \dfrac{3(x+y)}{5x-5y}$

★ 25. $\dfrac{a^2-7a}{a^2-16} \div \dfrac{a^2-9}{a^2-7a+12}$

26. $\dfrac{k}{x^3} \div \dfrac{1+m^2}{x^4}$

27. $\dfrac{x^2+10x+21}{x^2-2x-15} \div (x^2+2x-35)$

28. $\dfrac{x^3-y^3}{x-y} \div (x^2+xy+y^2)$

29. $\dfrac{x+y}{x^4-y^4} \div \dfrac{x-y}{x^2+y^2}$

30. $(1-z) \div \dfrac{1-z}{1-2z+z^2}$

31. $\dfrac{x+a}{x^4-a^4} \div \dfrac{(x+a)^2}{x^2-a^2}$

Complex Fractions

A fraction in which the numerator or the denominator or both are fractions is called a **complex fraction**. There are two ways of simplifying a complex fraction. One way is to multiply the numerator and the denominator by the lowest common denominator of the two fractions. The **lowest common denominator** or **L.C.D.**, of two denominators is the smallest number divisible by the two denominators. The second way is to divide the fractions by inverting the denominator and multiplying.

286 *ALGEBRA: ITS BIG IDEAS AND BASIC SKILLS*

Example for Study

Simplify: $\dfrac{\frac{1}{2}}{\frac{3}{4}}$

SOLUTION: Multiply both the numerator and the denominator by 4, the lowest common denominator of $\frac{1}{2}$ and $\frac{3}{4}$:

$$\frac{\frac{1}{2} \times 4}{\frac{3}{4} \times 4} = \frac{2}{3}$$

Or divide the fractions by inverting the denominator and multiplying:

$$\frac{1}{2} \div \frac{3}{4} = \frac{1}{2} \times \frac{4}{3} = \frac{2}{3}$$

PROBLEMS

Simplify the following complex fractions:

1. $\dfrac{\frac{3}{4}}{\frac{9}{8}}$ 　　2. $\dfrac{\frac{1}{2}}{\frac{1}{4}}$ 　　3. $\dfrac{\frac{4}{5}}{\frac{5}{4}}$ 　　4. $\dfrac{16}{\frac{8}{3}}$

5. $\dfrac{\frac{24}{6}}{x}$ 　　6. $\dfrac{\frac{a}{2}}{a}$ 　　7. $\dfrac{\frac{m}{3}}{m^2}$ 　　8. $\dfrac{\frac{10}{ab}}{\frac{5}{ab}}$

9. $\dfrac{\frac{x-2}{3}}{\frac{3}{x+2}}$ 　10. $\dfrac{9}{\frac{n^2-9}{9}}$ 　11. $\dfrac{\frac{x^2-16}{25-y^2}}{\frac{x+4}{5+y}}$ 　12. $\dfrac{\frac{m^2-mn}{n}}{m}$

13. $\dfrac{66\frac{2}{3}}{100}$ 　14. $\dfrac{87\frac{1}{2}}{100}$ 　15. $\dfrac{62\frac{1}{2}}{100}$ 　16. $\dfrac{33\frac{1}{3}}{100}$

★ 17. $\dfrac{\frac{3x^2}{5}-2}{\frac{3x^2}{5}-2}$ 　　18. $\dfrac{\frac{3x}{7}\cdot\frac{14}{x}}{\frac{x^2-y^2}{x+y}}$ 　　19. $\dfrac{\frac{7}{8}\div\frac{3}{4}}{\frac{3}{4}\div\frac{7}{8}}$

20. $\dfrac{2\frac{1}{2}\cdot\frac{3}{5}}{1\frac{3}{4}\cdot\frac{2}{3}}$ 　21. $\dfrac{0.83\frac{1}{3}}{0.62\frac{1}{2}}$ 　22. $\dfrac{93\frac{1}{5}}{100}$

23. $\dfrac{\frac{x^2-2x+1}{5-x}}{\frac{x-1}{5-x}}$ 　24. $\dfrac{\frac{x^2-y^2}{8}}{\frac{x+y}{4}}$ 　25. $\dfrac{\frac{a^3-b^3}{(a+b)}}{\frac{a^2-b^2}{(a+b)}}$

26. $\dfrac{\frac{x^3-y^3}{x-y}}{\frac{3x+2+3y+8}{x^2-y^2}}$ 　27. $\dfrac{\frac{4x^3}{8r^2}-3t}{\frac{4x^3}{8r^2}-3t}$ 　28. $\dfrac{\frac{8r^3}{4k}-2}{2-\frac{8r^3}{4k}}$

ALGEBRAIC FRACTIONS **287**

Multiply:

1. $\dfrac{3}{5} \cdot \dfrac{a}{b}$

2. $\dfrac{5}{8} \cdot a$

3. $c \cdot \dfrac{a}{b}$

4. $\dfrac{y^2 - 25}{y + 1} \cdot \dfrac{y^2 + 2y + 1}{y - 5}$

5. $\dfrac{5 \cdot 3^2}{2 \cdot 7} \cdot \dfrac{2^3 \cdot 7}{5^2 \cdot 3}$

6. $\dfrac{y}{4} \cdot \dfrac{16}{y(x + 1)}$

Divide:

7. $\dfrac{8}{9} \div \dfrac{2}{3}$

8. $9 \div \dfrac{3}{5}$

9. $\dfrac{7}{8} \div 4$

10. $\dfrac{5a + 5}{7} \div \dfrac{a + 1}{14}$

11. $\dfrac{x^2 + 10x + 25}{x^2 - 16} \div \dfrac{x + 5}{x + 4}$

12. $\dfrac{6x + 3y}{2x + y} \div \dfrac{3}{4}$

Simplify:

13. $\dfrac{\dfrac{15}{xy}}{\dfrac{5}{xy}}$

14. $\dfrac{\dfrac{y - 2}{4}}{\dfrac{y^2 - 4}{8}}$

15. $\dfrac{0.62\frac{1}{2}}{0.37\frac{1}{2}}$

Addition and Subtraction of Fractions Having the Same Denominator

An important point to remember when you add or subtract fractions is that you must first be sure all the fractions have the same denominator. When the denominators are the same, you add or subtract the numerators and write the sum or the difference as the numerator of the answer. The common denominator is the denominator of the answer.

Examples for Study

1. $\dfrac{4}{8} + \dfrac{3}{8} = \dfrac{4 + 3}{8} = \dfrac{7}{8}$

2. $\dfrac{5}{3} - \dfrac{3}{3} = \dfrac{5 - 3}{3} = \dfrac{2}{3}$

3. $\dfrac{2 + 3x}{a} + \dfrac{1 - 2x}{a} = \dfrac{2 + 3x + 1 - 2x}{a} = \dfrac{3 + x}{a}$

4. *Subtract:* $\dfrac{5a + b}{a - b} - \dfrac{2a - 3b}{a - b}$

SOLUTION: $\qquad \dfrac{5a + b}{a - b} - \dfrac{2a - 3b}{a - b} = \underline{\dfrac{?}{}}$

In subtracting algebraic fractions it is very important that you observe that the line separating the numerator from the denominator is a grouping symbol, just as parentheses are grouping symbols. Thus, $\frac{2x + 1}{3}$ means $(2x + 1) \div 3$. Hence, the first thing you should do is to enclose in parentheses the numerator of the fraction to be subtracted:

$$\frac{5a + b}{a - b} - \frac{(2a - 3b)}{a - b} = \underline{\quad ? \quad}$$

Now combine the numerators and place the result over the common denominator:

$$\frac{5a + b - (2a - 3b)}{a - b} = \frac{5a + b - 2a + 3b}{a - b} = \frac{3a + 4b}{a - b}$$

PROBLEMS

Add or subtract as indicated and reduce each answer to the simplest form:

1. $\frac{1}{6} + \frac{1}{6}$

2. $\frac{3}{5} - \frac{2}{5}$

3. $\frac{a}{4} + \frac{a}{4}$

4. $\frac{4}{a} + \frac{4}{a}$

5. $\frac{x}{7} - \frac{y}{7}$

6. $\frac{5}{c} - \frac{2}{c}$

7. $\frac{2a}{mn} + \frac{2a}{mn}$

8. $\frac{2a}{mn} + \frac{2}{mn}$

9. $\frac{a}{b} + \frac{a}{b} + \frac{a}{b}$

10. $\frac{m}{n} + \frac{m}{n} + \frac{r}{n}$

11. $\frac{a + 1}{3} + \frac{2a + 3}{3}$

12. $\frac{3m - 2}{6} - \frac{2m - 2}{6}$

13. $\frac{1}{2x} + \frac{1}{2x}$

14. $\frac{2a}{a - b} - \frac{a}{a - b}$

15. $\frac{16a}{b} - \frac{14a - 5}{b}$

16. $\frac{4}{s} - \frac{8 - d}{s}$

17. $\frac{a}{a + b} + \frac{b}{a + b}$

18. $\frac{x}{x - 2} - \frac{x}{x - 2}$

19. $\frac{3a - b}{a + b} - \frac{2a - 2b}{a + b}$

★ 20. $\frac{4x - 5}{xy} + \frac{3x + 5}{xy}$

21. $\frac{4}{3^2 \cdot 5} + \frac{7}{3^2 \cdot 5} + \frac{2}{3^2 \cdot 5}$

22. $\frac{a + b}{(a + b)^2} + \frac{1}{(a + b)^2}$

23. $\frac{3x}{9x^2} + \frac{9}{9x^2}$

24. $\frac{x + 1}{x + 1} + \frac{x^2 + 1}{x + 1}$

25. $\frac{5a}{15a + 1} + \frac{1}{15a + 1} + \frac{10a}{15a + 1}$

26. $\frac{7x^2}{3x^2 - 1} - \frac{4x^2}{3x^2 - 1}$

27. $\frac{6a^2 - 2}{3 - 12x^2} - \frac{3 + 7a^2}{12x^2 - 3}$

Addition and Subtraction of Fractions Having Unequal Denominators

You will find many practical problems involving addition and subtraction of fractions with denominators that are not the same. Before you can add or subtract such fractions, you must first change them to equivalent fractions having the same denominators.

To add the fractions $\frac{7}{15}$ and $\frac{5}{24}$, you must find a common denominator. One way to find a common denominator is to multiply 15 and 24. The product 15×24, or 360, is a common denominator, but it is not the lowest common denominator.

A useful method for finding the lowest common denominator is as follows:

(1) Factor the denominators 15 and 24 into prime factors.

$$15 = 5 \cdot 3 \quad \text{and} \quad 24 = 2 \cdot 2 \cdot 2 \cdot 3$$

(2) The lowest common denominator must contain each of the prime factors in 15 and 24, that is, 5, 3, and 2.

(3) Each factor must appear in the lowest common denominator as many times as it does in the denominator where it appears the greatest number of times. So the lowest common denominator of $\frac{7}{15}$ and $\frac{5}{24}$ must contain one 3, one 5, and three 2's as factors. The lowest common denominator is:

$$3 \cdot 5 \cdot 2 \cdot 2 \cdot 2 = 120$$

So $\frac{7}{15} + \frac{5}{24} = \frac{56}{120} + \frac{25}{120} = \frac{81}{120} = \frac{27}{40}$

Examples for Study

1. *Add:* $\dfrac{1}{8} + \dfrac{5}{6}$

SOLUTION: $\dfrac{1}{8} + \dfrac{5}{6} = \underline{\ ?\ }$

The lowest common denominator is 24, since 24 is the smallest number that is divisible by both 8 and 6. To make 24 the denominator of each fraction, you will have to multiply both the numerator and the denominator of the first fraction by 3 and multiply both the numerator and the denominator of the second fraction by 4:

$$\frac{3 \cdot 1}{3 \cdot 8} + \frac{4 \cdot 5}{4 \cdot 6} = \underline{\ ?\ }$$

$$\frac{3}{24} + \frac{20}{24} = \frac{23}{24}$$

2. *Subtract:* $\dfrac{1}{a} - \dfrac{1}{b}$

SOLUTION: $\dfrac{1}{a} - \dfrac{1}{b} = \underline{\ ?\ }$

The L.C.D. is ab, since this is the smallest expression that is divisible by both a and b. When denominators have no common factors, simply multiply them to find the L.C.D.

Next change each of the two fractions $\dfrac{1}{a}$ and $\dfrac{1}{b}$ to equivalent fractions having a common denominator ab:

$$\frac{1}{a} = \frac{1 \cdot b}{a \cdot b} = \frac{b}{ab} \quad \text{and} \quad \frac{1}{b} = \frac{1 \cdot a}{a \cdot b} = \frac{a}{ab}$$

so

$$\frac{1}{a} - \frac{1}{b} = \frac{b}{ab} - \frac{a}{ab} = \frac{b - a}{ab}$$

3. *Add:* $\dfrac{3}{5a^2} + \dfrac{4}{a^2 + a} + \dfrac{5}{(a + 1)}$

SOLUTION: Factoring the denominators completely:

$$5a^2 = 5 \cdot a \cdot a$$
$$a^2 + a = a(a + 1)$$
$$(a + 1) = (a + 1)$$

So the lowest common denominator must contain the factors 5, a, and $a + 1$. The factor a must appear twice because it appears twice as a factor of the first denominator. So the lowest common denominator is:

$$5 \cdot a \cdot a \cdot (a + 1) \quad \text{or} \quad 5a^2(a + 1)$$

$$\frac{3}{5a \cdot a} + \frac{4}{a(a + 1)} + \frac{5}{(a + 1)}$$

$$= \frac{3(a + 1)}{5a \cdot a \cdot (a + 1)} + \frac{4(5a)}{5 \cdot a \cdot a(a + 1)} + \frac{5(5a \cdot a)}{5a \cdot a(a + 1)}$$

$$= \frac{3(a + 1) + 4(5a) + 5(5a^2)}{5a^2(a + 1)}$$

$$= \frac{3a + 3 + 20a + 25a^2}{5a^2(a + 1)}$$

$$= \frac{25a^2 + 23a + 3}{5a^2(a + 1)}$$

4. Subtract: $\dfrac{3x}{x^2 + 5x + 6} - \dfrac{x - 5}{x^2 - 4}$

SOLUTION: Factoring the denominators completely:

$$x^2 + 5x + 6 = (x + 3)(x + 2)$$
$$x^2 - 4 \qquad = (x - 2)(x + 2)$$

So the lowest common denominator is:

$$(x + 3)(x + 2)(x - 2)$$

$$\frac{3x}{(x + 3)(x + 2)} - \frac{(x - 5)}{(x + 2)(x - 2)}$$

$$= \frac{3x(x - 2)}{(x + 3)(x + 2)(x - 2)} - \frac{(x - 5)(x + 3)}{(x + 3)(x + 2)(x - 2)}$$

$$= \frac{3x^2 - 6x - (x^2 - 2x - 15)}{(x + 3)(x + 2)(x - 2)}$$

$$= \frac{3x^2 - 6x - x^2 + 2x + 15}{(x + 3)(x + 2)(x - 2)}$$

$$= \frac{2x^2 - 4x + 15}{(x + 3)(x + 2)(x - 2)}$$

PROBLEMS

Find the lowest common denominator and add:

1. $\dfrac{4}{9} + \dfrac{5}{12}$ 2. $\dfrac{7}{30} + \dfrac{4}{45}$ 3. $\dfrac{5}{14} + \dfrac{4}{49}$

4. $\dfrac{4}{175} + \dfrac{6}{245}$ 5. $\dfrac{5}{54} + \dfrac{7}{45}$ 6. $\dfrac{3}{40} + \dfrac{5}{12}$

7. $\dfrac{5}{12} + \dfrac{7}{40} + \dfrac{4}{75}$ 8. $\dfrac{7}{30} + \dfrac{5}{154} + \dfrac{5}{12}$ 9. $\dfrac{5}{99} + \dfrac{3}{35} + \dfrac{7}{12}$

10. $\dfrac{3}{52} + \dfrac{3}{26} + \dfrac{7}{30}$ 11. $\dfrac{7}{30} + \dfrac{8}{15} + \dfrac{5}{6}$ 12. $\dfrac{2}{75} + \dfrac{8}{40} + \dfrac{3}{64}$

Combine by adding or subtracting as indicated:

13. $\dfrac{1}{5} + \dfrac{2}{3}$ 14. $\dfrac{3}{7} + \dfrac{4}{5} + \dfrac{1}{3}$ 15. $\dfrac{5}{2} + \dfrac{7}{8} + \dfrac{1}{4}$

16. $\dfrac{3}{7} - \dfrac{2}{5}$ 17. $\dfrac{a}{2} + \dfrac{a}{3}$ 18. $\dfrac{2m}{5} - \dfrac{m}{10}$

19. $\dfrac{1}{a} + \dfrac{2}{b}$ 20. $\dfrac{4}{a} + \dfrac{3}{2a}$ 21. $\dfrac{1}{3} - \dfrac{1}{x}$

22. $\dfrac{9}{4} - \dfrac{2}{a}$ 23. $\dfrac{1}{2} + \dfrac{1}{k}$ 24. $\dfrac{x}{10} - \dfrac{1}{5}$

25. $\dfrac{a}{b} - \dfrac{2}{a}$

26. $\dfrac{mn}{4} + \dfrac{mn}{2}$

27. $2\frac{1}{2} - \frac{2}{3}$

28. $\dfrac{1}{a} + \dfrac{1}{b} + \dfrac{1}{c}$

29. $\dfrac{x+y}{a} - \dfrac{x}{2a}$

30. $\dfrac{a}{b} - \dfrac{b}{a}$

31. $\dfrac{2}{3mn} - \dfrac{2}{5mn}$

32. $\dfrac{1}{2m} + \dfrac{a-3}{4m}$

33. $2 + \dfrac{1}{a}$

34. $3 + \dfrac{1}{b}$

35. $\dfrac{a}{3} + 4$

36. $\dfrac{5}{x} - 1$

37. $5 + \dfrac{3}{m}$

38. $6 - \dfrac{5}{n}$

39. $\dfrac{2}{a} - 2$

40. $\dfrac{a}{b} - c$

41. $\dfrac{10}{a} + a$

42. $\dfrac{a}{2b} - 1 + \dfrac{1}{b}$

43. $\dfrac{1}{a} + x - 3$

44. $\dfrac{2y}{x^2} + \dfrac{y^2}{x}$

45. $\dfrac{1}{r} + \dfrac{1}{s} - \dfrac{1}{t}$

46. $\dfrac{b}{3a} - \dfrac{a-1}{5b}$

47. $\dfrac{3}{4} - \dfrac{x-1}{5x} + \dfrac{x-2}{2x}$

48. $\dfrac{1}{2} - \dfrac{a-1}{a} + \dfrac{a-2}{a^2}$

49. $\dfrac{3a+2}{a} - 3$

50. $\dfrac{c+d}{c} + \dfrac{c-d}{d}$

51. $\dfrac{x-1}{2} + \dfrac{x-3}{4}$

52. $\dfrac{2x-6}{5} + \dfrac{x+2}{2}$

53. $\dfrac{3x+2}{4} + \dfrac{2x-1}{6}$

54. $\dfrac{x-2}{4} - \dfrac{x-3}{8}$

55. $\dfrac{a-1}{3} - \dfrac{2a-5}{4}$

56. $\dfrac{5-6x}{2} + \dfrac{3x+5}{5}$

57. $\dfrac{7b-3}{18} + \dfrac{1-b}{6}$

58. $\dfrac{1-3b}{8} - \dfrac{b-3}{12}$

59. $\dfrac{x^2+2x+1}{15} - \dfrac{x^2-3x-5}{5}$

60. $\dfrac{a^2+4a+4}{3} - \dfrac{a^2-2}{4}$

61. $\dfrac{1}{a^2} + \dfrac{1}{a} - a$

62. $\dfrac{3}{x^2} - \dfrac{2}{x} + 4$

63. $\dfrac{3}{x-y} - \dfrac{2}{x}$

64. $\dfrac{x}{x+y} + 3$

65. $\dfrac{5}{a+b} + \dfrac{3}{b}$

66. $\dfrac{4}{m-n} - \dfrac{8}{n}$

67. $\dfrac{1}{x-y} + \dfrac{1}{y}$

68. $\dfrac{1}{b-c} - \dfrac{1}{b}$

69. $\dfrac{x}{x-y} - 3$

70. $\dfrac{a}{a-d} - 1$

71. $\dfrac{x-2}{2} - \dfrac{3}{x+2}$

72. $\dfrac{3}{m-1} - \dfrac{2}{m-2}$

73. $\dfrac{2a}{(a-b)^2} + \dfrac{1}{(a-b)}$

74. $\dfrac{1}{a-b} - \dfrac{1}{a+b}$

75. $\dfrac{x}{x+5} + \dfrac{x}{x-4}$

76. $\dfrac{15}{4a-4b} - \dfrac{3}{a-b}$

77. $\dfrac{5}{(x-y)} + \dfrac{2}{(x+y)}$

78. $\dfrac{6}{4x+4y} - \dfrac{3}{4}$

79. $\dfrac{5x}{x^2-9} + \dfrac{7}{x+3}$

80. $\dfrac{3}{5x^2} - \dfrac{4}{2x}$

81. $\dfrac{2}{3x^3} + \dfrac{5}{4x}$

★ 82. $\dfrac{3x}{2x^2+4x} - \dfrac{5x}{x^2+4x+4}$

83. $\dfrac{5}{4x+4} + \dfrac{6}{x^2+2x+1}$

84. $\dfrac{4}{3a+3b} - \dfrac{7}{a^2-b^2}$

85. $\dfrac{5x}{x+3} + \dfrac{2}{x^2+5x+6}$

86. $\dfrac{2}{3a^2} + \dfrac{3b}{5a^3}$

87. $\dfrac{2}{3y} - \dfrac{y}{y+1}$

88. $\dfrac{3}{x-y} - \dfrac{2x}{x^2-y^2}$

89. $\dfrac{5a}{a^2+2ab+b^2} + \dfrac{2b}{(a+b)}$

90. $\dfrac{4x+1}{3x^2+33x+90} + \dfrac{3}{(x+6)}$

91. $\dfrac{4}{x} + \dfrac{3}{x+1} - \dfrac{5}{x^2}$

92. $\dfrac{1}{x} - \dfrac{1}{y} + \dfrac{3}{x^2 y}$

93. $\dfrac{3z}{x(y+z)} - \dfrac{2y}{(y+z)^2}$

94. $\dfrac{3}{a} - \dfrac{5}{b} - \dfrac{3}{a-b}$

95. $\dfrac{5}{x^2-y^2} + \dfrac{7}{x(x+y)}$

96. $\dfrac{2x}{x^2-36} - \dfrac{4(x-6)}{(x+6)}$

97. $\dfrac{5}{x^2+x-6} + \dfrac{3x}{x^2-4x+4}$

98. $\dfrac{3}{x^2+5x-14} - \dfrac{4}{x^2+14x+49} + \dfrac{7}{x^2-4x+4}$

99. $\dfrac{7(x+3)}{y^2} - \dfrac{4(y+1)}{(x+3)y}$

100. $\dfrac{16}{x^3-27} + \dfrac{3}{x-3}$

101. $\dfrac{a}{8a^3-1} - \dfrac{a-1}{2a^2-1}$

294 *ALGEBRA: ITS BIG IDEAS AND BASIC SKILLS*

Changing the Sign of a Fraction

Fractions have positive and negative signs. Just as negative 5 is written -5, so negative $\frac{3}{4}$ is written $-\frac{3}{4}$; and as positive 5 is written $+5$, so positive $\frac{3}{4}$ is written $+\frac{3}{4}$.

The sign in front of a fraction may be also thought of as attached to either the numerator or the denominator of the fraction. For example, the fraction $+\frac{3}{4}$ may be thought of as $\frac{+3}{4}$ or $\frac{3}{+4}$. Similarly, the fraction $-\frac{3}{4}$ may be thought of as $\frac{-3}{4}$ or $\frac{3}{-4}$.

The same is true of an algebraic fraction. For example, the fraction $+\frac{a}{b}$ may be thought of as $\frac{+a}{b}$ or $\frac{a}{+b}$. Similarly, the fraction $-\frac{a}{b}$ may be thought of as $\frac{-a}{b}$ or $\frac{a}{-b}$.

You recall that if you multiply -1 by -1 or divide -1 by -1, the result in each case is $+1$. You also know that any number multiplied by $+1$ is equal to that number. This fact can be used in changing the form of a fraction. Study the following examples to see how the form of a fraction is changed.

$$\frac{3}{4} = \frac{(-1) \cdot 3}{(-1) \cdot 4} = \frac{-3}{-4}$$

$$\frac{3}{4} = \frac{(-1)(-1) \cdot 3}{4} = -\left(\frac{-3}{4}\right)$$

$$\frac{3}{4} = \frac{3}{(-1)(-1) \cdot 4} = -\left(\frac{3}{-4}\right)$$

This fact that the factor -1 may be introduced twice in a fraction without changing the value of the fraction is a convenient one. You can use it very effectively in simplifying many algebraic fractions. A study of the following examples should make this clear.

Examples for Study

1. *Add:* $\dfrac{x}{x-4} + \dfrac{-3}{4-x}$

SOLUTION: You cannot add these fractions as they stand because they are not like fractions. But you can readily change them to like fractions by introducing -1 twice as a factor in either of the two fractions.

$$\frac{x}{x-4} + \frac{(-1)(-3)}{(-1)(4-x)} = \frac{x}{x-4} + \frac{+3}{-4+x}$$

$$= \frac{x}{x-4} + \frac{3}{x-4} = \frac{x+3}{x-4}$$

2. *Subtract:* $\dfrac{x}{x-5} - \dfrac{2}{5-x}$

SOLUTION: There are three possible places where you can introduce the -1 factors: in the numerator, in front of the fraction, or in the denominator. In Example 1, -1 was placed in the numerator and in the denominator. In Example 2 it is more convenient to place -1 in front of the fraction and in the denominator:

$$\frac{x}{x-5} - \frac{2}{5-x} = \underline{\ ?\ }$$

Introducing -1 twice in the second fraction changes it to:

$$\frac{x}{x-5} + \frac{2}{x-5} = \frac{x+2}{x-5}$$

PROBLEMS

Add or subtract as indicated:

1. $\dfrac{3}{x-3} + \dfrac{2}{3-x}$

2. $\dfrac{5}{a-b} - \dfrac{3}{b-a}$

3. $\dfrac{2}{m-2} - \dfrac{1}{2-m}$

4. $\dfrac{6}{a^2-a} - \dfrac{-2}{a-a^2}$

5. $\dfrac{12}{3x-1} + \dfrac{2}{1-3x}$

6. $\dfrac{x+1}{x-2} - \dfrac{-3}{2-x}$

7. $\dfrac{x-1}{x-8} + \dfrac{x-3}{8-x}$

8. $\dfrac{a+b}{a-b} + \dfrac{b+a}{b-a}$

9. $\dfrac{x-3}{2} + \dfrac{x+2}{-2}$

10. $\dfrac{a-b}{9} - \dfrac{a+b}{-3}$

11. $\dfrac{x}{x^2-1} - \dfrac{1}{1-x}$

12. $\dfrac{a^2}{a^2-b^2} - \dfrac{a}{b-a}$

Reduce the following fractions. Note: Introduce -1 in front of the fraction and in the denominator.

13. $-\dfrac{a-b}{b-a}$

14. $\dfrac{x-y}{y-x}$

15. $-\dfrac{m+n}{-m-n}$

16. $-\dfrac{2-c}{c-2}$

17. $\dfrac{8-k}{k-8}$

18. $\dfrac{m^2-n^2}{n-m}$

★ **19.** $\dfrac{a-5}{5-a}$

20. $\dfrac{15-5x}{x-3}$

21. $\dfrac{2x-12}{36-x^2}$

22. $\dfrac{x^2-x-20}{5-x}$

23. $\dfrac{a-3}{9-a^2}$

24. $\dfrac{c^3-d^3}{c^2-d^2}$

296 *ALGEBRA: ITS BIG IDEAS AND BASIC SKILLS*

Find the value of the following algebraic expressions if $a = \frac{1}{2}$, $b = \frac{3}{4}$, *and* $c = 2$:

25. $a + b + c$ **26.** $ab + bc$ **27.** $a^2 + b^2$

28. $\dfrac{a}{b}$ **29.** $\dfrac{b}{c}$ **30.** $\dfrac{a}{c}$

31. $\dfrac{1}{abc}$ **32.** $a^3 + b^3$ **33.** $ac - b$

34. $\dfrac{a - c}{a - b}$ **35.** $\dfrac{1}{a} + \dfrac{1}{b} - \dfrac{1}{c}$ **36.** $c - ab$

37. $\dfrac{\frac{a + b}{c}}{ab}$ **38.** $(ab)^c$ **39.** $(a - b)(a + b)$

40. $(a + b)^c$ **41.** $a^2(b - c)$ **42.** $\dfrac{bc - a}{a}$

43. $\dfrac{1}{a - b} \cdot \dfrac{1}{b + c}$ **44.** $(abc - b)(abc + b)$ **45.** $\dfrac{abc}{abc}$

If A, B, C, *and* D *have the values given below, write the following expressions in terms of* x. *Reduce each answer to the simplest form.*

$$A = \frac{x - 4}{2} \qquad B = \frac{x + 4}{2} \qquad C = \frac{x - 3}{3} \qquad D = \frac{x - 3}{x + 4}$$

46. $A + B$ **47.** $A - B$ **48.** AB

49. $A \div B$ **50.** $C + B$ **51.** CD

52. $A - C$ **53.** $B - A$ **54.** $A^2 + B^2$

55. $\dfrac{C}{D}$ **56.** $AB + C$ **57.** $\dfrac{1}{A} + \dfrac{1}{B}$

58. $\dfrac{1}{C} - \dfrac{1}{D}$ **59.** $(A + B)(A - B)$ **60.** $\dfrac{A}{B} + D$

61. $\dfrac{1}{D^2} - \dfrac{1}{C^2}$ **62.** $\dfrac{D}{C}$ **63.** $A + B - C$

Find the value of each of the following algebraic expressions if X, Y, *and* Z *have the values given below. Reduce each answer to the simplest form:*

$$X = \frac{33\frac{1}{3}}{a + b} \qquad Y = \frac{37\frac{1}{2}}{a - b} \qquad Z = \frac{66\frac{2}{3}}{a + 2b}$$

64. $X + Y$ **65.** $X - Y$ **66.** $\dfrac{X}{Y}$

67. YZ **68.** $\dfrac{Y}{Z}$ **69.** XYZ

SUMMARY OF IMPORTANT THINGS TO REMEMBER

1. Words and Expressions

algebraic fraction
complex fraction
equivalent fractions

lowest common denominator, or L.C.D.
reciprocal of a number

2. Understandings

Multiplying or dividing the numerator and the denominator of a fraction by the same number, except zero, does not change the value of the fraction.

Before fractions can be added or subtracted, they must have the same denominators.

To multiply two or more fractions, multiply the numerators to get the numerator of the product and multiply the denominators to get the denominator of the product. Sometimes you can divide the numerator and denominator by a common factor before multiplying.

To divide one fraction by another fraction, multiply the dividend by the reciprocal of the divisor.

A complex fraction can be changed to a common fraction by doing the indicated division.

To find the lowest common denominator:

(1) Factor the denominators completely.

(2) Include each different factor as a factor of the L.C.D.

(3) Include any factor in the L.C.D. as many times as it appears in the denominator in which it appears the greatest number of times.

3. Skills

You should be able to:

Change fractions to equivalent fractions.

Multiply fractions.

Divide fractions.

Add and subtract fractions with the same denominators.

Add and subtract fractions with unlike denominators.

Change the signs of fractions.

PROBLEMS ON YOUR AIMS

YOUR AIM 👉 **To get a better understanding of fractions.**

In what way are the expressions in each of the following alike?

1. $\dfrac{x-6}{2}$ and $(x-6) \div 2$

2. $-\dfrac{3a-4}{a+2}$ and $\dfrac{-1(3a-4)}{a+2}$

298 *ALGEBRA: ITS BIG IDEAS AND BASIC SKILLS*

3. $\dfrac{2}{x-2} - \dfrac{1}{2-x}$ and $\dfrac{2}{x-2} + \dfrac{1}{x-2}$ 4. $\dfrac{3}{4} - \dfrac{2}{5}$ and $3 \div 4 - 2 \div 5$

5. In Problem 4 which is the preferable form? Why?

What is true of the numerical value of the following fractions?

6. $\dfrac{x}{12}$ when x stands for any whole number greater than 12.

7. $\dfrac{x}{12}$ when x stands for any whole number less than 12 but greater than zero.

8. $\dfrac{x}{12}$ when x stands for zero.

9. $\dfrac{x}{12}$ when x stands for a number less than zero.

YOUR AIM 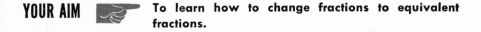 **To learn how to change fractions to equivalent fractions.**

In each of the following problems, what operation was performed on the fraction on the left to get the equivalent fraction on the right?

1. $\dfrac{3}{4} = \dfrac{6}{8}$ 2. $\dfrac{2}{5} = \dfrac{0.2}{0.5}$ 3. $\dfrac{x-1}{1-x} = -\dfrac{x-1}{x-1}$

4. $\dfrac{\frac{1}{2}}{\frac{3}{4}} = \dfrac{2}{3}$ 5. $\dfrac{x^2-4}{x^2-2x} = \dfrac{x+2}{x}$ 6. $\dfrac{0.1}{3} = \dfrac{1}{30}$

YOUR AIM **To learn how to add, subtract, multiply, and divide algebraic fractions.**

Find the lowest common denominator in each of the following sets of fractions:

1. $\dfrac{1}{2}, \dfrac{1}{3}, \dfrac{1}{9}$ 2. $\dfrac{2}{a}, \dfrac{3}{b}, \dfrac{4}{c}$ 3. $\dfrac{3}{ax}, \dfrac{1}{a^2x}, \dfrac{1}{x^2}$

4. $\dfrac{1}{x-1}, \dfrac{1}{x-2}$ 5. $\dfrac{1}{(a-b)^2}, \dfrac{1}{(a-b)}$ 6. $\dfrac{1}{x^2-9}, \dfrac{1}{x^2-2x-3}$

In the following problems find (1) the sum, (2) the difference (subtract the second from the first), (3) the product, and (4) the quotient (divide the first by the second):

7. $\dfrac{1}{3}, -2$ 8. $4, \dfrac{1}{x}$ 9. $\dfrac{1}{a}, a$

10. $\dfrac{1}{x-1}, \dfrac{2}{x^2-x}$ 11. $\dfrac{2}{a-b}, \dfrac{1}{b-a}$ 12. $\dfrac{m-n}{p}, \dfrac{-p}{m+n}$

ALGEBRAIC FRACTIONS **299**

VALUABLE SKILLS PRACTICE

1. Do the computations indicated below. Check your work by using the formula given at the bottom.

$a = 3.018 + 0.234 + 1.957 + 0.006$
$b = 4.302 - 3.168$
$c = 7.35 \times 0.079 - 0.00065$
$d = 24.276 \div 0.28 - 86.0$
$e = 12\%$ of 4.25
$f =$ forty-three thousandths
$g = 4\%$ of 2

CHECK: $a - b + c - d + e - f + g = 4.508$

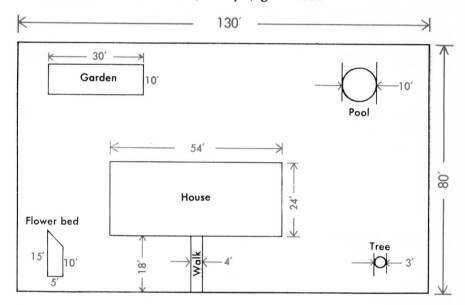

Study the diagram above. Find the area occupied by each of the following. (Use $\pi = 3.14$).

2. Lot   3. House   4. Flower bed
5. Walk   6. Tree   7. Pool

8. Find the fraction of the total area occupied by the house.
9. If all the area is in grass except the parts whose measurements are shown in the diagram, find the number of square feet of grass in the lot.

Add:

10. $\frac{7}{12} + \frac{2}{3} + \frac{3}{4}$ 11. $7\frac{2}{3} + 10\frac{1}{2} + 10\frac{3}{5}$ 12. $3\frac{1}{4} + 7\frac{3}{4} + 8\frac{1}{4}$
13. $\frac{9}{16} + 1\frac{1}{4} + 2\frac{3}{8}$ 14. $3\frac{3}{5} + 6\frac{1}{4} + 2\frac{1}{3}$ 15. $\frac{2}{15} + \frac{2}{9} + \frac{2}{3}$

Subtract:

16. $\frac{5}{12} - \frac{3}{8}$ 17. $14\frac{1}{2} - 8\frac{4}{5}$ 18. $\frac{7}{8} - \frac{3}{4}$
19. $\frac{3}{4} - \frac{3}{8}$ 20. $2\frac{1}{16} - 1\frac{1}{8}$ 21. $\frac{7}{12} - \frac{3}{8}$

Multiply:

22. $\frac{5}{6} \times \frac{3}{20}$

23. $8\frac{1}{3} \times 2\frac{1}{5}$

24. $14\frac{1}{3} \times 4\frac{1}{2}$

25. $\frac{4}{9} \times \frac{3}{8}$

26. $1\frac{2}{3} \times 2\frac{1}{4} \times 3\frac{1}{5}$

27. $\frac{3}{10} \times \frac{5}{6} \times \frac{4}{9}$

Divide:

28. $\frac{3}{8} \div \frac{3}{2}$

29. $10\frac{1}{2} \div \frac{3}{4}$

30. $96 \div 1\frac{1}{3}$

31. $\frac{3}{4} \div 1\frac{1}{8}$

32. $39 \div 4\frac{1}{3}$

33. $4\frac{1}{3} \div 4\frac{1}{6}$

CHAPTER TEST

Simplify:

1. $\frac{1}{x} + \frac{2}{x} + \frac{a}{x}$

2. $\frac{3}{2a} - \frac{1}{6a}$

3. $6 \cdot \frac{6}{a}$

4. $\frac{b^2}{12} \div \frac{b}{4}$

5. $\frac{a + x}{a^2 - x^2}$

6. $\frac{5}{x - y} - \frac{2}{x - y}$

7. $\frac{8}{x - y} - \frac{5}{x + y}$

8. $\frac{16}{m^2} \cdot \frac{3}{4a} \div \frac{2m}{a^3}$

9. $\frac{2x^2 + 11x + 15}{2x + 5}$

10. $\frac{4x - 8}{x^2 - 2x}$

11. $\frac{10 - 10a}{7a} \div \frac{a - a^2}{14}$

12. $5 + \frac{1}{a}$

13. $\frac{1}{x} + \frac{1}{y} - \frac{1}{z}$

14. $1 + \frac{2a}{3}$

15. $x - 3 - \frac{x - 4}{2}$

16. $\frac{3 - 1\frac{1}{2}}{5 - 2\frac{1}{2}}$

17. $\frac{a - 10}{10 - a}$

18. $\frac{b^2 - b}{b^2} \div \frac{b - 1}{b}$

19. $\frac{x - 7}{49 - x^2}$

20. $\frac{1}{a - 7} - \frac{1}{7 - a}$

21. How many minutes are there in $10s$ seconds and $\frac{1}{2}h$ hours? Express as one fraction.

22. How many months are there in $7w$ weeks and 15 days? Express as one fraction.

23. Mr. Clark's present age is a years and 3 months. Express this as one fraction.

If A, B, C, *and* D *have the values given below, write each of the following expressions in terms of* x. *Reduce each answer to its simplest form.*

$$A = \frac{x - 5}{x} \qquad B = \frac{x}{3x - 2} \qquad C = \frac{x + 5}{x} \qquad D = \frac{x - 5}{2 - 3x}$$

24. AB

25. AC

26. $A + C$

27. $A - C$

28. AD

29. CD

30. $A \div C$

31. $B - D$

32. $B + D$

ALGEBRAIC FRACTIONS **301**

CUMULATIVE REVIEW PROBLEMS
WORKING WITH ALGEBRAIC EXPRESSIONS

1. From the sum of $x^2 - 6xy + 2$ and $3x^2 + xy - 11$ subtract $-4x^2 - 8xy + 10$.
2. Simplify $5x^2 - 3y(x + y) - 3x(x - y)$.
3. Multiply $6x^2 - 17x + 11$ by $3x + 1$.
4. In $10ab - 5b = 6$, find a if $b = 1\frac{1}{2}$.
5. Write the square of the sum of $3x$, $-4x$, and y.
6. If $x + 1$ is the smallest of three consecutive numbers, what is the largest of these three numbers?
7. What will be Norma's age 5 years from now if her present age is $n - 1$ years?
8. Find the area of a rectangle whose length is y times the width x.
9. What is the perimeter of the rectangle in Problem 8?
10. How many dimes are there in D dollars and Q quarters?
11. How many feet are there in $\frac{1}{2}n$ yards and $2\frac{1}{4}$ feet?
12. How many yards are there in $4F$ feet and $1\frac{1}{2}$ feet? Express as one fraction.

Factor completely:

13. $2 - 18x^2$

14. $2a^2x^2 + 5a^2x - 12a^2$

15. $x^3 - x$

16. $a^2n + an - 2n$

Match each of the expressions in Column 1 with its algebraic equivalent in Column 2:

Column 1	Column 2
17. A trinomial square	**a.** $(a - 3)^2$
18. The difference between two squares	**b.** $n(a + b)$
19. The product of the sum of and the difference between two numbers	**c.** $x^2 - 2x + 1$
	d. $an + bn + cn$
20. The square of a binomial	**e.** $(x + 5)(x - 5)$
	f. $9x^2 - 16$

Find the products:

21. $(x - 5)(x + 6)$

22. $(-0.7a^3)^2 (10a)^3$

23. $(2m - 9)(2m + 9)$

24. $(x - 7)^2$

25. $(5 + 11k)(5 + k)$

26. $6(a + 1)(a - 1)$

27. $(2x)^2 (x + 2)^2$

28. $x(a - x)(a + x)$

29. $(y + \frac{1}{4})^2$

30. $(a + 1)^3$

Write each of the following as one fraction in the simplest form:

31. The number of pounds in $4w$ ounces.
32. The number of dimes in $5c$ cents.
33. The number of years in $8M$ months.
34. The number of dimes in D dollars and Q quarters.
35. The number of yards in F feet and 18 inches.
36. The number of dollars in N nickels and 3 quarters.

SOLVING EQUATIONS

Solve each of the following equations:

1. $4x - x(x - 8) = 0$
2. $\dfrac{3x}{4} = \dfrac{1}{4}$

3. $16 - (y - 5) = 20$
4. $\dfrac{-2y}{5} - 1 = 0$

5. $x - 7x = -10$
6. $x(x - 4) - 3(x + 7) = -3$

7. $\dfrac{x}{3} - \dfrac{x}{5} = 4$
8. $2.5 - (x - 0.6) + 5(2x + 0.1) = 0$

Solve each system of equations:

9. $x - 2y = 6$
   $x - 3y = 8$
10. $x - 5y = 6$
    $4x - y = 5$

WORKING WITH GRAPHS

1. Graph the equation $x + 2y = 4$ using a table of values and using the slope and y-intercept method.
2. In the equation $y = \frac{2}{3}x - 4$, when x increases by 1, by how much does y increase? At what point does the graph of this equation cross the y-axis?

WORKING WITH FORMULAS

Change the subject of each formula as directed:

1. If $m = \dfrac{b + 2x}{3}$, find the value of x.
2. If $a = m + x$, find the value of x.
3. If $a = \dfrac{bc + 1}{2}$, find the value of c.
4. If $m = 3a + b$, find the value of a.
5. If $p = \dfrac{4m - 6}{q}$, find the value of m.
6. $I = \dfrac{E}{R}$ is known as Ohm's law of electricity. Change the subject of this formula from I to E. From I to R.
7. $C = \frac{5}{9}(F - 32)$ is the relation between centigrade and Fahrenheit thermometer readings. Make F the subject of this formula.
8. $S = \frac{1}{2}gt^2$ is the formula for finding the distance a freely falling body travels in a given time. Make g the subject of this formula.
9. $A = \dfrac{h(a + b)}{2}$ is the formula for finding the area of a trapezoid. Change this formula so that h is the subject.
10. $F = \dfrac{wv^2}{gr}$ is the formula for centrifugal force—the force tending to pull an object like an airplane from its curved path when it is banking or pulling out of a dive. Make r the subject of this formula.

ALGEBRAIC FRACTIONS **303**

1. A rectangle is l inches long and w inches wide. If the length is increased by 2 inches and the width by 1 inch, by how much is the area increased?

2. A woman paid $79.50 for a watch. This price included a 10% special tax. What was the price of the watch before the tax?

3. The cost of an airplane ticket is $118.40. This price includes a special tax of 15%. Find the cost of the ticket before the tax.

4. A hardware store had a going-out-of-business sale. An electric coffeepot was sold at a loss of 1% of its cost. The selling price was $14.98. What was the cost of this coffeepot?

5. A saleman's commission is 5% of his sales. How much will he have to sell to make $500?

6. A ship, traveling 24 miles per hour, left a port. An airplane left the airport at the same port 2 hours and 30 minutes later and flew in the same direction as the ship. The plane flew at 240 miles per hour. How many minutes after taking off did the plane overtake the ship?

7. Mr. Adams and his son were painting their house. They found that 3 quarts of paint covered 384 square feet. At this rate, how much paint to the nearest quart will be needed to paint 740 square feet?

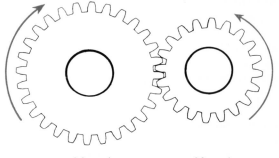

28 teeth   20 teeth

8. A gear having 28 teeth is driven by a gear having 20 teeth. The speed of the 28-tooth gear is 124 revolutions per minute. What is the speed of the other gear?

9. Find two consecutive odd numbers whose product is 8099.

10. A sports store has 43 pairs of two kinds of ice skates. One kind sells for $16.50 and the other for $19.98. If all the skates are sold, the store will receive $796.50. How many pairs of each kind of skates does the store have?

11. The ratio of the tens' and units' digits of a certain two-digit number is 3. The difference between the number and the number obtained by reversing the digits is 36. Find the number.

12. Two quarts of oil and 6 gallons of gasoline cost $2.44. One quart of oil and 9 gallons of gasoline cost $2.96. Find the cost of 1 quart of oil and 1 gallon of gasoline.

13. The number of revolutions a wheel makes in rolling a fixed distance varies inversely as the diameter of the wheel. A wheel 12 inches in diameter makes 190 revolutions in rolling a certain distance. What is the diameter of a wheel which makes 50 revolutions in rolling the same distance?

14. The speed required to travel a certain distance varies inversely as the time. It requires 3 hours to travel between two cities when traveling at an average speed of 42 miles per hour. How long will it take to make the same trip when traveling at an average speed of 50 miles per hour?

15. The sum of two numbers is 210. The larger number is one-third more than the smaller number. Find the numbers.

16. Divide $135 between Lois and Bob so that Lois will receive $1\frac{1}{2}$ times as much as Bob.

17. A line 100 inches long is divided into two parts. The smaller part is 4 inches less than three-fifths of the larger part. Find the two parts.

18. The perimeter of a rectangle is 46 inches, and its area is 120 square inches. Find the length and the width of the rectangle.

19. Arline is 5 years older than Donald. Ten years from now Donald will be seven-eighths as old as Arline. Find the present ages of Arline and Donald.

20. The difference between two numbers is 15. When the larger number is divided by the smaller number, the quotient is 2 and the remainder is 3. Find the two numbers.

21. What part of a dollar are k nickels and $2k$ dimes?

22. The formula for finding the area of a trapezoid is $A = \frac{1}{2}h(a + b)$. Rewrite this formula if $h = \frac{3}{4}a$ and $b = \frac{1}{2}a$.

23. The longer base of a trapezoid is $2\frac{1}{2}$ times the shorter base. Find the length of the bases if the altitude is 8 inches and the area is 280 square inches.

24. Separate a number represented by n into two numbers such that the larger number divided by the smaller number will give a quotient of k and a remainder of r.

AUTOMOBILE ENGINEERS USE ALGEBRA

Automobile engineers have a formula which they use to find the indicated horsepower of one cylinder of an automobile motor. Using this formula, they can find the total indicated horsepower of all the cylinders. The formula is:

$$H = \frac{P \cdot L \cdot A \cdot N}{33,000}$$

P stands for the average effective pressure in pounds per square inch on the piston.

L stands for the total length in feet that the pressure is applied.

A stands for the area of the piston, or cross section of the cylinder, in square inches.

N stands for the number of revolutions per minute divided by 2.

An engineer wished to find the horsepower of a 6-cylinder motor which has a 4-inch cylinder, a 3.6-inch stroke, 3200 revolutions per minute, and an average effective pressure of 100 pounds per square inch. He used the formula to find the answer.

$$H = \frac{P \cdot L \cdot A \cdot N}{33,000}$$

$$H = \frac{(100)(\frac{3.6}{12})(3.14 \times 2 \times 2)(1600)}{33,000}$$

$$H = \frac{602,880}{33,000}$$

$$H = 18.27$$

So the motor has 18.27 horsepower for 1 cylinder or 109.6 horsepower for all 6 cylinders.

306 *ALGEBRA: ITS BIG IDEAS AND BASIC SKILLS*

BIG IDEA | EQUATION

BASIC SKILLS | Using and interpreting symbols of algebra
Fundamental operations
Solving equations
Factoring
Solving verbal problems

CHAPTER **11** *Equations and Problems*

MANY PROBLEMS in business, industry, and science are solved by the use of equations. The ability to think in terms of equations and to solve problems by means of them is an advantage in finding employment in many fields.

You have already learned in this algebra course how useful equations are in solving problems. To become skillful in solving problems, you need to know how to solve equations and how to write as equations the facts given in problems. To improve these abilities is the purpose of this chapter.

YOUR AIM  **1. To improve your skill in solving equations of various types.**

2. To improve your ability to solve word problems.

307

First-degree Equations Involving Fractions

You have already learned how to solve first-degree, or linear, equations. Now you will learn how to solve linear equations which have fractions in them.

Examples for Study

1. *Solve:* $\dfrac{x}{2} + \dfrac{x}{6} = 10$

SOLUTION: The lowest common denominator is 6. Hence, to clear the equation of fractions, multiply each term by 6. Notice that multiplying each term by a number is the same as multiplying each side of the equation by that number.

$$6 \cdot \frac{x}{2} + 6 \cdot \frac{x}{6} = 6 \cdot 10 \qquad \text{CHECK: } \frac{15}{2} + \frac{15}{6} \overset{?}{=} 10$$

$$3x + x = 60 \qquad\qquad\qquad 7\tfrac{1}{2} + 2\tfrac{1}{2} \overset{?}{=} 10$$

$$4x = 60 \qquad\qquad\qquad\qquad 10 = 10$$

$$x = 15$$

2. *Solve:* $\dfrac{1}{x} + \dfrac{1}{x+4} = 0$

SOLUTION: The lowest common denominator is $x(x+4)$. Hence, multiply each term of the equation by $x(x+4)$:

$$x(x+4) \cdot \frac{1}{x} + x(x+4) \cdot \frac{1}{x+4} = x(x+4) \cdot 0$$

$$x + 4 + x = 0$$

$$2x = -4$$

$$x = -2$$

Check by substituting -2 for x in the original equation.

3. *Solve:* $\dfrac{5}{x+1} = \dfrac{15}{x+7}$

SOLUTION: Multiply each side of the equation by the lowest common denominator, $(x+1)(x+7)$:

$$\frac{5(x+1)(x+7)}{x+1} = \frac{15(x+1)(x+7)}{x+7}$$

$$5(x+7) = 15(x+1)$$

$$5x + 35 = 15x + 15$$

$$20 = 10x$$

$$2 = x$$

Check by substituting 2 for x in the original equation.

308 *ALGEBRA: ITS BIG IDEAS AND BASIC SKILLS*

PROBLEMS

1. $\dfrac{x}{3} + \dfrac{x}{2} = \dfrac{5}{2}$

2. $\dfrac{x}{4} + \dfrac{x}{2} = 9$

3. $\dfrac{3x}{5} - \dfrac{x}{5} = \dfrac{4}{5}$

4. $\dfrac{4x}{3} - \dfrac{3x}{4} = 7$

5. $\dfrac{x}{4} + 1 = 2$

6. $\dfrac{x}{3} - \dfrac{x}{4} = 2$

7. $\dfrac{2x}{5} + 1 = x$

8. $\dfrac{x}{4} = 0$

9. $\dfrac{1}{x} = 1$

10. $\dfrac{x}{5} = 0$

11. $\dfrac{2x}{5} = 2$

12. $\dfrac{1}{x} = 0.1$

13. $6 = \dfrac{x}{5}$

14. $10 = \dfrac{x}{10}$

15. $\dfrac{x-1}{3} = \dfrac{1}{7}$

16. $\dfrac{1}{x} + 2 = 0$

17. $\dfrac{x}{2} = \dfrac{1}{3}$

18. $\dfrac{2}{x} = \dfrac{1}{3}$

19. $\dfrac{x+1}{3} = 2$

20. $\dfrac{x}{a} = b$

21. $\dfrac{x}{b} = b$

22. $\dfrac{x}{m} - n = 0$

23. $\dfrac{3x+5}{6} = \dfrac{4+3x}{5}$

24. $\dfrac{x}{5} + \dfrac{x+5}{2} = 6$

25. $\dfrac{1}{x} - \dfrac{2}{x} = 6$

26. $\dfrac{2}{3x} - \dfrac{1}{4x} = \dfrac{1}{12}$

27. $\dfrac{3}{5x} - \dfrac{3}{4x} = \dfrac{1}{10}$

28. $\dfrac{x-10}{2} = \dfrac{2x+10}{3}$

29. $\dfrac{2}{x-3} = \dfrac{3}{x+2}$

30. $\dfrac{x-10}{3} - \dfrac{x+10}{7} = 0$

31. $\dfrac{6x+5}{8} - \dfrac{3x}{4} = \dfrac{x}{2}$

32. $\dfrac{x+6}{8} - \dfrac{x}{-16} = 0$

33. $\dfrac{4x+20}{5} + \dfrac{11+x}{10} = -\dfrac{6}{5}$

34. $\dfrac{8+x}{12} = \dfrac{1}{4} + \dfrac{4+x}{8}$

35. $\dfrac{5}{x-3} = \dfrac{5}{2(x-7)}$

36. $\dfrac{3x+2}{5} = \dfrac{-x}{-9} - 4$

37. $\dfrac{4x+3}{6} - \dfrac{x+3}{2} = 0$

★ 38. $\dfrac{5x-1}{5} - \dfrac{x-9}{3} = 2$

39. $\dfrac{1}{x-3} + \dfrac{3}{x-5} = 0$

40. $\dfrac{1}{2x-3} - \dfrac{3}{4x-15} = 0$

41. $\dfrac{x+2}{x+1} = \dfrac{x-1}{x+2}$

42. $\dfrac{1}{x+2} + \dfrac{1}{x-2} = \dfrac{1}{x^2-4}$

43. $\dfrac{1}{x-3} - \dfrac{1}{3-x} = \dfrac{1}{x^2-9}$

44. $\dfrac{x^2-5}{8-x} = \dfrac{1}{x-8} - x$

45. $\dfrac{4}{5-x} + \dfrac{5}{x-5} = 2$

46. $\dfrac{3}{x+3} + \dfrac{1}{x-3} = \dfrac{10}{x^2-9}$

47. $\dfrac{2}{x+4} + \dfrac{1}{4-x} = \dfrac{-15}{x^2-16}$

Second-degree Equations Involving Fractions

The equations in the following problems may appear to be first-degree equations. But as you eliminate the fractions in each equation, you will discover that they are second-degree equations. Turn back to pages 264–265 if you need to review how to solve second-degree, or quadratic, equations.

Example for Study

Solve: $x + \dfrac{5}{7x} = \dfrac{68}{21}$

SOLUTION: Multiply each side of the equation by $21x$:

$$21x^2 + 15 = 68x$$
$$21x^2 - 68x + 15 = 0$$
$$(21x - 5)(x - 3) = 0$$

$21x - 5 = 0 \qquad x - 3 = 0$

$x = \frac{5}{21} \qquad\qquad x = 3$

CHECK: Substitute both values for x in the original equation.

PROBLEMS

Solve and check each of the following equations:

1. $x + \dfrac{1}{x} = 2$

2. $x + \dfrac{12}{x} = 7$

3. $x - 1 = \dfrac{20}{x}$

4. $x + \dfrac{3}{4x} = 2$

5. $x - \dfrac{1}{x} = 0$

6. $\dfrac{4}{x} = \dfrac{x}{25}$

7. $\dfrac{6}{x} + 5 + x = 0$

8. $\dfrac{x}{3} - \dfrac{5}{3} = \dfrac{2}{x}$

9. $\dfrac{x}{2} + 1 = \dfrac{24}{x}$

10. $x = \dfrac{9}{x}$

11. $\dfrac{16}{3x} = 12x$

12. $x + \dfrac{1}{4x} = 0$

13. $\dfrac{2}{x} + 2\frac{3}{5} = \frac{3}{5}x$

14. $\dfrac{x}{a} - \dfrac{a}{x} = 0$

15. $\dfrac{x}{10} = \dfrac{3}{5} + \dfrac{4}{x}$

16. $\dfrac{x}{5b} = \dfrac{5b}{9x}$

17. $\dfrac{x^2}{25} - 1 = 0$

18. $\dfrac{1}{49} = \dfrac{1}{x^2}$

★ 19. $\dfrac{x - 5}{2} = \dfrac{12}{x + 5}$

20. $x - \dfrac{15}{2} + \dfrac{9}{x} = 0$

21. $\dfrac{x}{6} + \dfrac{4x^2 - 75}{18x} = \dfrac{2x}{9}$

22. $\dfrac{x^2}{x - 3} = \dfrac{9}{x - 3} + 10$

23. $\dfrac{x - 3}{x + 3} + \dfrac{x + 3}{x - 3} = 50$

24. $\dfrac{x + 2}{8} - \dfrac{4}{x} = \dfrac{3}{8x}$

25. $1 - \dfrac{1}{6x} - \dfrac{5}{12x^2} = \dfrac{5}{6x^2} - 1$

26. $\dfrac{1}{10} + \dfrac{21}{40x^2} = \dfrac{1}{x} - \dfrac{3}{10}$

310 *ALGEBRA: ITS BIG IDEAS AND BASIC SKILLS*

Systems of Two Linear Equations with Two Variables

You have learned to solve systems of two equations containing two variables by eliminating one of the variables. You can do this by the addition or subtraction method or by the substitution method.

Examples for Study

Solve by substitution: $4x - 5y = 100$
$3x - 4y = 78$

SOLUTION: Solve either equation for one of the variables in terms of the other:

$$4x - 5y = 100$$
$$4x = 5y + 100$$
$$x = \frac{5y + 100}{4}$$

Substitute $\dfrac{5y + 100}{4}$ for x in the second equation and solve for y:

$$3x - 4y = 78$$
$$3\left(\frac{5y + 100}{4}\right) - 4y = 78$$
$$\frac{15y + 300}{4} - 4y = 78$$
$$\frac{15y + 300}{4} - \frac{16y}{4} = \frac{312}{4}$$
$$15y + 300 - 16y = 312$$
$$-y = 12$$
$$y = -12$$

Find the value of x by substituting -12 for y in the equation $x = \dfrac{5y + 100}{4}$:

$$x = \frac{5y + 100}{4}$$
$$= \frac{5(-12) + 100}{4} = \frac{-60 + 100}{4} = \frac{40}{4}$$
$$x = 10$$

CHECK: Substitute the values of x and y in both of the original equations. Remember that it is not sufficient to check only one of the equations.

$$4x - 5y = 100 \qquad\qquad 3x - 4y = 78$$
$$4 \cdot 10 - 5(-12) \overset{?}{=} 100 \qquad 3 \cdot 10 - 4(-12) \overset{?}{=} 78$$
$$40 + 60 \overset{?}{=} 100 \qquad\qquad 30 + 48 \overset{?}{=} 78$$
$$100 = 100 \qquad\qquad\qquad 78 = 78$$

PROBLEMS

Solve the following systems of equations by the substitution method:

1. $3x - 2y = 9$
   $5x - 7y = 4$

2. $4x + 11y = 14$
   $3x - 4y = 35$

3. $4x - 9y = -7$
   $7x - 2y = -26$

4. $2x - 3y = 11$
   $3x + 2y = 36$

5. $6x - 5y = 21$
   $2x + 7y = 33$

6. $2x - 3y = 34$
   $4x + 5y = 2$

7. $10x + 3y = 7$
   $4x + 9y = 8$

8. $25x - 6y = 3$
   $15x + 12y = 7$

9. $7x + 3y = 9$
   $3x - 11y = 10$

10. $\dfrac{3x}{8} - \dfrac{2y}{3} = 2$
    $\dfrac{x}{8} - \dfrac{y}{4} = \dfrac{1}{2}$

11. $\dfrac{2x}{3} + \dfrac{1y}{2} = 4$
    $\dfrac{1x}{3} - \dfrac{1y}{4} = 0$

12. $\dfrac{x}{7} - \dfrac{y}{5} = 2$
    $\dfrac{x}{2} - \dfrac{y}{2} = 2$

You can best solve equations in which the variables appear as denominators of fractions by the addition or subtraction method. Using this method, you may eliminate one of the fractions and, thus, one of the variables.

Example for Study

Solve by addition: $\dfrac{1}{x} - \dfrac{1}{y} = 1$

$\qquad\qquad\qquad \dfrac{5}{x} + \dfrac{1}{y} = 2$

SOLUTION:

Adding these equations: $\dfrac{6}{x} = 3$

$\qquad\qquad\qquad\qquad\quad 6 = 3x$

Hence: $\qquad\qquad\qquad x = 2$

Complete the solution by substituting 2 for x in either equation.

Solve the following systems of equations by addition or subtraction:

13. $\dfrac{1}{x} + \dfrac{1}{y} = \dfrac{7}{10}$
    $\dfrac{1}{x} - \dfrac{1}{y} = \dfrac{3}{10}$

14. $\dfrac{1}{x} - \dfrac{1}{y} = \dfrac{1}{6}$
    $\dfrac{2}{x} + \dfrac{1}{y} = \dfrac{4}{3}$

15. $\dfrac{3}{x} - \dfrac{1}{y} = 1$
    $\dfrac{1}{x} - \dfrac{1}{y} = \dfrac{2}{3}$

16. $\dfrac{1}{x} - \dfrac{2}{y} = 10$
    $\dfrac{3}{x} - \dfrac{3}{y} = 21$

17. $\dfrac{1}{x} - \dfrac{1}{y} = 1$
    $\dfrac{2}{x} - \dfrac{3}{y} = 0$

18. $\dfrac{3}{x} - \dfrac{4}{y} = 5$
    $\dfrac{2}{x} + \dfrac{1}{y} = \dfrac{-1}{3}$

19. $\dfrac{1}{x} - \dfrac{1}{y} = 11$ 20. $\dfrac{5}{a} + \dfrac{1}{b} = 1$ 21. $\dfrac{12}{k} + \dfrac{1}{m} = 1$

$\dfrac{3}{x} + \dfrac{2}{y} = 3$ $\dfrac{1}{a} + \dfrac{1}{b} = 5$ $\dfrac{10}{k} + \dfrac{3}{m} = -10$

22. $\dfrac{1}{2p} + \dfrac{1}{w} = 12$ 23. $\dfrac{3}{x} + \dfrac{1}{y} = 0$ 24. $\dfrac{10}{x} - \dfrac{2}{y} = 14$

$\dfrac{1}{p} - \dfrac{2}{w} = -4$ $\dfrac{4}{x} + \dfrac{1}{3y} = 9$ $\dfrac{3}{2x} + \dfrac{5}{2y} = \dfrac{7}{2}$

★ *Solve and check the following miscellaneous equations:*

25. $\dfrac{3x}{8} - 5 = x$ 26. $\dfrac{5x^2}{2} - x - 8 = 0$

27. $3x(x - 6) + 2(5x - 4) = 8$ 28. $\dfrac{y - 2}{5} = \dfrac{3y - 1}{4}$

29. $\frac{1}{3}(x - 18) - \frac{2}{5}(2x + 20) = 0$ 30. $\dfrac{5}{x} + x = 4\frac{1}{2}$

31. $8x^2 + 10x = 5x^2 - 9x - 20$ 32. $\dfrac{x}{3} + \dfrac{x + 1}{2} = 3$

33. $4x + \dfrac{3}{x} = 13$ 34. $\dfrac{1}{x} + \dfrac{3}{x} = 1$

★ *Solve the following systems of equations:*

35. $\frac{1}{2}x + 6 = y$ 36. $\dfrac{1}{x} - \dfrac{1}{y} = \dfrac{1}{6}$ 37. $x = 2y$

$x + 5 = \frac{1}{2}y$ $\dfrac{2}{x} + \dfrac{1}{y} = 1\frac{1}{3}$ $3x - 2y = 1$

In each of the following problems (1) study the drawing, (2) write the equation or equations necessary for solving the problem, and (3) solve the equation or equations for the variable or variables. Some of the equations will be first-degree, some second-degree, and some will be systems of two equations with two variables. Remember, if there are two variables, two equations are required for finding the solution.

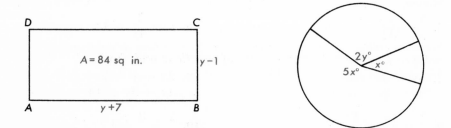

38. Find the lengths in inches of sides AB and AD in rectangle $ABCD$.

39. If $x + 2y = 140°$, find x and y.

40. Find m if the perimeter of triangle ABC is $82\frac{1}{2}$ inches.

41. Find the lengths in inches of sides AB and AD in rectangle $ABCD$.

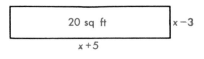

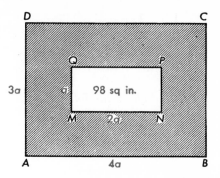

42. Find the length and the width of this rectangle in inches.

43. Find h if the area of this triangle is 121 square yards.

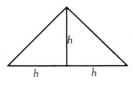

SELF TEST

Solve each of the following equations and check:

1. $\dfrac{3x}{5} + 4 = x$

2. $\dfrac{y-5}{8} = \dfrac{y-2}{10}$

3. $\dfrac{17}{7x} - \dfrac{1}{x} = \dfrac{10}{21}$

4. $\dfrac{1}{x^2-25} + \dfrac{x}{x+5} = \dfrac{x+1}{x+5}$

5. $\dfrac{2}{x} = \dfrac{x}{32}$

6. $y + \dfrac{1}{4y} = 1$

Solve each of the following systems of equations and check:

7. $8x - 3y = 1$
$3x - 2y = -4$

8. $2x + y = 7$
$4x + 2y = 14$

9. $\dfrac{1}{x} + \dfrac{1}{y} = \dfrac{13}{40}$
$\dfrac{2}{x} - \dfrac{1}{y} = \dfrac{1}{20}$

10. $\dfrac{2}{x} + \dfrac{3}{y} = 1$
$\dfrac{7}{x} - \dfrac{3}{y} = \dfrac{4}{5}$

314 *ALGEBRA: ITS BIG IDEAS AND BASIC SKILLS*

General Principles of Problem Solving

In solving problems, you set up one or more equations on the basis of the facts given in the problem. It is well to decide, before setting up equations, how many variables you are going to use. You will find that some problems may be solved by the use of one variable or by the use of two variables. Of course, you will probably want to select the easier way.

The best way to learn to solve problems is by actually solving various types of problems. The following pages contain a variety of problems for you to practice on.

Problems about Number Relationships

Examples for Study

1. The sum of two numbers is 36 and their quotient is $\frac{4}{5}$. Find the numbers.

SOLUTION USING TWO VARIABLES: Use x and y to stand for the unknowns:

Let x = the smaller number and y = the larger number

State the facts as a pair of equations:

$$x + y = 36 \quad \text{(Their sum is 36.)}$$
$$\frac{x}{y} = \frac{4}{5} \quad \text{(Their quotient is } \frac{4}{5}.\text{)}$$

Solve either equation for one variable in terms of the other variable:

$$x + y = 36$$
$$y = 36 - x$$

Substitute $36 - x$ for y in the other equation and solve for x:

$$\frac{x}{y} = \frac{4}{5}$$
$$\frac{x}{36 - x} = \frac{4}{5}$$
$$5x = 4(36 - x)$$
$$5x = 144 - 4x$$
$$9x = 144$$
$$x = 16$$

Substitute 16 for x in the first equation and solve for y:

$$x + y = 36$$
$$16 + y = 36$$
$$y = 20$$

CHECK: Their sum is 36; their quotient is $\frac{16}{20}$, or $\frac{4}{5}$.

SOLUTION USING ONE VARIABLE: Use one variable to express the unknowns:

$$\text{Let } x = \text{the smaller number}$$
$$\text{then } 36 - x = \text{the larger number}$$

State the facts as an equation: $\dfrac{x}{36 - x} = \dfrac{4}{5}$

Solve the equation:
$$5x = 4(36 - x)$$
$$5x = 144 - 4x$$
$$9x = 144$$
$$x = 16$$
$$36 - x = 20$$

By using one variable, you get the same answer with less work. Therefore, if a problem has two unknowns and you can easily express one of these unknowns in terms of the other, it is wasted effort to use two variables in solving the problem. In many problems this is true, but study the next example, which differs a little from this one.

2. A number consists of two digits whose sum is 9. If 39 is subtracted from the number, the result is four times the tens' digit. Find the number.

SOLUTION USING TWO VARIABLES:

$$\text{Let } t = \text{the tens' digit}$$
$$\text{and } u = \text{the units' digit}$$
$$\text{then } 10t + u = \text{the number}$$

NOTE: The reason that $10t + u = $ the number is this: When any digit is in the tens' position it has ten times the value it would have in the units' position. For example, $55 = 50 + 5$, or 5 tens $+ 5$ units. So t tens and u units equal $10t + u$.

From the facts stated in the problem, the equations are:
$$t + u = 9$$
$$(10t + u) - 39 = 4t \quad \text{or} \quad 6t + u = 39$$

Subtracting:
$$6t + u = 39$$
$$t + u = 9$$
$$\overline{5t = 30}$$
$$t = 6$$

Substituting 6 for t in either equation gives $u = 3$; hence, the number is 63.

CHECK: $6 + 3 = 9$ (The sum of the digits is 9.)
$63 - 39 = 24$ (39 subtracted from the number gives four times the tens' digit.)

316 *ALGEBRA: ITS BIG IDEAS AND BASIC SKILLS*

SOLUTION USING ONE VARIABLE:

$$\text{Let } t = \text{ the tens' digit}$$
$$9 - t = \text{ the units' digit}$$
$$10t + (9 - t) \quad \text{or} \quad 9t + 9 = \text{ the number}$$

$$(9t + 9) - 39 = 4t$$
$$5t = 30$$
$$t = 6 \text{ (the tens' digit)}$$
$$9 - t = 3 \text{ (the units' digit)}$$

Hence, the number is 63.

In problems of this type, you may easily express one variable in terms of the other. But the thinking processes are simpler to follow when you use two variables. Simplicity of thought is fundamental to clear thinking, and clear thinking is the key to problem solving. In any situation, then, use two variables instead of one if it facilitates the thinking necessary for solving the problem. If a problem when translated into algebra produces a second-degree equation, there will be two answers to the equation. Sometimes one of these answers will be meaningless. You should exclude any such answers from your solution of a problem.

Solve the following problems involving number relationships:

1. What number increased by five-sixths of itself is 55?
2. Find two numbers whose sum is 42 and whose quotient is $\frac{3}{4}$.
3. The sum of two numbers is 83 and their difference is 21. Find the numbers.
4. Two-thirds of a certain number is one more than five-eighths of the number. Find the number.
5. If five times the square of a number is decreased by nine times the number, the result is 2. Find the number.
6. What number plus its reciprocal equals 2?
7. Find the number which when added to both the numerator and the denominator of the fraction $\frac{5}{7}$ will produce a fraction equivalent to $\frac{4}{5}$.
8. The sum of the digits of a two-digit number is 10, and four times the units' digit is 4 more than the number. Find the number.
9. The product of two consecutive numbers is 36 more than ten times the first consecutive number. Find the numbers.
10. If three times a certain number is increased by six times its reciprocal, the result is 11. Find the number.
★ 11. The sum of the reciprocals of two numbers is $\frac{7}{10}$. The difference between the reciprocals of the numbers is $\frac{3}{10}$. Find the two numbers.
12. The square of a number divided by 25 equals 1. What is the number?

Problems about Money

Solve the following problems about money:

1. Divide $75 between two persons so that one person receives $\frac{7}{8}$ as much as the other person.

2. One month a school's lost and found department had $2.55 left unclaimed, all in dimes and quarters. There were 15 coins in all. How many coins were there of each kind?

3. Tom and Fred pooled their money for a party. They had a total of $3.25. If Tom gave 81 cents more than Fred, how much did each contribute?

4. A man invested $15,000 in two projects. On one he made a profit of 8% and on the other a profit of 3%. If his total profit was $1066, what was the amount of each investment?

5. The gate receipts at a football game were $1306 for 1258 cash customers. If the price for the reserved seats was $1.50 and for the general admission seats was $0.80, how many tickets of each kind were sold?

6. Mrs. Williams bought a davenport for $174.24. This was 12% less than the regular price. What was the regular price?

7. Mr. Stewart decided to invest $4000, some at 3% and the rest at 4%. How much should he invest at each rate to produce equal incomes?

★ 8. John had twice as many quarters as he had nickels, twice as many dimes as he had quarters, and twice as many pennies as he had dimes. In all he had $1.03. How many coins of each kind did he have?

9. How much money would a man have to invest at 4% interest so that at the end of a year the principal plus the interest would be $6000?

10. Mr. Stover buys and sells houses. Mr. Stover sold two houses, each for $15,000. One house was sold for 10% more than Mr. Stover paid for it. The other house was sold for 10% less than he paid for it. Did Mr. Stover make a profit or suffer a loss in selling the two houses?

11. Mr. Carver and Mr. Wallace agreed to divide the $4200 profit they made so that Mr. Carver received 15% more than Mr. Wallace. How much money did each man receive?

12. A grocer pays 16 cents a can for canned tomatoes. How much per can should he charge to make a profit of 10% of the selling price?

13. A retailer bought a coat for $28 wholesale. He wanted to mark the price of the coat in such a way that after he had a $\frac{1}{3}$ off sale he would still make a profit of 15% on the selling price. What should be the marked price of the coat?

Problems Involving Geometric Figures

Solve the following problems involving geometric figures:

1. The length of a rectangle is 10 inches more than the width. Find the length and the width of the rectangle if its area is 144 square inches.

2. The width of a rectangle is 3 inches less than the length. Find the length and the width of the rectangle if its area is 40 square inches.

3. The length of a rectangle is 6 inches more than the width. Find the length and the width of the rectangle if its perimeter is 40 inches.

4. The perimeter of a triangle is 57 inches. The second side is 8 inches more than $\frac{2}{3}$ of the first side, and the third side is 12 inches more than $\frac{4}{5}$ of the first side. Find the length of the sides of the triangle.

5. If one side of a square were reduced by 1 inch and one of the adjacent sides were increased by 2 inches, the area of the resulting figure would be 54 square inches. Find the length of a side of the square.

6. The first angle of a triangle is $\frac{4}{5}$ of the second angle, and the third angle is $\frac{1}{5}$ larger than the second angle. Find the sizes of the angles of the triangle.

7. The length of a rectangle is 6 inches more than the width. If the length and the width were each increased by 1 inch, the area would be increased by 17 square inches. Find the length and the width of the rectangle.

8. A rectangle has the same width as the side of a square. The length of the rectangle is 5 inches more than the side of the square. Find the length and the width of the rectangle and the side of the square if the area of the rectangle is 40 square inches more than the area of the square.

9. A line 49 inches long is divided into two parts. The first part is $\frac{3}{4}$ as long as the second part. How long is each part?

★ 10. The length of a rectangle is 3 inches more than $1\frac{1}{2}$ times the width. The perimeter is 31 inches. What are the length and the width of the rectangle?

11. The length of a rectangle is 5 inches more than the width. If the length were made 7 inches shorter and the width 3 inches shorter, the perimeter would be 102 inches. What are the length and the width of the rectangle?

12. If it were possible to have a telephone wire stretched snugly around the earth at the equator, it would be about 25,000 miles long. If the wire were to be placed on 6-foot poles, how much more wire would be needed?

Problems Involving Time, Rate, and Distance

Solve the following problems about time, rate, and distance:

1. Tourists traveled 1940 miles in 3 days. They traveled 90 miles farther during the second day than they did during the first, and 60 miles less during the third than during the first day. How many miles did they travel each day?

2. Two tourist parties traveled by automobile. One party averaged 45 miles per hour and the other 35 miles per hour. The faster party traveled 30 miles farther than the slower party and made the trip in two hours less time. How long did each party travel?

3. The cruising speed of an airline plane is 250 miles per hour. On a flight of 710 miles, against a strong wind, a flying time of $3\frac{1}{4}$ hours was required. What was the average speed on this trip? What was the average speed of the wind?

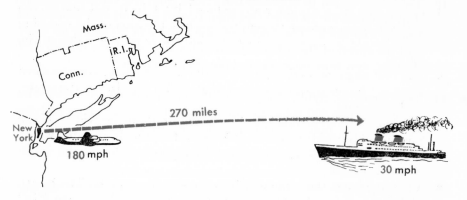

4. A ship was steaming toward New York City at an average rate of 30 miles per hour. It radioed that a sick person aboard should be flown to a hospital. When a plane left New York City for the ship, the ship was 270 miles away. The plane averaged 180 miles per hour. How long after it left New York City did the plane reach the ship?

5. An airplane traveling 280 miles per hour was reported over an airfield. Another plane took off from the airfield 6 minutes later and followed the first plane. The second plane's average speed was 320 miles per hour. Assuming the planes did not change speed or direction, how far from the airfield did the second plane overtake the first?

6. An airplane pilot is interested in knowing how far from a field he can fly and return without running out of gas. Suppose his plane can fly for 6 hours at an average speed of 120 miles per hour without running out of gas. How far from the airfield must he turn around so that he will be able to return without running out of gas?

7. Two automobiles leave Columbus at the same time, one traveling east and one west. One car averages 48 miles an hour and the second car 44 miles an hour. How many hours later will the automobiles be 529 miles apart?

8. Mr. Snyder's son Jim started driving home from a city 550 miles away. He had been driving for 2 hours when Mr. Snyder started driving from home to meet him. Mr. Snyder's speed was 50 miles an hour, and Jim's speed was 55 miles an hour. How far from home did they meet? How long did each drive before they met?

9. Two automobiles left Indianapolis at the same time, one traveling north and the other south. One car traveled at 45 miles per hour and the second car at 55 miles per hour for an hour. Then each car increased its speed 5 miles an hour. How long did it take the cars to drive 550 miles apart?

10. Two ships sailed in opposite directions from the same dock. Each ship traveled for 20 miles and then turned around and sailed back toward the dock. The speed of one ship was 20 miles an hour, and the speed of the other was 25 miles an hour. How far did each ship go, and how long did it take them to meet?

★ 11. Two airplanes flying in opposite directions pass each other. One plane is flying 300 miles per hour, and the second plane is flying 240 miles per hour. How long will they fly before they are 1200 miles apart?

12. At 8:30 A.M. Mary Kelsey started walking from her farm home to town. She walked $4\frac{1}{2}$ miles per hour. At 9:00 A.M. her brother Bill started after her riding his bicycle at 15 miles per hour. At what time will Bill catch up with Mary?

13. Two trains left the same station at the same time and traveled in opposite directions. One train averaged 18 miles per hour more than the other train. At the end of $2\frac{1}{2}$ hours the trains are 345 miles apart. What is the speed of each train?

14. St. Louis and New Orleans are 610 miles apart. At 10:00 A.M. a plane flying 180 miles per hour started from St. Louis toward New Orleans. At 10:45 A.M. a plane flying 140 miles per hour started from New Orleans for St. Louis. At what time will these planes pass each other?

EQUATIONS AND PROBLEMS **321**

Problems about Wind and Current

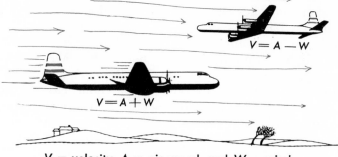

V = velocity, A = air speed, and W = wind.

Suppose that the speed of the airplane engine is such that in still air the plane would go 150 miles per hour. This plane may be going faster or slower than 150 miles per hour over the ground due to a wind. The plane's speed over the ground depends on which way the wind is blowing. If the wind is directly against the plane blowing 20 miles per hour, then the plane's speed over the ground is $150 - 20$, or 130 miles per hour. If the plane is flying with a wind of 20 miles per hour, then the plane's speed over the ground is $150 + 20$, or 170 miles per hour.

Example for Study

An airplane flew a distance of 96 miles one way with the wind in 36 minutes and returned against the wind in 48 minutes. How fast did the plane fly in still air, and what was the speed of the wind?

SOLUTION:

Let r = the number of miles per hour the plane flew in still air
Let w = the speed of the wind
$r + w$ = the plane's speed with the wind
$r - w$ = the plane's speed against the wind

Since 36 minutes is $\frac{3}{5}$ of an hour, and 48 minutes is $\frac{4}{5}$ of an hour, the equations are:

$$\frac{3}{5}(r + w) = 96$$
$$\frac{4}{5}(r - w) = 96$$

Solving the system of equations:

$$3(r + w) = 480$$
$$4(r - w) = 480$$

$$12r + 12w = 1920$$
$$\underline{12r - 12w = 1440}$$
$$24r \qquad\quad = 3360$$
$$r = 140$$
$$w = 20$$

CHECK: $\frac{3}{5}(r + w) = 96$ $\frac{4}{5}(r - w) = 96$

$\frac{3}{5}(140 + 20) \overset{?}{=} 96$ $\frac{4}{5}(140 - 20) \overset{?}{=} 96$

$\frac{3}{5}(160) \overset{?}{=} 96$ $\frac{4}{5}(120) \overset{?}{=} 96$

$96 = 96$ $96 = 96$

Solve the following problems about wind and current:

1. The current in a river was flowing at the rate of 3 miles per hour. A boat went downstream a certain distance in 2 hours. It took 3 hours to return the same distance against the current. What was the speed of the boat in still water? How far did the boat go downstream?

2. The wind was blowing at the rate of 18 miles per hour. An airplane flew with the wind a certain distance in 2 hours and returned against the wind in $2\frac{1}{2}$ hours. What was the speed of the plane in still air? What distance did the plane fly with the wind?

3. A motor boat went downstream a distance of 60 miles in 3 hours. The return trip against the current took 4 hours. What was the speed of the boat in still water, and what was the rate of the current?

4. An airplane flew with the wind for 140 miles in 35 minutes. The return trip against the wind took 40 minutes. What was the speed of the plane in still air, and what was the speed of the wind?

5. An airplane flew against the wind to a distant town in 70 minutes and returned with the wind in 55 minutes. The speed of the plane in still air was 150 miles per hour. What was the speed of the wind?

6. A pilot flew a plane 480 miles with the wind. For the same length of time he then flew against the wind, but only went 420 miles. The speed of the plane in still air was 300 miles per hour in both cases. What was the speed of the wind?

7. An airplane pilot can fly 350 miles per hour in still air. How far can he fly with a wind of 30 miles per hour and return against the wind to the starting place in 40 minutes?

★ 8. A river has a current of 2 miles per hour. How fast would a man have to row a boat in still water to take the boat 3 miles downstream and back again in 2 hours?

9. A pilot is to fly a plane with a wind of 35 miles per hour for 240 miles. He plans to return immediately, flying against the wind. At what speed must he fly the plane in still air to make the entire trip in 2 hours?

10. An aircraft carrier is steaming east at a speed of 20 miles per hour. An airplane leaves the carrier and flies west against a 15-mile-per-hour wind at 500 miles per hour (speed in still air). The plane has a 1-hour supply of fuel. How far west can the airplane fly before turning around if it must reach the carrier in 1 hour?

EQUATIONS AND PROBLEMS **323**

Problems Involving Rate of Work

Example for Study

If A can mow a lawn in 4 hours and B can mow the same lawn in 3 hours, how long will the job take if they work together?

SOLUTION:
What question is asked in the problem?
> How long will the job take if A and B work together?

What important facts are stated in the problem?
> A can mow a lawn in 4 hours.
> B can mow the same lawn in 3 hours.

Since A can mow the lawn in 4 hours, he could mow $\frac{1}{4}$ of the lawn in 1 hour, or in 2 hours he could do $\frac{2}{4}$ of the lawn, or in x hours he could do $\frac{x}{4}$ of the lawn. The same reasoning tells you that B could mow $\frac{x}{3}$ of the lawn in x hours.

Represent the unknowns by variables:
> $x =$ the number of hours needed to do the job if A and B work together

> Since $\frac{1}{4} =$ the part of lawn A can mow in 1 hour

> $\frac{x}{4} =$ the part A can do in x hours

> Since $\frac{1}{3} =$ the part of lawn B can mow in 1 hour

> $\frac{x}{3} =$ the part B can do in x hours

State the facts as an equation. Remember that the sum of the parts equals the whole.

The part mowed by A + the part mowed by B = 1 lawn

$$\frac{x}{4} \quad + \quad \frac{x}{3} \quad = 1$$
$$3x \quad + \quad 4x \quad = 12$$
$$7x \quad = 12$$
$$x \quad = 1\tfrac{5}{7}$$

CHECK: In $1\frac{5}{7}$ hours A will mow $\dfrac{1\frac{5}{7}}{4}$ of the lawn.

In $1\frac{5}{7}$ hours B will mow $\dfrac{1\frac{5}{7}}{3}$ of the lawn.

A and B together will mow $\dfrac{1\frac{5}{7}}{4} + \dfrac{1\frac{5}{7}}{3}$ of the lawn.

So $\dfrac{1\frac{5}{7}}{4} + \dfrac{1\frac{5}{7}}{3} = \dfrac{\frac{12}{7}}{4} + \dfrac{\frac{12}{7}}{3} = \dfrac{12}{28} + \dfrac{12}{21} = \dfrac{3}{7} + \dfrac{4}{7} = \dfrac{7}{7} = 1$, or the entire lawn.

Solve the following problems involving rate of work:

1. If Bob can clean the basement in his home in 3 hours, what part of it can he do in 1 hour? In 2 hours? In x hours?
2. If Walter can hike a mile in 20 minutes, what part of a mile can he hike in 10 minutes? In 12 minutes? In x minutes?
3. A swimming pool has two inlet pipes. One of them can fill the pool in 3 hours, the other in 2 hours. How long will it take to fill the tank when both pipes are used?
4. A tank can be emptied by one pipe in 30 minutes and by another pipe in 25 minutes. How long will it take to drain the tank if both pipes are used?
5. A farmer has two tractors. With the newer one he can plow a certain field in 12 hours, 3 hours faster than with his old machine. How long would it take to plow the field using both tractors?
6. Ivan can do a piece of work in 5 hours. After Ivan had worked for 2 hours, Bob joined him and together they completed the job in 2 more hours. If you assume that Bob would work at the same speed when working alone, how long would it have taken him to do the job by himself?
7. Alice can do a piece of work in $2\frac{1}{2}$ hours; Betty can do it in $3\frac{1}{4}$ hours. How long will it take them to do the job together?
8. Jack can mow a lawn in 3 hours, while his younger brother, Paul, can do it in 4 hours. If Jack works for 2 hours, how long will it take Paul to complete the job?

★ 9. A painter estimated that he could paint a house alone in 6 days and that with his helper he could do the job in 4 days. After both worked on the job for one day, the painter left for another job. If his time estimate for doing the work was correct, how long did it take his helper to complete the job?

10. A foreman assigned two men to a job. He estimated that the work would take them 5 hours. After they had worked for $1\frac{1}{2}$ hours, the foreman put two more men on the job. His estimate of the time needed by the second two men working together to do the entire work was 7 hours. Find the approximate time in hours and minutes it would take four men working together to do the job.

Problems Involving Mixture

Example for Study

How many pounds of water must be added to 50 pounds of brine solution containing 10% salt to reduce it to a 4% salt solution?

SOLUTION: Let x = the number of pounds of water added
The basis for the equation in this problem is:

The number of pounds of salt in the 4% solution	=	The number of pounds of salt in the 10% solution

$$0.04(50 + x) = 5$$
$$2 + 0.04x = 5$$
$$200 + 4x = 500$$
$$4x = 300$$
$$x = 75$$

CHECK: 75 pounds $+$ 50 pounds $=$ 125 pounds of the final solution
4% of 125 $=$ 5 pounds

Solve the following problems involving mixture:

1. If 2 gallons of water and 1 gallon of antifreeze are mixed, what part of the mixture is antifreeze? What percent of the mixture is antifreeze?
2. If a copper-zinc alloy is formed by dissolving 4 parts of copper with 6 parts of zinc, what part of the alloy is copper? What percent of the alloy is copper?
3. How much alcohol must be added to 20 gallons of a 10% solution to get a 12% solution?
4. A chemistry experiment calls for a 20% solution of sulfuric acid. If 500 cubic centimeters of concentrated solution (88%) is used, how many cubic centimeters of distilled water must be added to get the 20% solution?
5. How many quarts of distilled water must be added to 2 gallons of a 40% solution of nitric acid to get an 8% solution of acid?
6. A pharmacist has on hand a 50% solution of iodine. How many ounces of alcohol and how many ounces of the 50% solution must he use to make 12 ounces of a 20% solution?

★ 7. How much cream containing 25% butterfat must be added to 15 gallons of milk containing 2.6% butterfat to obtain a grade of milk that has 4% butterfat?
8. How many cubic centimeters of water must be added to m cubic centimeters of a $q\%$ solution of salt to reduce it to a $p\%$ solution?

★ *Mathematical Puzzles*

Each pupil in an algebra class made up a puzzle for the other members of the class to solve. Each puzzle can be solved by means of an equation. Here are some of the puzzles made up by the pupils.

Solve each of the following puzzles:

1. MARY ANN: "If Mother were one year older, she would be three times as old as I am. Two years from now, I shall be three-eighths as old as Mother. Find our present ages."

2. JOE: "Two-thirds of my age 3 years ago, plus one-sixth of my age 3 years from now, will equal my age 4 years ago. How old am I?"

3. BARBARA: "I am thinking of a number. Half of this number plus one-third of the number equals ten. What is the number?"

4. RICHARD: "My friend and I got a ride out of town, a distance of 6 miles. On our way back we walked for a while, at an average rate of 3 miles per hour. Then we got a ride in a truck for the rest of the way. The truck driver said that he drove 30 miles per hour. It took us 30 minutes to make the trip back to town. How far did my friend and I walk?"

5. PAUL: "I work in my father's store after school. Yesterday Dad told me to mix two grades of candy, one selling for 50 cents per pound and the other for 75 cents per pound. He wanted a mixture of 15 pounds that he could sell for 60 cents per pound. How many pounds of each grade of candy should I have used?"

6. LUCKY DAVIS: "As you know, people call me 'Lucky Davis.' Last week I really did have a lucky day. I was walking along State Street when I noticed a quarter on the sidewalk, then, a few feet away, a dime. By this time, of course, I was eagerly looking for more, and I found a total of 7 quarters and dimes, all within a few feet of each other. Apparently someone had a hole in his pocket. Anyway, I was $1.15 richer by the find. How many coins of each kind did I find?"

7. PAT: "My father's age is a number consisting of two digits, the sum of which is 7. If the order of the digits were reversed, he would be 27 years younger. How old is my father?"

8. Make up an example of a puzzle that can be solved by an equation or equations for the other members of your class to solve.

SUGGESTION: Three members of the class may act as a committee to study all the puzzles. Then they can select the ten best ones and have them mimeographed for the class to solve as a later assignment.

SUMMARY OF IMPORTANT THINGS TO REMEMBER

1. Understandings:

Many problems in business, industry, and science can be solved by the use of equations.

Many problems can be solved by using equations with either one or two variables. Sometimes it is more convenient to use two equations with two variables than it is to use one variable.

In checking word problems it is necessary to check the answer against the information in the problem.

2. Skills:

You should be able to:

Solve systems of two equations with two variables.

Solve equations involving fractions.

Solve various kinds of word problems.

PROBLEMS ON YOUR AIMS

YOUR AIM 👉 **To improve your skill in solving equations of various types.**

How many roots has each of the following equations?

1. $\dfrac{x}{4} - \dfrac{2}{3} = x$ 2. $\dfrac{7}{2x} - \dfrac{x}{2} = 3$ 3. $2x^2 + x = 1$

Explain, step by step, how to solve each of the following equations:

4. $\dfrac{x}{5} - \dfrac{x}{3} = \dfrac{1}{2}$ 5. $\dfrac{1}{x} - 3 = 0$ 6. $3x^2 = 1 - 2x$

7. Given the system of equations $x - 2y = 3$ and $2x - y = 3$, solve the system using the addition or subtraction method.
8. Given the system of equations $2x - y = 4$ and $3x + y = 12$, solve the system using the substitution method.

YOUR AIM 👉 **To improve your ability to solve word problems.**

Answer the following questions in terms of x:

1. If the sum of two numbers is 72 and x stands for the smaller number, write an expression to stand for the larger number.
2. One number exceeds another by 5. If x stands for the larger number, write an expression to stand for the smaller number.
3. The quotient of two numbers is 6. If x stands for the smaller number, write an expression to stand for the larger number.

328 *ALGEBRA: ITS BIG IDEAS AND BASIC SKILLS*

4. The perimeter of a rectangle is 24. If x stands for the length, write an expression to stand for the width.
5. If Ralph can do a certain job in x hours, what part can he do in 3 hours?

Write the equation or equations for finding x *or* x *and* y *in each of the following:*
6. An investment of $12,000 brings in an annual income of $520. Part of the $12,000 yielded $3\frac{1}{2}\%$ interest and the remainder 4%. Let x stand for the amount invested at $3\frac{1}{2}\%$ and y the amount invested at 4%.
7. A right angle is divided into two angles so that the larger angle is $10°$ less than twice the smaller angle. Let x stand for the number of degrees in the smaller angle.
8. An equilateral triangle and a square have equal perimeters. The side of the square is 3 inches less than the side of the triangle. Let x stand for one of the sides of the triangle.

VALUABLE SKILLS PRACTICE

Add to find A, B, C, *and* D:

1.	2.	3.	4.
$15\frac{3}{4}$	$3\frac{1}{6}$	65.42	27.45
$6\frac{1}{2}$	$27\frac{1}{2}$	128.37	98.70
$9\frac{1}{4}$	$72\frac{2}{3}$	495.31	36.86
$\underline{\quad ? \quad} = A$	$\underline{\quad ? \quad} = B$	$\underline{\quad ? \quad} = C$	$\underline{\quad ? \quad} = D$

Using the values of A, B, C, *and* D *found in Problems 1–4, complete the following:*
5. $2A = \underline{\ ?\ }$ 6. $2B = \underline{\ ?\ }$ 7. $2C = \underline{\ ?\ }$ 8. $2D = \underline{\ ?\ }$

Using the values of A, B, C, *and* D *found in Problems 1–4, solve the following:*

9. $A + B = m$
   $B - A = n$
   $m + n = \underline{\ ?\ }$
   $m - n = \underline{\ ?\ }$

10. $C + D = h$
    $D - C = k$
    $h + k = \underline{\ ?\ }$
    $h - k = \underline{\ ?\ }$

11. $\dfrac{A}{B} = x$
    $\dfrac{B}{A} = y$
    $xy = \underline{\ ?\ }$

Write in words each of the following numbers. Use an unabridged dictionary, if necessary, for the large numbers.

12. 801,000
13. $2\frac{4}{9}$
14. 1,000,100
15. 2,002,000
16. 1.001
17. 10,000,000,000
18. 7,992,143
19. 102.0012
20. 7,700,700,700,700
21. 111,000,111
22. 0.000001
23. 0.00013

Find the missing number or numbers in each of the following problems:

	This number	is this fractional part	or this percent	of this number
24.	3	$\frac{1}{2}$	?	6
25.	1	?	?	3
26.	2	?	?	8
27.	$\frac{1}{2}$	?	?	1
28.	$\frac{1}{2}$	?	?	$\frac{2}{3}$
29.	4	?	?	1
30.	?	$\frac{2}{3}$	?	9
31.	?	$\frac{3}{5}$	?	10
32.	?	$\frac{3}{2}$	?	2
33.	?	$\frac{15}{4}$	?	21
34.	?	$\frac{3}{1}$	?	3
35.	?	?	$83\frac{1}{3}\%$	6
36.	?	?	$66\frac{2}{3}\%$	3
37.	?	?	$37\frac{1}{2}\%$	8
38.	?	?	$33\frac{1}{3}\%$	16
39.	?	?	$62\frac{1}{2}\%$	24

Make a scale drawing for each of the following:

40. A room 18 by 15 feet, scale: 1 inch = 6 feet

41. A lot 60 by 110 feet, scale: 1 inch = 40 feet

42. A concrete foundation 36 by 50 feet, scale: 1 inch = 8 feet

43. A square lot, 0.9 acre in size, scale: 1 inch = 6 rods

To learn and to remember what you have been taught, you must do your own work. You may ask for help or suggestions from your teacher and from others, but do not ask them to do your work for you. By working and studying faithfully, you will improve your skill in algebra. By copying, you will gain nothing except writing and copying practice.

330 *ALGEBRA: ITS BIG IDEAS AND BASIC SKILLS*

CHAPTER TEST

Solve the following equations:

1. $\dfrac{x}{5} - \dfrac{x}{6} = 4$

2. $\dfrac{3}{x} - \dfrac{2}{x} = 7$

3. $\dfrac{5}{x-3} = \dfrac{8}{x+4}$

4. $\dfrac{x+4}{x+3} = \dfrac{x-1}{x+2}$

5. $\dfrac{x}{15} + \dfrac{8}{45} = \dfrac{7}{x}$

6. $\dfrac{2}{x+5} + \dfrac{-3}{x} + \dfrac{2}{5} = 0$

7. $x^2 - 11x + 24 = 0$

8. $x^2 - 14x - 15 = 0$

Solve the following systems of equations:

9. $7x - y = 4$
   $2x + y = 14$

10. $3x - 4y = 7$
    $5x + 6y = -1$

11. $\dfrac{4}{x} - \dfrac{1}{y} = \dfrac{5}{4}$
    $\dfrac{1}{x} - \dfrac{1}{y} = \dfrac{1}{2}$

12. $\dfrac{1}{x} - \dfrac{5}{y} = \dfrac{7}{18}$
    $\dfrac{3}{x} - \dfrac{2}{y} = -1$

13. If Sam can do a job in 10 days, what part can he do in 3 days? In x days?

14. If x stands for the units' digit and y stands for the tens' digit of a number, what is the number?

15. The product of two consecutive odd numbers is 195. Find the numbers.

16. If five times a number is added to its square, the result is 66. Find the number.

17. In triangle ABC, side AC is 2 inches longer than side AB and side BC is twice as long as AB. Find the three sides if the perimeter of the triangle is 18 inches.

18. The sum of the digits of a two-digit number is 9 and the number itself is 2 more than twice the units' digit. Find the number.

19. The perimeter of a rectangle is 40 inches and its area is 64 square inches. Find the length and the width of the rectangle.

20. One pump can fill a tank in 30 minutes and a second pump can do the job in 36 minutes. How long will it take for both pumps working together to fill the tank?

21. A pilot flew an airplane 207 miles with the wind in 46 minutes. The return trip against the wind took him 54 minutes. What was the speed of the plane in still air, and what was the speed of the wind?

CUMULATIVE REVIEW PROBLEMS

WORKING WITH ALGEBRAIC EXPRESSIONS

1. By how much does $5x + 18$ exceed $5x - 18$?

Make up an example of each of the following:
2. The product of the sum of and the difference between two numbers
3. A trinomial square
4. A system of equations with two variables
5. The difference between two squares

Find the product of each of the following:
6. $a^3(a^2 + a)$
7. $(a - b)(a - b)$
8. $a^m x^2 \cdot a^m x^2$
9. $(x + 3)^2$
10. $(x^3 - 1)(x^3 + 1)$
11. $a^x \cdot a^x$
12. $(x - 2)^3$
13. $a^m(a^m - a)$
14. $(ax - 1)(ax + 2)$
15. $a^{2n}(a^n + a^2)$
16. $\dfrac{x}{y} \cdot \dfrac{x}{y} \cdot \dfrac{x}{y}$
17. $(a^2 x^3)^4$
18. $\left(\dfrac{a}{b}\right)^2 \cdot \left(\dfrac{b}{a}\right)^3$
19. $(2x - 5)(x + 3)$
20. $c^2(c - c^4)$

Factor completely:
21. $a^3 + a^2 - 2a$
22. $x^4 - y^4$
23. $a^{2x+1} - a$
24. $(a + b)^2 - c^2$
25. $a^2 - (x - y)^2$
26. $(a + b)^2 - (c - d)^2$
27. $a^2 + 2ab + b^2 - m^2$
28. $c^3 + d^3$
29. $0.25 - b^2$
30. $16 - n^4$
31. $m^3 - n^3$
32. $ax + ax^2$
33. $(2r + s)^2$
34. $8t^3 - 27$
35. $(x^2 - y^2)^3$
36. $ab + ac + db + dc$
37. $xy + y^2 - zx - zy$
38. $2c^2 m - c^2 n^2 + dn^2 - 2dm$
39. $ac + 2a - 8 - 4c$

Write each of the following as an algebraic expression:
40. P is 3 more than the product of 5 and k.
41. Jane's age 5 years ago, if her present age is $5a$ years.
42. The number of feet there are in y yards and m inches.
43. The cost of x pounds of beans at p cents per pound and y pounds of flour at q dollars per hundred pounds.
44. The cost of m tablets if n tablets cost x cents.

Do the following problems without pencil and paper:
45. $\left(\dfrac{x}{3}\right)^3$
46. $\left(\dfrac{0.1a}{2b^2}\right)^3$
47. $(x - 10)^2$

332 *ALGEBRA: ITS BIG IDEAS AND BASIC SKILLS*

48. $x^2 \div \dfrac{1}{x^2}$ **49.** $(ab + d)(ab - d)$ **50.** $\left(a - \dfrac{1}{4}\right)\left(a + \dfrac{1}{4}\right)$

51. $\dfrac{1}{m} \div \dfrac{1}{n}$ **52.** $\dfrac{1}{a} \div \dfrac{1}{a}$ **53.** $\left(a - \dfrac{1}{2}\right)^2$

54. $(ab + c)^2$ **55.** $(x - y - 4)(x - y + 4)$

56. $\dfrac{1}{x^2 + 6xy + 9y^2} \div \dfrac{1}{x^2 - 9y^2}$ **57.** $\dfrac{4a^2 + 4ac + c^2}{c + 2a}$

APPLYING ALGEBRA TO GEOMETRIC FIGURES

What is the side of a square whose area is:

1. 25   **2.** $16x^4$ **3.** $a^2 - 2ab + b^2$

What is the length of the side of a cube whose volume is:

4. 27   **5.** a^3 **6.** $(a - 2)^3$

7. If the perimeter of an equilateral triangle is $12x + 9$, what is the length of its side?

8. If the perimeter of a square is $16m - 4$, what is the length of its side?

9. If the area of a square is $a^2 - 10a + 25$, what is its perimeter?

10. Find the number of degrees in angles A, B, and C below.
     11. Find d in the circle below.

12. Find x if the volume of the solid below is 432 cubic feet.
     13. Find h if $b = 2h$ and the area of the parallelogram below is 131.22 square inches.

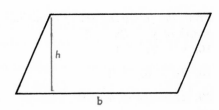

EQUATIONS AND PROBLEMS **333**

WORKING WITH GRAPHS

Answer the following questions from the graph below:

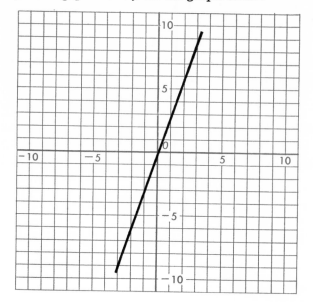

1. As one variable increases, what change takes place in the other variable?
2. Does the graph represent a direct or an inverse variation? How can you tell?

Which of the following points satisfy the equation of the graph:
3. $(1, 10)$ 4. $(-1, -3)$ 5. $(-3, -9)$
6. $(0, -6)$ 7. $(-2, 2)$ 8. $(0, 0)$

9. Write the equation of the graph above.

Tell without graphing what are the slopes and y-intercepts of the following lines:
10. $y = 7x - 3$ 11. $y = \frac{1}{2}x + 2$
12. $y = -3x + 5$ 13. $y = -\frac{3}{4}x + 15$
14. $5x + 2y = 7$ 15. $3x - 2y = 14$

From the following set of equations tell which have graphs parallel to the graph of $y = 3x - 5$:
16. $y = 2x - 4$ 17. $y = 3x + 8$
18. $2y = 6x - 3$ 19. $\frac{1}{3}y = x + 4$
20. $2x - 3y + 4 = 0$ 21. $3x - y + 6 = 0$

ELECTRICAL ENGINEERS USE ALGEBRA

Electrical engineers use a great amount of algebra in their work. In the following computation, an electrical engineer was trying to solve a problem about how big wires should be in transmission lines.

$$P = \sqrt{3}\ EI \cos \phi$$

$$I = \frac{P}{\sqrt{3}\ E \cos \phi}$$

$$aP = 3I^2R = 3\left(\frac{P}{\sqrt{3}\ E \cos \phi}\right)^2 R$$

$$\text{Since } W = \frac{kI^2}{R}$$

$$\text{and } R = \frac{aP}{\dfrac{P^2}{(E \cos \phi)^2}}$$

$$R = \frac{a(E \cos \phi)^2}{P}$$

$$\text{then } W = \frac{kI^2}{\dfrac{a(E \cos \phi)^2}{P}}$$

$$W = \frac{kP}{a}\left(\frac{I}{E \cos \phi}\right)^2$$

EQUATIONS AND PROBLEMS **335**

BIG IDEAS	NUMBER
	EQUATION
	EXPONENT
BASIC SKILLS	Using and interpreting symbols of algebra
	Fundamental operations
	Evaluating algebraic expressions
	Solving equations
	Factoring
	Solving verbal problems
	Using exponents

CHAPTER **12** *Exponents and Radicals*

SO FAR you have learned how to use positive whole numbers as exponents. In this chapter you will learn how to use zero, negative numbers, and fractions as exponents. You will also study the relationship between exponents and square roots, cube roots, and so on.

Exponents have many uses. They are convenient in writing very large and very small numbers. They are also used in multiplying, dividing, and finding roots of numbers.

YOUR AIM 1. To learn the meaning of zero, negative numbers, and fractions as exponents.

2. To learn how to write very large and very small numbers using powers of 10.

3. To be able to use the laws of exponents in their most general form.

4. To learn how to simplify, add, subtract, multiply, and divide radicals.

336

The Laws of Exponents

You will recall that the symbol a^n is read "a to the nth power" or "the nth power of a." In this symbol a is the base and n is the exponent. The entire symbol a^n is the power.

In your work with positive whole numbers as exponents you have used three **laws of exponents.** These laws stated in symbols are:

LAW I. $\quad a^m \cdot a^n = a^{m+n}$

LAW II. $\quad \dfrac{a^m}{a^n} = a^{m-n}$

LAW III. $(a^m)^n = a^{mn}$

These laws hold when m and n are positive numbers. In Law II, a cannot be equal to zero and m is greater than n.

Examples of Law I

$$a^2 \cdot a^3 = a^{2+3} = a^5$$
$$a^4 \cdot a^5 = a^{4+5} = a^9$$
$$3^2 \cdot 3^4 = 3^{2+4} = 3^6$$
$$a^x \cdot a^{2x} = a^{x+2x} = a^{3x} \text{ for } x > 0$$

Examples of Law II

$$\frac{a^5}{a^3} = a^{5-3} = a^2$$

$$\frac{c^7}{c^4} = c^{7-4} = c^3$$

$$\frac{4^3}{4^2} = 4^{3-2} = 4^1 = 4$$

Examples of Law III

$$(a^2)^3 = a^{2 \cdot 3} = a^6$$
$$(m^3)^4 = m^{3 \cdot 4} = m^{12}$$
$$(4^5)^2 = 4^{5 \cdot 2} = 4^{10}$$

Write each of the three laws of exponents in words. You might begin like this:

LAW I. To multiply powers of the same number, . . .

LAW II. To divide a power of a number by another power of the same number, . . .

LAW III. To raise a power of a number to another power, . . .

Errors are often made in applying the third law of exponents, $(a^m)^n = a^{mn}$.

Error 1. When a is replaced by $3x$, ab, or $a + b$:

$$(3x)^2 = \underline{\ ?\ } \qquad (ab)^3 = \underline{\ ?\ } \qquad (a + b)^2 = \underline{\ ?\ }$$

Incorrect answers that are often given are: $(3x)^2 = 3x^2$, $(ab)^3 = ab^3$, and $(a + b)^2 = a^2 + b^2$. Do you see what is wrong in each instance? You can easily avoid such errors by simply considering the meaning:

$(3x)^2$ means $(3x)(3x)$, or $9x^2$
$(ab)^3$ means $(ab)(ab)(ab)$, or a^3b^3
$(a + b)^2$ means $(a + b)(a + b)$, or $a^2 + 2ab + b^2$

Error 2. When a is a fraction:

$$\left(\frac{m}{4}\right)^2 = \underline{\ ?\ } \qquad \left(\frac{a - b}{3}\right)^2 = \underline{\ ?\ } \qquad \left(\frac{x}{y}\right)^3 = \underline{\ ?\ }$$

Incorrect answers often given are: $\left(\frac{m}{4}\right)^2 = \frac{m^2}{4}$, $\left(\frac{a - b}{3}\right)^2 = \frac{a^2 - b^2}{3}$,

and $\left(\frac{x}{y}\right)^3 = \frac{x^3}{y}$. Can you see what the mistakes are? Again, you will not make such errors when you consider the meaning:

$$\left(\frac{m}{4}\right)^2 \text{ means } \frac{m}{4} \cdot \frac{m}{4}, \text{ or } \frac{m^2}{16}$$

$$\left(\frac{a - b}{3}\right)^2 \text{ means } \frac{a - b}{3} \cdot \frac{a - b}{3}, \text{ or } \frac{a^2 - 2ab + b^2}{9}$$

$$\left(\frac{x}{y}\right)^3 \text{ means } \frac{x}{y} \cdot \frac{x}{y} \cdot \frac{x}{y}, \text{ or } \frac{x^3}{y^3}$$

When you square a fraction, you must square both the numerator and the denominator; when you cube a fraction, you must cube both the numerator and the denominator; and so on.

PROBLEMS

Write the following expressions in the simplest form:

1. $aaabbbb$
2. $2aabb \cdot 3aabbb$
3. $5aaa + 3aaa$
4. $m + m + m$
5. $aa + aa + aa$
6. $pppp \cdot ppp$
7. d^3d^2d
8. $\frac{a}{b} \cdot \frac{a}{b} \cdot \frac{a}{b} \cdot \frac{a}{b} \cdot \frac{a}{b}$
9. $abc + abc + abc$
10. $abc \cdot abc \cdot abc$

Square each of the following:

11. $\frac{1}{2}a$
12. $\frac{1}{9m}$
13. $\frac{xy}{4}$
14. $0.2m$
15. $\frac{-2x}{3}$
★ 16. $\frac{ab}{c^2}$
17. $\frac{2}{a^3}$
18. a^x
19. a^{2x}
20. y^{3a}

Cube each of the following:

21. $4x$ 22. $-\frac{1}{2}a$ 23. $-\frac{3}{4}x^{2y}$ 24. $0.2mn$ 25. $\dfrac{-3}{ab}$

★ 26. $\dfrac{5m}{n^2}$ 27. x^{2a} 28. a^a 29. y^{3a} 30. t^{a-1}

Perform the indicated operations:

31. $(\frac{1}{2}a)^2$ 32. $\dfrac{a^5b^4}{a^3b^2}$ 33. $x^4 \div x$

34. $mn^3 \div mn^2$ 35. $(2ab)^3$ 36. $(-1)^3(-1)^2$

37. $(-3a^4)^4$ 38. $(\frac{1}{4}x)^3$ 39. $(-ab)^2$

40. $(x - 2y)^2$ 41. $-27ab^4 \div 9ab^3$ 42. $\left(\dfrac{2}{a-b}\right)^2$

★ 43. $a^x \cdot a^x \cdot a^x$ 44. $3mn(2m^2)^3$ 45. $\left(\dfrac{2a}{b}\right)^3$

Find the value of each of the following if **x** $= 2$ *and* **y** $= 3$:

46. $\left(\dfrac{1}{x}\right)^x$ 47. y^x 48. x^{xy}

49. $\left(\dfrac{1}{x}\right)^y$ 50. $\left(\dfrac{x}{y}\right)^x$ 51. $\left(\dfrac{y}{x}\right)^y$

52. $x^x y^y$ 53. $\left(\dfrac{1}{y}\right)^y$ 54. $\left(\dfrac{1}{xy}\right)^x$

55. $(x^x y)^x$ 56. y^{xy} 57. $x^x + y^y$

★ 58. $(y^y - x^x)^x$ 59. $\left(\dfrac{1}{x} + \dfrac{1}{y}\right)^x$ 60. $\left(\dfrac{1}{x} \div \dfrac{1}{y}\right)^y$

Zero and Negative Numbers as Exponents

Look at the division law: $\dfrac{a^m}{a^n} = a^{m-n}$. Suppose $m = n$. Then $m - n = 0$ and the exponent of a is zero. Let us see what a^0 means. When $m = n$, $\dfrac{a^m}{a^n}$ becomes $\dfrac{a^n}{a^n}$. Notice that a^n is divided by itself. How much is $\frac{4}{4}$? $\frac{10}{10}$? $\frac{50}{50}$? The answer in each case is 1.

The symbol $\neq$ means "not equal to." Therefore $a \neq 0$ means "a is not equal to zero."

DO YOU SEE? 👉 Since $\dfrac{a^n}{a^n} = 1$ and $a^0 = \dfrac{a^n}{a^n}$, it is reasonable to define $a^0 = 1$.

$$\dfrac{a^n}{a^n} = a^{n-n} = a^0 = 1 \text{ when } a \neq 0$$

a can have any value except zero, and when raised to the zero power, its value is 1.

$$(\tfrac{1}{2})^0 = 1 \qquad (-10)^0 = 1 \qquad (ab)^0 = 1 \qquad (5a^2b)^0 = 1$$

Are there any situations in which you could obtain a negative exponent of a number by using the laws of exponents? Again the division law provides the answer. For example, you know that

$$\frac{a^3}{a^2} = a^{3-2}, \text{ or } a$$

But notice what happens when you reverse the position of these exponents:

$$\frac{a^2}{a^3} = a^{2-3} = a^{-1}$$

Here is a negative 1 as an exponent!

You can get a clue as to the meaning to give this negative exponent if you think of $\frac{a^2}{a^3}$ as a fraction and reduce it to lowest terms:

$$\frac{a^2}{a^3} = \frac{1}{a}$$

DO YOU SEE? 👉 Since $\frac{a^2}{a^3} = \frac{1}{a}$ and $\frac{a^2}{a^3} = a^{-1}$, it is reasonable to define

$$a^{-1} = \frac{1}{a} \text{ when } a \neq 0.$$

a can represent any number except zero, and when raised to the -1 power, it is the reciprocal of the positive power of a.

$$3^{-1} = \frac{1}{3} \qquad 10^{-1} = \frac{1}{10} \qquad (ab)^{-1} = \frac{1}{ab} \qquad (5x^2y)^{-1} = \frac{1}{5x^2y}$$

In general, $a^{-n} = \dfrac{1}{a^n}$ and $\dfrac{1}{a^{-n}} = a^n$ when $a \neq 0.$

Examples for Study

1. $6^{-1} = \dfrac{1}{6}$
2. $x^{-2} = \dfrac{1}{x^2}$
3. $2c^{-4} = \dfrac{2}{c^4}$

4. $\dfrac{1}{b^{-3}} = \dfrac{1}{\frac{1}{b^3}} = b^3$
5. $\dfrac{2}{m^{-1}} = \dfrac{2}{\frac{1}{m^1}} = 2m$
6. $\dfrac{a^{-2}}{b^{-3}} = \dfrac{\frac{1}{a^2}}{\frac{1}{b^3}} = \dfrac{b^3}{a^2}$

340 *ALGEBRA: ITS BIG IDEAS AND BASIC SKILLS*

PROBLEMS

Find the value of each of the following:

1. 5^2
2. 6^3
3. $(-1)^4$
4. $(-4)^3$
5. 1^{10}

6. 12^0
7. 6^{-3}
8. 2^{-1}
9. 25^0
10. 3^{-2}

11. $\dfrac{1}{2^{-1}}$
12. $\dfrac{3}{6^{-2}}$
13. $(-9)^{-3}$
14. $\dfrac{16}{(-4)^{-2}}$
15. $\dfrac{3^{-1}}{12^{-1}}$

★ 16. 85^0
17. $\left(\dfrac{1}{2}\right)^{-1}$
18. $\left(\dfrac{3}{4}\right)^0$
19. $\dfrac{1}{2^{-5}}$
20. $\dfrac{4^{-2}}{2^{-4}}$

21. b^{-1}
22. m^{-4}
23. $\dfrac{1}{x^{-5}}$
24. $a^0 \cdot a^{-2}$

25. $x^0 \cdot x \cdot x^{-1}$
26. $\dfrac{10}{n^{-3}}$
27. $\dfrac{a}{a^{-1}}$
28. $2y^{-4}$

29. $m^0 + n^0$
30. $m^0 \div m^{-1}$
31. $a^3 \div a^{-2}$
32. $\dfrac{a^{-3}}{b^{-2}}$

Divide using Law II. Remember that, when an exponent is not written, it is understood to be 1.

33. $\dfrac{a^2}{a^2}$
34. $\dfrac{a}{a}$
35. $\dfrac{6}{6}$
36. $\dfrac{s^3}{s}$
37. $\dfrac{2^4}{2}$

Example for Study

$$\frac{1}{4} = \frac{1}{2^2} = 2^{-2}$$

Write each of the following numbers as a power of 2:

38. 8
39. 16
40. 128
41. $\frac{1}{2}$
42. $\frac{1}{4}$

43. $\frac{1}{8}$
44. $\frac{1}{32}$
45. 1
46. 256
47. $\frac{1}{256}$

SELF TEST

Find the value of each of the following:

1. $\left(\dfrac{3}{2}\right)^2$
2. $\left(\dfrac{1}{5}\right)^3$
3. $\dfrac{(-4)^2}{(+2)^3}$
4. 1^8

5. $\left(\dfrac{35}{16}\right)^0$
6. 8^{-2}
7. 10^{-1}
8. $10^{+3} \cdot 10^{-2}$

9. $\dfrac{5^3}{5^{-2}}$
10. $\dfrac{6^{-2}}{6^{+2}}$
11. $\dfrac{2^{-3}}{2^{-4}}$
12. $\dfrac{3426^{-21}}{3426^{-21}}$

Write each of the following as a power of 3:

13. 9
14. 81
15. $\dfrac{1}{27}$
16. $\dfrac{1}{243}$

17. 1
18. $\dfrac{3^2}{3^{-3}}$
19. $3^{-5} \cdot 3^7$
20. $\dfrac{1}{3^{-4}}$

A Short Way of Writing Large and Small Numbers

Scientists often have to use numbers that are very small as well as numbers that are very large. They work with numbers that range from the diameters of the smallest particles of matter like electrons and protons to the distances between stars in the sky. If they had to write these numbers in the ordinary way, their work would be so cluttered with figures that they would be greatly handicapped. For example, the diameter of 1 molecule of water is estimated to be $\frac{2}{100,000,000}$ inch, and the distance to the nearest star is 25,000,000,000,000 miles.

Exponents provide an easy method of writing these numbers. The explanations and problems that follow will make this clear.

These boys have solved the same problem. The boy on the right used a short cut. Note how much more work the boy on the left made for himself by using the long method.

PROBLEMS

1. *Copy and complete the following table. Do not write in your book.*

$10^0 = 1$	$10^4 = \underline{?}$	$10^8 = \underline{?}$
$10^1 = 10$	$10^5 = \underline{?}$	$10^9 = \underline{?}$
$10^2 = 100$	$10^6 = \underline{?}$	$10^{10} = \underline{?}$
$10^3 = 1000$	$10^7 = \underline{?}$	$10^{11} = \underline{?}$

2. Write the long way: 10^{15} and 6×10^5.
3. Write one million as a power of 10. Write one hundred million as a power of 10.

342 *ALGEBRA: ITS BIG IDEAS AND BASIC SKILLS*

Example for Study

$5000 = 5 \times 1000 = 5 \times 10^3$

Write each of the following numbers as a product of a number between 1 and 9 and a power of 10:

4. 3000　　　5. 80,000　　　6. 4000　　　7. 90,000
8. 300,000　　9. 2,000,000　10. 800,000　　11. 60,000
12. 1000　　　13. 30,000,000　14. 800,000,000　15. 9,000,000,000
16. 7 million　17. 50 million　18. 600 million　19. 4 billion

Example for Study

$9500 = 9.5 \times 1000 = 9.5 \times 10^3$

Find the exponent in each of the following:

20. $8800 = 8.8 \times 10^?$　　　　21. $3500 = 3.5 \times 10^?$
22. $3670 = 3.67 \times 10^?$　　　　23. $23,000 = 2.3 \times 10^?$
24. $460,000 = 4.6 \times 10^?$　　　25. $975,000 = 9.75 \times 10^?$
26. $408,000 = 4.08 \times 10^?$　　27. $150 = 1.5 \times 10^?$
28. $4750 = 4.75 \times 10^?$　　　　29. $9,500,000 = 9.5 \times 10^?$
30. $3,760,000 = 3.76 \times 10^?$　31. $43,500,000 = 4.35 \times 10^?$

★ 32. $78,000,000,000 = 7.8 \times 10^?$　　33. $573,000,000 = 5.73 \times 10^?$
34. $98 = 9.8 \times 10^?$　　　　　　　　35. $34 = 3.4 \times 10^?$
36. $7.6 = 7.6 \times 10^?$　　　　　　　　37. $4 = 4 \times 10^?$

Study the following three examples. Then complete Problems 38–43.

$10^{-1} = \frac{1}{10} = 0.1$　　$10^{-2} = \frac{1}{100} = 0.01$　　$10^{-3} = \frac{1}{1000} = 0.001$

38. $10^{-4} = $ _?_　　　39. $10^{-5} = $ _?_　　　40. $10^{-6} = $ _?_
41. $10^{-7} = $ _?_　　　42. $10^{-8} = $ _?_　　　43. $10^{-9} = $ _?_

Write each of the following as a power of 10:

44. 0.01　　　45. 0.1　　　46. 0.001　　　47. 0.0001
48. 0.0000001　49. 0.00001　50. 0.00000001　51. 0.000000001

Example for Study

$0.003 = 3 \times 0.001 = 3 \times 10^{-3}$

Find the exponent in each of the following:

52. $0.02 = 2 \times 10^?$　　　　53. $0.18 = 1.8 \times 10^?$
54. $0.007 = 7 \times 10^?$　　　55. $0.083 = 8.3 \times 10^?$
56. $0.146 = 1.46 \times 10^?$　　57. $0.308 = 3.08 \times 10^?$
58. $0.0003 = 3 \times 10^?$　　　59. $0.00007 = 7 \times 10^?$
60. $0.0046 = 4.6 \times 10^?$　　61. $0.0473 = 4.73 \times 10^?$
62. $0.00049 = 4.9 \times 10^?$　　63. $0.03065 = 3.065 \times 10^?$

★ **64.** The weight of 1 molecule of hydrogen is estimated to be 33×10^{-24} gram. Write this number as a decimal.

65. The diameter of 1 molecule of water is estimated to be $\frac{2}{100,000,000}$ inch. Write this number using a negative exponent.

66. The distance from the earth to the nearest star is 25 million million miles. Write this number using an exponent.

67. The weight of the earth is about 6.3×10^{21} tons, and the weight of the moon is about 7×10^{17} tons. How many times as heavy is the earth as the moon?

68. The number of molecules in 1 gram of hydrogen is estimated to be 3,030,000,000,000,000,000,000, or $3.03 \times 10^{?}$. What is the exponent of 10?

69. It is estimated that one pint of water contains 1.6×10^{25} molecules and that each molecule weighs 1.04×10^{-24} ounce. Find the weight of 1 pint of water in ounces. Find the weight of 1 gallon of water in pounds. Find the answers using exponents.

Radicals and Roots

You have already used the idea of square root. If a number is the product of two identical factors, either of the factors is a square root of the number. For example, since $36 = (+6)(+6)$, $+6$ is a square root of 36. Since $36 = (-6)(-6)$, then -6 is also a square root of 36.

A RADICAL

Index → 3 $\sqrt{85}$ ← Radical sign ← Radicand

$\sqrt{}$ is called a **radical sign**. The symbol for the positive square root of 36 is $\sqrt{36}$. So we know $\sqrt{36} = +6$. The symbol for the negative square root of 36 is $-\sqrt{36}$. So $-\sqrt{36} = -6$. We sometimes say the square roots of 36 are $\pm\sqrt{36}$. The symbol $\pm$ is read "plus and minus." $+\sqrt{36}$ or simply $\sqrt{36}$ is called the **principal square root** of 36.

The number or expression written under the radical sign is called the **radicand.** Numbers and expressions like $\sqrt{25}$, $\sqrt{x + 1}$, and $\sqrt{3a^2}$ are called **radicals.**

Roots other than the square root are indicated by a small number, called the **index number,** in the $\sqrt{}$ of the radical sign. Thus $\sqrt[3]{N}$ means the principal cube root of N.

FOR EXAMPLE: $\sqrt[3]{27} = 3$ because $3 \cdot 3 \cdot 3 = 27$.

$\sqrt[3]{-27} = -3$ because $(-3)(-3)(-3) = -27$.

344 *ALGEBRA: ITS BIG IDEAS AND BASIC SKILLS*

The principal cube root of a positive number is a positive number. The principal cube root of a negative number is a negative number.

Raising a number to a power and finding a root are inverse operations.

Powers	*Roots*

2 to the third power is 8:
$$2^3 = 8$$

The cube root of 8 is 2:
$$\sqrt[3]{8} = 2$$

2 to the fourth power is 16:
$$2^4 = 16$$

The fourth root of 16 is 2:
$$\sqrt[4]{16} = 2$$

a to the fifth power is a^5:
$$a^5$$

The fifth root of a^5 is a:
$$\sqrt[5]{a^5} = a$$

PROBLEMS

Write the square of each of the following:

1. 9
2. -9
3. 0.5
4. 0.02
5. x^2
6. $3a^3$
7. $\frac{1}{4}mn$
8. x^3
9. $-x^3$
10. d^5

Find the square roots of each of the following. Remember that a positive number has two square roots.

11. 25
12. 49
13. $\frac{1}{4}$
14. $100a^2$
15. $\frac{1}{64}$
16. m^6
17. a^8
18. b^{14}
19. m^2n^4
20. $0.01a^4$

Find the cube of each of the following:

21. 2
22. -2
23. 5
24. -5
25. $\frac{1}{3}$
26. $\frac{3}{4}$
27. -0.1
28. a^2
29. a^3
30. a^5

Find the cube root of each of the following:

31. $\dfrac{1}{27}$
32. -64
33. $\dfrac{a^3}{8}$
34. a^6
35. a^{12}
36. $-m^{15}$
37. $\dfrac{x^6}{27}$
38. $125a^9$
39. $0.001a^6$
40. $-\dfrac{1}{64}b^3$

41. Look at your answers to Problems 11–20. What short cut can you use in finding the square of expressions like m^6, a^{10}, c^{16}?
42. Look at your answers to Problems 31–40. What short cut can you use in finding the cube root of expressions like a^6, m^{12}, c^{15}?

43. For what values of a is $\sqrt[3]{a}$ a positive number? For what values of a is $\sqrt[3]{a}$ a negative number?
44. For what values of a is $\sqrt[3]{a^2}$ a positive number? For what values of a is it a negative number?
45. For what values of x is $\sqrt[3]{3x+4}$ a positive number? For what values of x is $\sqrt[3]{3x+4}$ a negative number? For what value of x is it equal to zero?

EXPONENTS AND RADICALS **345**

What Fractional Exponents Mean

The first law of exponents stated that $a^m \cdot a^n = a^{m+n}$ where m and n were positive integers.

In mathematics we have to decide how to define $a^{\frac{1}{2}}$ where a is either positive or zero. We have never used the fraction $\frac{1}{2}$ as an exponent before. If we were to use the first law of exponents with the expression $a^{\frac{1}{2}} \cdot a^{\frac{1}{2}}$, we would get $a^{\frac{1}{2}+\frac{1}{2}} = a^1$.

$$a^{\frac{1}{2}} \cdot a^{\frac{1}{2}} = a^{\frac{1}{2}+\frac{1}{2}} = a^1$$

We also know that $\sqrt{a} \cdot \sqrt{a} = a$

DO YOU SEE?   **It is reasonable to define $a^{\frac{1}{2}} = \sqrt{a}$**

Similarly, $a^{\frac{1}{3}} \cdot a^{\frac{1}{3}} \cdot a^{\frac{1}{3}} = a^{\frac{1}{3}+\frac{1}{3}+\frac{1}{3}} = a$

and $\sqrt[3]{a} \cdot \sqrt[3]{a} \cdot \sqrt[3]{a} = a$

Therefore, $a^{\frac{1}{3}} = \sqrt[3]{a}$

In general, for the principal roots we define:

$$a^{\frac{1}{n}} = \sqrt[n]{a} \quad \text{and} \quad a^{\frac{m}{n}} = (\sqrt[n]{a})^m = \sqrt[n]{a^m}$$

Examples for Study

1. $\sqrt{x} = x^{\frac{1}{2}}$ 2. $\sqrt[3]{x} = x^{\frac{1}{3}}$ 3. $\sqrt{x^2} = (x^2)^{\frac{1}{2}} = x$

4. $\sqrt[3]{x^2} = x^{\frac{2}{3}}$ 5. $\sqrt{x^3} = (x^3)^{\frac{1}{2}} = x^{\frac{3}{2}}$ 6. $\sqrt[3]{x^3} = x^{\frac{3}{3}} = x$

PROBLEMS

Write each of the following using the radical sign:

1. $m^{\frac{1}{2}}$ 2. $b^{\frac{1}{3}}$ 3. $10^{\frac{1}{4}}$ 4. $(ab)^{\frac{1}{2}}$

5. $x^{\frac{1}{5}}$ 6. $5x^{\frac{1}{3}}$ 7. $36^{0.5}$ 8. $a^{0.5}$

9. $x^{\frac{3}{4}}$ 10. $a^{\frac{2}{3}}$ 11. $(ab)^{\frac{3}{2}}$ 12. $36^{\frac{3}{2}}$

13. $3a^{\frac{2}{3}}$ 14. $(3a)^{\frac{2}{3}}$ 15. $a^{1.5}$ 16. $b^{3\frac{1}{2}}$

Write each of the following using a fractional exponent:

17. $\sqrt[3]{x}$ 18. $\sqrt{a^3}$ 19. $\sqrt[4]{m}$ 20. $\sqrt{x^3}$

21. $\sqrt{ab}$ 22. $\sqrt[5]{y^3}$ 23. $\sqrt[b]{x^a}$ 24. $\sqrt[n]{x}$

25. $\sqrt[3]{a}$ 26. $\sqrt{a^5}$ 27. $\sqrt{a^6}$ 28. $\sqrt{a^8}$

29. $\sqrt[3]{a^3}$ 30. $\sqrt{(xy)^2}$ 31. $\sqrt[3]{(xy)^2}$ 32. $\sqrt[4]{m^2n^3}$

Write each of the following as a single number with no exponents:

33. $4^{\frac{1}{2}}$ 34. $64^{\frac{1}{2}}$ 35. $8^{\frac{1}{3}}$ 36. $64^{\frac{1}{3}}$

37. $125^{\frac{1}{3}}$ 38. $81^{\frac{1}{4}}$ 39. $16^{\frac{3}{4}}$ 40. $16^{\frac{1}{4}}$

41. $32^{\frac{2}{5}}$ 42. $125^{\frac{2}{3}}$ 43. $64^{\frac{2}{3}}$ 44. $256^{\frac{3}{4}}$

Methods of Finding the Square Root of a Number

In order to develop a method of finding the square root of any number, you will find the square root of a perfect-square trinomial first.

Examples for Study

1. Find the square root of $100a^2 + 20ab + b^2$.

SOLUTION: First find the square root of $100a^2$:

$$\sqrt{100a^2} = 10a$$

Write $10a$ in three places as shown. Multiply $10a \times 10a = 100a^2$. Subtract $100a^2$ from $100a^2 + 20ab + b^2$:

$$
\begin{array}{r r}
 & 10a \\
10a & \sqrt{100a^2 + 20ab + b^2} \\
10a & \underline{100a^2} \\
 & \qquad\quad 20ab + b^2
\end{array}
$$

Add the two $10a$'s on the left. Use $20a$ as the trial divisor. Divide $20a$ into $20ab$. The quotient is b. Write b in three places as shown:

$$
\begin{array}{r r}
 & 10a + \quad b \\
10a & \sqrt{100a^2 + 20ab + b^2} \\
10a & \underline{100a^2} \\
\overline{20a + b} & \qquad\quad 20ab + b^2 \\
 & \underline{\quad b}
\end{array}
$$

Multiply $20a + b$ by b. Subtract the product $20ab + b^2$ from $20ab + b^2$:

$$
\begin{array}{r r}
 & 10a + \quad b \\
10a & \sqrt{100a^2 + 20ab + b^2} \\
10a & \underline{100a^2} \\
\overline{20a + b} & \qquad\quad 20ab + b^2 \\
\underline{\quad + b} & \qquad\quad \underline{20ab + b^2} \\
\overline{20ab + b^2} &
\end{array}
$$

Since the remainder is zero, $10a + b$ is the square root of $100a^2 + 20ab + b^2$.

$10a + b$ is a square root of $100a^2 + 20ab + b^2$ because $(10a + b)^2$ is equal to $100a^2 + 20ab + b^2$. This method of finding a square root depended upon factoring $100a^2 + 20ab + b^2$ into $100a^2 + b(20a + b)$. You first found the square root of $100a^2$. You next found b such that $b(20a + b)$ was equal to the difference after subtracting $100a^2$ from $100a^2 + 20ab + b^2$.

2. Find the square root of 4096.

SOLUTION: Separate the digits in the number 4096 into groups of two digits starting from the right:

$$\sqrt{40\ 96}$$

The largest square in 40 is 36. Write 6, the square root of 36, in 3 places as shown. Multiply 6×6 and write the product 36 under 40. Subtract 36 from 40:

$$
\begin{array}{r}
6 \\
6\ \sqrt{40\ 96} \\
6\phantom{\ \sqrt{}}\ 36 \\
\hline
4
\end{array}
$$

Write the next two digits, 96, after the remainder 4. Add the two 6s on the left to get the trial divisor:

$$
\begin{array}{r}
6 \\
6\ \sqrt{40\ 96} \\
6\phantom{\ \sqrt{}}\ 36 \\
\hline
12\ \big|\ 4\ 96
\end{array}
$$

Estimate the next digit of the square root by dividing 12 into 49. Write the quotient 4 in 3 places as shown and multiply 124 by 4:

$$
\begin{array}{r}
6\ \ 4 \\
6\ \sqrt{40\ 96} \\
6\phantom{\ \sqrt{}}\ 36 \\
\hline
124\ \big|\ 4\ 96 \\
4\ \ 4\ 96 \\
\hline
\end{array}
$$

Since the remainder is zero, 64 is the square root of 4096.

3. $\sqrt{55,225} = \underline{\ ?\ }$

SOLUTION:

$$
\begin{array}{r}
2\ \ 3\ \ 5 \\
2\ \ \sqrt{5\ 52\ 25} \\
2\phantom{\ \sqrt{}}\ 4 \\
\hline
43\ \big|\ 1\ 52 \\
3\ 1\ 29 \\
\hline
465\ \big|\ \ 23\ 25 \\
5\ \ 23\ 25 \\
\hline
\end{array}
$$

Therefore, $\sqrt{55,225} = 235.$

4. Find $\sqrt{17.3}$ to the nearest hundredth.

SOLUTION:

$$
\begin{array}{r}
4.\ \ 1\ \ 5\ \ 9 \\
4\ \ \sqrt{17.\ 30\ 00\ 00} \\
4\phantom{\ \sqrt{}}\ 16 \\
\hline
81\ \big|\ 1\ 30 \\
1\ 81 \\
\hline
825\ \big|\ \ 49\ 00 \\
5\ \ 41\ 25 \\
\hline
8309\ \big|\ 7\ 75\ 00 \\
9\ 7\ 47\ 81 \\
\hline
\end{array}
$$

Therefore, $\sqrt{17.3} = 4.16.$

NOTE: To find the square root to the nearest hundredth, you must obtain 3 decimal places in the result. If the third place in the quotient is 5 or more, drop this digit and add one to the second-place decimal; if less than 5, simply drop the digit. Hence, the solution in example 4 is $\sqrt{17.3} = 4.16.$

PROBLEMS

Find the square root of each of the following numbers. If a number is not a perfect square, find its square root to the nearest hundredth.

1. 196
2. 65,025
3. 18
4. 145,161
5. 7
6. 1000
7. 23,481
8. 5,084
9. 0.0148
10. 8473
11. 18,417
12. 28

Write each of the following numbers as a decimal and find the square root to the nearest hundredth:

13. $3\frac{1}{4}$
14. $\frac{1}{2}$
15. $\frac{3}{4}$
16. $\frac{3}{5}$
17. $\frac{3}{8}$
18. $5\frac{2}{3}$
19. $1\frac{3}{4}$
20. $2\frac{1}{4}$

★ *Find the square root of each of the following numbers to the nearest thousandth:*

21. 2
22. 3
23. 5
24. 10
25. 229.65
26. 3021.78
27. 5.321
28. 4.635
29. 0.2356
30. 0.74351
31. 0.0428
32. 0.00365

SELF TEST

Find the missing exponents:

1. $95 = 9.5 \times 10^?$
2. $42,600,000 = 4.26 \times 10^?$
3. $45,000 = 4.5 \times 10^?$
4. $0.0083 = 8.3 \times 10^?$
5. $0.000006 = 6.0 \times 10^?$
6. $\frac{5}{500,000} = 1.0 \times 10^?$

Write each of the following as a single number with no exponent:

7. $16^{\frac{1}{2}}$
8. $16^{\frac{1}{4}}$
9. $27^{\frac{2}{3}}$
10. $(\frac{1}{8})^{\frac{1}{3}}$
11. $(0.01)^{\frac{1}{2}}$
12. $\sqrt[4]{256}$

Find the square root of each of the following to the nearest hundredth:

13. 625
14. 10,000
15. 145
16. 3.46
17. 0.0523
18. 326,425

★ ### *Irrational Numbers*

A number that can be written as a fraction in which the numerator and the denominator are whole numbers is called a **rational number**. Some examples of rational numbers are $\frac{1}{2}$, $\frac{3}{4}$, 5, 123, 0.5, 0.128, 5.73, $0.33\frac{1}{3}$, $0.16\frac{2}{3}$, and $0.14\frac{2}{7}$.

Each of the above numbers can be written in fraction form.

FOR EXAMPLE:
$$123 = \frac{123}{1}$$

$$0.128 = \frac{128}{1000}$$

$$0.16\frac{2}{3} = \frac{16\frac{2}{3}}{100} = \frac{\frac{50}{3}}{100} = \frac{50}{300} = \frac{1}{6}$$

EXPONENTS AND RADICALS **349**

A number that cannot be written as a fraction in which the numerator and the denominator are whole numbers is called an **irrational number**. Some examples of irrational numbers are $\sqrt{2}, \sqrt{3}, \sqrt{5}, \sqrt{11}, \sqrt[3]{2}, \sqrt[3]{3}, \sqrt[4]{2},$ and $\sqrt[5]{3}$.

All roots are not irrational numbers, however. For example, $\sqrt{16}$ is a rational number because $\sqrt{16} = 4 = \frac{4}{1}$. Also $\sqrt[3]{8}$ and $\sqrt[4]{81}$ are rational numbers. Why?

PROBLEMS

Tell which of the following are rational and which are irrational numbers:

1. $\frac{5}{8}$ 2. 0.35 3. $\frac{3}{4}$ 4. $0.12\frac{1}{2}$
5. $\sqrt{7}$ 6. $\sqrt{9}$ 7. $\sqrt{4}$ 8. $\sqrt{1}$
9. $\sqrt{13}$ 10. $\sqrt{10}$ 11. $0.66\frac{2}{3}$ 12. 0.875

Multiplying Radicals

Suppose you want to simplify $\sqrt{9 \cdot 16}$. There are two ways of doing this problem:

(1) $\sqrt{9 \cdot 16} = \sqrt{144} = 12$
(2) $\sqrt{9 \cdot 16} = \sqrt{9} \cdot \sqrt{16} = 3 \cdot 4 = 12$

This example illustrates an important property of radicals: If a and b represent positive numbers, then:

$$\sqrt{a}\sqrt{b} = \sqrt{a \cdot b}$$

PROBLEMS

Use the property of radicals $\sqrt{a}\sqrt{b} = \sqrt{a \cdot b}$ to find the following products:

1. $\sqrt{3}\sqrt{15}$ 2. $\sqrt{2}\sqrt{8}$ 3. $\sqrt{5}\sqrt{20}$ 4. $\sqrt{7}\sqrt{8}$
5. $\sqrt{16}\sqrt{25}$ 6. $\sqrt{4}\sqrt{36}$ 7. $\sqrt{23}\sqrt{5}$ 8. $\sqrt{9}\sqrt{49}$
★ 9. $\sqrt{x^2}\sqrt{x^2}$ 10. $\sqrt{y^2}\sqrt{5}$ 11. $\sqrt{7}\sqrt{a^2b^2}$ 12. $\sqrt{15}\sqrt{13}$

Simplifying Radicals

The property $\sqrt{a \cdot b} = \sqrt{a}\sqrt{b}$ for the positive numbers a and b can be used to write radicals in simpler form. For example, to simplify $\sqrt{75}$, you can note that $75 = 25 \cdot 3$ and that 25 is a perfect square. So

$$\sqrt{75} = \sqrt{25 \cdot 3} = \sqrt{25}\sqrt{3} = 5\sqrt{3}$$

To simplify a radical by this method, first factor the number into two factors, one of which is a perfect square. Next write the square root as the product of two separate square roots. Then find the square root of the perfect square.

Examples for Study

1. *Simplify:* $\sqrt{80}$

SOLUTION: $\sqrt{80} = \sqrt{16 \cdot 5}$
$= \sqrt{16}\sqrt{5}$
$= 4\sqrt{5}$

2. *Simplify:* $8\sqrt{27}$

SOLUTION: $8\sqrt{27} = 8\sqrt{9 \cdot 3}$
$= 8\sqrt{9}\sqrt{3}$
$= 8 \cdot 3\sqrt{3}$
$= 24\sqrt{3}$

PROBLEMS

Simplify:

1. $\sqrt{12}$
2. $\sqrt{48}$
3. $\sqrt{18}$
4. $\sqrt{50}$
5. $\sqrt{32}$
6. $\sqrt{20}$
7. $\sqrt{125}$
8. $\sqrt{72}$
9. $\sqrt{98}$
10. $\sqrt{96}$
11. $\sqrt{128}$
12. $\sqrt{162}$
13. $\sqrt{180}$
14. $\sqrt{175}$
15. $\sqrt{63}$
16. $\sqrt{5a^2}$
17. $3\sqrt{27}$
18. $6\sqrt{36}$
19. $2\sqrt{90}$
20. $\sqrt{324}$

★ 21. $\sqrt{196}$
22. $\sqrt{243}$
23. $\sqrt{200}$
24. $\sqrt{300}$
25. $\sqrt{900}$
26. $\sqrt{1000}$
27. $\sqrt{10,000}$
28. $\sqrt{5000}$

★ ## Computing Square Roots

The method of simplifying radicals by factoring out the perfect square factor is very useful in finding square roots of some numbers. For example, if you memorize that $\sqrt{2} = 1.414$ and $\sqrt{3} = 1.732$, you can very easily find square roots of some numbers to the nearest thousandth.

Examples for Study

1. $\sqrt{50} = \sqrt{25 \cdot 2} = \sqrt{25}\sqrt{2} = 5(1.414) = 7.070$

2. $\sqrt{72} = \sqrt{36 \cdot 2} = \sqrt{36}\sqrt{2} = 6(1.414) = 8.484$

3. $\sqrt{75} = \sqrt{25 \cdot 3} = \sqrt{25}\sqrt{3} = 5(1.732) = 8.660$

PROBLEMS

Use $\sqrt{2} = 1.414$, $\sqrt{3} = 1.732$, and $\sqrt{5} = 2.236$ to find each of the following to the nearest thousandth:

1. $\sqrt{32}$
2. $\sqrt{20}$
3. $\sqrt{12}$
4. $\sqrt{48}$
5. $\sqrt{125}$
6. $\sqrt{80}$
7. $\sqrt{45}$
8. $\sqrt{27}$
9. $\sqrt{200}$
10. $\sqrt{500}$
11. $\sqrt{98}$
12. $\sqrt{147}$
13. $\sqrt{432}$
14. $\sqrt{675}$
15. $\sqrt{338}$
16. $\sqrt{588}$

Dividing Radicals

You can find the answer to $\sqrt{\frac{4}{9}}$ in two ways.

(1) Change $\frac{4}{9}$ to a decimal: $\frac{4}{9} = 0.4444 \ldots$ Then find the square root:

$$
\begin{array}{r}
\quad 0.\ 6\ \ 6\ \ 6\ \ldots \\
6 \quad \sqrt{0.44\ 44\ 44\ \ldots} \\
6 \quad 36 \\
\overline{12\ 6}\quad \overline{8\ 44} \\
6 \quad 7\ 56 \\
\overline{13\ 26}\quad \overline{88\ 44} \\
49\ 56 \\
\overline{8\ 88\ \ldots}
\end{array}
$$

The answer is the repeating decimal $0.666 \ldots$ or $0.66\frac{2}{3}$, which is $\frac{2}{3}$.

(2) A second way to solve $\sqrt{\frac{4}{9}}$ is to find the square root of 4 and then find the square root of 9. Thus,

$$\sqrt{\frac{4}{9}} = \frac{\sqrt{4}}{\sqrt{9}} = \frac{2}{3}$$

This example shows a very important property of radicals: When a and b represent positive numbers, then:

$$\frac{\sqrt{a}}{\sqrt{b}} = \sqrt{\frac{a}{b}}$$

PROBLEMS

Use the property of radicals $\sqrt{\frac{a}{b}} = \frac{\sqrt{a}}{\sqrt{b}}$ to simplify each of the following:

1. $\sqrt{\frac{9}{16}}$
2. $\sqrt{\frac{4}{25}}$
3. $\sqrt{\frac{9}{100}}$
4. $\sqrt{\frac{16}{49}}$

5. $\sqrt{\frac{25}{64}}$
6. $\sqrt{\frac{81}{100}}$
7. $\sqrt{\frac{36}{49}}$
8. $\sqrt{\frac{49}{144}}$

9. $\sqrt{\frac{81}{121}}$
10. $\sqrt{\frac{144}{196}}$
11. $\sqrt{\frac{100}{225}}$
12. $\sqrt{\frac{529}{625}}$

13. $\frac{\sqrt{300}}{\sqrt{12}}$
14. $\frac{\sqrt{72}}{\sqrt{2}}$
15. $\frac{\sqrt{320}}{\sqrt{5}}$
16. $\frac{\sqrt{243}}{\sqrt{3}}$

17. $\frac{\sqrt{12}}{\sqrt{27}}$
18. $\frac{\sqrt{20}}{\sqrt{125}}$
19. $\frac{\sqrt{54}}{\sqrt{600}}$
20. $\frac{\sqrt{112}}{\sqrt{343}}$

★ 21. $\frac{\sqrt{5164}}{\sqrt{329}}$
22. $\frac{\sqrt{0.78}}{\sqrt{4.32}}$
23. $\frac{\sqrt{15}}{\sqrt{5}}$
24. $\frac{\sqrt{9.87}}{\sqrt{3.24}}$

Simplifying Radicals Containing Fractions

To simplify radicals having fractions whose denominators are not perfect squares, change the fractions to equivalent fractions whose denominators are perfect squares.

FOR EXAMPLE: $\sqrt{\dfrac{1}{3}} = \sqrt{\dfrac{1}{3} \cdot \dfrac{3}{3}} = \sqrt{\dfrac{3}{9}} = \dfrac{\sqrt{3}}{\sqrt{9}} = \dfrac{\sqrt{3}}{3} = \dfrac{1}{3}\sqrt{3}$

Examples for Study

1. *Simplify:* $\sqrt{\dfrac{7}{12}}$

SOLUTION: $\sqrt{\dfrac{7}{12}} = \sqrt{\dfrac{7 \cdot 3}{12 \cdot 3}} = \sqrt{\dfrac{21}{36}} = \dfrac{\sqrt{21}}{6} = \dfrac{1}{6}\sqrt{21}$

2. *Simplify:* $3\sqrt{\dfrac{x^3}{18}}$

SOLUTION: $3\sqrt{\dfrac{x^3}{18}} = 3\sqrt{\dfrac{2x^3}{36}} = \dfrac{3\sqrt{2x^3}}{6} = \dfrac{1}{2}\sqrt{x^2}\sqrt{2x} = \dfrac{1}{2}x\sqrt{2x}$

PROBLEMS

Simplify each of the following by making the denominator a perfect square:

1. $\sqrt{\dfrac{1}{2}}$ 2. $\sqrt{\dfrac{1}{3}}$ 3. $\sqrt{\dfrac{3}{4}}$ 4. $\sqrt{\dfrac{3}{5}}$

5. $\sqrt{\dfrac{5}{6}}$ 6. $\sqrt{\dfrac{5}{8}}$ 7. $\sqrt{\dfrac{9}{32}}$ 8. $\sqrt{\dfrac{25}{27}}$

9. $\sqrt{\dfrac{9}{20}}$ 10. $\sqrt{\dfrac{4}{11}}$ 11. $\sqrt{\dfrac{2}{15}}$ 12. $\sqrt{\dfrac{25}{72}}$

13. $\sqrt{\dfrac{15}{28}}$ 14. $\sqrt{\dfrac{32}{75}}$ 15. $\sqrt{\dfrac{45}{125}}$ 16. $\sqrt{\dfrac{12}{96}}$

When the denominator of a fraction is a radical, you can simplify the fraction by multiplying both the numerator and the denominator by the radical which makes the denominator a perfect square. This process is called **rationalizing the denominator.**

Examples for Study

1. *Simplify:* $\dfrac{7}{\sqrt{12}}$

SOLUTION: $\dfrac{7}{\sqrt{12}} = \dfrac{7\sqrt{3}}{\sqrt{12}\sqrt{3}} = \dfrac{7\sqrt{3}}{\sqrt{36}} = \dfrac{7\sqrt{3}}{6}$

2. *Simplify:* $\dfrac{5\sqrt{7}}{\sqrt{5}}$

SOLUTION: $\dfrac{5\sqrt{7}}{\sqrt{5}} = \dfrac{5\sqrt{7}\sqrt{5}}{\sqrt{5}\sqrt{5}} = \dfrac{5\sqrt{35}}{\sqrt{5}\sqrt{5}} = \dfrac{5\sqrt{35}}{5} = \sqrt{35}$

Rationalize the denominator in each of the following:

17. $\dfrac{3}{\sqrt{5}}$ 18. $\dfrac{2}{\sqrt{3}}$ 19. $\dfrac{5}{\sqrt{7}}$ 20. $\dfrac{8}{\sqrt{12}}$

21. $\dfrac{6}{\sqrt{10}}$ 22. $\dfrac{3}{\sqrt{20}}$ 23. $\dfrac{5}{\sqrt{50}}$ 24. $\dfrac{3}{\sqrt{48}}$

25. $\dfrac{2\sqrt{3}}{\sqrt{75}}$ 26. $\dfrac{15}{\sqrt{72}}$ 27. $\dfrac{8}{\sqrt{18}}$ 28. $\dfrac{3}{\sqrt{40}}$

★ 29. $\dfrac{5}{\sqrt{60}}$ 30. $\dfrac{5}{8\sqrt{12}}$ 31. $\dfrac{4}{7\sqrt{200}}$ 32. $\dfrac{\sqrt{3}}{\sqrt{5}}$

33. $\dfrac{5\sqrt{6}}{\sqrt{2}}$ 34. $\dfrac{\sqrt{5}}{4\sqrt{20}}$ 35. $\dfrac{2\sqrt{3}}{5\sqrt{8}}$ 36. $\dfrac{2\sqrt{5}}{\sqrt{12}}$

Solving Equations Containing Radicals

To solve an equation like $\sqrt{x + 3} = 5$, first square each side of the equation; then solve the equation as usual. Be sure to check in the original equation.

$$\sqrt{x + 3} = 5 \qquad \text{CHECK: } \sqrt{22 + 3} \overset{?}{=} 5$$
$$x + 3 = 25 \qquad\qquad \sqrt{25} \overset{?}{=} 5$$
$$x = 22 \qquad\qquad\quad 5 = 5$$

PROBLEMS

Solve for x:

1. $\sqrt{x} = 3$ 2. $\sqrt{x} = 7$ 3. $\sqrt{3x} = 6$
4. $\sqrt{2x} = 2$ 5. $\sqrt{x - 5} = 1$ 6. $\sqrt{2x + 1} = 7$
7. $\sqrt{3x + 2} = 6$ 8. $5 = \sqrt{2x + 5}$ 9. $4\sqrt{5x} = 20$
10. $3\sqrt{x} = 1$ 11. $\sqrt{2x + 1} = 2\sqrt{x}$ 12. $3\sqrt{x} = \sqrt{x + 8}$

13. $\sqrt{\dfrac{3x}{5}} = 6$ 14. $\sqrt{\dfrac{1}{x}} = 2$ 15. $\sqrt{\dfrac{4}{x}} = 4$

16. $\sqrt{\dfrac{5x + 1}{6}} = 1$ 17. $\sqrt{3x + 4} = 2$ 18. $\sqrt{x - \tfrac{1}{2}} = \tfrac{1}{2}$

★ 19. $\sqrt{x - \tfrac{1}{4}} = 1$ 20. $\sqrt{\dfrac{1}{x}} = \dfrac{1}{3}$ 21. $\sqrt{\tfrac{1}{2}x - \tfrac{3}{4}} = 0$

22. $\sqrt{3x} + 1 = 2$ 23. $\sqrt{\tfrac{1}{2}x} - \tfrac{1}{2} = 1$ 24. $6 = \sqrt{9x} - 3$

25. $\sqrt{x} - 5 = 18$ 26. $\sqrt{2x} + 6 = 23$ 27. $\sqrt{\dfrac{3}{x}} - 6 = \dfrac{1}{5}$

28. Why is it not possible to find a root of $\sqrt{x + 3} = -5$?

SELF TEST

Simplify each of the following by factoring out a perfect square factor from the radical:

1. $\sqrt{108}$ 2. $\sqrt{125}$ 3. $\sqrt{128}$ 4. $\sqrt{500}$

5. $\sqrt{98}$ 6. $\sqrt{567}$ 7. $\sqrt{20,000}$ 8. $\sqrt{1800}$

Simplify each of the following:

9. $\dfrac{\sqrt{8}}{\sqrt{32}}$ 10. $\dfrac{\sqrt{75}}{\sqrt{3}}$ 11. $\sqrt{\dfrac{125}{180}}$ 12. $\sqrt{\dfrac{48}{147}}$

13. $\dfrac{5}{\sqrt{3}}$ 14. $\dfrac{6}{\sqrt{50}}$ 15. $\dfrac{5\sqrt{5}}{\sqrt{80}}$ 16. $\dfrac{3\sqrt{5}}{\sqrt{24}}$

Solve and check the following equations:

17. $\sqrt{x} = 6$ 18. $\sqrt{5x} = 45$

19. $\sqrt{5x + 1} = 11$ 20. $\sqrt{\dfrac{7}{x}} = 7$

Adding and Subtracting Radicals

The distributive principle holds for irrational numbers. In some cases you can use this principle to simplify the sum of or the difference between radicals.

Examples for Study

1. *Simplify:* $5\sqrt{2} + 3\sqrt{5} - 2\sqrt{2} - 2\sqrt{5}$

SOLUTION:

$$\begin{aligned}
5\sqrt{2} + 3\sqrt{5} - 2\sqrt{2} - 2\sqrt{5} &= 5\sqrt{2} - 2\sqrt{2} + 3\sqrt{5} - 2\sqrt{5} \quad \text{Why?} \\
&= \sqrt{2}(5 - 2) + \sqrt{5}(3 - 2) \quad \text{Why?} \\
&= \sqrt{2}(3) + \sqrt{5}(1) \quad \text{Why?} \\
&= 3\sqrt{2} + \sqrt{5} \quad \text{Why?}
\end{aligned}$$

2. *Simplify:* $\sqrt{75} + \sqrt{12} + 6\sqrt{27}$

SOLUTION:

$$\begin{aligned}
\sqrt{75} + \sqrt{12} + 6\sqrt{27} &= \sqrt{25 \times 3} + \sqrt{4 \times 3} + 6\sqrt{9 \times 3} \quad \text{Why?} \\
&= \sqrt{25}\sqrt{3} + \sqrt{4}\sqrt{3} + 6\sqrt{9}\sqrt{3} \quad \text{Why?} \\
&= 5\sqrt{3} + 2\sqrt{3} + 6 \times 3\sqrt{3} \quad \text{Why?} \\
&= \sqrt{3}(5 + 2 + 18) \quad \text{Why?} \\
&= \sqrt{3}(25) \quad \text{Why?} \\
&= 25\sqrt{3} \quad \text{Why?}
\end{aligned}$$

PROBLEMS

Simplify as much as possible:

1. $3\sqrt{2} + 6\sqrt{2} - 2\sqrt{2}$
2. $10\sqrt{5} - \sqrt{5} - 3\sqrt{5}$
3. $9\sqrt{7} + \sqrt{7} + \sqrt{7}$
4. $6\sqrt{3} + \sqrt{3} - 5\sqrt{3}$
5. $4\sqrt{3} + 6\sqrt{5} - \sqrt{3}$
6. $\sqrt{3} + \sqrt{5} + \sqrt{3} + \sqrt{5}$
7. $\sqrt{8} + 16 + 10$
8. $9\sqrt{3} - 15 + 7\sqrt{3}$
9. $33 - \sqrt{5} - 3\sqrt{5}$
10. $\sqrt{16} + \sqrt{4} + \sqrt{36}$
11. $\sqrt{25} + 5\sqrt{5} + 17$
12. $3\sqrt{4} + 5\sqrt{3} - 2\sqrt{3} + 13$
13. $-\sqrt{5} - 3\sqrt{5} + 6\sqrt{3}$
14. $\sqrt{17} - 13\sqrt{17} - 15\sqrt{17}$
15. $\sqrt{18} + \sqrt{8} + \sqrt{32}$
16. $-3\sqrt{12} + 2\sqrt{3} + 5\sqrt{50}$
17. $2\sqrt{20} + 8\sqrt{2} - 3\sqrt{5}$
18. $\sqrt{6} + 2\sqrt{24} + 5\sqrt{54}$
19. $13\sqrt{2} - 4\sqrt{3} + 5\sqrt{147}$
20. $\sqrt{\frac{1}{2}} + 4\sqrt{2} - 6\sqrt{72}$

★ 21. $5\sqrt{\frac{1}{3}} + 6\sqrt{\frac{1}{2}} + \sqrt{50} - \sqrt{75}$
22. $\sqrt{225} + \sqrt{25} + \sqrt{75} + \sqrt{125}$
23. $\sqrt{\frac{2}{3}} + \sqrt{6} + \sqrt{24}$
24. $\sqrt{\frac{4}{9}} + 5 - \sqrt{\frac{16}{25}}$
25. $2\sqrt{7} + 5\sqrt{35} - \sqrt{49}$
26. $15\sqrt{15} + 5\sqrt{3} - 2\sqrt{27}$
27. $\sqrt{\frac{7}{8}} + \sqrt{\frac{5}{6}} - \sqrt{\frac{7}{2}}$
28. $\sqrt{3x} - 5\sqrt{18x} + 4\sqrt{12x}$
29. $3\sqrt{a} - 2\sqrt{a} + 16\sqrt{b}$
30. $14\sqrt{xy} - 3\sqrt{xy} + 6\sqrt{x}$

★ ## Computing by Exponents

Scientists, astronomers, and engineers use exponents in multiplying and dividing large numbers, multiplying and dividing decimals, finding square roots and cube roots, or in any combination of these operations. As an example, consider a complicated operation like this:

$$\sqrt[3]{\frac{64^2 \times 262,144}{512}} = \underline{\ ?\ }$$

You can simplify this expression quickly, as shown at the right, by using the table at the bottom of the page.

$(64)^2 = (2^6)^2 = 2^{12}$
$262,144 = 2^{18}$
$512 = 2^9$

Thus, $\sqrt[3]{\dfrac{64^2 \times 262,144}{512}} = \sqrt[3]{\dfrac{2^{12} \times 2^{18}}{2^9}} = \sqrt[3]{\dfrac{2^{30}}{2^9}} = \sqrt[3]{2^{21}} = 2^7 = 128$

$2^0 = 1$	$2^6 = 64$	$2^{12} = 4096$	$2^{18} = 262,144$
$2^1 = 2$	$2^7 = 128$	$2^{13} = 8192$	$2^{19} = 524,288$
$2^2 = 4$	$2^8 = 256$	$2^{14} = 16,384$	$2^{20} = 1,048,576$
$2^3 = 8$	$2^9 = 512$	$2^{15} = 32,768$	$2^{21} = 2,097,152$
$2^4 = 16$	$2^{10} = 1024$	$2^{16} = 65,536$	$2^{22} = 4,194,304$
$2^5 = 32$	$2^{11} = 2048$	$2^{17} = 131,072$	$2^{23} = 8,388,608$

Examples for Study

Using the table on page 356, do the following operations by means of exponents:

1. Multiply 512 by 128.

SOLUTION: $512 = 2^9$ and $128 = 2^7$
$$512 \times 128 = 2^9 \times 2^7 = 2^{16} = 65,536$$

2. Divide 524,288 by 8192.

SOLUTION: $\dfrac{524,288}{8192} = \dfrac{2^{19}}{2^{13}} = 2^{19-13} = 2^6 = 64$

3. Find the square root of 16,384.

SOLUTION: $\sqrt{16,384} = \sqrt{2^{14}} = (2^{14})^{\frac{1}{2}} = 2^7 = 128$

PROBLEMS

Using the table on page 356, do the following problems by means of exponents:

1. 64×32 **2.** 4096×16 **3.** $32 \times 128 \times 1024$

4. 256×256 **5.** $4096 \div 512$ **6.** $(64)^2$

7. $131,072 \div 8192$ **8.** $\sqrt{65,536}$ **9.** $\dfrac{32 \times 262,144}{1024}$

10. $\sqrt[3]{32,768}$ **11.** $(1024)^2$ **12.** $(1,048,576)^{\frac{1}{4}}$

13. $\dfrac{512 \times 256}{131,072}$ **14.** $\sqrt[3]{(4096)^4}$ **15.** $\dfrac{16,384 \times 2048}{8,388,608}$

Find the following powers:

16. 3^0 **17.** 3^4 **18.** 3^8 **19.** 3^{12}
20. 3^1 **21.** 3^5 **22.** 3^9 **23.** 3^{13}
24. 3^2 **25.** 3^6 **26.** 3^{10} **27.** 3^{14}
28. 3^3 **29.** 3^7 **30.** 3^{11} **31.** 3^{15}

Using your answers to Problems 16–31, do the following problems by means of exponents:

32. 729×81 **33.** $\dfrac{59,049}{2187}$ **34.** $27 \times 3 \times 81$

35. 2187×2187 **36.** $\sqrt{6561}$ **37.** $\dfrac{14,348,907}{243 \times 2187}$

38. $\dfrac{(19,683)^2}{81 \times 6561}$ **39.** $\sqrt[3]{531,441}$ **40.** $(243)^3$

41. $\dfrac{(27)^5 \times (81)^3}{14,348,907}$ **42.** $(531,441)^{\frac{3}{4}}$ **43.** $\sqrt[5]{59,049}$

EXPONENTS AND RADICALS **357**

The Pythagorean Theorem

You will recall that a right triangle is a triangle having one right angle. There is an interesting relationship between the sides of a right triangle. Pythagoras, a Greek mathematician who lived about 300 B.C., is believed to have been the first to prove this relationship, known today as the **Pythagorean theorem.**

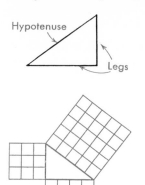

In any right triangle, the side opposite the right angle is called the **hypotenuse,** and the two sides forming the right angle are called the **legs**.

The Pythagorean theorem is: *The square of the hypotenuse of any right triangle is equal to the sum of the squares of the legs.*

If the hypotenuse of a right triangle is represented by the letter c and the two legs by the letters a and b, the Pythagorean theorem can be written:

$$c^2 = a^2 + b^2$$

Example for Study

If the hypotenuse of a right triangle is 15 and one of the legs is 12, find the other leg.

SOLUTION: Let a = the leg that is unknown; then $b = 12$ and $c = 15$.

Substituting in the formula $a^2 + b^2 = c^2$:

$$a^2 + 12^2 = 15^2$$
$$a^2 + 144 = 225$$
$$a^2 = 81$$
$$a = 9$$

NOTE: $a^2 = 81$ is reduced to $a = 9$ by finding the square root of each side of the equation. The square roots of 81 are $+9$ and -9. Since -9 for the length of the side of a triangle has no meaning, it is rejected as the answer.

PROBLEMS

If a and b are the legs of a right triangle and c is the hypotenuse, find the missing side of each of the following:

1. $a = 3, b = 4$
2. $a = 6, c = 10$
3. $a = 5, b = 12$
4. $b = 5, c = 13$
5. $a = 8, b = 15$
6. $a = 7, b = 24$
7. $b = 16, c = 20$
8. $a = 14, b = 48$
9. $a = 12, b = 5$
10. $a = 14, b = 51$

Use the Pythagorean theorem to find the value of the unknown in each of the following. If necessary, use the table of square roots on page 424. Find each answer to the nearest tenth.

11. Right triangles:

12. Rectangles:

13. Squares:

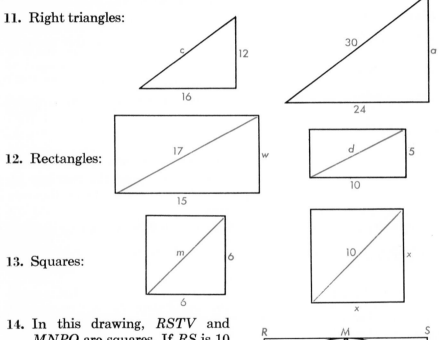

14. In this drawing, $RSTV$ and $MNPQ$ are squares. If RS is 10 inches, find the length of PQ to the nearest tenth of an inch. If QM is 8 inches, find the length of RS to the nearest tenth of an inch.

15. Find to the nearest tenth of a foot the diagonal of a room whose floor measurements are 20 by 15 feet and whose height is 10 feet. The first step is to find the diagonal of the floor.

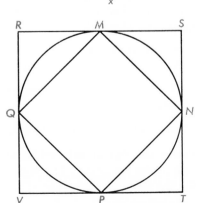

EXPONENTS AND RADICALS **359**

SUMMARY OF IMPORTANT THINGS TO REMEMBER

1. *Words and Expressions*

hypotenuse

index number

irrational numbers

laws of exponents

legs

negative exponents

principal square root

Pythagorean theorem

radical

radical sign

radicand

rational numbers

rationalizing the denominator

zero exponent

2. *Understandings*

The meaning of a zero exponent is defined by the equation $a^0 = 1$ when $a \neq 0$.

The meaning of negative exponent is defined by the equation $a^{-n} = \dfrac{1}{a^n}$ when $a \neq 0$.

The meaning of a fractional exponent is defined by the equation $a^{\frac{m}{n}} = \sqrt[n]{a^m}$.

The following rules hold for radicals having the same index number:

$$\sqrt{a}\,\sqrt{b} = \sqrt{a \cdot b} \text{ and } \frac{\sqrt{a}}{\sqrt{b}} = \sqrt{\frac{a}{b}}.$$

The rules for combining like terms are used in combining radicals.

Exponents are widely used in scientific fields to simplify work with very large and very small numbers.

It is possible to change a number written by the use of exponents into an equal number written by the use of radicals.

3. *Skills*

You should be able to:

Apply the four laws of exponents.

Use exponents to write very small and very large numbers in simplified form.

Simplify, add, subtract, multiply, and divide using radicals.

Use the Pythagorean theorem.

Find the square root of a number.

Solve an equation of the form $\sqrt{ax + b} = c$.

360 *ALGEBRA: ITS BIG IDEAS AND BASIC SKILLS*

PROBLEMS ON YOUR AIMS

YOUR AIM To learn the meaning of zero, negative numbers, and fractions as exponents.

Explain why the following definitions are reasonable:

1. $n^0 = 1$

2. $n^{-1} = \dfrac{1}{n}$

3. $a^{\frac{1}{2}} = \sqrt{a}$

Write the fraction $\dfrac{a^m}{a^n}$ as a power of a using only positive or zero exponents when:

4. $m = 4, n = 6$ 5. $m = 5, n = 6$ 6. $m = 3, n = 2\frac{1}{2}$
7. $m = 0, n = 1$ 8. $m = k, n = k$ 9. $m = 2, n = 7$

Find the value of each of the following:
10. 2^{-3} 11. 5^0 12. $(-8)^{\frac{2}{3}}$ 13. $(\frac{1}{4})^{-3}$
14. $(131)^0$ 15. $16^{-\frac{1}{2}}$ 16. $(-27)^{-\frac{1}{3}}$ 17. $(\frac{1}{8})^{-\frac{1}{3}}$

YOUR AIM To learn how to write very large and very small numbers using powers of 10.

Write each of the following as a power of 10:
1. 100 2. $100,000$ 3. $1,000,000,000$ 4. 0.01
5. 0.0001 6. 0.000001 7. 0.1 8. 1.0

Write each of the following as a single number without the use of exponents:
9. 10^6 10. 10^{-4} 11. 3.4×10^7 12. 1.73×10^{-5}
13. 5.81×10^{-3} 14. 7.6×10^{-2} 15. 9.87×10^3 16. 1.01×10^{-3}
17. 1.82×10^4 18. 1.00×10^0 19. 8.52×10^{-9} 20. 6.03×10^2

YOUR AIM To be able to use the laws of exponents in their most general form.

Simplify each of the following by writing as a positive or as a zero power of a:

1. $a \cdot a^6$ 2. $a^5 \cdot a^5$ 3. $\dfrac{a^4}{a^7}$ 4. $a^3 \cdot a^3$ 5. $\dfrac{a^6}{a^6}$

6. $a^0 \cdot a^{-3} \cdot a$ 7. $\dfrac{a^3 \cdot a^7}{a \cdot a^{14}}$ 8. $(aa^2)^3$ 9. $(a^5)^4$ 10. $(a^{-2})^{-3}$

11. $\dfrac{a^7}{a^{-3}}$ 12. $\dfrac{a^{-2}}{a^{-5}}$ 13. $\dfrac{a^{-4}}{a^3}$ 14. $\dfrac{a^{-15}}{a^{-15}}$

15. $a^{\frac{1}{3}} \cdot a^{\frac{2}{3}}$ 16. $\dfrac{a^{\frac{1}{2}}}{a^{-\frac{1}{2}}}$ 17. $(a^{\frac{1}{2}})^4$ 18. $\dfrac{(a^2)^{-\frac{1}{2}}}{a^{-2}}$

EXPONENTS AND RADICALS **361**

YOUR AIM   To learn how to simplify, add, subtract, multiply, and divide radicals.

Write in simplest form:

1. $\sqrt{\frac{1}{2}} - \sqrt{2}$ 2. $\sqrt{\frac{1}{3}}$ 3. $\sqrt{24} - \sqrt{6}$ 4. $6\sqrt{3} - 2\sqrt{27}$

5. $\sqrt{3} \cdot \sqrt{3}$ 6. $(\sqrt{7})^4$ 7. $(\sqrt{10})^2$ 8. $(\sqrt[3]{2})^3$

Find the value of:

9. $16^{\frac{1}{4}}$ 10. $9^{-\frac{1}{2}}$ 11. $8^{\frac{3}{2}}$ 12. $1000^{\frac{2}{3}}$

13. $\sqrt{9a^2}$ 14. $\sqrt{x^2y^4}$ 15. $\sqrt[3]{8}$ 16. $\sqrt[3]{27}$

17. $(0.5\sqrt{12})^2$ 18. $16^{\frac{1}{2}}$ 19. $8^{\frac{2}{3}}$ 20. $100^{\frac{3}{2}}$

21. $\dfrac{\sqrt{72}}{\sqrt{2}}$ 22. $\dfrac{\sqrt{180}}{\sqrt{5}}$ 23. $\sqrt{\dfrac{32}{75}}$ 24. $\sqrt{\dfrac{1}{20}}$

VALUABLE SKILLS PRACTICE

Write the answers to Problems 1–6 as mixed numbers and as decimals. Then find the sum of the mixed-number answers and the sum of the decimal answers. The sum of your decimal answers should equal 38.40 and the sum of your mixed-number answers should be the fractional equivalent of 38.40.

	Mixed number	Decimal
1. Add $4\frac{2}{5}$, $8\frac{1}{3}$, $1\frac{1}{15}$.	?	?
2. Subtract $6\frac{2}{3}$ from $13\frac{1}{4}$.	?	?
3. Multiply $9\frac{1}{2}$ by $1\frac{1}{2}$.	?	?
4. Divide 82.1 by 8210.	?	?
5. Divide $8\frac{1}{2}$ by $3\frac{3}{4}$.	?	?
6. Subtract 0.01 from $1\frac{1}{2}$.	?	?
	? Total	38.40

Count the units in sections a, b, c, d, *and* e *in the drawing above and write the following ratios as fractions:*

7. a to b   8. c to d   9. b to e   10. a to c

11. a to (b + c)   12. (d − c) to c   13. (d + e) to d   14. (a + c) to d

Divide:
15. $956 \div 10$
16. $268 \div 1000$
17. $4213 \div 100$
18. $1011 \div 100$
19. $10.12 \div 0.1$
20. $0.00639 \div 0.01$
21. $0.1798 \div 0.001$
22. $2.13100 \div 0.0001$

Write as improper fractions:
23. $3\frac{1}{4}$
24. $2\frac{5}{8}$
25. $7\frac{1}{3}$
26. 1.1
27. $2\frac{1}{12}$
28. 6.07
29. $10\frac{1}{6}$
30. $3\frac{1}{8}$

Change the following fractions to percents:
31. $\frac{1}{2}$
32. $\frac{1}{4}$
33. $\frac{1}{3}$
34. $2\frac{1}{5}$
35. $\frac{1}{6}$
36. $\frac{3}{8}$
37. $\frac{5}{6}$
38. $\frac{7}{8}$

Solve:
39. A bedroom represented on a blueprint of a house has the dimensions $3\frac{3}{4}$ by $6\frac{1}{4}$ inches. If the scale is $\frac{1}{4}$ inch to 1 foot, what are the actual dimensions of the room?

40. A bathroom represented on a blueprint has the dimensions $2\frac{1}{4}$ by 3 inches. Find the actual dimensions of the room if the scale is $\frac{1}{4}$ inch to 1 foot.

Find the missing measurements in each of the following:

	Scale used	Actual length	Scale length
41.	1 in. = 12 ft	80 ft	_?_
42.	$\frac{1}{8}$ in. = 1 ft	68 ft	_?_
43.	1 in. = 1 ft	_?_	$6\frac{1}{4}$ in.
44.	$\frac{1}{4}$ in. = 10 ft	_?_	$5\frac{1}{4}$ in.
45.	$\frac{1}{2}$ in. = _?_ ft	100 ft	$8\frac{1}{3}$ in.
46.	$\frac{1}{4}$ in. = _?_ ft	120 ft	$7\frac{1}{2}$ in.

Studying is more than mere reading, and the proper setting will help put you in the mood for work. The boy at the left is practicing good study habits. The boy at the right is not likely to remember much of what he is reading.

CHAPTER TEST

If $a = 2, b = 3, c = -1,$ *and* $d = 0,$ *find the value of the following:*

1. $a^a + b^b$
2. $(abc)^a$
3. $ab + bc + a^d$

4. $16^{\frac{b}{a}}$
5. $4^{\frac{b}{c}}$
6. $27^{\frac{a}{b}}$

7. c^c
8. $a^d + b^d + c^d$
9. $\dfrac{a^c}{b}$

Tell if the numbers in each of the following problems could represent the length of the sides of a right triangle:

10. $15, 20, 25$
11. $6, 9, 10$
12. $3, 7, 4$

Find the square root of each of the following to the nearest hundredth:

13. 48
14. 20
15. 102
16. 149.68

Write each of the following numbers as a power of 10:

17. $10,000$
18. 0.00001
19. 10
20. 0.0001

Write each of the following numbers as a power of 2:

21. 16
22. $\frac{1}{8}$
23. 128
24. 1
25. $\frac{1}{32}$

Write each of the following using a radical sign:

26. $(ab)^{\frac{1}{2}}$
27. $x^{\frac{1}{3}}$
28. $(a - 4)^{\frac{1}{2}}$
29. $5a^{\frac{1}{2}}$

Write each of the following using an exponent:

30. $\sqrt{m}$
31. $\sqrt{a^3}$
32. $\sqrt[3]{x^2}$
33. $\sqrt{ab}$

Simplify each of the following:

34. $\sqrt{27}$
35. $\sqrt{500}$
36. $\sqrt{125}$
37. $\sqrt{243}$

Find the square roots to the nearest hundredth:

38. $\sqrt{45}$
39. $\sqrt{175}$
40. $\sqrt{98}$
41. $\sqrt{1.037}$

Simplify each of the following:

42. $\sqrt{\dfrac{9}{32}}$
43. $\sqrt{\dfrac{32}{75}}$
44. $\dfrac{3}{\sqrt{50}}$
45. $\dfrac{5}{\sqrt{20}}$

46. Use the laws of exponents to find the value of $\dfrac{128 \times 1024}{32}$

$(1024 = 2^{10})$.

47. Find to the nearest tenth the hypotenuse of a right triangle whose legs are 4 and 8.

Solve for x:

48. $\sqrt{3 - x} = 3$
49. $\sqrt{\frac{1}{2}x} = 2$
50. $\sqrt{3x} = 3.6$

51. The diagonal of a rectangle is 17 inches, and its length is 15 inches. Find the width of the rectangle.

52. A circle has a radius of r inches. If this radius is increased by 4 inches, by how much will the area be increased?

CUMULATIVE REVIEW PROBLEMS

WORKING WITH EXPONENTS

Perform the indicated operations:

1. 3^4
2. $(\frac{1}{2})^2$
3. $(-3)^3$
4. $(\frac{1}{2})^4$
5. $(a^2)^4$
6. $(a^{\frac{1}{2}}b^4)^{\frac{1}{2}}$
7. $(a^3)^{-2}$
8. 3^0
9. $9^{\frac{1}{2}}$
10. $8^{\frac{1}{3}}$
11. $169^{\frac{1}{2}}$
12. $1000^{\frac{1}{3}}$
13. 8^0
14. 10^{-1}
15. 3^{-2}
16. 10^{-3}
17. $x^4 \cdot x^{-3}$
18. $x^{\frac{1}{2}} \cdot x^{-\frac{1}{2}}$
19. $16^{\frac{1}{4}}$
20. $(\frac{1}{2})^{-2}$
21. $100^{0.5}$
22. $(7500.32)^0$
23. 9^0
24. $9^{-\frac{1}{2}}$
25. $9 \div 9^{-1}$
26. $(9^{-1})^2$
27. 5^{-2}
28. $8^{-\frac{1}{3}}$

WORKING WITH FORMULAS

$$S_i = \frac{S_o D_i}{D_o}$$

In the formula above, D_i and D_o represent different variables. So do S_i and S_o. You read them as "D sub i," "S sub o," and so on. "Sub" is the word "subscript" abbreviated. It comes from Latin and means "under."

1. In the formula $S_i = \frac{S_o D_i}{D_o}$, find the value of S_i when $S_o = 100$, $D_i = 4.8$ and $D_o = 32$.

2. Solve the formula in Problem 1 for D_o.

In the formula in Problem 1, if S_o is constant, what change takes place in S_i when:

3. D_i increases and D_o is constant?

4. D_o increases and D_i is constant?

5. D_i decreases and D_o increases?

6. In the formula $d = \frac{m}{v}$, find d when $m = 224$ and $v = 20$.

7. Solve the formula $d = \frac{m}{v}$ for m.

In the formula $d = \frac{m}{v}$, describe the change that takes place:

8. In d if m is constant and v decreases.

9. In m if d is constant and v increases.

10. In v if d is constant and m decreases.

11. In the formula $I = \frac{c}{d^2}$, find I when $c = 100$ and $d = 4$.

12. Solve the formula in Problem 11 for c.

EXPONENTS AND RADICALS **365**

In the formula in Problem 11, what is the effect on I *when:*
13. c is doubled and d remains constant?

14. d is doubled and c remains constant?

15. c and d are both doubled?

16. In the formula $F = \dfrac{wv^2}{gr}$, find F when $w = 250$, $v = 9.8$, $g = 980$, and $r = 25$.

17. Solve the formula in Problem 16 for r.

In the formula in Problem 16, what will be the effect of each of the following on F?
18. Decreasing r, all other variables remaining constant.

19. Decreasing w, all other variables remaining constant.

20. Decreasing v, all other variables remaining constant.

Solve the following formulas for the variable indicated:
21. $W = I^2 R$ for R

22. $E = \frac{1}{2} mv^2$ for m

23. $e = kl_o(t - t_o)$ for l_o

24. $\dfrac{P_1 V_1}{T_1} = \dfrac{P_2 V_2}{T_2}$ for V_2

25. $t = \pi \sqrt{\dfrac{l}{g}}$ for l

26. $H = 0.24 Ri^2 t$ for i

SOLVING EQUATIONS

Solve the following systems of equations for x *and* y:
1. $x + 3y = 36$
$3x - y = 27$

2. $7x - 3y = -2$
$2x - 5y = -13$

Solve for x:

3. $x^2 = 14 - 5x$

4. $\dfrac{2}{x} - 3 = 8$

5. $\dfrac{3}{a} = \dfrac{b}{x}$

6. $x^2 = 10x$

7. $\dfrac{x}{4} - \dfrac{25}{x} = 0$

8. $\dfrac{3x}{5} - \dfrac{1}{4} = x$

9. $\dfrac{x}{4} - \dfrac{1}{x} = 0$

10. $\dfrac{3}{x} - \dfrac{x}{5} = \dfrac{2}{5}$

11. $\dfrac{x}{m} - \dfrac{m}{x} = 0$

12. $11x = 7x^2$

13. $\dfrac{x - 2}{3} - \dfrac{x - 1}{4} = 12$

14. $\dfrac{x}{a} - \dfrac{x}{b} = a$

Solve the following problems:

1. Mrs. Gray drove a certain distance in $4\frac{1}{2}$ hours, averaging 42 miles per hour. What would her average speed have to be to make the return trip in $3\frac{3}{4}$ hours?

2. The difference between the units' digit and the tens' digit of a certain two-digit number is 4. The units' digit is 1 larger than twice the tens' digit. Find the number.

3. Mr. LeRoy can spray an orchard in 6 hours using his power sprayer. His neighbor, Mr. Majeski, can do the same job with his sprayer in $4\frac{1}{2}$ hours. How long will it take to do the job if they work together in spraying the orchard?

4. The perimeter of a rectangle is 50 feet. If both the length and the width of the rectangle were increased by 5 feet, the new perimeter would be 70 feet. Find the dimensions of the original rectangle. Is more than one answer possible?

5. A certain grade of sirup contains 10% sugar. How many pounds of water must be removed from 70 pounds of the sirup to produce a 15% solution of sugar?

6. Pupils in a general science class made some hydrogen gas. They obtained 4800 cubic centimeters of hydrogen by using $\frac{1}{2}$ ounce of zinc with some acid. At this rate how much zinc would they need for obtaining 500 cubic centimeters of hydrogen?

7. A man invested $8000 in two business enterprises. On one he made a profit of 6% and on the other a profit of $3\frac{1}{2}$%. His total profit was $325. How much money did he invest in each enterprise?

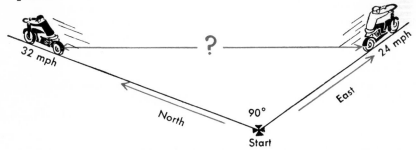

8. Two boys on motor scooters started from a point at the same time. One rode east at an average speed of 24 miles per hour. The other rode north at an average speed of 32 miles per hour. At the end of $2\frac{1}{2}$ hours, how far apart were they?

9. What is the length of a side of a square if the diagonal of the square is 12 inches?

10. A square is a units on a side. By how many units will the area of the square be increased if b units are added to each side?

11. The radius of a circle is r units. By how much will the area of the circle be decreased if the radius is decreased t units?

12. One side of a square is increased by 3 inches and the adjacent side is decreased by 1 inch so as to form a rectangle. The area of the rectangle is 117 square inches. What is the length of the side of the square?

13. Jack Benson made a round trip to a city 160 miles away. The driving time for the round trip was 9 hours. On the return trip his average speed was 8 miles per hour slower. Find his average speed going and returning.

14. You can find approximately how high a ball will rise when thrown directly upward by the formula $s = vt - 16t^2$. In this formula, s stands for the height in feet, v for the initial speed of the ball in feet per second, and t for the time in seconds. Find how long it will take a ball to reach 512 feet if thrown upward with an initial speed of 192 feet per second.

15. The energy of a speeding automobile is given by the formula $E = \frac{1}{2}mv^2$. In this formula E stands for the energy, m for the weight of the automobile in pounds, and v for its speed in feet per second. Find the speed that an automobile weighing 1600 pounds must attain to have 100,000 units of energy.

16. The approximate time t in seconds for an object to reach the ground when dropped from a height s in feet is given by the formula $s = 16t^2$. Find how long it will take a baseball to reach the ground when dropped from a helicopter, 1500 feet above the ground.

17. The square of a certain negative number exceeds ten times this number by 24. Find the number.

18. Two trucks were used to move 38 tons of supplies. One truck carried $1\frac{1}{2}$ times as much as the other. The smaller truck made 28 trips, and the larger truck made 32 trips. What was the average load carried by each truck per trip?

19. Catherine can type 4 pages of copy in 38 minutes. At this rate, how long will it take her to type 56 pages?

20. A telephone company uses a machine to dig a trench. The machine digs a trench 120 feet long in $4\frac{1}{2}$ hours. At this rate, how long will it take to dig a trench a mile long?

21. Traveling at an average speed of 46 miles per hour, Mr. Martin drives from his home to another city in $3\frac{1}{2}$ hours. How long would it take him to make the same trip when traveling at an average speed of 56 miles per hour?

22. A group of girls left school at 1:30 P.M. on a Saturday for a hike. They walked at an average speed of 3 miles per hour. At 2:00 P.M. Edna started after them on her bicycle. She rode at an average speed of 5 miles per hour. At what time did Edna overtake the group and at what distance from the school?

EDUCATORS USE ALGEBRA

Teachers and educational research persons use algebra. Large-scale testing programs involve a great amount of statistical study in which algebra is used. In designing educational research studies, specialists use algebra.

Here is a page from a test maker's notebook.

$$\sigma = \sqrt{\frac{\sum f x^2 - \frac{(\sum f x)^2}{n}}{n-1}}$$

$$\sigma = \sqrt{\frac{256,700 - \frac{(3500)^2}{50}}{49}}$$

$$\sigma = \sqrt{\frac{256,700 - 245,000}{49}}$$

$$\sigma = \sqrt{\frac{11,700}{49}}$$

$$\sigma = \sqrt{238.8}$$

$$\sigma = 15.4$$

BIG IDEAS	EQUATION
	FUNCTION
	GRAPH

BASIC SKILLS	Using and interpreting symbols of algebra
	Solving equations
	Factoring
	Solving verbal problems
	Using exponents
	Drawing and reading graphs

CHAPTER **13** *Quadratic Equations in One Variable*

IN YOUR study of algebra thus far you have had much experience in solving equations, and you have used equations in solving many problems. Most of this work, however, has been with first-degree equations. In this chapter you will learn more about second-degree equations. You will learn general methods of solving quadratic equations.

YOUR AIM  **1. To learn how to solve quadratic equations.**

2. To learn how to solve problems using quadratic equations.

3. To learn how to find approximate roots of quadratic equations by graphing.

370

What Are Quadratic Equations?

When an equation has at least one term in which the variable is squared and no term has a higher power of the variable, then the equation is a second-degree equation, or **quadratic equation in one variable.**

PROBLEMS

Tell which of the following equations are quadratic equations:

1. $x^2 - 2x + 6 = 0$ 2. $3x^2 + x + 15 = 0$ 3. $3x + 18 = 0$
4. $35x + 6 = 0$ 5. $17x^2 + 4x + 5 = 0$ 6. $5x^3 + 7x^2 + 2 = 0$
7. $7x^2 - 14 = 0$ 8. $18x^2 + 6x = 0$ 9. $4 + 3x^2 = 6$
10. $5 + 2x + 7x^2 = 0$ 11. $17x^2 = 2x + 4$
12. $3x^3 = 6x + 7$ 13. $x^2 = 5x - 6x^3 + 7$
14. $\frac{1}{2}x^2 - 2x + \frac{1}{8} = 0$ 15. $3x = 7x^2 + \frac{1}{2}$
16. $\frac{3}{4}x - \frac{5}{8}x^2 = \frac{7}{8}$ 17. $-3x - 6x^2 = 15$
18. $25 = x^2$ 19. $21x = -3x^2$
20. $6x^5 + 3x^2 = 7$ 21. $18x = -3$

The General Quadratic Equation in One Variable

Every quadratic equation in one variable can be written in the form
$$ax^2 + bx + c = 0$$
where x is the variable and a, b, and c are coefficients. For example, the equation $x^2 - 16 = 0$ can be written as:
$$1 \cdot x^2 + 0 \cdot x - 16 = 0$$
which is in the general form $ax^2 + bx + c = 0$, where $a = 1$, $b = 0$, and $c = -16$.

Examples for Study

1. Write the equation $x^2 = -5x$ in the general quadratic form and find the values of a, b, and c.

SOLUTION: $x^2 = -5x$ can be written $x^2 + 5x = 0$. In general quadratic form, $ax^2 + bx + c = 0$, this would be:
$$1x^2 + 5x + 0 = 0$$
So
$$a = 1$$
$$b = 5$$
$$c = 0$$

2. Write the equation $2x^2 + 18x = -28$ in general quadratic form find the values of a, b, and c.

SOLUTION: $2x^2 + 18x = -28$ can be written in general quadratic form:
$$2x^2 + 18x + 28 = 0$$
So
$$a = 2$$
$$b = 18$$
$$c = 28$$

PROBLEMS

Write each of the following equations in the general quadratic form and find the values of a, b, *and* c:

1. $x^2 = 25$
2. $5x^2 - 125 = 0$
3. $x^2 = -5x$
4. $3x^2 + 18x = 0$
5. $x^2 = 15x$
6. $x^2 + 5x + 6 = 0$
7. $x^2 = -7x - 12$
8. $2x^2 + 18x = -28$
9. $\frac{2}{3}x + 15x^2 - 6 = 0$
10. $x^2 + 7x + 15 = 0$
11. $3x^2 - 6x = -14$
12. $-x^2 + 6x - 15 = 0$
13. $3x = 7x^2 - 15$
14. $42 = 16x^2$
15. $5x - 7 = -2x^2$
16. $19x^2 = 38$
17. $25 = 7x^2$

★
18. $2 = 6x + 14x^2$
19. $-\frac{1}{2}x^2 + 6x - 18 = 0$
20. $2 = 7x - 15x^2$
21. $\frac{5}{8} = 12x^2 - 6x$
22. $19x^2 = 57$
23. $4x = 7x^2$
24. $-3x^2 = 5x$
25. $\frac{1}{2}(3 - 2x + x^2) = 4$

Solving Quadratic Equations of the Form $ax^2 + c = 0$

In quadratic equations of the form $ax^2 + c = 0$, a cannot be **zero** because the equation would reduce to $c = 0$. Also $\dfrac{c}{a}$ must represent a negative number; otherwise you would have to find a square root of a negative number.

To solve the equation $5x^2 - 125 = 0$, you proceed as follows:

$$5x^2 - 125 = 0$$
$$5x^2 = 125$$
$$x^2 = 25$$
$$x = \pm\sqrt{25} = \pm 5$$

CHECK: Substituting $x = +5$ Substituting $x = -5$

$$\begin{aligned}
5x^2 - 125 &= 0 \\
5(+5)^2 - 125 &\overset{?}{=} 0 \\
125 - 125 &\overset{?}{=} 0 \\
0 &= 0
\end{aligned} \qquad \begin{aligned}
5x^2 - 125 &= 0 \\
5(-5)^2 - 125 &\overset{?}{=} 0 \\
125 - 125 &\overset{?}{=} 0 \\
0 &= 0
\end{aligned}$$

So $+5$ and -5 are roots of $5x^2 - 125 = 0$.

Examples for Study

1. *Solve:* $3x^2 - 15 = 0$

SOLUTION:
$$3x^2 - 15 = 0$$
$$3x^2 = 15$$
$$x^2 = 5$$
$$x = \sqrt{5} \text{ and}$$
$$x = -\sqrt{5}$$

372 *ALGEBRA: ITS BIG IDEAS AND BASIC SKILLS*

CHECK:
$$3x^2 - 15 = 0 \qquad\qquad 3x^2 - 15 = 0$$
$$3(\sqrt{5})^2 - 15 \overset{?}{=} 0 \qquad 3(-\sqrt{5})^2 - 15 \overset{?}{=} 0$$
$$3(5) - 15 \overset{?}{=} 0 \qquad\qquad 3(5) - 15 \overset{?}{=} 0$$
$$15 - 15 \overset{?}{=} 0 \qquad\qquad 15 - 15 \overset{?}{=} 0$$
$$0 = 0 \qquad\qquad\qquad 0 = 0$$

2. *Solve:* $3y^2 - 96 = 0$

SOLUTION:
$$3y^2 - 96 = 0$$
$$3y^2 = 96$$
$$y^2 = 32$$
$$y = +\sqrt{32} \text{ and}$$
$$y = -\sqrt{32}$$

Simplifying the answers:
$$y = +\sqrt{32} = +4\sqrt{2}$$
$$y = -\sqrt{32} = -4\sqrt{2}$$

CHECK:
$$3y^2 - 96 = 0 \qquad\qquad 3y^2 - 96 = 0$$
$$3(+4\sqrt{2})^2 - 96 \overset{?}{=} 0 \qquad 3(-4\sqrt{2})^2 - 96 \overset{?}{=} 0$$
$$3(32) - 96 \overset{?}{=} 0 \qquad\qquad 3(32) - 96 \overset{?}{=} 0$$
$$96 - 96 \overset{?}{=} 0 \qquad\qquad 96 - 96 \overset{?}{=} 0$$
$$0 = 0 \qquad\qquad\qquad 0 = 0$$

3. *Solve:* $\dfrac{x}{4} + \dfrac{3}{x} = x$

SOLUTION: Multiply each side by the lowest common denominator, $4x$.

$$4x\left(\frac{x}{4} + \frac{3}{x}\right) = 4x \cdot x$$
$$x^2 + 12 = 4x^2$$
$$-3x^2 = -12$$
$$x^2 = 4$$
$$x = +2 \text{ and}$$
$$x = -2$$

CHECK:
$$\frac{x}{4} + \frac{3}{x} = x \qquad\qquad \frac{x}{4} + \frac{3}{x} = x$$
$$\frac{+2}{4} + \frac{3}{+2} \overset{?}{=} +2 \qquad \frac{-2}{4} + \frac{3}{-2} \overset{?}{=} -2$$
$$\frac{1}{2} + \frac{3}{2} \overset{?}{=} 2 \qquad\qquad -\frac{1}{2} - \frac{3}{2} \overset{?}{=} -2$$
$$\frac{4}{2} \overset{?}{=} 2 \qquad\qquad\qquad -\frac{4}{2} \overset{?}{=} -2$$
$$2 = 2 \qquad\qquad\qquad -2 = -2$$

PROBLEMS

Solve the following:

1. $x^2 = 16$
2. $y^2 = 25$
3. $k^2 = 81$
4. $-x^2 = -100$
5. $49 = x^2$
6. $x^2 - 36 = 0$
7. $2y^2 - 128 = 0$
8. $3x^2 - 48 = 0$
9. $x^2 = 2$

10. $z^2 = 15$
11. $x = \dfrac{25}{x}$
12. $4a^2 - 72 = 0$

13. $2x^2 - 150 = 0$
14. $3x^2 = 960$
15. $\dfrac{5}{b} = \dfrac{b}{2}$

16. $98 = x^2$
17. $-3x^2 = -36$
18. $x^2 = 1.44$

19. $y^2 = \dfrac{9}{4}$
20. $x^2 = \dfrac{1}{4}$
21. $\dfrac{16}{k} = k$

22. $\dfrac{24}{x} + \dfrac{x}{3} = x$
23. $3y = \dfrac{2}{y}$
24. $6x = \dfrac{36}{2x}$

⭐ 25. $64x^2 = 1$
26. $\dfrac{x}{5} + \dfrac{6}{x} = x$
27. $x^2 = 3a^2$

28. $x^2 = 3\frac{3}{4}$
29. $\dfrac{x}{5} = \dfrac{2\frac{1}{2}}{x}$
30. $4x^2 = \dfrac{2}{3}$

31. $\dfrac{x^2}{a} = \dfrac{b}{a}$
32. $0.01 = x^2$

33. $5(x^2 - 3) - 6(x^2 + 1) = -46$
34. $\dfrac{5x^2 + 6x - 7}{3x^2 + 6x - 5} = 1$

35. $\dfrac{(x+2)}{(x-2)} + \dfrac{(x-2)}{(x+2)} = 3$
36. Solve $V = \frac{1}{3}\pi r^2$ for r.

37. What is the length of a side of a square whose area is 529 square inches?
38. What number is equal to its reciprocal?
39. What number is equal to twenty-five times its reciprocal?
40. What is the radius of a circle whose area is 113 square inches?
41. The formula for the volume of a cone is $V = \frac{1}{3}\pi r^2 h$. A certain cone has a volume of 332 cubic inches and a height of 18 inches. What is the radius of the base of the cone?
42. Four equal squares of paper cover a table top whose area is 8.8 square feet. Find the length of a side of each of the squares.
43. The ratio of 80 to some number is equal to the ratio of that number to 45. What is the number?
44. Find three consecutive numbers such that the product of the first two numbers is 62 larger than the third number.
45. The formula for the area of a triangle is $A = \frac{1}{2}bh$. The area of a certain triangle is 121 square inches. The height of this triangle is twice as great as the length of the base. Find the height and the base of the triangle.

Solving Quadratic Equations of the Form $ax^2 + bx = 0$

In equations of the form $ax^2 + bx = 0$, a and b cannot be zero. Such equations can be solved by factoring. For example, to solve the equation $3x^2 + 4x = 0$, you factor as follows:

$$x(3x + 4) = 0$$

Since the product of two numbers can be equal to zero only if one or both of the factors are equal to zero:

$$x = 0 \quad \text{or} \quad 3x + 4 = 0$$

Solving these two linear equations, you find:

$$x = 0 \quad \text{and} \quad x = -\frac{4}{3}$$

CHECK: $\qquad 3x^2 + 4x = 0 \qquad\qquad\qquad 3x^2 + 4x = 0$

$$3(0)^2 + 4(0) \overset{?}{=} 0 \qquad\qquad 3\left(-\frac{4}{3}\right)^2 + 4\left(-\frac{4}{3}\right) \overset{?}{=} 0$$

$$0 = 0 \qquad\qquad\qquad 3\left(+\frac{16}{9}\right) - \frac{16}{3} \overset{?}{=} 0$$

$$\frac{16}{3} - \frac{16}{3} \overset{?}{=} 0$$

$$0 = 0$$

So the two roots are 0 and $-\frac{4}{3}$.

DO YOU SEE? ☞ **One of the roots of an equation of the form $ax^2 + bx = 0$ when $a \neq 0$ is always zero.**

Example for Study

Solve: $7x^2 = 6x$

SOLUTION: First get all the terms on one side of the equation:

$$7x^2 - 6x = 0$$

Factor: $\qquad\qquad\qquad\qquad x(7x - 6) = 0$

Set each factor equal to zero and solve for x:

$$x = 0 \qquad 7x - 6 = 0$$
$$7x = 6$$
$$x = \frac{6}{7}$$

CHECK: $\quad 7x^2 = 6x \qquad\qquad 7x^2 = 6x$

$$7(0)^2 \overset{?}{=} 6(0) \qquad 7\left(\frac{6}{7}\right)^2 \overset{?}{=} 6\left(\frac{6}{7}\right)$$

$$0 = 0 \qquad\qquad \frac{36}{7} = \frac{36}{7}$$

So the two roots are 0 and $\frac{6}{7}$.

PROBLEMS

Solve the following equations:

1. $x^2 - 12x = 0$
2. $x^2 + 5x = 0$
3. $y^2 = 6y$
4. $3m^2 = 6m$
5. $4z^2 = z$
6. $3x^2 - 3x = 0$
7. $16x^2 = -4x$
8. $4x^2 = 1$
9. $32x^2 = 2$
10. $25x^2 + 50x = 0$
11. $6k = k^2$
12. $-4t = 5t^2$

★ 13. $\dfrac{x}{4} = \dfrac{15x^2}{2}$

14. $\dfrac{6}{5x^2} = \dfrac{3}{x}$

15. $\dfrac{x+3}{x-3} = \dfrac{2x-3}{x+3}$

16. $\frac{3}{5}x = -\frac{2}{3}x^2$

17. $0.6x^2 = 0.3x$

18. $3\frac{1}{5}x^2 + \frac{4}{5}x = 0$

19. $\dfrac{5}{x^2} = \dfrac{8}{x}$

20. $4x^2 = 0.16$

21. $0.09x^2 = 0.27x$

22. Three times some number is equal to three times the square of the number. What is the number?
23. Three times the square of a number is equal to six times the number. What is the number?
24. The number of square units in the area of a circle is the same as the number of length units in the circumference of the circle. What is the radius of the circle?

SELF TEST

Write the following in general quadratic form $ax^2 + bx + c = 0$ *and tell the value of* a, b, *and* c *in each equation:*

1. $3x^2 = 4x - 6$
2. $5x + 2 = -x^2$
3. $36x^2 = 1$
4. $4x^2 + 2x = 0$

Solve and check the following equations:

5. $18 = x^2$
6. $y^2 = 1.69$
7. $\dfrac{9}{k} = k$
8. $x^2 - 7x = 0$
9. $3y = y^2$
10. $5x^2 = 9x$

Solving Equations of the Form $ax^2 + bx + c = 0$

Quadratic equations of the form $ax^2 + bx + c = 0$ in which neither a, b, nor c is zero can be solved by factoring if the trinomial $ax^2 + bx + c$ can be factored. Equations in which the trinomial cannot be factored will be considered later.

To solve the equation $x^2 + 5x + 6 = 0$, first factor:
$$(x + 3)(x + 2) = 0$$
If either factor is zero, the product is zero. So set each factor equal to zero and solve for x:
$$x + 3 = 0 \qquad x + 2 = 0$$
$$x = -3 \qquad x = -2$$

Now if $x = -3$ and $x = -2$ make the original equation a true statement, then they are roots.

CHECK:
$$x^2 + 5x + 6 = 0$$
$$(-3)^2 + 5(-3) + 6 \overset{?}{=} 0$$
$$9 - 15 + 6 \overset{?}{=} 0$$
$$0 = 0$$

$$x^2 + 5x + 6 = 0$$
$$(-2)^2 + 5(-2) + 6 \overset{?}{=} 0$$
$$4 - 10 + 6 \overset{?}{=} 0$$
$$0 = 0$$

So the roots are -3 and -2.

Examples for Study

1. *Solve:* $x^2 - 3x - 28 = 0$

SOLUTION:
Factor: $\qquad\qquad (x - 7)(x + 4) = 0$
Set each factor equal to zero and solve for x:
$$x - 7 = 0 \qquad\qquad x + 4 = 0$$
$$x = 7 \qquad\qquad x = -4$$

CHECK:
$$x^2 - 3x - 28 = 0$$
$$7^2 - 3(7) - 28 \overset{?}{=} 0$$
$$49 - 21 - 28 \overset{?}{=} 0$$
$$0 = 0$$

$$x^2 - 3x - 28 = 0$$
$$(-4)^2 - 3(-4) - 28 \overset{?}{=} 0$$
$$16 + 12 - 28 \overset{?}{=} 0$$
$$0 = 0$$

So the roots are 7 and -4.

2. *Solve:* $6z^2 + 23z - 18 = 0$

SOLUTION:
Factor: $\qquad\qquad (3z - 2)(2z + 9) = 0$
Set each factor equal to zero and solve for z:
$$3z - 2 = 0 \qquad\qquad 2z + 9 = 0$$
$$3z = 2 \qquad\qquad 2z = -9$$
$$z = \frac{2}{3} \qquad\qquad z = \frac{-9}{2}$$

CHECK:
$$6z^2 + 23z - 18 = 0$$
$$6\left(\frac{2}{3}\right)^2 + 23\left(\frac{2}{3}\right) - 18 \overset{?}{=} 0$$
$$6\left(\frac{4}{9}\right) + \frac{46}{3} - 18 \overset{?}{=} 0$$
$$\frac{24}{9} + \frac{46}{3} - 18 \overset{?}{=} 0$$
$$\frac{24}{9} + \frac{138}{9} - 18 \overset{?}{=} 0$$
$$\frac{162}{9} - 18 \overset{?}{=} 0$$
$$0 = 0$$

$$6z^2 + 23z - 18 = 0$$
$$6\left(\frac{-9}{2}\right)^2 + 23\left(\frac{-9}{2}\right) - 18 \overset{?}{=} 0$$
$$6\left(\frac{81}{4}\right) - \frac{207}{2} - 18 \overset{?}{=} 0$$
$$\frac{243}{2} - \frac{207}{2} - 18 \overset{?}{=} 0$$
$$0 = 0$$

QUADRATIC EQUATIONS IN ONE VARIABLE **377**

PROBLEMS

Solve:

1. $x^2 + x - 6 = 0$
2. $x^2 - x - 20 = 0$
3. $t^2 - 4t - 12 = 0$
4. $x^2 + 7x + 12 = 0$
5. $x^2 = 2x + 35$
6. $z^2 = 9z - 18$
7. $y^2 + 30 = 11y$
8. $x^2 - 32 = 4x$
9. $x^2 + 36 = -13x$
10. $56 = -x^2 + 15x$
11. $2k^2 - 5k - 3 = 0$
12. $3x^2 - 20x + 12 = 0$
13. $6x^2 - 2x - 8 = 0$
14. $-5x^2 - 9x + 18 = 0$
15. $8x^2 + 10x - 3 = 0$
16. $64x^2 + 48x - 40 = 0$
17. $4x^2 = 7x$
18. $3x = 16x^2$
19. $12x^2 + 6x = 0$
20. $5x^2 - 3x = 0$
21. $x^2 + 8x - 9 = 0$
22. $x^2 + 6x + 9 = 0$

★ 23. $x^2 + 4.02x + 0.08 = 0$
24. $x^2 + 0.07x + 0.0012 = 0$

25. $1 - \dfrac{3}{5x} - \dfrac{2}{5x^2} = 0$
26. $1 - \dfrac{11}{6x} - \dfrac{5}{3x^2} = 0$

27. $x^2 - ax + bx - ab = 0$
28. $x^2 - 2ax + a^2 = 0$

29. $x^2 + \dfrac{1}{4}x - \dfrac{3}{8} = 0$
30. $\dfrac{x+1}{x-3} + \dfrac{1}{x+3} = 1$

Solve each of the following problems using quadratic equations:

31. The square of a number is 48 larger than eight times the number. What is the number?

32. The square of a number is equal to eight times the number. What is the number?

33. One leg of a right triangle is 8 inches and the second leg is 6 inches. How long is the hypotenuse?

34. What is the length of a diagonal of a square in which each side is 12 inches long?

35. The square of what number is 6 less than five times the number?

36. The area of a triangle is 24 square inches. The base is $\frac{1}{3}$ as long as the height. What are the base and the height of the triangle?

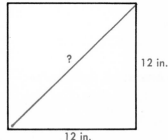

37. The length of a rectangle is 12 inches more than the width. The area is 220 square inches. What are the length and the width of the rectangle?

38. A rectangle has a perimeter of 28 feet and an area of 48 square feet. What are the length and the width of the rectangle?

39. A box is 6 inches high. The length is 8 inches longer than the the width. The volume of the box is 1080 cubic inches. What are the length and the width of the box?

★ **40.** In a right triangle the hypotenuse is 1 inch longer than one of the legs. This leg is 7 inches longer than the other leg. Find the length of each leg and the hypotenuse.

41. The area of a circle is 400 square inches. What is the radius of the circle?

42. If one of the sides of a square is increased by 3 and one of the adjacent sides is decreased by 3, the area of the rectangle so formed will be 135 square inches. How long is each side of the square?

Completing the Square

You have already learned how to square a binomial. You will now see whether there is a relationship between the coefficients in a trinomial which is the result of squaring a binomial. Examine the following four binomials which have been squared:

$$(x + 6)^2 = x^2 + 12x + 36$$
$$(x - 5)^2 = x^2 - 10x + 25$$
$$(x + \tfrac{1}{2})^2 = x^2 + x + \tfrac{1}{4}$$
$$(x + a)^2 = x^2 + 2ax + a^2$$

The last term in each of the above trinomials was obtained by squaring one-half of the coefficient of the x-term.

Thus, $36 = \left(\dfrac{12}{2}\right)^2 \qquad 25 = \left(\dfrac{-10}{2}\right)^2 \qquad \left(\dfrac{1}{4}\right) = \left(\dfrac{1}{2}\right)^2 \qquad a^2 = \left(\dfrac{2a}{2}\right)^2$

If you are given two terms of a trinomial, such as $x^2 + 16x + \underline{\ ?\ }$, you now are able to tell what the third term should be so that the trinomial will be a perfect square. Take one-half of 16 and square it:

$$\left(\dfrac{16}{2}\right)^2 = 8^2 = 64$$

So the trinomial is $x^2 + 16x + 64$, which is equal to $(x + 8)^2$.

Examples for Study

1. *Find the third term:* $x^2 + 14x + \underline{\ ?\ }$

SOLUTION: $\qquad\qquad\qquad \tfrac{1}{2}$ of $14 = 7$
$$7^2 = 49$$
So the perfect square trinomial is $x^2 + 14x + 49$, since
$$x^2 + 14x + 49 = (x + 7)^2$$

2. *Find the third term:* $x^2 + \tfrac{2}{3}x + \underline{\ ?\ }$

SOLUTION: $\qquad\qquad\qquad \tfrac{1}{2}$ of $\tfrac{2}{3} = \tfrac{1}{3}$
$$(\tfrac{1}{3})^2 = \tfrac{1}{9}$$
So the perfect square trinomial is $x^2 + \tfrac{2}{3}x + \tfrac{1}{9}$, since
$$x^2 + \tfrac{2}{3}x + \tfrac{1}{9} = (x + \tfrac{1}{3})^2$$

QUADRATIC EQUATIONS IN ONE VARIABLE **379**

PROBLEMS

Find the third term which will make each of the following a perfect square:

1. $x^2 - 8x + \underline{\ ?\ }$
2. $x^2 + 24x + \underline{\ ?\ }$
3. $y^2 + 12y + \underline{\ ?\ }$
4. $k^2 - 18k + \underline{\ ?\ }$
5. $x^2 + 20x + \underline{\ ?\ }$
6. $a^2 - 40a + \underline{\ ?\ }$
7. $m^2 - 16m + \underline{\ ?\ }$
8. $x^2 + 24x + \underline{\ ?\ }$
9. $x^2 + 26x + \underline{\ ?\ }$
10. $z^2 - 22z + \underline{\ ?\ }$
11. $x^2 - x + \underline{\ ?\ }$
12. $x^2 - 4x + \underline{\ ?\ }$
13. $b^2 + 7b + \underline{\ ?\ }$
14. $x^2 - 14x + \underline{\ ?\ }$
15. $t^2 + 9t + \underline{\ ?\ }$
16. $x^2 - 5x + \underline{\ ?\ }$
17. $k^2 + k + \underline{\ ?\ }$
18. $x^2 - \frac{4}{3}x + \underline{\ ?\ }$
19. $x^2 + \frac{6}{5}x + \underline{\ ?\ }$
20. $a^2 - \frac{8}{5}a + \underline{\ ?\ }$
21. $x^2 + \frac{5}{4}x + \underline{\ ?\ }$
22. $x^2 - \frac{9}{5}x + \underline{\ ?\ }$

★

23. $y^2 - 1.6y + \underline{\ ?\ }$
24. $z^2 + \frac{8}{9}z + \underline{\ ?\ }$
25. $x^2 - 2.8x + \underline{\ ?\ }$
26. $b^2 + 0.6b + \underline{\ ?\ }$
27. $r^2 + 4rs + \underline{\ ?\ }$
28. $k^2 - 3mk + \underline{\ ?\ }$
29. $y^4 + 3y^2 + \underline{\ ?\ }$
30. $\underline{\ ?\ } + 2y + y^2$

Solving Quadratic Equations by Completing the Square

The method of completing the square may be used to solve a quadratic equation even when the polynomial $ax^2 + bx + c$ cannot be factored. For example, to solve the equation $x^2 + 6x + 6 = 0$, proceed this way:

(1) First subtract 6 from each side of the equation:
$$x^2 + 6x = -6$$

(2) Next find a third term that will make the trinomial on the left side of the equation a perfect square. That term is 9.

(3) Next add 9 to each side of the equation:
$$x^2 + 6x + 9 = -6 + 9$$
$$x^2 + 6x + 9 = 3$$

(4) Write the left side of the equation as the square of a binomial:
$$(x + 3)^2 = 3$$

(5) Take the square root of each side. Thus,
$$x + 3 = +\sqrt{3} \quad \text{and} \quad x + 3 = -\sqrt{3}$$

So
$$x = -3 + \sqrt{3} \quad \text{and} \quad x = -3 - \sqrt{3}$$

(6) Check your answer:
$$x^2 + 6x + 6 = 0$$
$$(-3 + \sqrt{3})^2 + 6(-3 + \sqrt{3}) + 6 \overset{?}{=} 0$$
$$9 - 6\sqrt{3} + 3 - 18 + 6\sqrt{3} + 6 \overset{?}{=} 0$$
$$0 = 0$$

$$x^2 + 6x + 6 = 0$$
$$(-3 - \sqrt{3})^2 + 6(-3 - \sqrt{3}) + 6 \stackrel{?}{=} 0$$
$$9 + 6\sqrt{3} + 3 - 18 - 6\sqrt{3} + 6 \stackrel{?}{=} 0$$
$$0 = 0$$

So the roots are $-3 + \sqrt{3}$ and $-3 - \sqrt{3}$.

Example for Study

Solve: $3x^2 + 4x - 7 = 0$

SOLUTION: Add 7 to each side of the equation:
$$3x^2 + 4x = 7$$

Next divide each side of the equation by 3 so that the left side will be in the form $x^2 + bx +$ _?_. You have learned how to complete the square only when the coefficient of x^2 is 1.

$$x^2 + \frac{4}{3}x = \frac{7}{3}$$

Complete the square and add $\frac{4}{9}$ to each side:

$$x^2 + \frac{4}{3}x + \frac{4}{9} = \frac{7}{3} + \frac{4}{9}$$

Write the left side as the square of a binomial:

$$\left(x + \frac{2}{3}\right)^2 = \frac{25}{9}$$

Take the square root of each side:

$$x + \frac{2}{3} = +\frac{5}{3}$$
$$x + \frac{2}{3} = -\frac{5}{3}$$

So
$$x = \frac{5}{3} - \frac{2}{3} = 1$$
$$x = -\frac{5}{3} - \frac{2}{3} = -\frac{7}{3}$$

CHECK:

$$3x^2 + 4x - 7 = 0 \qquad\qquad 3x^2 + 4x - 7 = 0$$
$$3(1)^2 + 4(1) - 7 \stackrel{?}{=} 0 \qquad 3(-\tfrac{7}{3})^2 + 4(-\tfrac{7}{3}) - 7 = 0$$
$$3 + 4 - 7 \stackrel{?}{=} 0 \qquad\qquad 3(\tfrac{49}{9}) - \tfrac{28}{3} - 7 \stackrel{?}{=} 0$$
$$0 = 0 \qquad\qquad\qquad \tfrac{49}{3} - \tfrac{28}{3} - 7 \stackrel{?}{=} 0$$
$$\tfrac{21}{3} - 7 \stackrel{?}{=} 0$$
$$0 = 0$$

So 1 and $-\frac{7}{3}$ are roots of the equation.

PROBLEMS

Solve each of the following by completing the square and check the answer:

1. $x^2 + 6x + 8 = 0$
2. $y^2 + 8y + 15 = 0$
3. $x^2 - 2x = 35$
4. $m^2 + 10m + 21 = 0$
5. $x^2 - 12x + 27 = 0$
6. $b^2 - 2b = 8$
7. $x^2 + 10x = 24$
8. $x^2 + 6x = 7$
9. $k^2 - 14k + 48 = 0$
10. $x^2 - 2x - 1 = 0$
11. $x^2 - 2x = 80$
12. $z^2 + 4z = 96$
13. $2x^2 - 20x = 22$
14. $3x^2 + 12x = 135$
15. $y^2 - 5y + 6 = 0$
16. $x^2 + 3x - 10 = 0$
17. $x^2 - x = 2$
18. $2t^2 + t - 1 = 0$
19. $2x^2 - x = 3$
20. $2x^2 - 5x = -2$
21. $x^2 + 6x = 3$
22. $z^2 - 10z + 12 = 0$
23. $x^2 - 14x + 30 = 0$
24. $x^2 + 16x + 50 = 0$
25. $x^2 = 2x + 19$
26. $\dfrac{3}{x} + \dfrac{5}{x^2} = 1$

★ 27. $\dfrac{3}{y} = \dfrac{5}{y^2}$
28. $x - 20 - \dfrac{5}{x} = 0$
29. $x^2 + \dfrac{5}{4}x = 15$
30. $y^2 + 0.6y = 0$
31. $z^2 + 10z - k = 0$
32. $x^2 + kx = 0$
33. $ax^2 + 4x + 8 = 0$
34. $k^2 + 6k + c = 0$
35. $x^2 + bx + 5 = 0$
36. $ax^2 + bx + c = 0$
37. $\dfrac{x^2}{k} + \dfrac{x}{m} + \dfrac{1}{n} = 0$
38. $\dfrac{a}{x} + \dfrac{b}{x^2} = 2$

SELF TEST

Solve each of the following by factoring:

1. $x^2 - 3x - 40 = 0$
2. $a^2 - 14a + 48 = 0$
3. $2y^2 - 9y - 18 = 0$
4. $8x^2 - 10x - 3 = 0$
5. $2x^2 + x - 15 = 0$
6. $8x^2 - 2x - 3 = 0$

Solve each of the following by completing the square:

7. $x^2 + 6x = 16$
8. $y^2 + 12y - 13 = 0$
9. $k^2 + 12 = 10k$
10. $2a^2 - 5a - 3 = 0$
11. $x^2 - 6x - 7 = 0$
12. $5x^2 - 4x + \frac{1}{2} = 0$

Solve each of the following by any method you wish:

13. $5y = \dfrac{7}{y}$
14. $8x^2 - 7x = 0$
15. $x^2 + 4x - 6 = 0$
16. $x^2 + \dfrac{3x}{2} - 1 = 0$
17. $5x^2 - 3x = 0$
18. $6x^2 - 7 = 0$

382 *ALGEBRA: ITS BIG IDEAS AND BASIC SKILLS*

Solving Quadratic Equations by Formula

Since $ax^2 + bx + c = 0$ is the general form of a quadratic equation in one variable, you may solve this equation by completing the square and thus obtain its roots in terms of a, b, and c.

(1) $ax^2 + bx + c = 0$

(2) Subtract c from each side:
$$ax^2 + bx = -c$$

(3) Divide each side by a so that the coefficient of x^2 will be 1:
$$x^2 + \frac{b}{a}x = \frac{-c}{a}$$

(4) Add the square of one-half of $\frac{b}{a}$ to each side of the equation:
$$x^2 + \frac{b}{a}x + \frac{b^2}{4a^2} = \frac{b^2}{4a^2} - \frac{c}{a}$$

(5) Write the left side of the equation as the square of a binomial:
$$\left(x + \frac{b}{2a}\right)^2 = \frac{b^2 - 4ac}{4a^2}$$

(6) Take square root of each side:
$$x + \frac{b}{2a} = -\frac{\sqrt{b^2 - 4ac}}{2a} \quad \text{or} \quad +\frac{\sqrt{b^2 - 4ac}}{2a}$$

(7) Solve for x:
$$x = \frac{-b}{2a} - \frac{\sqrt{b^2 - 4ac}}{2a} \quad \text{or} \quad x = \frac{-b}{2a} + \frac{\sqrt{b^2 - 4ac}}{2a}$$

$$x = \frac{-b \pm \sqrt{b^2 - 4ac}}{2a}$$

You can solve any quadratic equation by substituting the values of a, b, and c in the formula above. To use this method, then, you must remember the formula.

Examples for Study

1. *Solve:* $2x^2 - 5x + 3 = 0$

SOLUTION: $a = 2, b = -5, c = 3$

$$x = \frac{-b \pm \sqrt{b^2 - 4ac}}{2a}$$

$$= \frac{-(-5) \pm \sqrt{25 - 4 \cdot 2 \cdot 3}}{2 \cdot 2}$$

$$= \frac{5 \pm \sqrt{1}}{4} \quad \text{or} \quad \frac{5 \pm 1}{4}$$

Hence,
$$x = \frac{5+1}{4} \quad \text{and} \quad x = \frac{5-1}{4}$$
$$x = \frac{3}{2} \qquad\qquad x = 1$$

CHECK: $2\left(\frac{3}{2}\right)^2 - 5\left(\frac{3}{2}\right) + 3 \stackrel{?}{=} 0 \qquad 2(1)^2 - 5(1) + 3 \stackrel{?}{=} 0$

$$\frac{9}{2} - \frac{15}{2} + 3 \stackrel{?}{=} 0 \qquad\qquad 2 - 5 + 3 \stackrel{?}{=} 0$$
$$0 = 0 \qquad\qquad\qquad 0 = 0$$

So $\frac{3}{2}$ and 1 are the roots of the equation $2x^2 - 5x + 3 = 0$.

2. Find the roots of $3x^2 + 10x = 1$ to the nearest hundredth.

SOLUTION: $3x^2 + 10x - 1 = 0; a = 3, b = 10, c = -1$
$$x = \frac{-b \pm \sqrt{b^2 - 4ac}}{2a}$$
$$= \frac{-10 \pm \sqrt{100 - 4 \cdot 3(-1)}}{2 \cdot 3}$$
$$= \frac{-10 \pm \sqrt{112}}{6} \quad \text{or} \quad \frac{-10 \pm 10.583}{6}$$

The square root of 112 may be obtained from the table on page 424:
$$x = \frac{-10 + 10.583}{6} = 0.097 \quad \text{and} \quad x = \frac{-10 - 10.583}{6} = -3.430$$

Hence, the roots to the nearest hundredth are 0.10 and -3.43.

Notice that it is necessary to find the root to three decimal places in order to round off to the nearest hundredth. Check in the usual manner. Since the square roots are only approximate numbers, the checks, likewise, will be only approximate.

CHECK:
$$3x^2 + 10x = 1 \qquad\qquad 3x^2 + 10x = 1$$
$$3(0.097)^2 + 10(0.097) \stackrel{?}{=} 1 \qquad 3(-3.430)^2 + 10(-3.430) \stackrel{?}{=} 1$$
$$0.028 + 0.97 \stackrel{?}{=} 1 \qquad\qquad 35.29 - 34.30 \stackrel{?}{=} 1$$
$$0.998 \stackrel{?}{=} 1 \qquad\qquad 0.99 \stackrel{?}{=} 1$$

Since 0.998 and 0.99 are about 1 the answer checks.

PROBLEMS

What are the values of a, b, *and* c *in the following quadratic equations? First rewrite each equation, if necessary, so that it will be in the form* ax² + bx + c = 0.

1. $3x^2 + 2x - 8 = 0$ 2. $x^2 - 6x = 14$
3. $x^2 = x - 1$ 4. $0 = 2x^2 - 5x + 3$
5. $5x^2 - 3 = 10x + 3$ 6. $x^2 - x = 7 + x$
7. $3 - x + x^2 = 6 - 2x - 4x^2$ 8. $12 = x - x^2 + 12$

Solve each of the following equations using the quadratic formula. Check each answer. Leave roots that are irrational numbers in simplest radical form.

9. $x^2 + x - 20 = 0$

10. $2x^2 - 7x + 3 = 0$

11. $x^2 - 3x = 10$

12. $8x^2 = 2x + 1$

13. $x^2 + 8 = 9x$

14. $2x^2 = x + 3$

15. $5x - 2 = 3x^2$

16. $0 = 7x - 2 + 15x^2$

17. $x^2 + \frac{1}{2}x - \frac{1}{2} = 0$

18. $x^2 - 4 = 0$

19. $2x^2 - 4x + 1 = 0$

20. $x^2 - 5x - 2 = 0$

21. $4x^2 + 9x + 3 = 0$

22. $3x^2 - 2 = 8x$

23. $5x^2 - x = 1$

24. $7x^2 + 10x + 2 = 0$

25. $2x^2 + 5x - 12 = 0$

26. $3x^2 + 5x - 2 = 0$

27. $x^2 - 17x + 72 = 0$

28. $x^2 - 6x = 1$

29. $4x^2 - 15x = 25$

30. $x^2 + 16x = 9x$

31. $4x^2 - 1 = 0$

32. $x^2 + 2x = 5$

33. $3x^2 - 12 = 0$

34. $x^2 - 16x = -40$

35. $\dfrac{6}{x} - x = 5$

36. $x(x + 1) + 2x = 4$

37. $(x + 1)^2 = 3x + 5$

38. $\dfrac{3x^2}{x + 1} - x = -10$

★ 39. $(2x - 1)^2 - x(x - 2) = 16x - 4$

40. $\dfrac{5}{x + 3} - \dfrac{x + 3}{x + 2} = \dfrac{1}{x + 3}$

41. $(2x - 1)(x - 2) + 8 = 2(x + 4) + 11$

42. $\dfrac{x + 4}{x - 5} - \dfrac{x + 2}{2x + 1} = 5$

43. $\dfrac{3}{x} + \dfrac{6}{5x - 1} = \dfrac{3x}{5x - 1}$

44. $\dfrac{2}{x^2 - 4} + \dfrac{5}{3(x - 2)} = 7$

45. $\dfrac{2x - 1}{x^2 + 5x + 6} + \dfrac{2x}{x + 3} = \dfrac{8x}{5(x + 2)}$

46. $\dfrac{5}{y} - \dfrac{2y + 1}{3y + 2} = \dfrac{7y}{3y + 2}$

47. $\dfrac{5x}{x^2 + x - 12} + \dfrac{2}{x^2 - 6x + 9} = \dfrac{3}{x + 4}$

48. $\dfrac{k}{x} + \dfrac{x}{k} = \dfrac{k^2 - x^2}{kx}$

49. $\dfrac{7}{x + a} + \dfrac{6}{x - a} = 4$

50. $\dfrac{b}{x + a} + \dfrac{a}{x + b} = 5$

Find the roots of the following equations to the nearest hundredth. Use the table of square roots on page 424.

51. $x^2 + 2x - 5 = 0$

52. $y^2 - 7y + 3 = 0$

53. $3x^2 + x - 6 = 0$

54. $2y^2 - 15y + 3 = 0$

55. $r^2 - 3r - 9 = 0$

56. $5x^2 + 12x + \frac{1}{2} = 0$

57. $x^2 - 0.3x - 0.4 = 0$

58. $y^2 + 3.2y + 0.7 = 0$

★ 59. $x^2 + 5.32x - 4.18 = 0$

60. $0.3y^2 + 1.4y + 0.2 = 0$

61. $1.6 = 3.2x - 1.4x^2$

62. $5.21 = 4.32y^2 - 5.16y$

QUADRATIC EQUATIONS IN ONE VARIABLE **385**

*Solve the following problems by any method you wish. Leave roots which
are irrational numbers in simplest radical form.*

63. $3x^2 = 126$ **64.** $x^2 - 5x = 0$
65. $x^2 + 6x + 8 = 0$ **66.** $y^2 - 9y + 18 = 0$
67. $y^2 - y = 56$ **68.** $3k^2 = 7k$
69. $z^2 + 3z - 15 = 0$ **70.** $29 = 4x^2$
71. $m^2 - 2m - 9 = 0$ **72.** $15m^2 - 14m = 0$
73. $k^2 + 5k - 24 = 0$ **74.** $28 - 5k^2 = 0$
75. $1 = 2r^2 - r$ **76.** $3y - 4y^2 = 0$
77. $5r^2 - 8r + 1 = 0$ **78.** $x^2 - \frac{3}{4}x - \frac{3}{8} = 0$
79. $3x^2 - 52 = 0$ **80.** $7z = 20 - 3z^2$
81. $16z = 3z^2$ **82.** $-4x = 3 - 4x^2$
83. $2y^2 - 5y + 2 = 0$ **84.** $\frac{3}{4}m^2 = \frac{7}{8}$
85. $3k^2 - 5k + 2 = 0$ **86.** $3x^2 + 5x = -1$
87. $2x^2 + 14x + 6 = 0$ **88.** $\frac{3}{4}k^2 - \frac{1}{4}k - \frac{1}{8} = 0$
89. $\frac{1}{5}x = 3x^2$ **90.** $y^2 - 18y + 81 = 0$
91. $\frac{1}{8}x^2 = \frac{3}{5}x$ **92.** $0.3y = 0.9y^2$

93. One number is 6 larger than another number. The square of the larger number is 132 greater than the square of the smaller number. What are the numbers?

94. One number is 4 larger than another number. The sum of the squares of the two numbers is 136. What are the numbers?

95. Joe Thompson, an usher at the football stadium, was responsible for a certain number of rows of seats. In each row of seats there were 15 more seats than the number of rows Joe had. The total number of seats Joe had was 594. How many seats were there in each row?

96. Tom collected and sold stamps. He had two large sheets of United States stamps each worth $3. One sheet had 25 more stamps in it, but each stamp was worth 6 cents per stamp less than the stamps in the other sheet. How many stamps did Tom have?

97. Bill planned to cut a piece of wood 18 feet long into a certain number of short blocks. However, he changed his mind and decided to make the blocks 2 inches shorter than he had originally planned. He cut 18 blocks more than he would have cut if he had followed his original plan. How many blocks did he cut?

98. A pilot flew an airplane with the wind to a city 315 miles away and returned against the wind in a total of 4 hours. The wind was blowing at the rate of 20 miles an hour. What was the speed of the airplane in still air?

99. Two fast passenger trains make runs between two cities 300 miles apart. One train averages 20 miles an hour faster than the other train and makes the trip in $1\frac{1}{4}$ less hours. What is the average speed of each train?

Graphing a Quadratic Function

On page 199 you learned how to graph a second-degree equation in which y is a function of x. For example, to graph the function

$$y = x^2 - 2x - 8$$

you can proceed as follows:

(1) Prepare a table of corresponding values of x and y.

(2) Plot the points representing these pairs of numbers on the coordinate plane.

(3) Draw a smooth curve through the points you have plotted.

PROBLEMS

Draw a graph for each of the following quadratic functions. First prepare a table of corresponding values of x *and* y. *Then plot the points on the graph and draw a smooth curve through the points.*

1. $y = x^2 + 6x + 5$ 2. $y = x^2 + x - 20$ 3. $y = x^2 - x - 6$
4. $y = 2x^2 + 2x - 12$ 5. $y = 3x^2 - 12$ 6. $y = x^2 - 6x$

7. Draw the graph of $x^2 - x - 12$. One axis of your graph paper will be the x-axis, the other will be the $(x^2 - x - 12)$-axis.

8. The table for $y = x^2 - 2x - 8$ is given here. Check the pairs of numbers in the table by substituting in the function $y = x^2 - 2x - 8$.

x	-4	-3	-2	-1	0	$+1$	$+2$	$+3$	$+4$	$+5$	$+6$
y	$+16$	$+7$	0	-5	-8	-9	-8	-5	0	$+7$	$+16$

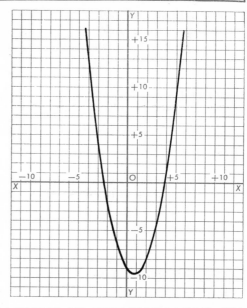

Note where the graph crosses the x-axis. It crosses at $x = -2$ and $x = +4$.

9. If you substitute $x = -2$ and $x = +4$ in $y = x^2 - 2x - 8$, what value will y have? Remember the graph crosses the x-axis at these points.

10. What value will $x^2 - 2x - 8$ have if $x = -2$ and $x = +4$?

11. What are the roots of the quadratic equation $x^2 - 2x - 8 = 0$?

12. The following table is for the function $y = x^2 + 4x + 3$. Copy and complete this table and plot the graph of $y = x^2 + 4x + 3$.

x	$+2$	$+1$	0	-1	-2	-3	-4	-5
y	?	?	?	?	?	?	?	?

13. Solve the quadratic equation $x^2 + 4x + 3 = 0$ by any method you wish. What are the roots?

14. At what points does the graph you drew in Problem 12 cross the x-axis?

15. What is the value of $x^2 + 4x + 3$ at the points where the graph crosses the x-axis?

DO YOU SEE? The coordinates of points at which the graph of the function $y = ax^2 + bx + c$ crosses the x-axis are the roots of the equation $ax^2 + bx + c = 0$.

Solving Quadratic Equations by Graphing

The fact that the x-value of the points where the graph of the function $y = ax^2 + bx + c$ crosses the x-axis are the roots of the quadratic equation $ax^2 + bx + c = 0$ can be used to find the roots of a quadratic equation. First you must draw the graph of the function. Then read the values of the roots—the abscissas of the points where the curve crosses the x-axis—from the graph. Since the method depends on reading numbers from a graph, the answers are approximate. It sometimes happens that the number you read from the graph turns out to be the exact root. However, you cannot depend on this. You must substitute the numbers you read from the graph in the equation to see if they are exact or approximate roots.

PROBLEMS

Find the roots of each of the following quadratic equations by graphing the quadratic function and reading the abscissas of the points at which the graph crosses the x-axis:

1. $x^2 - 4 = 0$
2. $x^2 + 2x - 3 = 0$
3. $x^2 - x - 20 = 0$
4. $x^2 - 9 = 0$
5. $x^2 + 5x + 4 = 0$
6. $x^2 - 8x + 12 = 0$
7. $x^2 + 4.5x - 2.5 = 0$
8. $x^2 - 4x = 0$
9. $x^2 + 6x = 0$
10. $x^2 + 12x - 5 = 0$
11. $2x^2 - x - 5 = 0$
12. $3x^2 - 8x = 0$

★ 13. $x^2 - 3.2x - 4 = 0$
14. $x^2 + 12x + 5 = 0$
15. $x^2 - \frac{19}{4}x - \frac{33}{8} = 0$
16. $x^2 + 2.5x - 11 = 0$

Use a quadratic equation to solve each of the following problems:

17. The square of a certain number exceeds five times the number by 84. Find the number.
18. The product of two consecutive numbers is 240. Find the numbers.
19. What number increased by twelve times its reciprocal equals 7?
20. The length of a rectangle is 3 inches less than twice the width. The area is 104 square inches. Find the length and the width.
21. The altitude of a triangle is a; its base is $2a + 5$. Find the base and the altitude if the area is 26 square inches.
22. The sum of a number and its reciprocal is $2\frac{4}{15}$. Find the number.
23. The sum of the areas of two squares is 117 square inches. Find the length of a side of each square if a side of the larger square is 3 inches longer than a side of the smaller square.
24. The diagonal of a rectangle is $3x - 2$, its width is x, and its length is $2x + 2$. Find the length and the width of the rectangle.
25. The volume of a rectangular solid is 80 cubic feet. The length is $2m - 1$ feet, the width is $m + 1$ feet, and the height is 4 feet. Find the length and the width of the solid.

SUMMARY OF IMPORTANT THINGS TO REMEMBER

1. *Words and Expressions*

   completing the square   quadratic equation in one variable
   general quadratic equation   quadratic formula

2. *Understandings*

   A quadratic equation has two roots. Sometimes these two roots are the same number.

   When the product of two factors is zero, one of the factors must be zero.

   Quadratic equations can be solved by several different methods.

   In a perfect-square trinomial of the form $x^2 + bx + c$, c is equal to the square of one-half of b.

   The abscissas of the points where the graph of $y = ax^2 + bx + c$ crosses the x-axis are the roots of the equation $ax^2 + bx + c = 0$.

   The two roots of the quadratic equation $ax^2 + bx + c = 0$ are

   $$x = \frac{-b + \sqrt{b^2 - 4ac}}{2a} \text{ and } x = \frac{-b - \sqrt{b^2 - 4ac}}{2a}.$$

3. *Skills*

   You should be able to:
   Identify and solve a quadratic equation using various methods.
   State from memory the quadratic formula.
   Graph a quadratic function.

QUADRATIC EQUATIONS IN ONE VARIABLE **389**

YOUR AIM 👉 **To learn how to solve quadratic equations.**

1. How can you tell if an equation is a quadratic equation by looking at it?
2. What does it mean to solve a quadratic equation?
3. Name three methods which may be used in solving quadratic equations.

Solve each of the following by completing the square:
4. $x^2 + 2x = 0$ 5. $x^2 - x = 2$

Solve each of the following by using the quadratic formula:
6. $6x^2 - x = 1$ 7. $x^2 - \frac{1}{4}x - \frac{1}{8} = 0$

Solve each of the following by the most convenient method:
8. $x^2 - 10 = 0$ 9. $2x^2 - x = 4x - x^2$ 10. $x^2 - x - 1 = 0$

YOUR AIM 👉 **To learn how to solve problems using quadratic equations.**

The time in seconds for a pendulum to make one complete swing can be found by the use of the formula $t = 2\pi\sqrt{\dfrac{L}{g}}$. In this formula L = length in feet and g = acceleration constant due to gravity.

1. Find t when $L = 2$ feet and $g = 32$.
2. Find L when $t = 1$ second and $g = 32$.

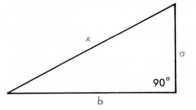

The length of legs a and b of this right triangle are consecutive even numbers.

3. If x represents the hypotenuse of this right triangle, find the expression for side a. For side b.

4. Write the equation for finding the sides of the triangle when $x = 10$.
5. Solve the equation in Problem 4 and find the length of each side.

YOUR AIM 👉 **To learn how to find approximate roots of quadratic equations by graphing.**

1. In a quadratic function such as $f(x) = x^2 - x - 2$, what is the value of $x^2 - x - 2$ at the points where the graph of the function crosses the x-axis?
2. Without graphing, tell where the graph of the function in Problem 1 crosses the x-axis.
3. Find the roots of $x^2 - 2x = 15$ by graphing.

VALUABLE SKILLS PRACTICE

1. Copy the following table and complete it as indicated:

a	b	$M = a + b$	$N = a - b$	$P = ab$	$Q = \dfrac{a}{b}$	$M + N + PQ$
-5	8	?	?	?	?	?
4	$-2\frac{1}{5}$	?	?	?	?	?
3	-1.5	?	?	?	?	?
0.6	-0.8	?	?	?	?	?
0.6	0.7	?	?	?	?	?
					CHECK:	Total $= 57.12$

2. First find the values of a, b, and c. Then find the values of p, q, r, and s to the nearest hundredth. Use the formula to check your work.

$a = 5 + 4 + 15 + 24 + 35$

$b = 6 + 7 + 16 + 27 + 36$

$c = 3 + 8 + 23 + 38 + 43$

CHECK: $p + q + r + s = 68.66$

$$p = \frac{a + b}{c}$$

$$q = \frac{b - a}{c}$$

$$r = \frac{c}{a + b}$$

$$s = \frac{ab}{c}$$

3. Copy the following table and complete it as indicated. Use the formula to check your work.

$0.6 \times 0.5 = \underline{?}$	$1.2 \div 0.25 = \underline{?}$
$0.62 \times 0.45 = \underline{?}$	$0.18 \div 0.36 = \underline{?}$
$0.3 \times 0.3 = \underline{?}$	$0.007 \div 0.005 = \underline{?}$
$0.003 \times 17 = \underline{?}$	$0.039 \div 0.03 = \underline{?}$
Total $= a$	Total $= b$
CHECK: $ab + \dfrac{a}{b} = 5.85$	

QUADRATIC EQUATIONS IN ONE VARIABLE **391**

CHAPTER TEST

Tell which of the following are quadratic equations:

1. $3x + 5 = 17$
2. $\dfrac{3}{x} = 8$
3. $5x^2 - 16 = 0$
4. $2x^3 + 4x + 7 = 0$
5. $x^2 + 4x + 3 = 0$
6. $2x + 3 = 5$
7. $(x - 7)(x + 2) = 0$
8. $3 + 6x = -8x^2$
9. $-2 = +3x - 5x^2$
10. $1 + \dfrac{4}{x} = \dfrac{5}{x}$
11. $9x^2 = -5x$
12. $3x^2 + 2x + 1 = 0$

Solve and check each of the following equations:

13. $5x^2 = 75$
14. $4x^2 - 20x = 0$
15. $x^2 - 5x + 6 = 0$
16. $3x^2 - 42 = 0$
17. $x^2 + x - 30 = 0$
18. $x^2 - 5x + 24 = 0$
19. $18 = 4x^2$
20. $-5x = 2x^2$
21. $x^2 - 1 = 0$
22. $2x^2 + 3x - 6 = 0$
23. $3x^2 - x - 1 = 0$
24. $x^2 - 5x + 3 = 0$
25. $\dfrac{5}{x} + \dfrac{2}{x+1} = 7$
26. $\dfrac{5}{x+3} - \dfrac{6}{2x} = 8$
27. $\dfrac{2}{x} + \dfrac{x}{6} = 14$

Find the roots of the following equations to the nearest hundredth:

28. $x^2 + 3x - 8 = 0$
29. $x^2 - 2x - 5 = 0$
30. $x^2 + 3x + 2 = 0$
31. $x^2 - 8x + 5 = 0$
32. $2x^2 - 6 = 0$
33. $4x^2 - 7x = 0$

Solve:

34. The length of a rectangle is 4 inches longer than the width. The area of the rectangle is 165 square inches. What are the length and the width of the rectangle.
35. One number is 8 more than another number and their product is 460. What are the two numbers?
36. The square of a number is 12 less than eight times the number. What is the number?
37. The area of a rectangle is 54 square inches. The perimeter is 30 inches. What are the length and the width of the rectangle?

CUMULATIVE REVIEW PROBLEMS

WORKING WITH ALGEBRAIC EXPRESSIONS

Factor:

1. $5ax + 5a$
2. $a^2 + ab - a$
3. $x^2 - 16$
4. $x^2 - 5x + 6$
5. $6m^2 - 5m + 1$
6. $p^2 + 7p + 10$
7. $b^3 - 4b$
8. $x^2 - 11x + 30$
9. $y^2 - 6y - 27$
10. $m^2 + 4m - 5$
11. $aM + bM$
12. $a(x - y) + b(x - y)$
13. $5 + 16k + 3k^2$
14. $x(m + n) - y(m + n)$
15. $49 - 7x - 6x^2$
16. $2x^2 - 19x - 10$
17. $6a^2 + 25a - 9$
18. $x^3 - x$
19. $m^4 - n^4$
20. $m^2n^2 - 1$

21. $p^3 - p^2 - 42p$

22. $1 + x - 72x^2$

23. $a^3 - 4a$

24. $ab - a^3b^3$

25. $9 - 6c + c^2$

26. $a^2b^2 + 2ab + 1$

27. $x^2 - 2x - 48$

28. $6xy - 3x$

29. $a^2 - 7ab - 30b^2$

30. $m^3n + m^2n - 6mn$

31. $15x^2 + 19x - 8$

32. $6x^2 - 11x + 4$

33. $\dfrac{b^2}{16} - \dfrac{c^2}{4}$

34. $a^2 - \frac{1}{4}$

35. $3n^3 - 3n$

36. $m^3 - m^5$

37. $12r^2 - 16rs + 5s^2$

38. $2a^3 - 2ab^2$

39. $\dfrac{x^4}{16} - \dfrac{1}{81}$

40. $\dfrac{a^3}{b} - \dfrac{ac^2}{b}$

41. $3ax + 5a + 5b + 3xb$

42. $12ax + 3cx + 3cy + 12ay$

43. $6ax + 2xb + 3ay + by$

44. $16rm + ns + 4rm + 4ms$

45. $15xy + 3xs + 5y^2 + ys$

46. $ax - ay + bx - by$

47. $x^3 - y^3$

48. $z^3 + 1$

49. $x^3 - 1$

50. $m^4 - n^4$

51. $27k^3 + 8m^3$

52. $x^2 - a^2 - 2ab - b^2$

53. $4(x + y + z) + 7(x + y + z) + a(x + y + z)$

54. $3a^2 + ya^2 + 3ab + yab$

55. $a^5b + 8a^2b$

WORKING WITH FRACTIONS

For each of the following pairs of fractions, find (1) the sum, (2) the difference of the first subtracted from the second, (3) the product, and (4) the quotient of the first divided by the second:

1. $\dfrac{5}{6}, \dfrac{3}{4}$

2. $\dfrac{a}{b}, \dfrac{a}{b}$

3. $\dfrac{3m}{7}, \dfrac{2m}{5}$

4. $\dfrac{1}{x}, \dfrac{1}{y}$

5. $\dfrac{2}{3a}, \dfrac{2}{5a}$

6. $\dfrac{4 + x}{x}, \dfrac{5 - x}{x}$

7. $\dfrac{a}{a + b}, \dfrac{b}{a + b}$

8. $\dfrac{a}{a - b}, \dfrac{b}{a + b}$

9. $\dfrac{1}{x^2 - 1}, \dfrac{1}{x + 1}$

10. $\dfrac{a + b}{b}, \dfrac{a - b}{a}$

Write each of the following as one fraction:

11. $\dfrac{1}{a} + \dfrac{2}{a} + \dfrac{3}{a}$

12. $\dfrac{1}{a} + \dfrac{1}{b}$

13. $\dfrac{3}{a + b} - \dfrac{2}{a + b}$

14. $\dfrac{1}{x - 2} + \dfrac{1}{2}$

15. $\dfrac{5a}{a - 1} - \dfrac{2a}{a + 1}$

16. $\dfrac{1}{x + 1} - \dfrac{1}{x - 1} + \dfrac{1}{x^2 - 1}$

QUADRATIC EQUATIONS IN ONE VARIABLE **393**

17. $\dfrac{1}{a} + \dfrac{1}{b} + \dfrac{1}{c}$

18. $\dfrac{1}{a-b} - \dfrac{1}{b-a}$

19. $\dfrac{1}{a} - \dfrac{1}{a^2} - \dfrac{1}{a^3}$

20. $\dfrac{3x}{2} - \dfrac{4x}{3} + \dfrac{5}{4}$

21. $\dfrac{x}{x^2-y^2} - \dfrac{y}{y^2-x^2}$

22. $1 + \dfrac{a}{b}$

23. $x - \dfrac{1}{x}$

24. $2x - 1 + \dfrac{x-1}{x}$

25. $x + 2 + \dfrac{4}{x-2}$

26. $\dfrac{a}{a-b} - \dfrac{b}{a+b} + 1$

WORKING WITH EXPONENTS AND RADICALS

Express each of the following in the simplest form using positive exponents only:

1. $2m \cdot 2m \cdot 2m \cdot 2m$ 2. $(\tfrac{1}{2})^3$ 3. $x^2 \cdot x \cdot x^3 \cdot x^0$
4. $c^6 \cdot c^{-4} \cdot c$ 5. $2^0 \cdot 2^{-2} \cdot 2^3$ 6. $m^m \cdot m^m \cdot m^m$
7. $x^{\frac{1}{2}} \cdot x^{-1} \cdot x^{\frac{1}{2}} \cdot x^{\frac{1}{2}}$ 8. $m^2n^3 \div mn^2$ 9. $(a^4b^6)^{\frac{1}{2}}$
10. $2^{-1} \cdot 4^{\frac{1}{2}}$ 11. $x^0 \div y^0$ 12. $25^{\frac{1}{2}}$
13. $25^{1.5}$ 14. $81^{\frac{3}{4}}$ 15. $64^{0.5}$

16. Write one hundred million as a power of 10.
17. Write one-billionth as a power of 10.

Express each of the following without the use of exponents:
18. 9×10^{10} 19. 6.5×10^6
20. 10^{-4} 21. 4.2×10^{-5}

Express each of the following without the use of the radical sign:
22. $\sqrt{x}$ 23. $\sqrt[3]{a^2}$ 24. $\sqrt{ab}$

Write each of the following using the radical sign:
25. $x^{\frac{1}{2}}$ 26. $y^{\frac{1}{4}}$ 27. $(mn)^{\frac{1}{2}}$ 28. $a^{\frac{2}{3}}$

29. If the hypotenuse of a right triangle is 25 inches and one of the legs is 20 inches, what is the length of the other leg?

Find the square root of each of the following numbers:
30. 2709   31. 6084   32. 2.56

Find the square root of each of the following numbers to the nearest hundredth:
33. 8   34. 19   35. 85   36. 218.86

37. How much is a to the a power if a represents $\tfrac{1}{2}$? Answer to the nearest hundredth.

Simplify the following radicals:
38. $\sqrt{72}$ 39. $\sqrt{300}$ 40. $\sqrt{98}$ 41. $\sqrt{75}$

394 *ALGEBRA: ITS BIG IDEAS AND BASIC SKILLS*

SOLVING EQUATIONS

Find the roots of each of the following equations:

1. $\dfrac{x}{5} - 8 = x$

2. $3x + 16 + x + 12 = 49 + x$

3. $x^2 - 47 = 3$

4. $\dfrac{x}{9} - \dfrac{1}{4} = 0$

5. $x^2 + 13x = 0$

6. $4(x - 16) - (x - 22) = 0$

7. $\dfrac{1}{x} + \dfrac{2}{x} = 1$

8. $\dfrac{8}{x} - 2 = \dfrac{4}{2x}$

9. $x^2 + 3x - 28 = 0$

10. $x^2 - 6x = 7$

11. $\dfrac{2}{3x} - \dfrac{1}{2x} = \dfrac{x}{6}$

12. $(x + 2)(x - 3) - (x - 1)^2 = 0$

13. $\dfrac{2}{x - 2} - \dfrac{3}{2 - x} = 1$

14. $x^2 - 81 = 0$

15. $28 = 2x^2$

16. $x^2 - 7x = 44$

17. $\dfrac{x}{6} - \dfrac{1}{2} = \dfrac{x}{3}$

18. $8x - 40 - 17x = 16x - 40$

19. $2(x - 5) - 3(2x - 8) = 2$

20. $\dfrac{x + 4}{3} + \dfrac{x - 3}{2} = 0$

21. $\dfrac{1}{x} - x = 0$

22. $9(x - 2) - 3(x - 8) = 0$

23. $\dfrac{2}{9} - \dfrac{1}{x} = \dfrac{1}{3}$

24. $\dfrac{x}{b} - a = 0$

25. $\dfrac{ax}{b} - b = 0$

26. $ax + bx = a^2 + b^2$

Find the roots of each of the following systems of equations:

27. $2x - 5y = 14$
    $4x - 3y = 0$

28. $x = y + 1$
    $2x = y - 5$

29. $x - 3y = 8$
    $4x - 3y = 8$

30. $x = 2y - 3$
    $x - 3y = -7$

31. $x + y = b$
    $x - y = 7b$

32. $6x + y = 8$
    $3x + 4y = 4$

33. $x - y = 6$
    $9x - y = -10$

34. $x = 3y + 5$
    $2x - 5y = 13$

35. $\dfrac{x}{3} = 2y + 12$

    $\dfrac{x}{4} = y + 7\tfrac{1}{4}$

36. $\dfrac{2x}{5} + \dfrac{y}{4} = 2$

    $\dfrac{3x}{5} - \dfrac{y}{2} = 10$

37. $\dfrac{3x}{2} + y = \dfrac{7}{2}$

    $5x + y = 21$

38. $bx + cy = a$

    $dx + ey = f$

QUADRATIC EQUATIONS IN ONE VARIABLE **395**

Solve each of the following problems:

1. The sum of two numbers is 70. The larger number is 7 less than twice the smaller number. Find the numbers.
2. What number increased by its reciprocal equals 2?
3. A man has $2 in nickels and dimes. How many coins of each kind has he if he has 4 more nickels than dimes?
4. Express P and Q in terms of a and b if the sum of P and Q is a and the difference of Q subtracted from P is b.
5. Find the length and the width of a rectangle if its perimeter is 46 inches and its area is 120 square inches.
6. A real-estate dealer sold a house for $9600, which was 20 per cent less than the cost. What was the cost?
7. In $c^2 = a^2 + b^2$, c is 9 more than b and a is 7 more than b. Find a, b, and c.
8. Jack can mow a lawn in $1\frac{1}{2}$ hours, while Bill needs 2 hours to do the job. How long, to the nearest minute, will it take the boys to do the job if they work together?
9. One of the Air Force's medium bombers on a test flight traveled 1080 miles in 2 hours' flying time with the wind and made the return flight in $2\frac{1}{2}$ hours' flying time. Find the air speed of the plane and the velocity of the wind for this flight.
10. The formula for the distance s that a freely falling body will travel in t seconds is $s = \frac{1}{2}gt^2$. How long will it take for a body to fall 900 feet? g is a constant due to the pull of gravity and equals approximately 32.
11. The radiator of a car is filled with a mixture of water and antifreeze that is 20% antifreeze. What part of this mixture must be drawn off and replaced with antifreeze so that the resultant mixture will be 50% antifreeze?
12. How many pounds of water must be evaporated from p pounds of $c\%$ salt solution if the resulting solution is to be $k\%$?
13. $ABCD$ at the right is a square. If the side of the square is 6 inches, find the radius of the circle to the nearest hundredth of an inch.

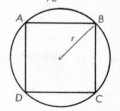

14. One number is $\frac{3}{4}$ of another number. The product of the numbers increased by their sum is 335. Find the numbers.
15. A sports dealer sells tennis balls at m dollars per can. To fill a $12 order, he needed 3 more cans of the particular kind asked for. How many of these cans did he have in stock?
16. Draw a square and label its vertices A, B, C, and D. Mark side AB as s. What is the area of the square? Its perimeter? What is the area and the perimeter of a square in which each side is $s + 5$?

BIG IDEA | FUNCTION

BASIC SKILLS | Using and interpreting symbols of algebra
Solving equations
Solving verbal problems
Drawing and reading graphs

CHAPTER **14** *Indirect Measurement*

YOU CAN measure directly your height or the width of a room with a yardstick. You can use a tape measure to mark off a number of yards for a foot race. But you cannot use either of these measuring devices to find the distance to the moon or the length of a projected tunnel through a mountain. To find lengths like these, you need to know a method of measuring indirectly.

In this chapter you will learn how to use relationships between the sides and the angles of a triangle to make indirect measurements.

YOUR AIM 👉 **1.** To learn some basic facts about angles and triangles.

2. To learn three important ratios between the sides of a right triangle.

3. To learn why the three ratios are functions of the size of an acute angle in a right triangle.

4. To learn how measurements may be made by use of the three trigonometric ratios.

397

Importance of Indirect Measurement

Many scientific and industrial developments depend upon indirect measurements. For example, the weight and the size of small particles of matter like atoms or electrons and protons, which make up the atoms, can be measured only indirectly. No one has ever seen these particles, yet their size and weights have been measured accurately— as accurately as you can measure your height with a yardstick.

The kind of indirect measurement you will study in this chapter depends on a part of mathematics called trigonometry. The word "trigonometry" means "measuring by triangles." It is an important part of mathematics because its use is not limited to triangles but is far-reaching in its applications. The following are a few examples of the uses of trigonometry:

(1) Astronomers measure the distance from the earth to heavenly bodies like the sun, moon, and planets.

(2) Surveyors determine distances, measure heights, and establish boundaries.

(3) Engineers collect data for building bridges and digging tunnels.

(4) Electrical engineers use trigonometry in working with alternating currents in electricity.

Angles

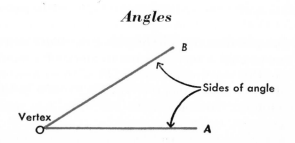

In your previous study of mathematics you no doubt learned that an angle is a figure formed by two lines drawn from a point. The figure above is an **angle.** The lines OA and OB are called the "sides" of the angle. The point O, where the sides meet, is called the "vertex" of the angle.

To read, say, "Angle E or angle DEF."

398 *ALGEBRA: ITS BIG IDEAS AND BASIC SKILLS*

Now to understand how an angle is made, place your pencil length-wise on line OA in the drawing shown below. Keep one end of the pencil at point O and rotate the pencil toward line OB. When the pencil coincides with the line OB, you have rotated the pencil through the angle AOB. The direction of the pencil has changed. Continue rotating your pencil to line OC. You have now rotated the pencil through angle AOC. Has the direction in which the pencil is pointing changed?

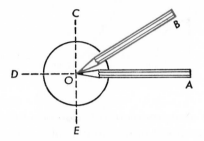

Now continue rotating the pencil about point O to line OD and to line OE. You have rotated the pencil through angles AOD and AOE respectively. Has the direction in which the pencil is pointing changed?

The size of an angle is determined by the amount of turning of one side about the vertex to make it coincide with the other side. The larger the amount of turning, the larger the angle is. The length of the sides of an angle has nothing to do with the size of the angle.

The unit of measure of an angle is a **degree**. A degree is $\frac{1}{360}$ of a complete rotation of a line about a point. When you rotated your pencil about point O, through how many degrees did your pencil sweep in making the complete rotation? Through how many degrees did the direction of your pencil change in rotating from point A to C? From A to D? From A to E?

The symbol for a degree is a small circle written to the right of a number and slightly above it.

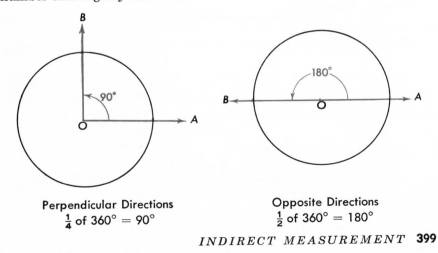

Perpendicular Directions
$\frac{1}{4}$ of $360° = 90°$

Opposite Directions
$\frac{1}{2}$ of $360° = 180°$

INDIRECT MEASUREMENT **399**

An angle is said to be *acute, right, obtuse,* or *straight* depending upon the amount of rotation. When the rotation is:

Less than 90°, the angle is an *acute angle.*
Equal to 90°, the angle is a *right angle.*
Greater than 90° but less than 180°, the angle is an *obtuse angle.*
Equal to 180°, the angle is a *straight angle.*

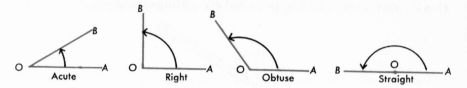

PROBLEMS

1. If there are 360° in a complete rotation of a line about a point, how many degrees are there in one-fourth of a rotation?
2. If the angle between two lines is 90°, the lines are said to be perpendicular. How much turning would be required to make one of two perpendicular lines coincide with the other?
3. The angle formed by one-fourth of a complete rotation of a line about a point is called a "right angle." How many degrees are in a right angle?
4. If line OA in the drawing on the right is rotated about point O so that it moves to the position OB, through how many degrees has OA been rotated?
5. If you walked south and then turned and walked east, through what size angle would you turn?
6. An airplane pilot is flying west. He makes a turn and flies north. Through what size angle does he turn?
7. In Problem 6 in what direction is the airplane pilot flying after he makes a 180° turn?

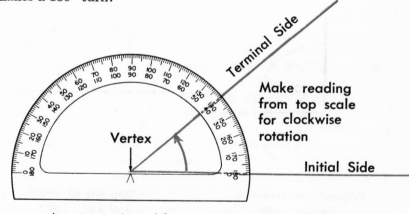

A protractor is used for measuring angles on paper.

400 *ALGEBRA: ITS BIG IDEAS AND BASIC SKILLS*

1. How many degrees are in a straight angle?
2. Define an acute angle.
3. Define an obtuse angle.
4. How many degrees are in $\frac{1}{6}$ of a complete rotation?
5. An angle of 45° is what fraction of a complete rotation?

Triangles

A **triangle** is a figure formed by three intersecting straight line segments. The line segments are called the "sides" of the triangle. The points of intersection of the sides are called the "vertices" of the triangle.

A triangle which contains a right angle, 90°, is called a "right triangle."

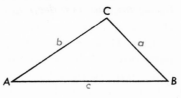

Capital letters are used to label the vertices of a triangle, as A, B, and C. The sides may be called "side AB" or "side c," "side AC" or "side b," and "side BC" or "side a." Notice that if a small letter is used to label a side, it corresponds to the opposite angle: side c is opposite angle C, side b is opposite angle B, and side a is opposite angle A.

The angles may be called angle A, angle B, and angle C and may be written $\angle A$, $\angle B$, $\angle C$. Angles may be identified by three letters, as $\angle BAC$ for $\angle A$, and $\angle ABC$ for $\angle B$. When three letters are used, the middle letter always names the vertex.

The sum of the angles of a triangle is 180°.

PROBLEMS

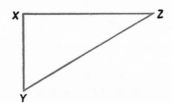

1. Name the three angles in triangle ABC shown above using one letter for each angle. Using three letters for each angle.
2. Which angle in triangle XYZ on the right appears to be a right angle?
3. Two angles in a triangle are 32° and 90°. What is the size of the third angle?
4. Is it possible for a triangle to have two right angles? Why?
5. In a triangle one angle is three times a second angle. The third angle is equal to the sum of the other two angles. Find the size of each angle.

Ratios

If one line segment is 3 inches long and another line segment is 4 inches long, the ratio of the first line segment to the second is $\frac{3}{4}$. The ratio of two numbers represented by a and b is $\frac{a}{b}$. The ratio $\frac{3}{4}$ may also be written as $3 \div 4$. Every ratio can be written as a decimal.

FOR EXAMPLE: $\dfrac{3}{4} = 0.75$ $\qquad \dfrac{15}{8.2} = 1.83$ $\qquad \dfrac{2}{11.2} = 0.179$

PROBLEMS

In each of the following drawings, count the number of units in the segments a and b. Then express the ratio of the length of a to the length of b as a fraction and as a decimal:

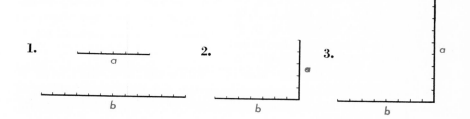

1.   2.   3.

Express the ratio of a to c as a fraction and as a decimal:

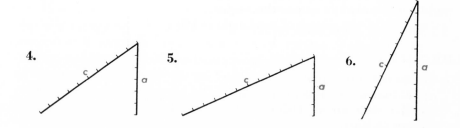

4.   5.   6.

Express the ratio of b to c as a fraction and as a decimal:

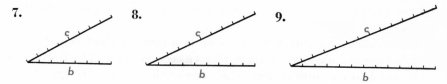

7.   8.   9.

402 *ALGEBRA: ITS BIG IDEAS AND BASIC SKILLS*

Study the following diagram and find the value of each ratio given below.

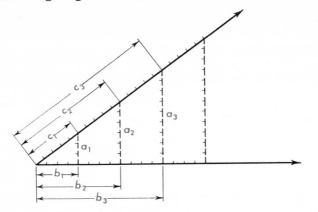

10. $\dfrac{a_1}{b_1} = \underline{\ ?\ }$ 11. $\dfrac{a_2}{b_2} = \underline{\ ?\ }$ 12. $\dfrac{a_3}{b_3} = \underline{\ ?\ }$

13. $\dfrac{a_1}{c_1} = \underline{\ ?\ }$ 14. $\dfrac{a_2}{c_2} = \underline{\ ?\ }$ 15. $\dfrac{a_3}{c_3} = \underline{\ ?\ }$

16. $\dfrac{b_1}{c_1} = \underline{\ ?\ }$ 17. $\dfrac{b_2}{c_2} = \underline{\ ?\ }$ 18. $\dfrac{b_3}{c_3} = \underline{\ ?\ }$

19. Compare the values of the three ratios in Problems 10–12. What did you discover?
20. Compare the values of the three ratios in Problems 13–15. What did you discover?
21. Compare the values of the three ratios in Problems 16–18. What did you discover?

Two intersecting lines are perpendicular when they intersect at right angles.

22. Draw an acute angle of any size. Locate two points on one side of the angle you drew. From these two points draw lines perpendicular to the other side. Now measure the length of the perpendiculars and the segments cut off on the other side. Compare the lengths by dividing the length of the perpendicular by the length of the segment cut off on the other side. Do the same for both pairs of lines.
23. Make some more perpendiculars to the side of the angle as you did in Problem 22. Compare again by division. What do you discover?

DO YOU SEE?  **If perpendiculars are drawn from any two points on one side of an angle to the other side, the ratio of the perpendicular to the line segment cut off on the other side is constant.**

INDIRECT MEASUREMENT **403**

24. Draw an angle of 45° on your paper. Find the ratio of the length of a perpendicular line to the length of the line cut off on the other side of the angle.

25. Do the same for an angle of 60°. If you do not have a protractor, you can draw an angle of 60° by drawing a triangle with all sides equal. Each of the angles of this triangle is an angle of 60°.

26. How does the ratio you computed for 60° compare with the ratio you computed for 45°?

In this drawing, angle A is 40°. Perpendiculars have been drawn from points 1, 2, 3, 4, and 5 on side AC of angle A to side AB. Call the perpendiculars a_1, a_2, a_3, and so on, and their corresponding bases b_1, b_2, b_3, and so on.

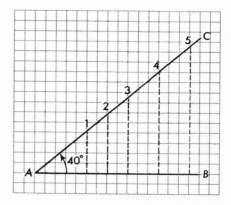

Count the number of divisions and compute the ratios in the following problems to the nearest tenth:

NOTE: In Problem 31, a_n may be any perpendicular from any point along AC that you choose, except the points 1, 2, 3, 4, and 5. The first ratio is worked out for you.

$$\frac{a_1}{b_1} = \frac{4.2}{5.0} = 0.84$$

27. $\dfrac{a_2}{b_2}$ 28. $\dfrac{a_3}{b_3}$ 29. $\dfrac{a_4}{b_4}$ 30. $\dfrac{a_5}{b_5}$ 31. $\dfrac{a_n}{b_n}$

32. Compare the values of the ratios for Problems 27–31. What did you discover?

33. On graph paper draw angles, such as 30°, 50°, and 60°. In each angle draw five perpendiculars from one side to the other and compute the ratios, to the nearest tenth, of the perpendiculars to their corresponding bases, as you did in Problems 27–31.

DO YOU SEE? The ratio of the length of a perpendicular drawn from one side of an angle to the length of the line segment cut off on the other side varies with the size of the angle.

404 *ALGEBRA: ITS BIG IDEAS AND BASIC SKILLS*

The Tangent Ratio

From one side of an angle like angle A shown below, you can draw a perpendicular, BC, to the other side of the angle. This gives you a right triangle ACB. The right angle is angle C.

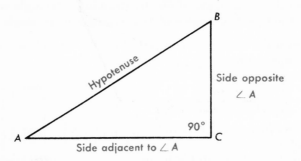

Side AB, which is one of the sides of angle A and is opposite the right angle, is called the "hypotenuse." Side AC, which forms the other side of angle A, is called the **adjacent side.** "Adjacent" means "next to." The remaining side is called the **opposite side.**

The ratio of the length of the side opposite an acute angle in a right triangle to the length of the side adjacent to the angle is called the **tangent of the angle.**

$$\text{tangent } A = \frac{\text{opposite side}}{\text{adjacent side}} = \frac{BC}{AC}$$

Different size angles have different tangent ratios. The table below shows the tangent ratios of several angles.

Angle	Tangent	Angle	Tangent
0°	0.00	45°	1.00
5°	0.09	50°	1.19
10°	0.18	55°	1.43
15°	0.27	60°	1.73
20°	0.36	65°	2.14
25°	0.47	70°	2.75
30°	0.58	75°	3.73
35°	0.70	80°	5.67
40°	0.84	85°	11.43

Engineers use tables like this one to solve quickly problems involving indirect measurement.

INDIRECT MEASUREMENT **405**

Example for Study

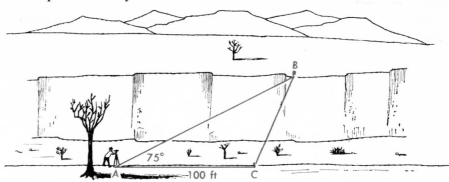

What is the distance BC across the canyon pictured above?

NOTE: In solving this problem an engineer would use an instrument for measuring angles called a **transit.** Study the labeled drawing of a transit at the right.

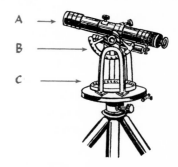

A is a telescope for sighting. **B** is a vertical protractor for measuring angles in a vertical plane. **C** is a horizontal protractor for measuring angles in a horizontal plane.

SOLUTION: To find the distance BC across the canyon, you would first set up a transit at point C to establish a sight line to the tree on the opposite side of the canyon. Then you would rotate the telescope on the transit 90° to get the direction of the base line AC. Next you would use a steel tape and stake out point A 100 feet from C, or some other distance you might decide. Finally, you would set up the transit at point A and find the angle between AB and AC, which is 75°.

The solution to the problem is now very simple:

$$\text{tangent } A = \frac{BC}{AC}$$

Let x = length of BC in feet

$$\text{tangent } 75° = \frac{x}{100}$$

Look up the value of tangent 75° in the table on page 405.

$$\text{tangent } 75° = 3.73$$

$$3.73 = \frac{x}{100}$$

$$x = 373 \text{ feet}$$

406 *ALGEBRA: ITS BIG IDEAS AND BASIC SKILLS*

PROBLEMS

Using the table of tangents on page 405, find the value of **x** *in the following right triangles:*

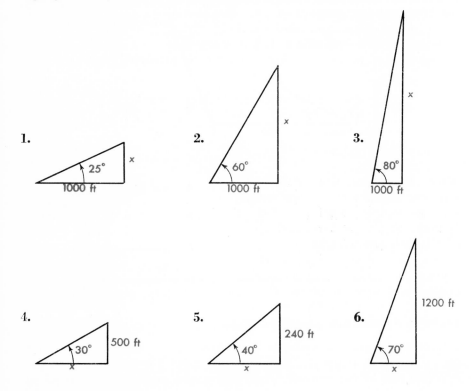

1. 25° 1000 ft x

2. 60° 1000 ft x

3. 80° 1000 ft x

4. 30° 500 ft x

5. 40° 240 ft x

6. 70° 1200 ft x

Find the height of the objects in the following:

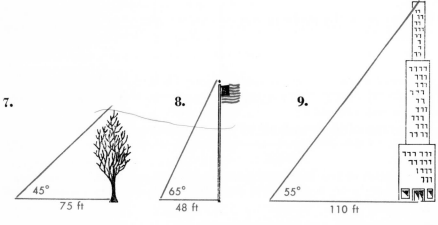

7. 45° 75 ft

8. 65° 48 ft

9. 55° 110 ft

Sine and Cosine Ratios

In this triangle it is easy enough to find side a if you have a table of tangent ratios available to give you the tangent of 20°. But if you wish to find side c, you need a ratio involving side b, 300 feet, and side c. If you know side a and wish to find c, then you need a ratio involving a and c.

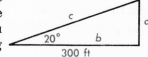

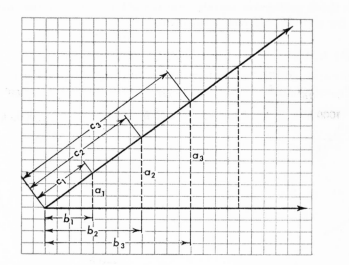

$$\frac{a_1}{b_1} = \frac{3}{4} \qquad \frac{a_2}{b_2} = \frac{6}{8} = \frac{3}{4} \qquad \frac{a_3}{b_3} = \frac{9}{12} = \frac{3}{4}$$

$$\frac{a_1}{c_1} = \frac{3}{5} \qquad \frac{a_2}{c_2} = \frac{6}{10} = \frac{3}{5} \qquad \frac{a_3}{c_3} = \frac{9}{15} = \frac{3}{5}$$

$$\frac{b_1}{c_1} = \frac{4}{5} \qquad \frac{b_2}{c_2} = \frac{8}{10} = \frac{4}{5} \qquad \frac{b_3}{c_3} = \frac{12}{15} = \frac{4}{5}$$

Study the above diagram. Notice that not only is the ratio $\frac{a}{b}$ constant for the various perpendiculars, but the ratios $\frac{a}{c}$ and $\frac{b}{c}$ are also constant for the different perpendiculars. These three ratios include all the sides of a right triangle and, hence, are the three important ratios used in trigonometry.

The ratio of the length of the side opposite an acute angle of a right triangle to the length of the hypotenuse is called the **sine of the angle.**

The ratio of the length of the side adjacent to an acute angle of a right triangle to the length of the hypotenuse is called the **cosine of the angle.**

408 *ALGEBRA: ITS BIG IDEAS AND BASIC SKILLS*

$$\text{sine } A = \frac{\text{opposite side}}{\text{hypotenuse}} = \frac{BC}{AB}$$

$$\text{cosine } A = \frac{\text{adjacent side}}{\text{hypotenuse}} = \frac{AC}{AB}$$

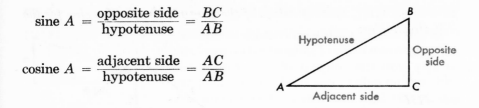

The three ratios are usually abbreviated as tan A for tangent A, sin A for sine A, and cos A for cosine A.

PROBLEMS

Read the sine, cosine, and tangent ratios for angles D, E, F, G, *and* H *in the following figures:*

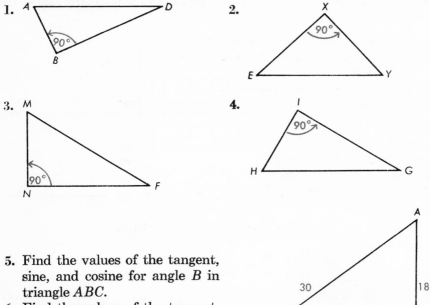

1.

2.

3.

4.

5. Find the values of the tangent, sine, and cosine for angle B in triangle ABC.
6. Find the values of the tangent, sine, and cosine for angle A in triangle ABC.

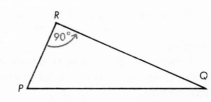

7. What are the tangent, the sine, and the cosine for angle Q in triangle PQR?
8. What are the tangent, the sine, and the cosine for angle P in triangle PQR?

INDIRECT MEASUREMENT **409**

In triangle GHI, *find the values of the tangent, sine, and cosine for the following angles:*

9. *IGJ*

10. *GIJ*

11. *JIH*

12. *JHI*

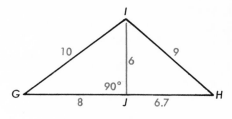

SELF TEST

1. What does the word "trigonometry" mean?
2. How many degrees are there in a right angle?
3. If one acute angle of a right triangle is 58°, what is the size of the other acute angle?

4. Define the tangent of an acute angle.
5. Write the ratio equal to sin N in triangle MNO.
6. Write the ratio equal to cos O in triangle MNO.

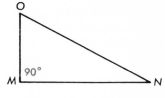

In the triangle XYZ *find:*
7. tan Y 8. sin X
9. cos Y 10. sin Y

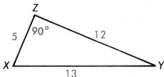

Trigonometric Functions

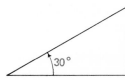

tan 30° = 0.577
sin 30° = 0.500
cos 30° = 0.866

J. P. Doe
Every person has his own characteristic fingerprints.

Every angle has its own "fingerprints," that is, its own characteristic ratios.

Since every angle has its own ratios, tables of trigonometric ratios for angles between 0° and 90° have been developed. These tables make problems in indirect measurement very simple—problems that would otherwise be difficult if not impossible to solve.

On page 425 there is a table giving the values of the **trigonometric ratios** for various angles.

410 *ALGEBRA: ITS BIG IDEAS AND BASIC SKILLS*

PROBLEMS

Use the table of trigonometric ratios to find the following:

1. $\sin 72°$
2. $\sin 18°$
3. $\sin 36°$
4. $\sin 65°$
5. $\tan 21°$
6. $\tan 34°$
7. $\tan 45°$
8. $\tan 80°$
9. $\cos 6°$
10. $\cos 58°$
11. $\cos 42°$
12. $\cos 77°$

13. As an angle increases from $0°$ to $90°$, does the tangent increase or decrease?
14. As an angle increases from $0°$ to $89°$, what change takes place in the sine?
15. How does the cosine change as an angle increases?
16. Do the values of the trigonometric ratios depend on the size of an angle? Explain.

DO YOU SEE? Sine A, cosine A, and tangent A are functions of angle A.

Since the values of the trigonometric ratios—sine, cosine, and tangent—depend on the size of an angle, they are called **trigonometric functions**.

Solving Right Triangles

By using trigonometric tables you can solve many problems concerning triangles.

Example for Study

In the right triangle ABC, $\angle A = 66°$ and $c = 84$ feet. Find a and b.

SOLUTION: Since you know the value of c, to find a you must use a ratio involving a and c.

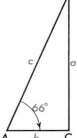

Hence:
$$\sin 66° = \frac{a}{c}$$

Find the value of $\sin 66°$ in the table on page 425:
$$\sin 66° = 0.914$$

$$0.914 = \frac{a}{84}$$

$$a = 77 \text{ feet approximately}$$

To find b:
$$\cos 66° = \frac{b}{c}$$

$$0.407 = \frac{b}{84}$$

$$b = 34 \text{ feet approximately}$$

INDIRECT MEASUREMENT **411**

PROBLEMS

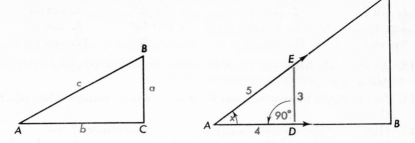

Find the indicated parts of the following right triangles. Use triangle ABC at the left above for reference.

1. If $\angle A = 34°$, $c = 24$ feet, find a and b.

2. If $\angle A = 52°$, $c = 112$ yards, find a and b.

3. If $\angle A = 30°$, $a = 29.6$ feet, find b and c.

4. If $\angle A = 85°$, $a = 100$ feet, find b and c.

5. If $\angle A = 45°$, $b = 200$ yards, find a and c.

6. If $\angle B = 30°$, $b = 250$ yards, find a and c.

7. If $\angle A = 42°$, $c = 32$ feet, find a and b.

8. If $\angle A = 48°$, $a = 48$ feet, find b and c.

9. If $\angle A = 60°$, $b = 100$ yards, find a and c.

★ 10. Find the length of AB in the right-hand figure above if BC is 120 yards.

11. Find the area of triangle *MNP*.

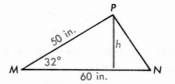

12. Find the height of the chimney *FG* above the building.

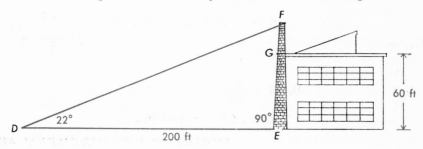

412 *ALGEBRA: ITS BIG IDEAS AND BASIC SKILLS*

Angles of Elevation and Depression

The terms **angle of elevation** and **angle of depression** are used by engineers and surveyors. They are angles between the line of sight of an object and the horizontal line.

If the telescope in a transit has been elevated in sighting an object, like angle 1 in this drawing, then the angle between the line of sight and the horizontal is the *angle of elevation.*

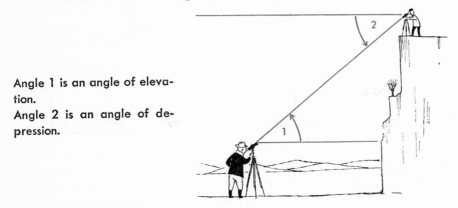

Angle 1 is an angle of elevation.
Angle 2 is an angle of depression.

If the telescope has been depressed in sighting an object, like angle 2 in this drawing, then the angle between the line of sight and the horizontal is the *angle of depression.*

PROBLEMS

In solving each of the following problems, first make a diagram and label the known and the unknown parts. Then decide what trigonometric ratio to use in finding the unknown parts.

1. A 25-foot ladder is placed against the side of a building. If it makes an angle of 72° with the ground, at what height does it touch the building?
2. The angle of elevation of a mountain peak is 10°. If the mountain is about 20 miles from the observer, what is the approximate height of the mountain above the level of the observer?
3. A lighthouse is 185 feet high. If its angle of elevation as observed from a ship is 11°, find the distance between the ship and the lighthouse.
4. An observer in an airplane at a height of 10,000 feet over the ocean reads the angle of depression of a distant coastline to be 9°. A ship is directly under the plane when the reading is made. How far is the ship from the coast?
5. The diagonal of a rectangle makes an angle of 39° with one of its longer sides. Find the width of the rectangle if its length is 20 inches.
6. Find the diagonal of a square if one of its sides is 70 inches.

7. A kite string is 250 feet long. Find the height of the kite if the string makes an angle of 48° with the ground.

8. Use cos A to find the base of the triangle at the right.

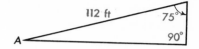

★ 9. In triangle MNP below, find the ratio of the altitude x to side MN. Find the length of MN.

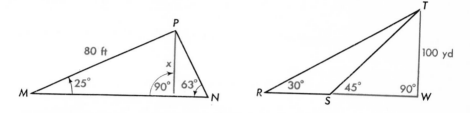

10. Find the lengths of the three sides of triangle RST.
11. Select a tall tree, chimney, or steeple and plan how to find its height by using trigonometry. Make the necessary measurements with your measuring instruments (see pages 426–427) and find the height of the object you selected.
12. Select a tree on the side of a street opposite the side you are on. Pretend the street is a river which will prevent you from measuring from the base of the tree. Plan how to find the height of the tree and then find it.
13. Select a tall house, church, or building and plan how to find the distance from a second-story window to the roof. Then take the necessary measurements and find the height.
14. Describe the plan which you would use in measuring the distance from the ground to the highest point in the house or apartment building in which you live. After your plans are carefully made, take the necessary measurements and find the distance.

SELF TEST

Find each of the following to three decimal places:
1. $\sin 21°$
2. $\cos 80°$
3. $\tan 45°$
4. $\sin 30°$
5. $\cos 60°$
6. $\tan 89°$

Solve for x:

7. $\tan 30° = \dfrac{x}{500}$
8. $\dfrac{325}{x} = \cos 60°$
9. $\sin 45° = \dfrac{0.013}{x}$

10. How high is an airplane that is 15 miles away from an airport if the angle of elevation of the plane sighted from the airport is 5°?

414 *ALGEBRA: ITS BIG IDEAS AND BASIC SKILLS*

★ The Tangent as a Function of the Sine and Cosine

There is a relationship between the three trigonometric functions you have studied. You will discover this relationship by doing the following problems.

PROBLEMS

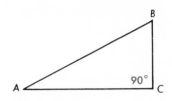

In right triangle ABC *at the right:*
1. Find sin A and cos A.
2. Divide the value of sin A by the value of cos A.
3. Find tan A.
4. Compare your answers to Problems 2 and 3. What did you discover?
5. Find sin B and cos B.
6. Divide the value of sin B by the value of cos B.
7. Find tan B.
8. Compare your answers to Problems 6 and 7. What did you discover?

DO YOU SEE? ☞ **If A is any acute angle, tan A $= \dfrac{\sin A}{\cos A}$.**

9. Using the values of the trigonometric functions for several angles (page 425) show that tan $A = \dfrac{\sin A}{\cos A}$.

10. Explain why the tangent of an angle is a function of the sine and the cosine of the angle.

SUMMARY OF IMPORTANT THINGS TO REMEMBER

1. Words and Expressions

adjacent side	sine of an angle
angle	tangent of an angle
angle of depression	transit
angle of elevation	triangle
cosine of an angle	trigonometric functions
degree	trigonometric ratios
opposite side	trigonometric tables

2. Understandings

If perpendiculars are drawn from any two points on one side of an angle to the other side, the ratio of the perpendicular to the line segment cut off on the other side is constant.

The ratio of the length of a perpendicular drawn from one side of an angle to the length of the line segment cut off on the other side varies with the size of the angle.

The values of the sine, cosine, and tangent of an acute angle are given in a table of trigonometric ratios.

Since the values of the sine, cosine, and tangent of an angle depend on the size of the angle, the sine, cosine, and tangent are functions of the angle.

Trigonometric functions can be used to find measurements indirectly.

3. Skills
You should be able to:

Write the sine, cosine, and tangent ratios of an angle of a right triangle in terms of the sides of the triangle.

Find the value of trigonometric functions of an angle from a table of trigonometric ratios.

Use trigonometric functions in solving a right triangle.

Use trigonometric functions to find measurements indirectly.

PROBLEMS ON YOUR AIMS

YOUR AIM **To learn some basic facts about angles and triangles.**

Read each statement, decide if it is true or false, and explain why:
1. The size of an angle is determined by the length of its sides.
2. A triangle may have two angles that are right angles, but it cannot have three right angles.
3. In triangle ABC at the right, angle 1 may be read as angle B or as angle ACB.
4. In triangle ABC at the right, $\angle A + \angle B = 180°$.

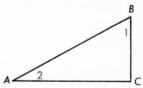

5. If angle 2 in triangle ABC measures 40°, then angle 1 measures 60°.

YOUR AIM 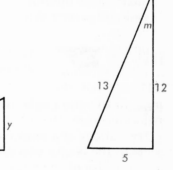 **To learn three important ratios between the sides of a right angle.**

416 *ALGEBRA: ITS BIG IDEAS AND BASIC SKILLS*

Use the three drawings at the bottom of page 416 to complete the statements in Problems 1–9:

1. $\tan A$ = _?_
2. $\tan B$ = _?_
3. $\tan m$ = _?_
4. $\sin A$ = _?_
5. $\sin B$ = _?_
6. $\sin m$ = _?_
7. $\cos A$ = _?_
8. $\cos B$ = _?_
9. $\cos m$ = _?_

10. Draw any right triangle DEF, with E the vertex of the right angle. Write the sine, tangent, and cosine ratios of angle D in terms of the sides of triangle DEF.

YOUR AIM  **To learn why the three ratios are functions of the size of an acute angle in a right triangle.**

In the figure at the right the numbers 1, 2, and 3 show the position of the rotating side OB of angle x. Note that angle x increases in size as OB rises.

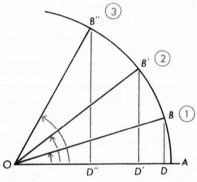

1. Which angle—AOB, AOB', or AOB''—represents angle x when OB is in position 1? Position 2? Position 3?
2. Which side is opposite angle x when OB is in position 1? Position 2? Position 3?
3. In Problem 2, are the sides opposite angle x increasing or decreasing in length as angle x increases?
4. Which side is adjacent to angle x when OB is in position 1? Position 2? Position 3?
5. In Problem 4, are these adjacent sides increasing or decreasing in length as angle x increases?
6. Since the tangent ratio of an angle is $\dfrac{\text{opposite side}}{\text{adjacent side}}$, is tangent x an increasing or decreasing function as OB rotates?
7. Examine the table of trigonometric ratios on page 425. Do the tangent ratios increase or decrease as the size of the angle increases from 0° to 90°? What is true of the sine ratios? Cosine ratios?

YOUR AIM 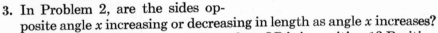 **To learn how measurements may be made indirectly by the use of the three trigonometric ratios.**

Explain how you would use trigonometric ratios to measure the following. Use diagrams.

1. The width of a river.
2. The height of a tree or tall building.

VALUABLE SKILLS PRACTICE

1. Copy the following table and do the necessary operations to complete the table. Check your work using the total given at the bottom of the table.

a	b	$\dfrac{a}{b} = x^*$	$ab = y$	$x + y^*$	$\dfrac{1}{x + y}$ †
$\frac{1}{4}$	$\frac{2}{3}$	?	?	?	?
$\frac{1}{5}$	$\frac{8}{15}$	?	?	?	?
1	$\frac{2}{9}$	?	?	?	?
$\frac{3}{6}$	$\frac{1}{4}$	?	?	?	?
0.1	0.45	?	?	?	?
1.2	0.45	?	?	?	?
					Total 8.66

* Express as fractions or mixed numbers.
† Express as decimals to the nearest hundredth.

Write each of the following numbers without the use of exponents:

2. $(\frac{1}{2})^2$
3. $(\frac{3}{2})^2$
4. 4^3
5. $(0.1)^2$
6. $(0.1)^3$
7. $(\frac{1}{5})^2$
8. $(\frac{1}{3})^2$
9. $(\frac{3}{2})^3$
10. $(\frac{1}{3})^3$
11. $(0.2)^4$
12. $(0.02)^2$
13. $(0.3)^3$
14. $(0.1)^4$
15. $(0.07)^3$
16. $(-0.1)^4$

Write the following using exponents. Simplify wherever possible.

17. $\sqrt[3]{27}$
18. $\sqrt{\frac{1}{4}}$
19. $\sqrt[3]{\frac{1}{64}}$
20. $\sqrt{144}$
21. $\sqrt{\frac{9}{25}}$
22. $\sqrt[3]{\frac{1}{8}}$
23. $\sqrt{121}$
24. $\sqrt{169}$
25. $\sqrt{0.36}$
26. $\sqrt{225}$
27. $\sqrt[3]{0.008}$
28. $\sqrt[5]{0.03}$

Find each of the following to the nearest hundredth. Use the table of squares and square roots on page 424.

29. $\sqrt{5}$
30. $\sqrt{8}$
31. $\sqrt{3}$
32. $\sqrt{2}$
33. $\sqrt{27}$
34. $\sqrt{50}$
35. $\sqrt{112}$
36. $\sqrt{148}$
37. $\sqrt{80}$
38. $\sqrt{90}$
39. $\sqrt{72}$
40. $\sqrt{30}$

Find each of the following to the nearest whole number. Use the table of squares and square roots on page 424.

41. $(1.732)^2$
42. $(1.414)^2$
43. $(2.236)^2$
44. $(4.472)^2$
45. $(3.464)^2$
46. $(9.798)^2$
47. $(9.950)^2$
48. $(5.099)^2$

418 *ALGEBRA: ITS BIG IDEAS AND BASIC SKILLS*

Write the following ratios in fractional form and reduce to lowest terms:

49. 24 to 48   **50.** 16 to 36   **51.** 21 to 49

52. 12 to 42   **53.** $9\frac{1}{2}:12\frac{1}{2}$ **54.** $5\frac{1}{4}:3\frac{1}{4}$

55. 3π to 4π **56.** π to 2π **57.** 3 ft to 4 yd

58. 1 yd to 1 ft   **59.** 3 qt to 3 gal   **60.** 4 mo to 2 yr

Measure the lines shown at the right with whatever measuring tools you have. Write your measurements on a piece of paper, then find the following ratios:

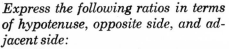

61. a to b **62.** c to d **63.** d to b

64. a to c **65.** a to $a+b$ **66.** c to $c+d$

CHAPTER TEST

Express the following ratios in terms of hypotenuse, opposite side, and adjacent side:

  1. $\sin x$ **2.** $\cos x$ **3.** $\tan x$

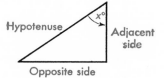

Express the following ratios in terms of the sides represented in the figures at the right:

  4. $\tan x$

  5. $\cos x$

  6. $\sin y$

  7. $\cos y$

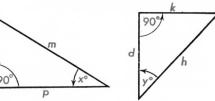

Find the following to three decimal places:

  8. tangent A

  9. sine A

10. cosine A

Solve for x using the table of trigonometric ratios:

11. $x = 90 \tan 35°$ **12.** $\tan 88° = \dfrac{x}{110}$ **13.** $\dfrac{125}{x} = \tan 40°$

14. $\sin 30° = \dfrac{1000}{x}$ **15.** $\cos 16° = \dfrac{400}{x}$ **16.** $\cos 60° = \dfrac{x}{85}$

17. The diagonal of a square 3.1 inches on a side makes an angle of 45° with each of the sides. Find the length of the diagonal of the square.

18. The wire supporting a pole 48 feet high makes an angle of 76° with the ground. How long is the wire?

19. The shadow of a tree is 102 feet. Find the height of the tree if the angle of elevation of the sun is 42°.

20. If a vertical pole 12 feet high casts a shadow equal to its own length, what is the angle of elevation of the sun?

21. At the height of 2500 feet an observer in an airplane notes that the angle of depression of the ground light of an airport is 6°. How far is the plane from the airport? Find the ground distance to the airport from a point on the ground directly beneath the plane at the time the observer took the reading.

22. A tree 34 feet high casts a shadow 8 feet long. What is the angle of elevation of the sun?

23. A 14-foot ladder is leaning against a building. The foot of the ladder is 4 feet from the base of the building. What angle does the ladder make with the ground?

24. Each angle in an equilateral triangle is 60°. Find the altitude of an of an equilateral triangle whose sides are 9 inches long.

25. A railroad track rises 2 feet vertically for every 23 feet measured along the track. What angle does the track make with a horizontal line?

CUMULATIVE REVIEW PROBLEMS

WORKING WITH ALGEBRAIC EXPRESSIONS

1. What is the rule for squaring a binomial? Make up five binomials and find the square of each.

2. When two binomials, such as $3x + 4$ and $4x - 1$, are multiplied, how many terms are there in the product? Describe the method of finding such products by inspection.

3. Under what condition will the product of two binomials give an expression consisting of two terms? Make up five examples of such binomials.

4. Write a formula for multiplying a polynomial by a monomial. Make up five examples.

5. Write the formula $(a + b)^2 = a^2 + 2ab + b^2$ in words.

6. Write the formula $(a + b)(a - b) = a^2 - b^2$ in words.

7. How can you tell that a trinomial is a perfect square? Make up five examples of trinomials that are perfect squares.

8. What is the relation between factoring and multiplying?
9. If a binomial is the difference between two squares, what are its factors? Make up five examples.
10. From $3x - y$ subtract $6x - y$.
11. From the sum of $2a - 3b - c$ and $4a - 8b - c$ subtract $3a - 6b - 2c$.
12. Subtract $5x^2 - 10xy - 2y^2$ from $4x^2 - 12xy - 7y^2$.
13. From the square of $2 - 3a$ subtract the product of $a - 8$ and $2a - 7$.

Do the indicated operations:
14. $a^4 \cdot a^2 \cdot a$
15. $(-a)^2 (a^2)^2$
16. $(-a^2b)(-ab)$
17. $(-2a^2b)^2 (-3ab^2)$
18. $(a^3)^4$
19. $(-2a^2b)^5$
20. $(5ab)(3a)^2 (-2a)$
21. $(-2a)^3 (2a)^4$
22. $(3a)^2 - (2a)^3$
23. $(4a^2)^3 - (-2a^3)^2$
24. $3^2 \cdot 2^3 - 3^3 \cdot 2^2$
25. $(2^2 - 3^2)(2^2 + 3^2)$

Rewrite the following expressions in the simplest form:
26. $3x - (2x - 4)$
27. $2x - (-4x + 5)$
28. $2(2x - 1) - 3(x - 4)$
29. $x(x - 2) + 2x(x - 1)$
30. $(x + 2)^2 + (x - 3)^2$
31. $(a - 3)^2 (a + 3)^2$
32. $(x - 3)(x + 5) + (2x + 1)(3x + 2)$
33. $(2a - 3)(4a + 5) - 3a(2a - 3)$
34. $(x - 6)(x + 6) + (6 + x)(6 - x)$
35. $(m + 4)(m - 4) - (4 + m)(4 - m)$
36. $(1 - x)^2 - (1 - x)(1 + x)$
37. $(2a - 7)^2 - (3a - 5)^2$

Divide:
38. $8a^2 + 2ab$ by $2a$
39. $15xy^2 - 18x^2y$ by $-3xy$
40. $8x^2 - 2x - 15$ by $4x + 5$
41. $3x^2 + 2x - 21$ by $x + 3$
42. $5x^2 - 14x - 24$ by $x - 4$

Find the value of each of the following if $m = 2$ *and* $n = -3$:
43. $5m - 10mn$
44. $3m + 3(m + n)$
45. $4m + 5(m - n)$
46. $m(6m + 1) + n(n + 1)$
47. $(mn)^2 - (m + n)^2$
48. $(2m - n)^2$

49. The side of a cube is $a + 2$ inches. Write a formula for the area of its total surface. For its volume.
50. The volume of a rectangular solid may be found by the formula $V = lwh$. Write a formula for the volume of a rectangular solid in which the length is twice the width and the height is 3 units less than the width.

SOLVING EQUATIONS

1. Compare the method of solving first-degree equations with that of solving second-degree equations.
2. If the root of an equation is -5, what is the degree of the equation?
3. If the roots of an equation are 2 and 3, what is the degree of the equation? Find the equation.
4. Solve the system of equations $x - 3y = 10$ and $2x + y = 6$ both graphically and algebraically.

SOLVING VERBAL PROBLEMS

1. A brick near the top of a tall building becomes loosened and falls 784 feet to the ground. How long will it take for it to reach the ground?
2. A circle has a radius of r inches. If the radius is increased by 1 inch, by how much will the area be increased?
3. Thirty times a number subtracted from eight times the square of the number is 8. Find the number.
4. One number is 53 more than another. Their product is -492. Find the two numbers.
5. A motorist left Lincoln for Prentice, 320 miles away. Two hours later a second motorist left Lincoln for Prentice, traveling over the same route. The second motorist traveled 8 miles per hour slower than the first motorist and arrived at Prentice 4 hours later than the first. What is the time required by each motorist to make the trip?
6. The sum of two numbers is 17. The sum of their squares is 157. Find the numbers.
7. A farmer bought some cows for $1260. If each cow had cost $84 more, the farmer would have bought 4 fewer cows for the same money. How many cows did he buy?
8. The sum of the digits of a two-digit number is 12. The number is 12 more than the product of the digits. What is the number?
9. The difference between the digits of a two-digit number is 8. The number is 9 more than the sum of the squares of the digits. What is the number?
10. A rectangle has the same width as the side of a square. The length of the rectangle is 6 inches more than the side of the square. Find the length and the width of the rectangle and the side of the square if the area of the rectangle is 54 square inches more than the area of the square.
11. In a right triangle the hypotenuse is 6 inches longer than one of the legs. This leg is 6 inches longer than the other leg. Find the length of each leg and the hypotenuse.
12. The area of a circle is 500 square inches. What is the radius of the circle?

APPENDIX

TABLE 1. ROMAN NUMERALS

I.........1	IX......9	XVII....17	LXX...70	DC......600
II........2	X.......10	XVIII...18	LXXX..80	DCC....700
III......3	XI......11	XIX.....19	XC.....90	DCCC...800
IV.......4	XII.....12	XX......20	C.......100	CM......900
V........5	XIII....13	XXX....30	CC.....200	M.......1000
VI.......6	XIV.....14	XL......40	CCC....300	MD.....1500
VII......7	XV......15	L........50	CD.....400	MM.....2000
VIII....8	XVI.....16	LX......60	D......500	$\bar{\text{V}}$.......5000

TABLE 2. WEIGHTS AND MEASURES

Linear Measure

12 inches	= 1 foot
3 feet	= 1 yard
$16\frac{1}{2}$ feet	= 1 rod
40 rods	= 1 furlong
5280 feet	= 1 mile
3 miles	= 1 league

Avoirdupois Weight

$27\frac{1}{3}$ grains	= 1 dram
16 drams	= 1 ounce
16 ounces	= 1 pound
100 pounds	= 1 hundredweight
2000 pounds	= 1 ton (short)
2240 pounds	= 1 ton (long)

The English system of weights and measures is used in Great Britain and the United States, and the metric system is used in most of the other countries of the world. The metric system was developed by the French during the latter part of the eighteenth century. It is based on the meter (approximately 39.37 inches), which, according to the best scientific measurement at the time, was believed to be one ten-millionth of the distance from the equator to either pole. The measurement was later proved to be somewhat inaccurate, but the estimate is still the standard for the meter (and is preserved today on a platinum-iridium rod kept at the International Metric Commission in Paris). It is unfortunate that the metric system is not used in all countries, for it is simpler than the English system. It is on a decimal plan somewhat like our monetary system.

Metric System

Length:
10 millimeters = 1 centimeter
 (Abbreviated 10 mm = 1 cm)

100 centimeters = 1 meter
 (Abbreviated 100 cm = 1 m)

1000 meters = 1 kilometer
 (Abbreviated 1000 m = 1 km)

Capacity:
1000 cubic centimeters = 1 liter
 (Abbreviated 1000 cc = 1 l)

Weight:
1000 milligrams = 1 gram
1000 grams = 1 kilogram
1000 kilograms = 1 metric ton

TABLE 3

SQUARES AND SQUARE ROOTS OF NUMBERS

No.	Squares	Square Roots	No.	Squares	Square Roots	No.	Squares	Square Roots
1	1	1.000	51	2,601	7.141	101	10,201	10.050
2	4	1.414	52	2,704	7.211	102	10,404	10.100
3	9	1.732	53	2,809	7.280	103	10,609	10.149
4	16	2.000	54	2,916	7.348	104	10,816	10.198
5	25	2.236	55	3,025	7.416	105	11,025	10.247
6	36	2.449	56	3,136	7.483	106	11,236	10.296
7	49	2.646	57	3,249	7.550	107	11,449	10.344
8	64	2.828	58	3,364	7.616	108	11,664	10.392
9	81	3.000	59	3,481	7.681	109	11,881	10.440
10	100	3.162	60	3,600	7.746	110	12,100	10.488
11	121	3.317	61	3,721	7.810	111	12,321	10.536
12	144	3.464	62	3,844	7.874	112	12,544	10.583
13	169	3.606	63	3,969	7.937	113	12,769	10.630
14	196	3.742	64	4,096	8.000	114	12,996	10.677
15	225	3.873	65	4,225	8.062	115	13,225	10.724
16	256	4.000	66	4,356	8.124	116	13,456	10.770
17	289	4.123	67	4,489	8.185	117	13,689	10.817
18	324	4.243	68	4,624	8.246	118	13,924	10.863
19	361	4.359	69	4,761	8.307	119	14,161	10.909
20	400	4.472	70	4,900	8.367	120	14,400	10.954
21	441	4.583	71	5,041	8.426	121	14,641	11.000
22	484	4.690	72	5,184	8.485	122	14,884	11.045
23	529	4.796	73	5,329	8.544	123	15,129	11.091
24	576	4.899	74	5,476	8.602	124	15,376	11.136
25	625	5.000	75	5,625	8.660	125	15,625	11.180
26	676	5.099	76	5,776	8.718	126	15,876	11.225
27	729	5.196	77	5,929	8.775	127	16,129	11.269
28	784	5.292	78	6,084	8.832	128	16,384	11.314
29	841	5.385	79	6,241	8.888	129	16,641	11.358
30	900	5.477	80	6,400	8.944	130	16,900	11.402
31	961	5.568	81	6,561	9.000	131	17,161	11.446
32	1,024	5.657	82	6,724	9.055	132	17,424	11.489
33	1,089	5.745	83	6,889	9.110	133	17,689	11.533
34	1,156	5.831	84	7,056	9.165	134	17,956	11.576
35	1,225	5.916	85	7,225	9.220	135	18,225	11.619
36	1,296	6.000	86	7,396	9.274	136	18,496	11.662
37	1,369	6.083	87	7,569	9.327	137	18,769	11.705
38	1,444	6.164	88	7,744	9.381	138	19,044	11.747
39	1,521	6.245	89	7,921	9.434	139	19,321	11.790
40	1,600	6.325	90	8,100	9.487	140	19,600	11.832
41	1,681	6.403	91	8,281	9.539	141	19,881	11.874
42	1,764	6.481	92	8,464	9.592	142	20,164	11.916
43	1,849	6.557	93	8,649	9.644	143	20,449	11.958
44	1,936	6.633	94	8,836	9.695	144	20,736	12.000
45	2,025	6.708	95	9,025	9.747	145	21,025	12.042
46	2,116	6.782	96	9,216	9.798	146	21,316	12.083
47	2,209	6.856	97	9,409	9.849	147	21,609	12.124
48	2,304	6.928	98	9,604	9.899	148	21,904	12.166
49	2,401	7.000	99	9,801	9.950	149	22,201	12.207
50	2,500	7.071	100	10,000	10.000	150	22,500	12.247

TABLE 4

TRIGONOMETRIC RATIOS

Angle	sin	cos	tan	Angle	sin	cos	tan
0°	.0000	1.0000	.0000	45°	.7071	.7071	1.0000
1°	.0175	.9998	.0175	46°	.7193	.6947	1.0355
2°	.0349	.9994	.0349	47°	.7314	.6820	1.0724
3°	.0523	.9986	.0524	48°	.7431	.6691	1.1106
4°	.0698	.9976	.0699	49°	.7547	.6561	1.1504
5°	.0872	.9962	.0875	50°	.7660	.6428	1.1918
6°	.1045	.9945	.1051	51°	.7771	.6293	1.2349
7°	.1219	.9925	.1228	52°	.7880	.6157	1.2799
8°	.1392	.9903	.1405	53°	.7986	.6018	1.3270
9°	.1564	.9877	.1584	54°	.8090	.5878	1.3764
10°	.1736	.9848	.1763	55°	.8192	.5736	1.4281
11°	.1908	.9816	.1944	56°	.8290	.5592	1.4826
12°	.2079	.9781	.2126	57°	.8387	.5446	1.5399
13°	.2250	.9744	.2309	58°	.8480	.5299	1.6003
14°	.2419	.9703	.2493	59°	.8572	.5150	1.6643
15°	.2588	.9659	.2679	60°	.8660	.5000	1.7321
16°	.2756	.9613	.2867	61°	.8746	.4848	1.8040
17°	.2924	.9563	.3057	62°	.8829	.4695	1.8807
18°	.3090	.9511	.3249	63°	.8910	.4540	1.9626
19°	.3256	.9455	.3443	64°	.8988	.4384	2.0503
20°	.3420	.9397	.3640	65°	.9063	.4226	2.1445
21°	.3584	.9336	.3839	66°	.9135	.4067	2.2460
22°	.3746	.9272	.4040	67°	.9205	.3907	2.3559
23°	.3907	.9205	.4245	68°	.9272	.3746	2.4751
24°	.4067	.9135	.4452	69°	.9336	.3584	2.6051
25°	.4226	.9063	.4663	70°	.9397	.3420	2.7475
26°	.4384	.8988	.4877	71°	.9455	.3256	2.9042
27°	.4540	.8910	.5095	72°	.9511	.3090	3.0777
28°	.4695	.8829	.5317	73°	.9563	.2924	3.2709
29°	.4848	.8746	.5543	74°	.9613	.2756	3.4874
30°	.5000	.8660	.5774	75°	.9659	.2588	3.7321
31°	.5150	.8572	.6009	76°	.9703	.2419	4.0108
32°	.5299	.8480	.6249	77°	.9744	.2250	4.3315
33°	.5446	.8387	.6494	78°	.9781	.2079	4.7046
34°	.5592	.8290	.6745	79°	.9816	.1908	5.1446
35°	.5736	.8192	.7002	80°	.9848	.1736	5.6713
36°	.5878	.8090	.7265	81°	.9877	.1564	6.3138
37°	.6018	.7986	.7536	82°	.9903	.1392	7.1154
38°	.6157	.7880	.7813	83°	.9925	.1219	8.1443
39°	.6293	.7771	.8098	84°	.9945	.1045	9.5144
40°	.6428	.7660	.8391	85°	.9962	.0872	11.4301
41°	.6561	.7547	.8693	86°	.9976	.0698	14.3007
42°	.6691	.7431	.9004	87°	.9986	.0523	19.0811
43°	.6820	.7314	.9325	88°	.9994	.0349	28.6363
44°	.6947	.7193	.9657	89°	.9998	.0175	57.2900
45°	.7071	.7071	1.0000	90°	1.0000	.0000	

HOW TO MAKE SIMPLE MEASURING INSTRUMENTS

There are two kinds of measuring instruments a person must have to be able to use the principles of trigonometry: (1) a measuring tape, and (2) a device for measuring angles. In case your school does not have these, here are some suggestions for making these instruments. Ask your teacher to help you get started.

Making Measuring Tapes

You can make rough but serviceable measuring tapes from clothesline. Get some new clothesline from a store. Stretch it tight. Using a yardstick, paint a thin mark at every foot along the clothesline. Use a different color of paint for every tenth foot so that you can easily count the number of feet. Make the measuring tape 50 or 100 feet long. Your tape will be more accurate if you can find a steel measuring tape to help you lay off the feet on the clothesline.

Making Instruments for Measuring Angles

You probably used a protractor in your other mathematics classes to measure and construct angles. You can use the principle of the protractor to make an instrument for measuring angles in a vertical plane.

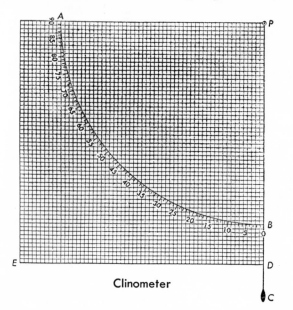

Clinometer

Take a large sheet of graph paper. Use a point (such as P) in the upper right-hand corner of the graph paper. With a radius of 10 units (approxi-

426 *APPENDIX*

mately 10 inches) draw with a compass a quarter circle from A to B. Using a protractor, mark off the arc AB in degrees. With rubber cement paste the graph paper on a backing of ply wood or stiff cardboard. Cut out the backing to fit the graph paper. Tie a small length of thin string to a thumbtack and stick the thumbtack into the board at P. Tie a small weight to the other end of the string, that is, at C. Make sure the angles APD and PDE are right angles (90 degrees).

The instrument you have made is called a clinometer. To use the clinometer to measure angles in the vertical plane, sight at the object, for example, the top of the tree X, along line DP. Allow the string to

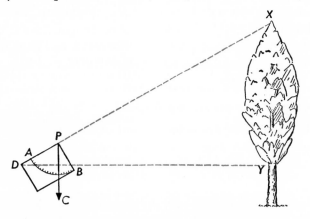

hang free. Put your finger over the string to hold it in place and then read angle BPC from the scale, AB. This angle equals angle XDY, the one you want to measure.

INDEX

428